KU-209-370

Practical
Knowledge for All

Our Colour Plates

(1) BAYEUX'S STORIED TAPESTRY

One of the most interesting and indubitably authentic relics of Britain's yesterday is a flimsy creation of embroidered stuff, housed—strangely enough, until we remember that when it came into being England was an appanage of the Norman duke—in a hall in Bayeux. Over 200 feet long and 19 inches wide, the world-famous Bayeux Tapestry comprises 72 scenes depicting English history from the time of Harold's departure for Normandy to his death on the stricken field of Hastings in 1066. Three of the incidents are illustrated in our colour plate ; note the explanations in Latin and the ornamental borders with motifs from Æsop's Fables and figures of some of the fabulous animals that filled the medieval fancy.

BRITISH HISTORY 3

(2) MASTERPIECE OF RENAISSANCE ART

Just as the Bayeux Tapestry is a priceless "document" in the historical record of the eleventh century, so the masterpieces of the Renaissance painters give us an insight into the colourful life of the age when Europe was being reborn under the inspiration of classical culture and scientific and geographical discovery. In such pictures as Giovanni Bellini's masterly portrait of Loredano, Doge of Venice in 1501, we have not only a superb example of a great painter's art, but an actual reminder of one of the most brilliant and fascinating chapters in the human story. The picture is now among the treasures of the National Gallery, London.

ART AND ARCHITECTURE 14

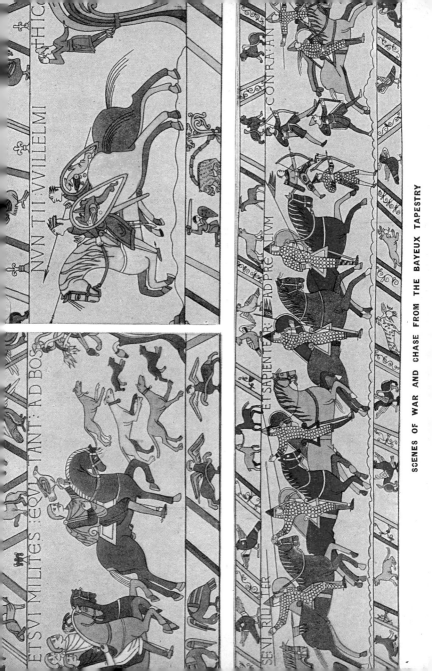

SCENES OF WAR AND CHASE FROM THE BAYEUX TAPESTRY

PRACTICAL
KNOWLEDGE FOR ALL

Sir John Hammerton

Comprising Easy Courses in Literature Language
History Geography the Arts and Sciences Written
by Experts and Arranged for Home Study

NEWLY REVISED EDITION

In Six Handy Volumes with over 360 Special
Plates including Twelve in Full Colours
and about 1300 other Illustrations

THIRD VOLUME

LONDON
THE WAVERLEY BOOK COMPANY LTD.
A3

Printed in Great Britain by The Amalgamated Press, Ltd., London.

LITERARY CONTENTS
OF VOLUME III

COMPLETE LIST OF COURSES

ACCOUNTANCY	ECONOMICS	LATIN
AERONAUTICS	ENGINEERING	MATHEMATICS
ART & ARCHITECTURE	ENGLISH LANGUAGE	MODERN HISTORY
ASTRONOMY	ENGLISH LITERATURE	PHILOSOPHY
BIOLOGY	FRENCH	PHYSICS
BOTANY	GEOGRAPHY	PHYSIOGRAPHY
BRITISH HISTORY	GEOLOGY	PHYSIOLOGY
CHEMISTRY	GERMAN	SHORTHAND
DRAWING & DESIGN	HISTORY : ANCIENT &	SPANISH
ECONOMIC GEOGRAPHY	MEDIEVAL	ZOOLOGY

LIST OF SPECIAL PLATES
IN VOLUME III

Frontispieces in Colour

Bayeux's Storied Tapestry ;   Masterpiece of Renaissance Art

(7)

Maps and Plans in the Text

ACCOUNTANCY

Basic Principles of Double Entry Book-Keeping

THE importance of a reliable and accurate system of accounting to the modern business is manifest to all. The executive of today demands of the accountant more detailed information and more intelligent arrangement of figures than in the past, and it is his duty to collect and arrange information about the operations and position of the business in such a way as to enable the management to make its plans for the future in the secure knowledge that nothing has been overlooked.

The first and most important task of all is to grasp clearly the meaning of double entry book-keeping. All business transactions involve exchange, which necessarily implies two parties. If I part with anything having value, someone has received it ; if I acquire anything of value, somebody has parted with it ; if I receive money, clearly somebody has parted with that money. A proper record of the transaction, then, must show how all the parties to it have been affected.

This brings us to " debit " and " credit," corresponding respectively to the conceptions of receiving and imparting. If I lend a sum of money to John Smith, I will *debit* John Smith in my books, because he has *received* the money. If W. Jones, on the other hand, lends me a sum of money, I will *credit* W. Jones, because he has parted with the money. Every transaction is recorded in what are termed accounts, and, under the double entry system, every transaction is recorded in two accounts. Each account is divided by a line running down the middle of the page ; the left-hand side of the account is termed the debit side, and the right-hand side the credit side. When I lend John Smith £100, I debit his account ; that is to say, I write £100 on the left-hand side of an account headed John Smith. When I borrow £100 from W. Jones, I credit his account ; that is to say, I write £100 on the credit side of an account headed W. Jones.

We have seen that every transaction must be recorded in two accounts. One of the recording entries must be on the debit side, and the other on the credit side. This is an absolutely unvarying rule, to which there are no exceptions. For every amount that appears on the debit side of an account, a similar amount appears on the credit side of another account. For every debit there is an equal and opposite credit, and vice versa. This rule is based on the principle that was stated above, viz. that every transaction has a twofold aspect, of imparting and receiving. The debit entry is the record of the receiving ; the credit entry is the record of the imparting.

When I lent £100 to John Smith, I debited his account, because he received the money. What account am I to credit ? I paid him the money. Am I to credit myself ? In so far as transactions affect other individuals, the course is clear ; in so far as the transactions affect the proprietor of the business in whose books the records are being made, he does not debit himself, but debits an account which indicates the *nature* of the benefit which he receives ; when the business parts with a benefit, the credit is made to an account which indicates the *nature* of the benefit imparted.

It may be convenient for the beginner to regard these accounts as the accounts of imaginary persons inside the business. When £100 was paid to John Smith, the business parted with cash. The credit entry will be made in an account termed the cash account, which may be regarded as the account of the cashier. If £20 is spent on the purchase of goods, the procedure is to credit the cash account, because we have parted with cash, and to debit a goods account, thus indicating the nature of the benefit received. This goods account may also be regarded as the account of the storekeeper whose duty it is to look after the goods. We look upon him as having received something worth £20, and we debit him accordingly.

Let us consider the transactions of a man who conducts all his business on a cash basis, no credit being given or received. Every transaction will involve an entry in the cash account. The cash account is debited with all sums received, and credited with all payments made. We will deal first of all with the payments. For every payment an entry must be made on the credit side of the cash account. The debit entry will, in every case, indicate the nature of the payment made. £2 is spent on a railway fare ; the debit will be made in an account termed travelling expenses. It would, of course, be possible to record

the transaction in greater detail. The debit could be made to
the account of the " person " who received the money, i.e. the
railway company. We should then, however, be compelled to
credit the railway company with £2, since we have received *from*
the railway company the benefit of travelling ; and, to complete
the double entry, travelling expenses account must be debited.
The account of the railway company would show £2 on each
side, and we should be left as we were before, with a credit to
cash, and a debit to travelling expenses. No purpose, therefore,
is served by the more roundabout method.

Further payments are made. £20 is paid out in wages ; £50
is spent in buying furniture ; £4 on rent, and £100 on machinery.
In every case cash account will be credited, since we have parted
with cash. In every case a debit will be made to an account
which indicates the nature of the benefit received in exchange
for the money. Wages account will be debited with £20 ;
furniture account with £50 ; rent account with £4 ; and machinery account with £100.

At this stage we are in a position to state the principle that all
debit balances are either assets or losses. At first sight this
appears contradictory. One is inclined to regard an asset as
being opposed to a loss, rather than as being in any way similar.
A little reflection on the transactions mentioned above will make
its truth apparent. If money is spent, it is spent for some
purpose ; some benefit must be obtained in exchange ; no one
pays cash for nothing. Now, the benefit received in exchange
for cash may be represented by a physical object, having some
degree of permanency, such as a table or a building. The debit on
furniture or buildings account represents an asset. On the other
hand, the benefit we receive may be of a transitory nature, and
not represented by any physical object. If I pay £3 for a railway
ticket, I receive the benefit of travelling in a train. This benefit
is exhausted when the journey terminates. No object of lasting
utility remains. The debit on travelling expenses account is
said to be a loss.

LESSON 2

How Accounts are Classified

EVERY item of cash received will be debited to the cash account, and will be posted to the credit of an account which indicates the source from which it has come. The corollary of the axiom that all debit balances are either assets or losses is that all credit balances are either liabilities or gains.

Let us examine this statement in relation to the business which conducts all its transactions on a cash basis. If I receive cash it is under one of two conditions : either I am under an obligation to repay it, or else I am not. There is no third choice. If I borrow £100 from W. Jones, I debit cash and credit W. Jones. This credit to W. Jones' account indicates that I received the money from Jones, and that I owe this amount to him. That is to say, the credit item on Jones' account is a liability.

On the other hand, if I perform a service for Robinson and he pays me £30 by way of commission, I will debit cash and credit an account headed commission. I am under no obligation to repay the £30 to Robinson ; it has become mine without any obligations attaching to it. The credit on commission account represents my gain, or profit, on the transaction.

Credit in Accountancy. So far we have discussed the case of a business with cash transactions only. We have now to consider transactions where payment is deferred, or, in ordinary language, on a credit basis. " Credit " in this sense is not to be confused with the special term used in accountancy in opposition to debit.

It is possible to acquire benefits without paying cash for them immediately. If I obtain the benefit of using a building, and pay for that benefit in cash, the double entry necessary to record the transaction is a credit to cash and a debit to rent account. If, instead, I owe the money to my landlord, the double entry is to debit rent as before, and to credit, not cash, but the account of my landlord. The credit on my landlord's account is a liability, representing my obligation to pay him in the future. Conversely, I may impart a benefit without receiving cash immediately. If I perform a service for Robinson, for which he agrees to pay me a commission, the double entry is a credit to commission account and a debit to Robinson's account. The credit on commission account is a profit, and the debit on Robinson's account is an asset representing my right to receive the money from Robinson at a later date.

Personal Accounts. Accounts can be classified into certain well-defined groups. First, there are personal accounts. These are the accounts of individuals or firms with whom business transactions have been conducted. Personal accounts are debited with all benefits received by the persons concerned. If we part with cash, and pay it to a person with whom business is being transacted, that person's account is debited, cash being credited. If we sell goods to a person without receiving immediate payment, that person's account is debited and goods account credited. A debit balance on a personal account (that is, an excess of debits over credits) is an asset representing our right to receive a certain sum of money at some time in the future.

Personal accounts are credited with the benefits imparted by those persons, and therefore received by us. If we buy goods without paying for them immediately, we credit the personal account and debit a goods account. If we receive cash, we debit cash and credit the person from whom we received that cash. Of course, where there is no obligation to return the money, as in the sale of goods for cash, the credit is made direct to the goods account. But where there is an obligation to return the money, the personal account is credited ; and where we receive cash in discharge of a debt due to us, a debt represented by a previous debit to a personal account, the personal account of the debtor is credited. The effect of this is to leave no balance on the personal account, the debit and credit sides being of equal amount. This indicates that the debt is no longer due to us.

Real Accounts. Secondly, there are real accounts. Real accounts are assets. If we buy £100 worth of furniture or spend £1,000 on machinery, cash will be credited, and furniture or machinery account will be debited correspondingly. It is clearly impossible for a credit balance (that is, an excess of credits over debits) to exist on a real account.

Nominal Accounts. Then, thirdly, there are nominal accounts. Nominal accounts are either profits or losses. A debit balance on a nominal account, such as rent, wages, or travelling expenses, is a loss or an expense. The existence of the debit balance does not necessarily imply that we have parted with cash. It only signifies that an expense has been incurred. If payment has not been made the credit goes to a personal account. When the cash is subsequently paid, cash is credited and the debit then goes, not to the expense, but to the personal account.

We may illustrate the two cases as follows :

1. Stationery worth £20 is purchased and cash is paid immediately. The entries will be a credit to cash, and a debit to stationery account, viz. :

Stationery	Cash
To cash £20	By stationery £20

2. Stationery worth £20 is purchased from A.B., Ltd., on January 1st, but payment is not made until February 3rd. The entries will be a debit to stationery account, and a credit to A.B., Ltd., on January 1st, followed on February 3rd by a credit to cash and a debit to A.B., Ltd., viz. :

Stationery

Jan. 1. To A.B., Ltd.   £20

A.B., Ltd.

Feb. 3. To Cash   £20   Jan. 1. By stationery   £20

Cash

Feb. 3. By A.B., Ltd.   £20

The ultimate effect of the second method is the same as that of the first. We are left with a debit to stationery and a credit to cash. A.B.'s account is said to be closed, both sides being equal, and there being no balance.

The point, however, is that we could not make a direct entry from cash to stationery before February 3rd, whereas we incurred the expense on January 1st. This fact must be recorded. If an inquirer were to examine the books on, say, January 21st, he would expect to find a record of the state of affairs at that point of time. The state of affairs on January 21st is that an expense of £20 has been incurred, and that there is an undischarged liability to A.B., Ltd.

Where the payment of cash is coincident with the incurring of the expense, no personal account is necessary. An entry can be made direct from cash to the expense account. This, of course, is an everyday occurrence. Consider cash paid for travelling expenses, goods purchased for cash, the payment of wages, etc.

Similarly, a credit balance on a nominal account, which is a profit or a gain, does not necessarily imply that the money has been received, but only that it has been earned. If there is a lapse of time between the earning of the profit and its receipt in cash, then a personal account intervenes.

To sum up. It should now be clear that double entry book-keeping is not a mere mechanical device but a reflection of facts. When a profit is earned, that fact is recorded by a credit in a nominal account. But it is also reflected by a debit to an asset account, thus increasing the assets of the business. The asset account may be real, i.e. cash, furniture, etc., or personal—a debt due. In any event the profit, which is a credit balance, is represented by an increase of assets. This is common sense. If a man says : " I have made a profit of £100," one is entitled to ask : " Where is it ? " The answer is that it is represented by assets, whether in cash or something else.

In the same way, if an expense or a loss is incurred, it is shown as a debit balance on a nominal account. But that debit balance on the nominal account is reflected in a credit to cash, which diminishes assets, or else in a credit to a personal account, which increases liabilities. Thus, the incurring of expenses is necessarily accompanied by a decrease of assets or an increase of liabilities.

LESSON 3

A Further Step in the Theory of Double Entry

WE have seen that the basis of double entry book-keeping is that every transaction has a twofold aspect, that of receiving and that of imparting. To present a complete picture of any transaction, both these aspects must be recorded. If I acquire assets, I must show how I have acquired them ; if I have parted with cash in exchange my cash account is credited ; if I have not yet paid for them I have incurred a liability, and a personal account is credited. If I incur expenses in the conduct of my businesses, I either part with cash or increase my liabilities. Both aspects must be recorded ; the appropriate expense account is debited, and cash account or a personal account is credited.

It is clear, then, that double entry book-keeping is not a mere arithmetical device, but a reflection of an actual state of affairs. Every debit to a nominal (expense) account involves a credit to an asset or liability account, which has the effect of decreasing the net assets. Conversely, every credit to a nominal (profit or gain) account involves a debit to an asset or liability account, which has the effect of increasing the net assets. In other words, profits necessarily imply an increase in net assets, and losses or expenses imply a decrease in net assets, which is what ordinary common sense would lead us to expect.

Trial Balance. Inasmuch as every transaction requires two entries, one to the debit and one to the credit, it follows that the total of debit entries in any set of books must be equal to the total of credit entries. If, therefore, at any point of time, a list of all debit entries is set down on paper, together with a list of all credit entries, the totals of the two lists must necessarily be equal. This is the principle of the trial balance. It is not, however, customary to draw up a trial balance showing total debits and total credits. It is sufficient if the balance of each account is extracted. For instance, John Smith's account may appear in the books as follows :

John Smith

	£		£
To goods	100	By cash	95
.. goods	250	,, discount	5

In a list of total debits and total credits, John Smith's account would appear as a debit of £350 and a credit of £100. The usual practice, however, is to offset the credit against the debit items, and to show a debit balance only of £250. It is clear that the two columns (debit and credit) of the trial balance must still be equal. All that has been done is to deduct £100 from each column. It is most important to recognize that the trial balance is not an integral part of the double entry system ; the figures on the trial balance are not entries that require a complementary credit or debit, as the case may be. All that has been done is to set down on paper a list of the balances existing in the books at a given point of time. This list includes all the balances on all accounts, both assets and liabilities, and losses and gains—real, personal, and nominal accounts.

The next step is the preparation of the trading and profit and loss account. This account is a summary of all the balances on the nominal accounts, that is to say, of expenses and gains. If one were to take a trial balance, collect all the nominal accounts together, cancel out compensating debit and credit items, and thus leave only the net balance of all the nominal accounts, the two sides of the trial balance would still agree.

The principle of cancelling compensating debits and credits in each individual account has simply been carried a stage farther. By cancelling out debit balances against credit balances on nominal accounts, equal amounts have been deducted from both sides of the trial balance. We are left with real and personal account balances, together with the final balance of all nominal items. That is to say, we are left with a list of assets and liabilities, together with the net profit or loss.

This collection of all nominal account balances we term the profit and loss account. The list of asset and liability balances, together with the net balance on the profit and loss account, we term the balance sheet. The balance sheet is a statement of the financial position of a business at a given point of time. It is a summary of possessions, or assets, on the one side, and a summary of obligations, or liabilities, on the other. The possessions are debit balances ; the obligations are credit balances.

Capital Account. It becomes necessary at this point to explain an account of a special character, viz. the capital account. The capital account may perhaps be best defined as the personal account of the proprietor. The business must be regarded as having a separate existence, distinct from the proprietor. If an outside individual lends a sum of money to a business, the double entry is a debit to cash account and a credit to the personal account of the lender. This credit balance represents the liability to repay the lender the sum he has advanced. If the proprietor advances a sum of money to his own business, his personal account, which is termed the capital account, is credited. In everyday language, any sums put into a business by its proprietor are his capital. The debit indicates the nature of the asset the business receives ; the credit indicates where the asset has come from—in this case, from the proprietor himself.

Now, it is clear that if business is being successfully carried on, the assets will exceed the liabilities to external persons. The excess of the assets over the liabilities is what the business owes to the proprietor ; it is the measure of what he is worth.

To return to the profit and loss account. If the credit balances on all the nominal accounts exceed the debit balances, the net credit balance is the measure of the profit earned for the period under review. This is the new profit, as disclosed by the profit and loss account.

We have, however, seen that the credit items on the nominal accounts, which have been transferred to the profit and loss account, were reflected by debits to asset accounts of one kind or another, and that the debit items on nominal accounts,which appear on the expenses side of the profit and loss account, were reflected by credit entries to asset or liability accounts. That is to say, net assets have been increased to the extent of the credit items in the profit and loss, and have been diminished to the extent of the debit items in the profit and loss. In other words, we shall expect to find that our net assets have been increased to the extent of the excess of the credit side of the profit and loss over the debit side, that is, to the extent of the net profit, which is, as we have remarked, what common sense would lead us to expect.

If no additional sums have been introduced by the proprietor during the trading period, and if he has withdrawn no sums for his personal use, a credit balance on profit and loss account must be accompanied by a corresponding increase in the assets, which, it will be remembered, are debit balances.

Now, when the nominal accounts appearing in the trial balance are collected together to form the profit and loss account, we are left with asset and liability balances, including the proprietor's capital account. A list of these asset and liability balances, together with the net balance on nominal accounts (the net profit), must clearly agree. This list we term the balance sheet. If we compare the balance sheet at the end of a trading period with that at the beginning, then, if a profit has been earned, and the proprietor has neither introduced nor withdrawn anything, we shall find that both sides of the balance sheet have been increased by an equal amount. Among the credit items we find the figure for net profit—the credit balance on the profit and loss account. Corresponding to, and representing this net profit, we find that the assets have increased by a similar amount. We are here, of course, speaking of net assets. It is always possible to increase both assets and liabilities by equal amounts without affecting the profit and loss account. Net assets equal total assets minus total liabilities to external persons.

LESSON 4

Double Entry in Actual Practice

WE have traced the steps by which, under double entry book-keeping, the final results of all the transactions of a business appear in the profit and loss account and in the balance sheet. This process may be seen more clearly by means of an example. Consider the following set of facts :

Arthur Harris commences business on January 1st with a capital of £1,000 in cash. During January the following transactions take place :

Harris buys £100 of furniture, and pays in cash ; buys £500 worth of goods on credit from W. Robinson ; buys £400 worth of goods for cash ; pays Robinson £200 on account ; sells part of the goods to R. Jameson for £800, on credit ; sells the remainder of the goods for cash, £400 ; pays wages £50, and sundry expenses £25 in cash.

The first entry in Harris's books will be to debit cash £1,000 and to credit his capital account. The ledger accounts will be as follow :

Cash

To—				By—			
Capital	..	..	.. £1,000	Furniture	..	..	£100
Goods	..	..	.. 400	Goods	..	..	400
				W. Robinson	..	..	200
				Wages	..	..	50
				Sundry Expenses	..	25
				Balance	..	..	625
			£1,400				£1,400
Balance	..	..	.. 625				

Goods

To—		By—	
W. Robinson	£500	R. Jameson	£800
Cash..	400	Cash..	400
	900		
Balance	300		
	£1,200		£1,200
		Balance	300

W. Robinson

To—		By—	
Cash..	£200	Goods	£500
Balance	300		
	£500		£500
		Balance	300

Wages

To—	
Cash..	£50

Capital

		By—	
		Cash..	£1,000

Furniture

To—	
Cash..	£100

R. Jameson

To—	
Goods	£800

Sundry Expenses

To—	
Cash..	£25

It will be noticed that those accounts containing more than one entry have been "balanced." Take the cash account, for instance; the debit entries exceed the credit entries by £625. By making a balancing entry of £625 on the credit side, the two sides of the account agree, and can be ruled off. The double entry is preserved by making a debit entry of £625 below the ruled line ; the effect is that we can see the balance at a glance.

We are now in a position to extract a trial balance. It must always be borne in mind that the trial balance is simply a *list* of the balances appearing in the books, and is no part of the double entry.

TRIAL BALANCE

	Debit Balances			Credit Balances		
Cash	£625	0	0	£		
Capital				1,000	0	0
Goods				300	0	0
Furniture	100	0	0			
W. Robinson..				300	0	0
R. Jameson	800	0	0			
Wages	50	0	0			
Sundry Expenses..	25	0	0			
	£1,600	0	0	£1,600	0	0

The balances may be classified as follows :
(1) real—cash and furniture.
(2) personal—W. Robinson and R. Jameson.
(3) nominal—goods, wages, and sundry expenses.

The proprietor's capital account is in a class by itself ; if it must be included in the above tabulation, it will be as a personal account. The goods account is not a real account. The goods, when purchased, were physical and tangible ; but, at the end of the period, they have gone—no physical object remains.

A second and more instructive classification is as follows :
(A) debit balances : Assets (cash, furniture, and R. Jameson) and losses or expenses (wages and sundry expenses).
(B) credit balances : Liabilities (W. Robinson) and gains or profits (goods).

The proprietor's capital is again in a class by itself ; it may, however, be regarded as the liability of the business to the proprietor.

The next step is to prepare the profit and loss account. All the nominal accounts must be collected together. It must be borne in mind that, unlike the trial balance, the profit and loss account *is* an integral part of the double entry. Every entry in the profit and loss account has its equal and opposite debit or credit, as the case may be. In order that this principle may be made absolutely clear, the balances as they appear in the books are again reproduced :

Cash

To—
Balance £625

Goods

To—   By—
Profit and Loss % .. £300   Balance.. .. .. £300

W. Robinson

By—
Balance.. .. .. £300

Wages

To—   By—
Cash .. .. £50   Profit and Loss %   £50

Capital

By—
Cash £1,000
Net Profit 225

Furniture

To—
Cash £100

R. Jameson

To—
Goods £800

Sundry Expenses

To—   By—
Cash .. .. £25   Profit and Loss %   £25

(22)

PROFIT AND LOSS ACCOUNT

To—		By—	
Wages	£50 0 0	Goods	£300 0 0
Sundry expenses	25 0 0		
Balance, being net profit transferred to capital account	225 0 0		
	£300 0 0		£300 0 0

In our trial balance, we saw that there was a credit balance on goods account of £300. This has been " transferred " to the profit and loss account, by debiting the goods account and crediting the profit and loss account with £300. The goods account is now said to be " closed " ; the debit side equals the credit side ; there is no balance either way. This account has now served its purpose, and its place is taken by the entry in the profit and loss account.

Similarly, wages account and sundry expenses account have been " closed off " to profit and loss account. They have fulfilled their function and are no longer required : their places are taken by the entries on the debit side of the profit and loss account.

The profit and loss account presents a picture of the operations of the period ; a net profit of £225 has been earned. Harris sold the goods for £300 more than he paid for them : out of this he had to pay £75 in expenses, leaving a net profit of £225.

If we examine the books *after* the nominal accounts have been closed off to profit and loss account, we find the following balances remaining :

	Debit Balances	Credit Balances
Cash	£625 0 0	
Capital		£1,000 0 0
Profit and Loss		225 0 0
Furniture	100 0 0	
W. Robinson		300 0 0
R. Jameson	800 0 0	
	£1,525 0 0	£1,525 0 0

It will be noticed that, with the exception of the capital account and the profit and loss account, only assets and liabilities remain

When Harris commenced business on January 1st, his assets totalled £1,000 (all cash) and he had no liabilities. If we examine the list of balances remaining on January 31st, we find that his assets are :

Cash	£625
Furniture	100
R. Jameson	800
	£1,525

He has also a liability of £300 to Robinson. His net assets are, therefore, £1,225. If he were to pay W. Robinson, he would be left with assets totalling £1,225. It will be observed that his net assets have increased from £1,000 to £1,225 during the month, i.e. by £225. It will also be noticed that £225 is the amount of the net profit.

The meaning of the statement that double entry book-keeping is not a mere mechanical device but a reflection of an actual state of affairs, now becomes clear. A profit is not something abstract—something hanging, as it were, in the air. A profit is represented by something solid—either money or money's worth. The nominal accounts summarized in the profit and loss account show us how the profit has been earned ; the asset accounts, minus the liability accounts, show us *where* the profit is.

These remaining balances are usually summarized in a document termed the " balance sheet." This, like the trial balance, is merely a *list* of balances standing in the books. Like the trial balance, but unlike the profit and loss account, it forms no part of the double entry system. For historical reasons, the credit balances appear on the left-hand side of the balance sheet, and the debit balances appear on the right-hand side. In some cases, the prefixes " to " and " by " are used in the balance sheet, but their use is misleading. It conveys the impression that the balance sheet is an " account " ; that is to say, that debit items in the balance sheet have a corresponding credit, and vice versa. This impression is unfortunate and is entirely incorrect. The prefixes " to " and " by " are now usually omitted. The fact that the items appear on the reverse sides must be accepted as an historical survival, but should not be allowed to obscure the true nature of the balance sheet.

The balance sheet of Arthur Harris on January 31st will be as follows :

BALANCE SHEET

Credit Balances				*Debit Balances*			
Capital (including				Cash	£625	0	0
net profit) ..	£1,225	0	0	Debtors (R.			
				Jameson) ..	800	0	0
Creditors (W.				Furniture	100	0	0
Robinson) ..	300	0	0				
	£1,525	0	0		£1,525	0	0

One final word. The balance of the profit and loss account (the net profit) is transferred to the proprietor's capital account. The reason for this is that the business is deemed to be accountable to the proprietor for profits just as much as for the cash he originally invested in the business.

To put it in more everyday terms. The capital account is the measure of what the business is worth. When Harris started with a capital in cash of £1,000 he was worth £1,000. During the month of January he has increased his net worth by £225, by earning a profit of that amount. His net worth is always the amount by which his assets exceed his liabilities, and, as we have seen, a profit is always accompanied by an increase in net assets.

The balance sheet is a statement of the " real " position at a point of time, while the profit and loss account is a record of transactions *over a period of time.* Each, in a sense, confirms the other. The profit and loss shows what has been happening ; the balance sheet shows the *result* of these events.

LESSON 5

Principal Books of First Entry

W E have, up to the present, sketched the theoretical working of the double entry system, and examined the final results, as shown by the profit and loss account and the balance sheet. The object of the next three Lessons in this Course will be to consider the working of the system in practice, and, in particular, to examine the purpose of the various books.

We have, at the outset, to make a very important distinction between books of original entry, as they are called, and the financial books. Strictly speaking, only the financial books are an integral part of the double entry system. Every transaction has its place in the financial books ; all the debits and credits about which we have been speaking, and all the ledger accounts given by way of illustration in the preceding Lesson, are in the financial books. The financial books are nothing more or less than divisions or parts of the theoretical ledger. The ledger is, in theory, the book containing all debits and credits and all the accounts, personal, nominal, and real. In practice, transactions are too numerous to be conveniently recorded in one book. Such a book would be excessively bulky. The ledger is therefore split up, for the sake of convenience, into a number of ledgers, all of which, combined, constitute the essential double entry system.

Divisions of the Ledger. The usual divisions of the ledger are 1. The bought (or purchases) ledger, which contains all the personal accounts of creditors. 2. The sales (or sold) ledger, which contains all the personal accounts of customers or debtors. Personal accounts only are found in the bought and sales ledgers. 3. The private, or general ledger. which contains real and nominal accounts and the proprietor's capital account. 4. The cash book, which contains the cash account only.

In most businesses daily routine transactions are very numerous. It would clearly be difficult for the book-keepers to make a double entry in the ledger every moment a transaction took place. Many people might require the book at the same time.

The books of original entry, or books of first entry, are designed to meet this practical difficulty. Just as, in earlier times, one ledger was sufficient to contain all the accounts, etc., at one time one book of first entry was sufficient to record all transactions. This book was known as the *journal*, or day book.

The purpose of the journal was to serve as a kind of notebook, in which all transactions were jotted down, in chronological order, and at the time they occurred. At the end of the day, or at some time when he had leisure, the book-keeper would enter the transactions in the ledger, making a double entry for every transaction. The entry in the journal was not a part of the double entry. Two entries were made in the ledger in respect of every transaction, in addition to the record in the journal. At accounting periods, the trial balance was extracted in its entirety from the ledger. without reference to the journal. The latter was simply used as a matter of convenience. In the rush of business it would not always be possible for the book-keeper to find time to make the full ledger entries.

The journal might be regarded as a sort of diary or memorandum notebook, in which the book-keeper, in the busy hours of the day, made notes to serve as a reminder that certain transactions had occurred and that he must, at a more appropriate time, record these transactions in the ledger. To avoid duplications, it became the rule that *all* transactions must first be entered in the journal before they were entered in the ledger.

In modern practice the journal, like the ledger, is divided into specialized books. There is one exception to the rule that all transactions must first be recorded in a book of first entry : cash transactions are entered direct in the cash book, which is itself a part of the ledger. All cash received is entered on the left-hand or debit side of the cash book ; the corresponding credits are made to the appropriate accounts in the other divisions of the ledger. Similarly, cash payments are entered on the right-hand (or credit) side of the cash book, the corresponding debits being made to the appropriate ledger accounts. No book of first entry is used in respect of cash items.

All other transactions must first be recorded in a book of first entry. The principal books of first entry are : the purchases day book ; the sales day book ; the journal proper.

Purchases Day Book, All purchases on credit are recorded in this book in chronological order. Spaces are provided for the date of the transaction, for the name of the supplier, and for the money value of the goods. A narrow column is provided for a note of the page in the bought ledger containing the personal account of the supplier. Each individual item is " posted," as the term is, to the credit of the appropriate personal account in the bought ledger. At the end of a definite period, usually a month, the items in the day book are added up and debited in total to the goods or purchases account in the private ledger. We shall return to this aspect later.

It is now apparent that the purchases day book serves an additional purpose. By debiting totals only to the goods or purchases account the private ledger does not become over-crowded. The details appear in the day book. The totals, which give a compact view of a series of transactions, appear in the private ledger. It will be appreciated that it is a very desirable thing to keep the private ledger as compact as possible. The double entry is preserved. The total debit to goods equals the sum of all credits in the bought ledger, as may be seen from the following :

PURCHASES DAY BOOK

		Credited to Bought Ledger Folio	Amount
			£ s. d.
1931 Jan. 1	R. Jones	17	73 10 1
„ 15	W. Richards	103	165 0 0
„ 25	J. Wilkins..	88	40 8 3
			£278 18 4

Debited to Goods % in private ledger

Sales Day Book. The purpose of this book is analogous to that of the purchases day book. In this book all sales on credit are entered in chronological order. The individual amounts are debited to the appropriate personal accounts in the sales ledger, and the total, which is usually made up monthly, is credited to the sales or goods account in the private ledger.

Purchases which are paid for immediately are not entered in the purchases day book. The double entry is made direct, the cash account (in the cash book) being credited and goods account being debited. In the same way, cash sales do not appear in the sales day book ; the double entry is made direct from the debit side of the cash book to the credit of goods account in the private ledger. It has already been observed that cash transactions are an exception to the rule that all transactions must first be recorded in a book of original entry. Other specialized books of first entry will be dealt with later.

Journal Proper. This book is the survivor of the old journal, in which at one time all transactions were recorded. Its use is now limited to transactions of a peculiar or unusual character, which are not sufficiently numerous to make a specialized day book necessary. Ordinary day-to-day routine transactions, such as the purchase and sale of goods, are recorded in the special day books just referred to. Receipts and payments of cash are entered direct in the cash book. The use of the journal is thus strictly limited.

Closing entries, that is to say, the entries by which nominal account balances are transferred to the profit and loss account, are recorded in the journal. Other matters, which we will discuss in subsequent Lessons, such as provision for depreciation, bad debts, and outstanding expenses, are the subject of journal entries. The form of the journal should be noted. By way of illustration, consider the following transaction :

I perform on March 1st a special service for Arthur Jackson, for which he agrees to pay me £20 commission on April 1st. I must record this transaction on March 1st thus :

JOURNAL

			Debit Column	Credit Column
March 1	Arthur Jackson Dr. .. .. To commission .. .. Being amount due from A. J. for services rendered ..	40 78	£20 0 0	£20 0 0

I will then proceed to make a double entry in my private ledger. I will open an account for Jackson on page 40, which I will debit with £20 ; I will then credit commission account, which is on page 78, with £20. The credit balance on commission account is a profit, which will eventually be transferred to the profit and loss account.

The journal entry is nothing more than a memorandum that a double entry is *to be* made, and indicating which account is to be debited, and which account is to be credited, and with how much. The entry of the figures 40 and 78 in the narrow column is an

(29)

indication that the double entry has been made. Prior to the actual entry in the ledger, this narrow column is left blank. It will also be noted that the journal entry is followed by an explanation of the nature of the transaction, which is termed a " narration."

LESSON 6

On the Trading Account

IN Lesson 4 (page 19) we showed a specimen set of transactions, with trial balance, profit and loss account and balance sheet. On one point—the goods account—a very simplified assumption was made. It was assumed that, when goods were purchased, the goods account was debited, and that, when goods were sold, the goods account was credited with the proceeds : in this illustration, *all* the goods were sold during the period under review. In practice, the purchase and sale of goods are dealt with in two separate accounts. Furthermore, only in very exceptional cases are all the goods that have been purchased in a given period sold within the same period, since nearly all traders find it necessary to keep a stock of goods continuously in hand. This being so, the next thing we have to do is to trace the evolution of the goods account.

Suppose a trader buys goods for £1,000, and sells them all for £1,500, in both cases for cash. In its simple form the goods account would appear thus :

Goods

To—	By—
Cash £1,000	Cash.. .. .. £1,500

The credit balance of £500 on the goods account represents the profit on the transaction.

Now let us suppose that the trader only sells half of the goods for £750 :

Goods

To—	By—
Cash £1,000	Cash.. .. .. £750

TRADING ACCOUNT

We have a debit balance of £250 on the goods account. What does this balance represent ? It is really a composite of two things. The trader has sold half the goods only, the other half remaining in his possession ; that is to say, the unsold half of the goods constitutes an asset, value £500, which is half the total cost price. The half that has been sold for £750 also cost £500. Therefore, there is a profit of £250 on the sale. Now, assets are debit balances, and profits are credit balances. This debit balance of £250 on the goods account is really made up of a debit balance of £500, being the value of the stock still on hand, and a credit balance of £250, being the profit on the sale of half the goods.

We can, therefore, balance the goods account in this way :

Goods

To—		By—	
Cash	£1,000	Cash	£750
Profit..	250	Stock (balance) ..	500
	£1,250		£1,250
To Balance (stock) ..	£500	By Balance (profit) ..	£250

Now, in practice, the goods account is split up in the following manner. When goods are purchased the debit is made to a " purchases " account, and when goods are sold the credit is made to a separate account, called the " sales " account. At the end of an accounting period, the total of the purchases account is transferred to the debit of a trading account, and the total of the sales account is transferred to the credit of this account. The value of stock on hand at the end of the period is credited to the trading account, and debited to a stock account.

Using the same figures as above, the ledger accounts would be :

Purchases

To—	
Cash	£1,000

After transferring to the trading account :

Sales

By—	
Cash	£750

Purchases

To—		By—	
Cash	£1,000	Trading account ..	£1,000
	£1,000		£1,000

Sales

To—		By—	
Trading Account ..	£750	Cash	£750
	£750		£750

TRADING ACCOUNT

To—		By—	
Purchases	£1,000	Sales	£750
Gross profit, carried down	250	Stock..	500
	£1,250		£1,250

To—		By—	
		Gross profit	£250

(Here appear the various expense accounts.)

STOCK ACCOUNT

To—	
Trading account ..	£500

It will be observed that the trading account here shown is identical with the old goods account, with the exception that the stock is not brought down as a balance, but is debited to a new account. which remains in the books, and is shown in the balance sheet as an asset.

The profit on the sale (which is termed the gross profit) is brought down as a balance. Against this balance are debited the various loss or expense accounts. In other words, the profit and loss account is a continuation of the trading account. The distinction between trading account and profit and loss account is made for the sake of clarity. It is desirable to be able to see at a glance what is the extent of the margin between cost price of goods and selling price, and then to compare this gross profit with the expenses, rather than to lump all nominal debits and

TWO VIEWS OF THE 'AIRSPEED COURIER.' **Fig. 1.** With undercarriage in normal position. **Fig. 2.** With undercarriage retracted into the wings, giving the machine an increased speed of 13 miles per hour. AERONAUTICS 15

Courtesy of "Flight"

AEROPLANE CONTROL. **Fig. 2.** Tail plane and rudders of the de Havilland Albatross commercial aeroplane. AERONAUTICS 16

Courtesy of "Flight"

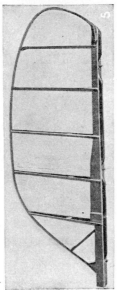

TAIL PLANES AND AILERONS. Fig. 3. Tail plane, rudder and fin of the Avro 621 Tutor. **Fig. 4.** Skeleton of the de Havilland Moth tail plane. **Fig. 5.** Half of an elevator of the Moth. **Fig. 6.** Fin and rudder of the Moth. **Fig. 7.** Skeleton of the Moth aileron. **Fig. 9.** Handley Page automatic slot fitted to the Moth. AERONAUTICS 16

Fig. 3, courtesy of The Royal Aeronautical Society

Plate 2

Volume III

FLYING BOAT CONSTRUCTION. Fig. 2. Hull of the Saunders-Roe Cutty Sark amphibian. **Fig. 3** (left). Interior view of the Short Sunderland, military version of the famous Empire flying boats. AERONAUTICS 17

Fig. 2, courtesy of The Royal Aeronautical Society ; Fig. 3, courtesy of "Flight"

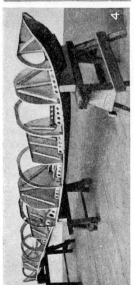

SEAPLANE CONSTRUCTION. Fig. 4. Avro metal float partly constructed; the float is built up to this stage in one jig and then placed in a second jig for completion. **Fig. 5.** Avro metal float completed with metal skin. **Fig. 6.** Short type **wing-tip floats**; these floats prevent the planes being broken by buffeting on the waves. **Fig. 7.** Long float under construction of the racing seaplane, Supermarine S5. AERONAUTICS 17

Courtesy of The Royal Aeronautical Society

Plate 4

Volume III

credits indiscriminately in one account. The balance on the profit and loss account, which is the gross profit minus expenses, is termed the net profit.

It might be asked, if the trading account is so similar to the goods account, why go to the trouble of opening separate purchases and sales accounts ? The answer is that, in the course of a year, the entries in the purchases and sales accounts are fairly numerous. If the purchase and sale of goods were recorded direct in the trading account, this account would become unwieldy. It is the purpose of the trading account to present a summarized, bird's-eye view of the whole transactions for a given period.

Just as one of the purposes of the purchases day book is to avoid too great a multiplicity of detail in the purchases account, so the purpose of the purchases account is to avoid unnecessary details in the trading account. Every individual transaction is recorded in detail in the purchases day book. The trading account shows us in a concise form the *final* effect of the transactions of a period.

We have seen that the trading account is credited with the value of the closing stock, and that a new account is opened, to which the same figure is debited. This account appears in the balance sheet as an asset. It is evident, however, that this balance will remain in the ledger unchanged throughout the whole of the following accounting period. As fresh goods are bought the cost is debited, not to the stock account but to the purchases account ; as goods are sold, sales account is credited. What is to be done with the stock account ?

The procedure is this. At the end of the subsequent accounting period, the balance on the stock account, which has remained in the ledger since the close of the preceding period, is transferred to the *debit* of the trading account. The value of the stock at the end of the subsequent period is found by a physical stocktaking, and this figure is credited to this new trading account, and debited to a new stock account. The old stock account has been closed by transfer to the debit of the trading account. In order to make the procedure perfectly clear, let us consider the following illustration :

A man commences business on Jan. 1st, 1930, without any stock. During 1930 his purchases are £4,000, his sales £7,000, and his stock on hand at Dec. 31st, 1930, is £1,000.

The ledger accounts and trading account for the year will appear as follows:

Purchases

To—		By—	
Sundries £4,000		Trading ᵃ⁄꜀ £4,000	

Sales

To—		By—	
Trading ᵃ⁄꜀ £7,000		Sundries £7,000	

TRADING ACCOUNT (Dec. 31st, 1930)

To—		By—	
Purchases £4,000		Sales £7,000	
Gross profit, to		Stock, Dec.	
P. & L. 4,000		31st 1,000	
	£8,000		£8,000

STOCK ACCOUNT

1930		1931	
Dec. 31st. To—		Dec. 31st. By—	
Trading account .. £1,000		Trading account .. £1,000	

The balance of £1,000 on the stock account on Dec. 31st, 1930, appears as an asset in the balance sheet at that date. During 1931 the purchases are £7,000, sales £10,000, and the stock on Dec. 31st, 1931, is £3,000. The stock on hand at the commencement of 1931 is transferred to the debit of the trading account and a new stock account is opened, being debited with £3,000, while the trading account is credited.

The trading account for 1931 will appear thus:

TRADING ACCOUNT (Dec. 31st, 1931)

To—		By—	
Stock, Jan. 1st .. £1,000		Sales £10,000	
Purchases 7,000		Stock, Dec.	
Gross profit 5,000		31st 3,000	
	£13,000		£13,000

TRADING ACCOUNT

STOCK ACCOUNT

1931
Dec. 31st. To—

  Trading account .. £3,000

The purpose of the trading account is to compare the cost of the goods sold with the selling price of those goods. The stock in hand on Jan. 1st plus purchases during the year is the total of goods to be accounted for. But not all of these goods have been sold. Clearly, if we deduct from the sum of opening stock and purchases the cost price of the stock in hand at the close of the year, the difference is the cost price of the goods sold.

We have on the debit side of the trading account opening stock plus purchases, with closing stock on the credit side. Now an addition to the credit side is the same thing as a subtraction from the debit side. The trading account thus gives a true picture of the actual state of affairs.

Our Course in Accountancy is continued in Volume 4.

LESSON 13

Detail Design of Main Planes

IN this and the next few Lessons some of the more important details of construction will be dealt with. The main plane structure of an aeroplane consists of the main spars, ribs, external and internal bracings and the wing covering. The most usual type of spar used by British manufacturers is made of metal. It consists of top and bottom flanges and two webs, fastened together by rivets, forming roughly a box. Fig. 1 shows a Westland spar and Fig. 2 a Boulton Paul spar. The latter has separator plates between the webs and flanges and tubular stiffeners or distance pieces between the webs, a form of construction which adds to the strength of the spars.

It will be noticed that metal sheets bent into special shapes for both the flanges and webs are used. It is the ingenious use of metal sheet which has enabled metal spar construction and metal construction generally in aircraft to reach such a high standard, and at the same time keep the weight down to the lowest possible. The sheet is passed through special rolling machines which roll it into the sections required ready for riveting. In most aircraft which are metal covered the thin metal sheet which is used is corrugated for the same reason, and prevents local buckling.

SPARS AND THEIR FITTINGS. **Fig. 1.** Westland spar. **Fig. 2.** Boulton Paul spar, the structure of which affords greater strength. **Fig. 3.** Armstrong Whitworth steel strip spar.

The Armstrong Whitworth steel strip spar is shown in Fig. 3. This form of spar is made of steel strip riveted together, and is one of the most efficient spars in use. In later forms of spars efforts have been made to get rid of the necessity for riveting. Fig. 4 shows a Bristol spar. In this spar the steel strips forming the webs and flanges are grooved at their edges and interlock. The four strips are prevented from moving relatively along one another by the rivets which secure the fittings and ribs. The actual shape of these duralumin or steel strips for spars is still a matter of experiment, with the object of saving weight. Certain forms of drawn metal tubes are used,

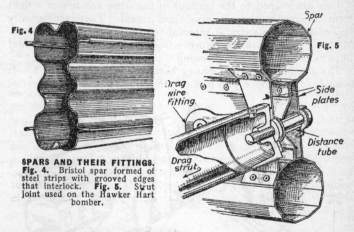

SPARS AND THEIR FITTINGS. Fig. 4. Bristol spar formed of steel strips with grooved edges that interlock. **Fig. 5.** Strut joint used on the Hawker Hart bomber.

but though this type of construction is very much simpler than the strip construction, it suffers from being heavier. In most forms of aircraft construction there has to be a compromise between simplicity and weight.

There are many varieties of joints used between the spars, ribs and interplane struts, and only a few typical joints can be illustrated and described. The whole objects of joint design are simplicity, weight-saving and strength, and considerable ingenuity has to be exercised to keep these objects constantly in view. Fig. 5 shows an intermediate drag strut joint on the Hawker Hart light bomber. The drag struts in the wings are fastened to plates by a plug fitting, threaded to take a bolt which passes through the tubular distance piece of the spar. The plates themselves are riveted to the main spar.

The rear interplane strut fitting on the De Havilland Moth is shown in Fig 6. The spruce interplane strut is fitted into a metal strut socket, which is held to the fitting by a bearing pin. The wiring fitting takes the incidence wire and the landing wire. This is one of the simplest forms of main plane strut and wiring fitting. Fig. 7 shows a more complicated fitting round a Boulton Paul spar. Here the lift and anti-lift or landing wires are doubled, and lugs are provided for the drag wires and sockets for the interplane and drag struts.

Ribs are shaped to the contour of the wing and are of a light form of construction in wood and metal. They are usually spaced along the spars at intervals of twelve to sixteen inches. With a greater span, the fabric covering between them sags and impairs the efficiency of the wing.

The standard rib on a Fairey bomber is shown in Fig. 8. It is made of a stamped web of sheet duralumin and flanges of rolled

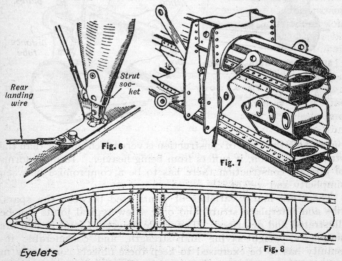

Rear landing wire

Strut socket

Fig. 6.

Fig. 7

Eyelets

Fig. 8

SPARS AND THEIR FITTINGS. Fig. 6. Form of main plane strut and wiring fitting used on the De Havilland Moth. **Fig. 7.** More elaborate fitting round a Boulton Paul spar. **Fig. 8.** Part of a main plane rib on a Fairey bomber. There are fourteen of these ribs spaced along the spars at 12–16-inch intervals.

duralumin attached by tubular aluminium rivets, which also serve as eyelets for the lacing of the fabric. The ribs are clipped to the main spars.

Interplane struts are of three general types—round tube, streamline section tube and built up from metal strip. A round tube is always fitted with a streamline fairing to reduce resistance when the aeroplane is flying. For small tubes the fairing is often a piece of wood as a tail-piece (as in Fig. 9), but for larger tubes a complete fairing is fitted round the tube, as in Fig. 10. These fairings are made from wood formers spaced at 4 to 6 inches, and covered with 1 mm. ply, which is fabric covered.

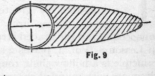

Fig. 9

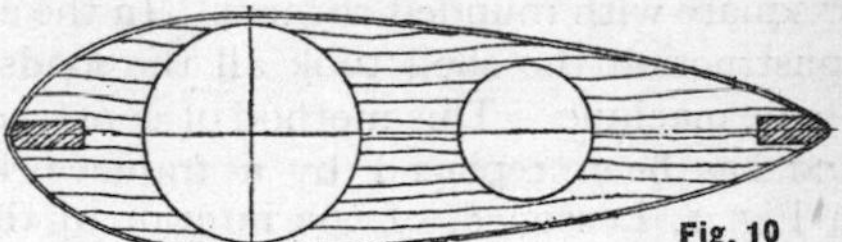

Fig. 10

FAIRINGS FOR INTERPLANE STRUTS. Fig. 9. Fairing for small, tube strut, consisting of a wooden tail-piece. **Fig. 10.** Fairing which is fitted round a larger tube.

There is an increasing tendency in aeroplane construction to use the thick monoplane wing, and also to fair the junction of wing and fuselage by means of streamlined fillets.

In the stressed-skin wing a metal cover is used instead of fabric, and this metal cover is made to take the forces on the wings. In this form of construction ribs are not used, and the number of spars and the method of construction vary within wide limits. Some designers prefer metal box spars, while others believe in multi-cellular construction, in which a number of light-weight stringers are attached to the skin and short fore and aft members. All-metal construction in small aircraft will always present difficulties, because of the thinness of the metal sheet which must be used. Such thin sheets always fail by local buckling, though in theory they may be strong enough.

An ingenious type of construction which comes between the monocoque and the girder is the Vickers-Wallis geodetic, applicable to both wings and fuselage. This involves the use of a kind of basket-work of intersecting diagonal members, the tension members stabilizing the compression members and vice versa. Three R.A.F aircraft of geodetic construction broke the world's distance record in 1938.

LESSON 14

Some Details of Fuselage Design

THE construction of the bodies or fuselages of aircraft shows a considerably greater variety than that of the main planes. There are, however, two broad types, the monocoque and the braced structure, both of which are illustrated in Lesson 8 (Vol. 2, plates 2 and 3). The monocoque fuselage in principle is a hollow shell, roughly circular or elliptical in section, or square with rounded corners. In the early forms of monocoque construction the shell took all the loads coming upon the body of the machine. This method of construction is, however, heavy, and has been replaced by a framework such as is illustrated in Fig. 1, Lesson 8, of the interior of the D.H. Flamingo. The skin covering of the fuselage of this machine is Alclad sheet stiffened by longitudinal stringers of light aluminium alloy.

Thin metal sheets have a tendency to buckle or cockle at the slightest strain, but by corrugating the sheets this tendency is greatly lessened. An example of the corrugated sheet covering was that used by the Junkers. The metal-covered monocoque or semi-monocoque fuselage is now the most popular type, while a form of construction which has given remarkable results in practice is the Vickers-Wallis geodetic system described in the preceding page.

The braced fuselage is still, nevertheless, a most widely used form. It consists generally of a tubular steel structure with mechanical or welded joints or a structure made from metal strip. Fig. 1 shows a side view of the fuselage of the Fairey 111 F. The centre and rear portions are wire braced tubular structures and are separate units. The front portion or engine mounting is also a separate unit, and is constructed of tubular steel members welded

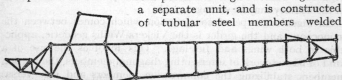

DETAILS OF FUSELAGES. Fig. 1. Braced fuselage of the Fairey 111 F. It is in three separate units for convenience of replacement.

together as shown in Fig. 2. Fig. 3 shows the type of fitting which is used in the centre section at the point where the under-carriage, also leg or shock absorber, comes and the front spar of the main plane.

A typical joint in the De Havilland Moth two-seater light aeroplane is illustrated in Fig. 4. In this joint both welding and bolting are made use of. The whole of the fuselage framework is steel tubing, either rounded or square in section, and follows the usual practice of being built in three portions, engine mounting, front and rear portions. Bracing is not used in the all-welded type of fuselage, but in the earlier types wire bracing is employed in the top and bottom panels of the rear portion.

The engine mounting is usually separated from the front portion of the fuselage by a fireproof

DETAILS OF FUSELAGE DESIGN. **Fig. 2.** Engine mounting of the Fairey 111 F.

bulkhead. The front portion is covered with three-ply over a spruce or ash framing shaped for the cockpit openings. The sides of the front portion and the whole of the rear portion are fabric covered. The engine is covered in by panels of aluminium.

This construction is general for most types of braced or partly braced and partly welded fuselages. The use of welding is much more widespread abroad than in Great Britain, where it is restricted. There is no doubt that the use of welded joints, however, will become more general as confidence in the methods is established. The restrictions of welding have led British designers to evolve ingenious mechanical joints, which are light and efficient. By the mechanical joint is meant one which is made up with bolts, pins or rivets and can be easily taken apart. The welded joint, of course, is one which is permanent. The mechanical joint has the advantage that a greater range of materials is available than in the case of the welded joint—stainless and high-

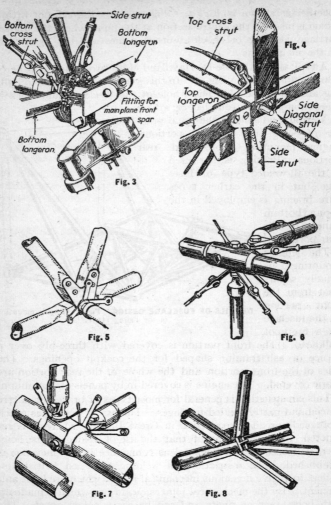

Side strut

Bottom cross strut

Bottom longeron

Fitting for mainplane front spar

Bottom longeron.

Fig. 3

Top cross strut

Fig. 4

Top longeron

Side Diagonal strut

Side strut

Fig. 5

Fig. 6

Fig. 7

Fig. 8

DETAILS OF FUSELAGE DESIGN. Fig. 3. Fitting at the bottom of the engine mounting of the Fairey 111 F, shown in the previous page. **Fig. 4.** Joint in the De Havilland Moth light aeroplane. **Fig. 5.** Hawker joint. **Fig. 6.** Armstrong Whitworth joint. **Fig. 7.** Boulton Paul joint of heavy tubular construction **Fig. 8.** Bristol joint.

tensile steels, duralumin, etc. Fig. 5 shows a typical mechanical joint used by the Hawker Aircraft company. This type of joint is of easy construction, and with different-sized plates and tubes can be used on a wide range of machines.

The Armstrong Whitworth joint is shown in Fig. 6. A metal sleeve, fitted over the longeron, is held in place by two bolts. The vertical bolt takes the end of the vertical fuselage strut, and the horizontal bolt the horizontal cross strut.

Tubular construction is in general heavy, and the Boulton Paul joint, shown in Fig. 7, is an effort to reduce the weight. Instead of the usual type of tube a locked joint tube is made from steel or duralumin strip. Steel strip is used in the fuselage construction of the Bristol

Fig. 9

Aeroplane Company. Two semicircular sections are used to make the tube, being interlocked at their edges. In order to increase the strength of this form of tubing it is

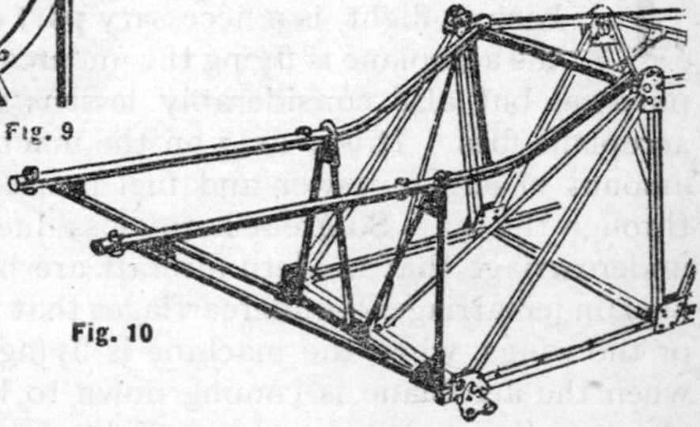

Fig. 10

ENGINE MOUNTINGS. Fig. 9. Ring mounting for Bristol engine. Fig. 10. Mounting of horizontal girder type.

often corrugated. The steel strip tube enables a different type of joint from those described to be used. The Bristol strip fuselage is a lighter form of construction than the normal tubular mechanical-joint fusclage. Fig. 8 shows the method of making the Bristol joint, and the construction of the strip steel tubes can be clearly seen.

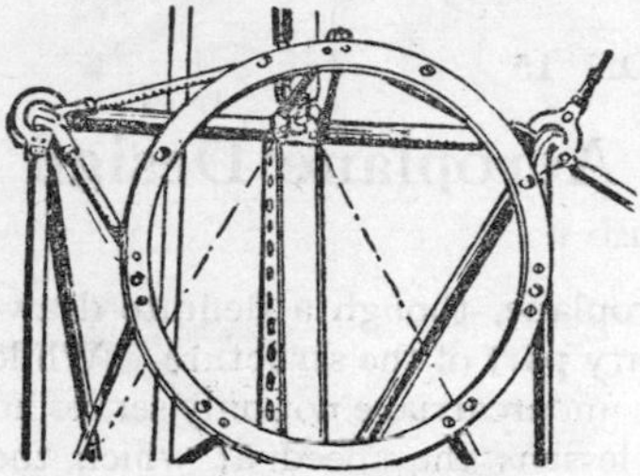

Engine mounting arrangements can be seen in Figs. 2, 9 and 10. There are no standard methods of fixing the engine, the various types of engine making standardization impossible. With the radial air-cooled engine, as the Bristol Pegasus or Pobjoy, the engine is attached to a vertical circular plate or ring concentric with the cylinders and crankcase. In the case of the in-line or

V air-cooled or liquid-cooled engines as the Gipsy or Merlin the engine is attached by two horizontal fore and aft girders. The whole mounting is held by struts to the main structure of the machine.

A circular ring mounting for a Bristol engine is illustrated in Fig. 9. Fig. 10 is the horizontal girder type, as used for the Cirrus or Gipsy engines. It is made of mild steel tube, welded. The engine is held in position by four vertical bolts.

LESSON 15

Undercarriages in Aeroplane Design

(See plate 1)

THE undercarriage of an aeroplane, though a definite drawback in flight, is a necessary part of the structure. While the aeroplane is flying the undercarriage not only serves no purpose, but also considerably lessens the speed at which the aeroplane flies. It is a drag on the machine, in fact, and a great amount of engine power and fuel is used up merely to carry it through the air. So great is the loss due to the resistance of the undercarriage that modern aircraft are being made with retractable undercarriages—undercarriages that fold up into the fuselage, or the wings, when the machine is flying, and are lowered again when the aeroplane is coming down to land. Some idea of the effect of the undercarriage in flight may be realised when it is stated that, on an average, it forms roughly an eighth of the total weight of the aeroplane and has about one-eighth of its total resistance to flight. A machine which flies at 100 miles an hour normally, would fly, with no increase in engine power or fuel consumption, at 112 miles an hour without its undercarriage.

The Airspeed Courier in flight with its undercarriage is shown in Fig. 1 (plate 1) ; in Fig. 2 the same machine is seen with its undercarriage retracted into the wings. By this retraction the top speed of the Courier was increased some 13 miles an hour with the same engine.

The undercarriage was the first part of the aeroplane to be constructed in metal ; the very strongest steels are used to keep down the weight as much as is consistent with the required strength. The most usual form of undercarriage consists of a two-wheel chassis and a skid or small wheel at the tail. Fig. 3 shows the simplest form of chassis, consisting of two wheels joined by an axle, and sprung on telescopic compression legs. These compression legs consist of an oil dashpot, helical springs or rubber blocks. The radius rod shown in Fig. 3 allows the compression leg to swing forward as it is compressed. It is jointed at both ends with a view to giving it freedom of movement.

The split axle type of undercarriage, illustrated in Fig. 4, is widely used. In the axle type shown in Fig. 3 there is always the possibility of the axle fouling some obstruction, and so causing the machine to crash over on its nose. In the split axle type this danger is avoided. Steel tubing is used instead of wires. The actual details of construction of aeroplane chassis vary, but the main principles remain the same as shown in Figs. 3 and 4. As to the distance between the wheels, this should be about one-fifth to one-quarter of the span of the wings of the aircraft.

The compression leg or shock absorber is a most important part of the structure of the undercarriage. In the simplest form the shock is taken in tension, and the absorber consists of a number of rubber rings or a length of rubber cord wound continuously; but the unreliability of the cord

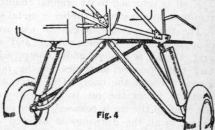

Fig. 4

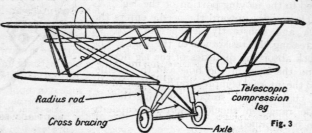

Radius rod

Cross bracing

Axle

Telescopic compression leg

Fig. 3

UNDERCARRIAGE DESIGN. **Fig. 3.** Diagram showing the most usual form of undercarriage. **Fig. 4.** Split axle type of chassis.

has caused this type to be superseded in most modern aircraft. Rubber is better in compression, and it is in this form that it is now chiefly employed. In most modern aircraft, however, especially in the larger machines, a combination of oil, compressed air, rubber or steel springs is used.

In the oil dash-pot system oil is forced through a small hole from one chamber to another, the resistance to the movement of the leg depending on the size of the hole.

Oleo-pneumatic *Oleo-rubber* *Oleo-spring*

COMPRESSION LEGS. Fig. 5. Three types generally used on medium-sized aircraft. In theory, the oleo-pneumatic form is the best and lightest, but it is difficult in practice to construct an absolutely air-tight joint.

The oil is returned to its original chamber, as soon as the load is removed, by a system of rubber or metal springs, or compressed air.

The three systems in general use are shown in Fig. 5 : the oleo-pneumatic, the oleo-rubber and the oleo-spring. In the first, the air is always under compression, and the pressure increases as the oil is forced through the hole. This increase of pressure forces the oil back the moment the load on the leg is released. The needle shown in all the drawings is tapered and fixed to the moving portion of the leg. As the leg moves upward the needle enters the hole and constantly lessens its size, so increasing the resistance to the load. The shock absorbing qualities of the leg depend upon the sizes of the hole and the needle, and the internal compression of the air in the air chamber ; by suitably varying these a wide range in shock absorbing capacity can be obtained.

FIG. 6. Details of the tail skid of the De Havilland Puss Moth.

The oleo-rubber and oleo-spring shock absorbing legs work on the same principle, rubber and metal springs being used.

UNDERCARRIAGES

A standard feature of all modern aircraft is the use of large-section low pressure tires. In light aircraft such tires have been very successful, and the low pressure tire has the further advantages of offering less resistance to the air and being more satisfactory on soft landing grounds than the normal high pressure tires. The low pressure tire, often called the doughnut wheel, is illustrated in Volume 2, Plate 3, Fig. 5.

As the landing speeds of aeroplanes have increased, with a consequent increase in landing run, wheel brakes have developed, so making a forced landing very much safer. The use of good wheel brakes reduces the landing run of the average aeroplane by as much as 50 per cent, and they have the further advantage of making the machine easier to manœuvre on the ground. With the use of wheel brakes, however, the chassis has to be thrown farther forward to prevent the aeroplane from turning over on its nose when the brakes are applied. Brakes add considerably to the weight of the chassis, as, apart from the weight of their own mechanism, braking throws greater loads on the undercarriage, which must, therefore, be more strongly constructed.

Two general types of brakes are used. In both the tire and rim move round the brake drum. In one case the braking action is brought into play by the pressure of expanding shoes against the rim through friction linings, and in the other by the pressure of a flexible circular expansion chamber against the rim.

Tail skids or wheels are a necessary part for landing. Fig. 6 shows the tail skid of the De Havilland Puss Moth. Its direction can be controlled by the rudder controls. Until the introduction of wheel brakes this type of tail skid, with a metal shoe, was widely used, as the friction between it and the ground served to slow up the aeroplane. But with the use of wheel brakes a steerable tail wheel has replaced the tail skid, and it has the advantage of imposing less strain on the tail structure.

The tricycle undercarriage, which embodies a wholesale revolution in design, has the subsidiary wheel under the nose instead of under the tail. This gives increased stability on the ground and improved vision.

LESSON 16

How Aeroplanes are Controlled in Flight

(See plates 1 and 2)

THE control surfaces of an aeroplane are the tail plane, the fin and rudder and the ailerons, and (usually) the landing flaps. Part of the tail plane, known as the elevators, the rudder, the ailerons, and the flaps are movable. Handley Page slots are also fitted to some British aircraft, and there is great variety in the design of modern high-lift devices. The function of the elevators, ailerons and rudder are explained in Lesson 2 (Volume 1, page 13), and those of the Handley Page slot in Lesson 1 (Volume 1, page 9). Here the construction of these controls and control surfaces will be considered.

In diagrammatic form Fig. 1 shows the flying controls of an aeroplane. The control column or wheel at D controls the ailerons and elevators through cables A and E. The cables A to the ailerons pass over pulleys to a drum at the front side of the handwheel at the top of the control column. Turning the wheel to the left lowers the right aileron and raises the left through the balance cable B, enabling the aeroplane to bank over for turning to the left without side-slipping. The reverse movement of the wheel raises the right aileron and lowers the left, and the aeroplane banks for turning to the right. It will be noticed that the cable B raises one aileron when the other is lowered, so decreasing the lift on one wing and increasing it on the other simultaneously, to enable the aeroplane to bank correctly without side-slipping.

The control column as a whole can be moved forward or back about hinges on the bottom cross tube shown in the figure. Control cables run from levers on this tube to the elevators. Moving the control column forward lowers the elevators, raises the tail of the machine and forces the nose down. Pulling the control column back raises the elevators, lowers the tail and forces the nose up. The rudder is connected by cables to the rudder bar F by cables G. By pushing the left foot forward the nose of the aeroplane is swung to the left, and vice versa.

AEROPLANE CONTROLS

The above gives the general principles of the controls. Instead of cables, pull and push rods may be used, and in small aeroplanes the control column is universally jointed at the lower end, so that the column can move fore and aft, as well as sideways, and give aileron and elevator control without the necessity of the handwheel. For large aircraft and training aircraft, dual controls are fitted and interconnected for the use of the instructor and the passenger learning to fly.

The construction of the tail plane, fin and rudder follows in general that of the main planes. In most aeroplanes the tail plane is a monoplane and a single rudder is used, but in large

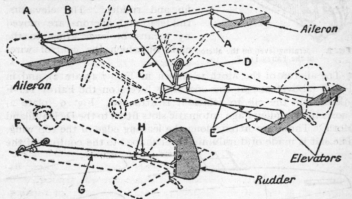

AEROPLANE CONTROLS. Fig. 1. Diagram of flying controls. A, cable to ailerons ; B, balance cable; C, aileron cables ; D, control column ; E, cable to elevators; F, rudder bar ; G, cable to rudder ; H, turnbuckles.
Courtesy of " Flight "

types of aircraft, large passenger machines and heavy bombers, a biplane tail may be used and two or more rudder surfaces Fig. 2 (plate 1) shows the tail plane and the twin rudders of the De Havilland Albatross commercial aeroplane. The fin, the fixed surface in front of the rudder, is usually set at a slight angle to the vertical centre line in small single-engined aeroplanes, to balance the effect of the propeller. Fig. 3 (plate 2) shows the construction of the tail plane and rudder and fin of the Avro 621 Tutor, a machine widely used in the Royal Air Force for the training of pilots. The construction resembles very closely that of the main planes of most aeroplanes. Spruce for light aeroplanes and metal for the heavier machines are the materials generally used.

In the tail unit shown the whole construction is of welded steel tubing. The rudder and elevators are mounted on ball bearings to give greater freedom of movement and control. Figs. 4, 5 and 6 (plate 2) show the skeletons of the tail plane, elevators, fin and rudder respectively of the two-seater light aeroplane, the De

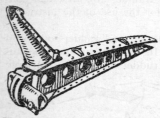

Havilland Moth. All are covered with fabric, finally. The spars of the tail plane are of spruce, and the ribs are of spruce and three-ply. Spruce and three-ply are used for the construction of the elevators, fin and rudder. The elevators, rudders, and ailerons are moved by means of lever arms, to the ends of which the control wires come.

Fig. 8. Operating lever on the aileron of the Fairey 111 F.

The aileron of the Moth is shown in Fig. 7 (plate 2), and in Fig. 8 (above) one of the operating levers on the Fairey 111 F aileron and the rib to which it is attached. Fig. 9 (plate 2) shows the Handley Page automatic slots fitted to the De Havilland Moth. These are fitted along the leading edge of the top wing. The slot is made of duralumin sheet shaped to the contour of the

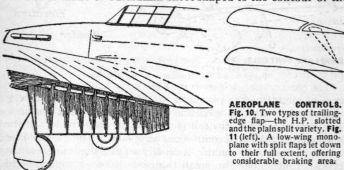

AEROPLANE CONTROLS. **Fig. 10.** Two types of trailing-edge flap—the H.P. slotted and the plain split variety. **Fig. 11** (left). A low-wing monoplane with split flaps let down to their full extent, offering considerable braking area.

nose of the wing. The control surfaces called flaps are used for increasing both lift and drag, the gliding angle of the aircraft being steepened and the landing speed reduced when they are let down. In Fig. 10 are seen two of the many types of flaps now in use. The **lower** illustrates the split trailing-edge flap, fitted as standard to many modern aircraft. The **upper** shows the H.P.

slotted flap, hinged in such a way that a slot is formed between the main wing and the flap when the latter is operated. Other developments of the flap are leading to greater safety of the aeroplane at the take-off and landing when it would be out of control if such devices were not used. Landing flaps in the fully lowered position are seen in Fig. 11.

LESSON 17

Construction of Sea-going Aircraft

(See plates 3 and 4)

THERE is little doubt that the big aircraft of the future flying over the great air routes of the world will be flying boats and seaplanes. Not only do such types of aircraft offer certain advantages of construction over the land machines, but they have the great advantage of not requiring specially-built aerodromes on which to alight. The hull of a flying boat takes the place of the fuselage or body of the land machine, and carries passengers, mails, goods, petrol, etc.

The great difficulty of hull construction is to make the hull of such a shape that it offers the least possible resistance when taxying on and getting off the water, and also when the boat is in flight. A compromise in shape has to be struck, as these two qualities are rarely in accord with one another. The hull has, in addition, to be seaworthy, and the flying boat must be stable on the water as it is in the air.

The chief terms used in flying boat construction are explained in Fig. 1. Most of the terms are self-explanatory, and are those used by shipbuilders. Tumble home is the inward slope of the side from chine to gunwale, and flare the outward slope. The two may occur in the same hull—flare at the stern and tumble home along the rest of the length. Light aluminium alloys, as duralumin or Alclad, are used in hull construction, and also stainless steel. Sea-water has a powerful corroding effect, and the metal-work of hulls has to be protected by paints or other methods against corrosion, adding considerably to the weight of the hull.

The hull of the Saunders-Roe Cutty Sark, under construction, is shown in Fig. 2 (plate 3). It is built of Alclad light alloy. In the boats built by Messrs. Short Bros., transverse rings are used supported by fore and aft stiffeners. Fig. 3 (plate 3) shows the interior construction of the Short Sunderland looking aft from the rear luggage compartment.

Certain types of flying boat, notably the American Consolidated and the German Dornier, have the wing raised above the hull on a streamlined fairing, but in most cases the wing is high enough above the water-line for the engines to be faired into its leading edge. In the Short "C" and "G" class boats there are two decks, the crew occupying the upper and the passengers the lower.

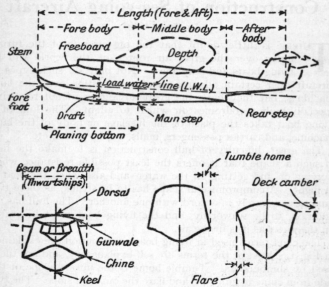

FLYING BOAT CONSTRUCTION. Fig. 1. Diagram explaining the terms used in the construction of flying boat hulls.

The hulls of the Rohrbach boats had sharp, high bows, resembling ships' hulls more than most flying boats, which usually have rather a blunt forward end. The Keystone-Loening flying boats, built in America, were unusual in their construction, in that they had a wooden framework covered with a metal skin, while most modern flying boats are of metal construction throughout.

The joints between the metal plates were sealed with fabric tape impregnated with marine glue, which gave a greater watertightness than is possible with the all-metal riveted joint. The advantage of wooden hulls over metal ones is that they are more resilient and so lessen the landing shock. But the all-wooden hull absorbs so much water that it may cease to be a commercial proposition. The Keystone-Loening type of construction combined the advantages of the wooden and the metal types.

The design and construction of floats for seaplanes follow very much those of hull construction. In most seaplane floats there is a strong fore and aft girder in the form of a keelson and dorsal, on to which are built the transverse frames, in halves each side. The float is usually divided into a number of watertight compartments and at the point of attachment of the fuselage struts the float is strengthened. In the normal twin-float seaplane each float is capable of taking the weight of the machine fully loaded.

The construction of the Avro all-metal float (Fig. 4, plate 4) shows the method of building up the transverse frames on the keelson. Fig. 5 shows the completed float with the metal skin riveted on and ready for finishing. Fig. 6 illustrates the wing-tip floats used on a Short commercial flying boat. These floats prevent the planes being broken by buffeting on the waves. Modern types often incorporate seawings or sponsons (*see* Vol. I, plate 3, fig. 3) or retractable wing-tip floats.

Floats for racing seaplanes are much longer than those designed for normal seaplanes. Fig. 7 shows the Supermarine S5 float, under construction. The strong keelson will be noticed, and the longitudinal stringers. These are the floats used on the machine which won the Schneider Trophy of 1927. One of these floats was provided with a petrol tank.

Taken all round, marine aircraft of over 8,000 lb. in weight are built as flying boats, and below that weight as seaplanes. An exception is the German Blohm und Voss seaplane, with a loaded weight of 37,000 lb. This has been specially constructed for catapulting from floating aerodromes in the Atlantic. The weight of the floats is about 10 per cent of the total weight of the machine.

The metal plating used on flying boat hulls and seaplane floats is 14–20 gauge, according to the part of the construction. In most flying boats, as in seaplanes, a number of watertight bulkheads are fitted, and the riveting is very closely spaced to provide watertightness where other precautions are not used.

LESSON 18

How to Become a Pilot

FLYING is, every year, becoming more and more simple. At one time it required a high degree of skill, but the modern aeroplane has become almost fool-proof if certain simple rules are observed. Anyone who is reasonably physically fit and a good car driver can learn to fly.

The best thing for anyone to do who has a wish to fly is to have a trial lesson at any one of the many flying clubs or schools. Aeroplanes for learning to fly are fitted with dual controls, and the instructor can give you an elementary lesson and accustom you to the sensation of flying. He can in a few minutes of practical lessons judge what your ability is for flying and how long you are likely to take to learn.

That time depends largely upon the individual and how regularly he or she can take lessons. The oftener the better, so that the feel of the controls is not lost between the lessons. The more regularly it is possible to take lessons the cheaper it is, in general, to learn to fly. The average pupil should take between ten and twelve hours to learn to become a pilot. Fees for instruction vary from £1 to £3 an hour, and the total cost of learning is usually about £30. This figure is substantially reduced for those volunteering for the Civil Air Guard, which now has sections attached to most clubs.

Licence and Certificate. No person is allowed to fly, unless under instruction, until he or she is the holder of a pilot's licence. There are two kinds of licences issued by the Air Ministry, the A or private pilot's licence, and the B or commercial flying licence. A pilot must have the A licence before he can obtain a B licence. The Royal Aero Club issues a certificate, and the holder of such a certificate will, subject to certain requirements, be granted an A licence by the Air Ministry.

To obtain a Royal Aero Club certificate a pilot must have had three hours at least flying experience as the sole occupant of the aircraft. He or she must take off and climb to a height, and must descend from not less than 2,000 feet with the engine cut off, and land within 150 yards of a given spot. The prospective pilot must also pass the following test. He must fly at a height of not more than 600 feet around two marks 500 yards apart in a series of five figure-of-eight turns. He must land afterwards, with his engine cut off, within 50 yards of a spot previously chosen. Finally, he must pass a *viva voce* examination on the Air Convention Rules as to lights, the general rules of Air Traffic, and International Air Legislation.

The Royal Aero Club certificate does not allow cross-country flying, and for that purpose it is necessary to obtain the A licence. To obtain this it is necessary to pass a medical examination, which may be held by the candidate's own doctor. If this examination, which is not a very rigorous one, is satisfactory, a candidate receives his A licence without any further flying tests. Qualified Royal Air Force pilots are exempted from the medical and flying tests for their A licences, but they must pass the *viva voce* examination outlined above. Licences must be renewed annually, and when application is made for a renewal, evidence must be produced that the pilot has flown solo for not less than three hours within the previous twelve months. The cost of the Royal Aero Club certificate is half a guinea and of the A licence 5s.

Identification Marks. The choice of an aeroplane for the private owner is entirely governed, as with a motor-car, by his requirements. He has a wide choice, from fast single-seaters to large machines carrying half a dozen or more passengers. Machines can be bought in exactly the same way as cars, for cash or by a series of payments. Every aeroplane has to be registered by the Air Ministry, for which a fee of £1 1s. is charged. Each aeroplane is given a series of registered letters, corresponding to the number plates on cars, and these letters must be painted a prescribed size on the fuselage and wings of the aeroplane. In addition, the name and address of the owner must be carried on a metal plate on the fuselage.

Every aeroplane must also have a certificate of airworthiness, for which a fee of £5 5s. is payable. This certificate of airworthiness —a certificate which means, in effect, that the aeroplane has been thoroughly inspected and is safe to fly—must be renewed annually.

Like motor-cars, aeroplanes can be bought secondhand, but the secondhand plane has the advantage over the secondhand car that it is known to be in first-class condition. It cannot be flown without the certificate of airworthiness, which means that it has not only been thoroughly inspected by a government inspector, but that all worn parts have been renewed and the machine is structurally perfect and as fit to fly as a new machine. It is safer to buy a secondhand aeroplane than a secondhand motor-car.

A pilot should carry four log books : (1) an engine log book, showing the number of hours the engine has done, together with any overhauls and adjustments which have been made ; (2) an aircraft log book, showing repairs, adjustments, etc., apart from the engine ; (3) a journey log book, giving an account of any journeys done by the aircraft, with a list of mishaps, etc. ; and (4) a pilot's log book, giving the hours flown by the pilot.

A private owner should insure his machine. The cost of insurance varies inversely with the skill of the pilot. The more experienced he is the less the insurance rate. Overhauls and repairs to private aircraft must be certified as correct by a licensed ground engineer or, alternatively, by the authorized representative of a firm approved by the Air Ministry.

Anyone wishing to fly abroad from Great Britain must leave from one of the Customs aerodromes, such as Croydon, Lympne or Heston. He should obtain a carnet from the Royal Aero Club or the Automobile Association. These carnets save the pilot from having to deposit sums for Customs dues in countries where there are duties on aircraft. Certain other Customs forms have to be filled in before leaving the Customs aerodrome, and these are supplied with the carnet, which is issued at a nominal cost.

B Licence. The B licence is a much more difficult licence to obtain than the A licence. The B licence is for commercial pilots who are allowed to take up paying passengers. In brief, the requirements for a B licence are (1) a cross-country flight of 200 miles solo with two obligatory landings en route, and a similar flight with an examiner on board, to include three forced landings ; (2) a general flight, with an examiner on board, for half an hour ; (3) a night flight of at least thirty minutes carried out from an aerodrome ; (4) proof of at least 100 hours' solo flying in the preceding two years and at least 30 landings, and (5) the passing of a technical examination dealing with theoretical and practical knowledge of aircraft engines and running repairs. In addition, the professional pilot usually holds what is known as the second-class navigator's licence. After four years' air experience and 600 hours' flying he can sit for his first-class navigator's licence and after five years' experience and 1,000 hours' flying he may obtain his master pilot certificate. Every British aeroplane used for international carrying of passengers or goods and having to fly over 100 miles by day or 16 miles by night without landing must have a navigator on board who holds a second-class certificate. For flights of more than 625 miles a first-class certificate is required, and two pilots, or a pilot and a navigator, must be carried. Holders of B licences have to be medically examined at regular intervals.

The regulations for B licences are necessarily severe, and the tendency is to make them harder to obtain. On the other hand, those for the A licence may be made easier in some ways, and certain other regulations at present in force will undoubtedly be relaxed in order to make it easier for the private owner to fly. The cost of flying is high at present, but it is becoming less every year, and with the increasing demand for aeroplanes they are also becoming cheaper. When aircraft are in as great demand as motor-cars their cost will be little greater than that of a car of the same seating capacity.

LESSON 19

Mapping the Earth from the Air

(See plates 5—7)

ONE of the most important uses of the aeroplane is for the purpose of making maps and carrying out survey work. In countries like Africa, Canada and Australia the difficulties of making detail maps from the ground are so great, and the cost is so high, that no accurate maps exist at all of many great areas of the world's surface. There are huge unexplored areas where gold and silver and other valuable minerals exist. The opening up and examination of these areas in the first place from the ground will take many years.

The aeroplane is able to overcome all these difficulties rapidly and accurately, and now air survey for the purpose of map making is superseding the slower methods of ground survey. An immense amount of time is saved in this way. An air survey, for example, was made in Egypt over an area of 120,000 square miles. The ground was difficult, and the survey in the ordinary way would have taken fifteen years to complete. The whole of the region was photographed from the air and maps prepared in a year and a half by aerial survey.

In Canada over 640,000 square miles have been mapped from the air, and the work of years carried out in a corresponding period of months. By means of these air photographs great areas of forest have been located containing valuable timbers, mining areas developed, and new water-power supplies discovered. Supplies are taken regularly by air to the big mining camps in a few hours, where formerly the time used to be many weeks. In this way the mining season has been considerably extended. Hundreds of men and tons of machinery are also taken to the camps, and from them fresh areas are being regularly surveyed from the air. The chief towns throughout the world are now photographed from the air, because the plan of the streets can be seen so much better that way.

In making a map from the air, the first thing which has to be done is to take a complete set of photographs of the ground which has to be covered. These photographs are afterwards pieced together, rather like a huge jig-saw puzzle, and from them the maps are finally drawn. To make certain that the ground is covered, a definite course is marked out for the aeroplane, and photographs are taken at regular intervals while it is flying this course. The intervals are so arranged that each photograph taken overlaps at least half the previous one. Fig. 1 (plate 5) shows the course of the aeroplane and the overlapping photographs. The dotted line indicates the course taken by the aeroplane, and the full lines the area covered by each photograph. Fig. 2 (plate 6) shows the developed prints being roughly pieced together to form what is known as the mosaic. The photographic mosaic serves as a second check that no ground should be missed.

Vertical and Oblique Photographs. There are two kinds of photographs taken for air survey work, the vertical and the oblique. Vertical photographs are taken with a camera fixed in the aeroplane so that the lens points straight downwards to the ground being photographed. The corresponding photographs give a very accurate plan of the ground below, but they have the disadvantage of not always being easy to understand. The oblique photograph is taken at an angle—very much the same kind of photograph as is taken from the top of a hill of the surrounding country. In the case of oblique photographs all the ground photographed is distorted and foreshortened, and the outlines so obtained have to be corrected before the map is made. In order to do this a grid of white lines is placed over the print, and by means of this the correct outlines can be drawn. Very often a combination of the vertical and the oblique methods is used. Fig. 3 (plate 5) shows a photograph of a large stretch of country taken for map making and the grid applied to it.

Even the vertical photographs have to be corrected to obtain accurate results, as it is not always possible to fly an aeroplane in such a way that the camera remains strictly vertical. Nor is it possible to make sure that every photograph is taken at the same height. Each photograph has to be enlarged or reduced in keeping with the proper scale decided on for the final map. To make sure of getting final accurate results, every photograph has on it, printed automatically, certain information. This is printed to one side, on what is known as the information strip.

For example, a photograph of a railway junction is shown in Fig. 4 (plate 6). On the right is the information strip. The top dial records the height at which the photograph was taken— here 10,000 feet. Below it is the number of the photograph, and below that a double kind of spirit level, which works horizontally and vertically and shows whether the aeroplane was flying level or not at the instant the photograph was taken. At the bottom of the strip is given the time at which the photograph was taken. All this information is recorded on every single photograph, so that everything which should be known about the resulting print is automatically recorded. The prints are all reduced to some standard height, and those which have been taken when the camera was not vertical are corrected. It is very useful to know the exact time of day at which the photograph was taken because, if that is known, it is possible to calculate, from the length of the shadows on the ground, the heights of buildings, hills, trees, and so on.

The upper part of Fig. 5 (plate 7) shows a hundred and fifty photographs which have been corrected and pieced together to form a photographic map, and the lower part shows the actual map which has been drawn from the photographs. The area covered is about eleven square miles, and the whole of the photographs were taken in three hours ; it would have taken as many months to make the same survey from the ground.

Increasing use is being made of aerial survey for town planning, for the control of big engineering projects, and for mining, forestry and other purposes To those skilled in reading aerial photographs it becomes possible to survey country with a view to its possibilities for minerals, oil, and so on. Many important mineral deposits have first been discovered by air survey in the North-West Territories of Canada, for example. Huge forest areas have not only been surveyed from the air, but it has been possible to discover, from the photographs, the types of trees growing and their extent, so that a close approximation can be made to the value of the timber.

The camera designed for air survey work uses a film capable of taking a hundred photographs, each five to seven inches square. The camera is automatic in action, and is usually actuated by a small electric motor.

Our Course in Aeronautics is continued in Volume 4.

LESSON 13

European Art in the Age of the Renaissance

(See plate 8)

IN the early days of the Italian Renaissance the Florentine school of painting took the lead, Siena occupying the second place. The subsequent history of the movement in the arts reveals the rise and development of several other local schools, each of them being identified with the name of at least one great master ; in fact, there was hardly a town of any importance that did not have its school of artists. Thus the schools of Rome and Venice developed when the influence of Florence began to wane ; Milan, Bologna and Genoa, Parma, Naples and Modena, Ferrara, Pisa and Lucca—all had their periods of artistic activity and fame. Most art historians do not adopt a severely local classification, but range the painters under more general headings, such as Tuscan or Umbrian or Lombard, finding in those within the category some common bond in style or technique. Many of the great artists travelled and were influenced by other schools or imparted their own knowledge to them.

It is not always easy to distinguish between these schools, especially those of central Italy, where the influence of Florence was dominant. But, so far as pictorial art is concerned, a difference developed in the early part of the 16th century between the Florentine school and that of Venice. Whereas the Florentines thought mainly in terms of form and line, the Venetians were, first and foremost, colourists. During the 15th century Venetian art was strongly influenced by the neighbouring school of Padua, represented by Schiavone (c. 1435–1474) and Mantegna (1431–1506) ; and these were essentially classical painters, exponents of the new humanism. Mantegna added his enthusiasm for archaeological construction and the asceticism of the engraver's line. He stands above his contemporaries as a classical artist with a Roman rather than a Greek interpretation. Then two great painters, Tura and Encole, rose in Ferrara, but they show, not the new humanism, but the tormented spirit of the north.

Venice was always less concerned with the revival of the ancient learning than with the colourful amenities of her own life—the pomp and ceremony of government, the pageants of her canals, the domestic luxuries—anything that gave pleasure and relaxation from the daily cares of this sternly mercantile republic. These wealthy traders demanded an art that should be neither academic nor didactic, an art that should not reflect classic knowledge or otherwise exact an effort of the intellect, but that should reproduce the splendour of their surroundings and appeal directly to the senses through harmony of colour. Venice had never lost touch with those aesthetic motifs that had come from Byzantium ; and Byzantine art was an art of colour.

Effect of the Renaissance in France. We may now glance at the effects of the Italian Renaissance upon the art of other countries. In France the influence was felt much earlier than elsewhere. This was due to the almost continuous political connexion between the two countries during the 15th century. Social manners in France became Italianised ; French scientists and men of letters visited the lecture rooms of Tuscany and Lombardy ; Italian artists, notably Andrea del Sarto and Leonardo da Vinci, received warm welcome from the French Court. Early in the 16th century French architects began to plan along the lines of the classic Renaissance builders. Yet, as is shown by Chambord and other examples of château architecture at this date, the vitality of the French style was such that it never became completely dominated by the Italian example. Then, as now, it was the striking achievement of French artistic genius to borrow and recreate. When the real Renaissance in French architecture matured in the 17th century, it had achieved a synthesis of northern feeling with classical abstraction.

In church building the Gothic ideals realized in the cathedrals died very hard. Lemercier's church of the Sorbonne, built in the days of the Grand Monarch, is one of the few examples that show a purely classic spirit. The châteaux of the previous century mostly represent either the imposition of classic details upon a Gothic plan or Gothic details retained in a classic plan. In painting, Italian ideas did not really manifest themselves until Nicolas Poussin (1594–1665) translated them into the French language of art. Poussin lived and worked in Rome as well as in Paris ; he was profoundly influenced by antique sculpture, and his mastery in the use of geometrical shapes and solid composition (the comprehension of form which makes things appear solid) has had a lasting influence on French art. He has been called the " father of the Post-Impressionists."

The Renaissance in Germany and Flanders. In Germany and Flanders the influence of the Renaissance had an individual rather than an artistic significance. The northerners were not greatly interested in the revival of learning in so far as it related to Greek and Roman philosophy ; but their scholars and churchmen were interested in the Greek and Hebrew texts of the Bible as a department of " learning," and there was much intercourse with Italy for the purpose of elucidating these texts and so preparing the way for the spreading of the Reformers' gospel. Thus, by the irony of events, humanism, which in Italy connoted the pagan classics, became an active instrument of the Christian Reformation ; although Protestantism, developing into Puritanism, was the negation of the Renaissance spirit. The Italian influence hardly affected either German or Flemish art during the 16th century. There is, indeed, nothing more striking, in view of the intellectual intercourse with Italy, than the consistently national character of the austerely great art of Albrecht Dürer (1471–1528) and of the Holbeins, or of the contemporary Flemish painters. Later both Germans and Flemings took something from Renaissance architecture, but the former never appreciated its simplicity, and overloaded their " classic " buildings with exuberant Teutonic ornament. In the Low Countries Renaissance architecture was more discreetly adapted, and in the 17th century painting began to reveal, in the art of Rubens and Van Dyck, a nobility of conception and grandeur of scale associated with Renaissance ideals ; but by this time the Renaissance in Italy was dead.

Cultural Activity in Spain. Any direct impression that humanism might have made on Spain was checked by the Counter-Reformation. The Church held life and art alike in a firm grip. Yet the writings of Cervantes and Calderon, the mystical paintings of El Greco and the realistic paintings of Velazquez, the exploration of the oceans by Columbus, the conquest of Mexico and Peru—all indicate a time of intense mental and physical activity arising at the same period of history as the Renaissance. In architecture, as we have seen, there were already several points of contact between the Moorish and classic styles ; but Italy's influence made no appreciable difference. The Escurial, indeed, built in the 17th century, is a " classical " building, but of a cold and slightly uninspired type that suggests an origin in passing fashion rather than in feeling.

England's Aesthetic Revival. Of English art it may be said that it was at first but lightly touched by the Renaissance. In painting, England was virtually attached to the Netherlands till the 18th century. The Tudor style of architecture has been described as an attempt to translate the Renaissance style into the English vernacular. Yet the numerous and stately country mansions it produced have an individuality at least as attractive and appropriate as the characteristic French château. Later, Inigo Jones—working when Van Dyck and Rubens were painting in England and dominating English art—gave us in " Palladian " an austere but dignified Greek classical architecture. Sir Christopher Wren (1632–1723), builder of St. Paul's and other beautiful London churches, evolved an independent style that was peculiarly suited to English aesthetic needs. In painting and sculpture there was no native soil prior to the 18th century in which Renaissance ideas could take root.

LESSON 14

Supreme Artists of the Italian Renaissance

(See Colour Frontispiece and plates 9—12)

Two great sculptors of the early Renaissance period are Ghiberti (1378–1455) and Donatello (1386–1466). Ghiberti's greatest work is the two bronze gates of the Baptistery at Florence. The grandeur and yet graceful composition displayed in this work are unexcelled, though his treatment of bas-relief has been criticized adversely.

Donatello also worked in metals, being first apprenticed to a goldsmith. He was the greatest of the early Tuscan sculptors, and his work created an epoch in the art of sculpture, of which he has been called the founder in its modern aspect. He had complete mastery in the art of relief. Although influenced and inspired by the antique he caught the personal character of the subject ; and his work thrills with life. His bronze

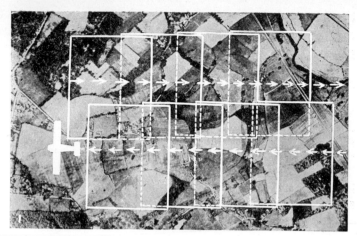

MAP MAKING FROM THE AIR. Fig. 1. A section of country to be photographed, showing the course taken by the aeroplane and the area of land covered by each photograph. **Fig. 3.** General view of the land to be mapped, showing the grid applied to it.

AERIAL MAP-MAKING. Fig. 2.
Developed prints being roughly pieced together to form a photographic mosaic. As indicated in Plate 5, they overlap in order to ensure that no part of the ground to be covered is missed.
AERONAUTICS 19

TYPICAL AIR PHOTOGRAPH. Fig. 4. Example of an aerial survey photograph showing a railway junction. On the right is the information strip, giving details of the height, the time, spirit level reading and number of the photograph.
AERONAUTICS 19

Courtesy of The Royal Aeronautical Society

Plate 6   *Volume III*

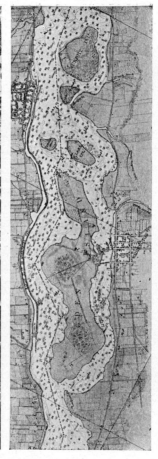

AERIAL SURVEY. **Fig. 5.** Above, one hundred and fifty photographs carefully corrected and pieced together as a mosaic and forming an accurate photographic map. Below, actual chart which has been drawn from the above mosaic. The area shown is roughly eleven square miles. AERONAUTICS 19

Courtesy of The Royal Aeronautical Society

TWO RENAISSANCE MASTERPIECES. Above, Poussin's "Bacchus and Ariadne"; below, Mantegna's "Triumph of Caesar."
ART AND ARCHITECTURE 13

Plate 8   *Volume III*

equestrian statue at Padua, the "Gattamelata," challenges the more famous Colleoni monument in Venice, the work of Verrocchio, for impressiveness and dignity.

Luca della Robbia (c. 1400–1482), a Florentine sculptor in bronze and marble, and the founder of a complete dynasty of workers in majolica or glazed and enamelled terra cotta, broke fresh ground in his masterly and sympathetic interpretations of the homelier human emotions : the mother's love, the happiness of children. Amongst his works are medallions in polychrome and enamelled reliefs. He is also specially famed for the two panels of children carved in marble for the singing gallery of Florence Cathedral.

Two Monkish Painters. Of the painters working in the 15th century, Fra Angelico, called Giovanni da Fiesole (1387–1455), a Dominican monk, who is associated with the Florentine school, stands on the threshold of the Renaissance, yet nevertheless apart. His was the triumph of the Gothic style. His frescoes in the museum of San Marco in Florence, and those in the chapel of Nicholas V in the Vatican, at Cortona and elsewhere, are considered examples of purest religious art. In the National Gallery, London, is one of his easel pictures : a " Glory " of Christ with 265 saints. The deeply sincere yet joyous nature of his art has often been stressed.

A later monkish painter, Fra Filippo Lippi (c. 1409–1469), expressed emotions of a different character. He studied under Masaccio (1401–c. 1428), a master who improved perspective in art and the relation of figures and objects to the background. Fra Filippo found beauty in Italian peasants, painting religious subjects from the human rather than from the idealistic viewpoint. His art reveals emancipation from the exaggerated religious fervours of some of his contemporaries. His greatest pupil, Sandro Botticelli (c. 1444–1510), was perhaps the most frankly Greek in spirit of all the 15th century Italians. With unequalled beauty of decorative line and rhythm, Botticelli stood apart from the scientific aims introduced into the art of the Renaissance by such masters as Donatello, Masaccio and Pollaiuolo. Though Botticelli could express blithe and lovely pagan feeling—for example, in his famous " Primavera " or Allegory of Spring—he also possessed the capacity for deep and sincere feeling. From 1482–92 his style, from the brilliant and exquisitely fanciful, becomes more austere. Examples of this period are his religious pictures of the Annunciation and the lovely circulars of the Madonna ; also the magnificent pagan decorative painting of " The Birth of Venus." His frescoes in the Sistine Chapel of the Vatican are representative of his greatest work.

Filippino Lippi (1457–1504), son of Fra Filippo, became the pupil of his father's pupil Botticelli. Though possessing an individual style, he shows the influence of both artists in his work. His most celebrated painting is comprised in the frescoes illustrating legends of St. John and St. Philip in Santa Maria Novella at Florence, and in those of incidents in the life of St. Thomas Aquinas, which are in the Minerva Church at Rome.

Piero della Francesca (c. 1416–1492) gave to his paintings a crystalline purity of light and colour. He was a master of perspectival composition and regularity of form. A pupil of his, Luca Signorelli (c. 1441–1523), painted a number of frescoes, and of his easel pictures there are several examples in the National Gallery, London. He shows himself in these, and in his frescoes in the Cathedral at Orvieto, as excelling in the painting of the human body in terms of muscular activity. Pietro Perugino (1446–1523) is perhaps chiefly noted as the master and forerunner of Raphael, but his paintings of religious subjects, though charming in colour and graceful in form, possess an almost cloying sweetness.

Raphael. Modern critical opinion has somewhat modified the former acceptance of Raphael Santi (1483–1520)—born at Urbino and commonly known as Raphael—as the greatest artistic figure of the Renaissance. His earlier work closely resembles Perugino's—which was natural, as he helped him in painting pictures, after the custom of the time for apprentices in the studio of a master. Later, having acquired all the graceful sense of form that Florence could teach him, he was influenced by both Michelangelo and Leonardo da Vinci. In common with them, Raphael passed easily from religious to pagan themes. He was, however, on his own account a technically perfect painter. It has been said of him that he was the symbol of the Italian spirit of sublime grace. Of the new classical humanist school, he reproduced antique character in fine designs expressive of lovely movement and action. Correggio (1494–1534), unrivalled as a master of chiaroscuro, possessed excellent command of technique and of his medium.

Leonardo da Vinci. The two greatest artists of the Renaissance are Leonardo da Vinci (1452–1519) and Michelangelo Buonarroti (1475–1564). The former is best known to the world by reproductions of his pictures " The Last Supper " on the wall of the church of St. Maria delle Grazie at Milan, and the " Mona Lisa " at the Louvre. Leonardo advanced towards a new synthesis of the scientific aims of the precursors of the Renaissance. Now linear perspective was not enough—aerial perspective is added. The figures in the composition are subordinated in detail to the whole and conform to effects of light. Leonardo is the great structural painter, investigating everything and putting his knowledge clearly into his drawing of forms.

Michelangelo. Painter, sculptor, engineer and architect, Michelangelo astounds in all four branches with the grandeur and vastness of his artistic conception. It would seem almost incredible that the man who executed the fresco of the " Last Judgement " on the vault of the Sistine Chapel, with its titanic tortured figures, its overwhelming sense of violence, should also have carved the classically beautiful and infinitely solemn figures of the Medicean tombs (in San Lorenzo, Florence), and yet again found energy and time to carry out the duties of architect-in-chief of St. Peter's and design a dome for that mighty cathedral. Michelangelo carries to its limits the modelling of the human form. His output of sculpture alone is enormous. He could strike the classical note impressively, as in the Medicean figures, or more lightly, as in his " David " (Florence Academy). He could also express the most tender and sincere religious feeling, as seen in the Pietà in St. Peter's, Rome. In none of his work does he consciously aim at beauty, but at grandeur, sublimity and the expression of passion.

Venetian School. The Venetian school may be said to have been founded with Giovanni Bellini (c. 1430–1516) and Gentile Bellini (c. 1426–1507) in the 15th century, in so far that both these artists were in search of that rich and harmonious colour that was to become characteristic of the later school. But maturity was not reached till the turn of the century, the age of Giorgione (1477–1510) and Titian (c. 1480–1576), and, in its latter half, of Tintoretto and Paolo Veronese. Giorgione is the real creator of the Venetian school ; he liberated Venetian art from servitude to Florentine form and established a new relationship between colour and light and shade. Titian, his greatest pupil, took the art of Giorgione as a starting point, but in later life developed and created new tonal harmonies splendid in their strength.

Giorgione as a portraitist was surpassed by Titian, who ranks in this branch with Velazquez and Rembrandt. The great men of Venice, their characters, their pomp and trappings, live again vividly in the pictures of this aristocratic artist and citizen. The religious side of the most sumptuous colourist of any age is revealed in his gorgeous yet solemn " Assumption " in the Venice Academy. Tintoretto (1518–1594) and Veronese (1528–1588) upheld and developed the traditions of Venetian painting when the Renaissance in the rest of Italy had lost its fire.

An important figure in the later Renaissance is Benvenuto Cellini (1500–1571), the greatest goldsmith of all time, who sculptured also in bronze. His " Perseus and Medusa," executed for Cosimo de' Medici, is a superb plastic creation in bronze ; but he displayed the same passion for perfection in designing and making so small a piece as a gold salt-cellar for the king of France.

LESSON 15

"Old Masters" of Northern Europe

(See plates 12 — 15)

LITTLE is known of the personalities and lives of the early artists in Germany. In the fourteenth and fifteenth centuries there were fairly vigorous schools of art at Prague, Cologne, Augsburg and some of the cities on the Rhine, but the "masters" preferred to remain anonymous. The asceticism of the medieval spirit was translated in Germanic art into terms of the stark horror of realism. This is especially noticeable in the treatment of religious subjects, such as martyrdoms or the Crucifixion. At best, these painters desired to be truthful at all costs, their work possessing a tortured passion of sincerity ; at worst, they twisted the truth into unendurable ugliness. The work of Mathias Grünewald shows both aspects.

Albrecht Dürer. Towards the end of the 15th century Albrecht Dürer (1471–1528), with his freedom from Italian influence and the Renaissance cult of classical beauty before all, represents everything that was greatest in German national art, which was intellectual rather than aesthetic. He brought to his work immense dignity and supreme technical ability; it combines characteristics of his nation in its homeliness and mysticism and of himself in its expression of his search after scientific and moral truth. In such works as the Nativity triptych in the Dresden Gallery and his " Adam and Eve " at Madrid, these qualities and his talent for forcible composition are magnificently asserted. Had he never painted a picture, he would, however, still be among the world's greatest artists ; his magnificently designed woodcuts and copper-plates for engravings exhibit the highest degree of finish with boldness of line, imagination, and grasp of the technical requirements of his materials. His drawings, of which there are many examples in the British Museum, show his supreme skill as a draughtsman. During his later years the thought of this profound artist was influenced by Luther—himself fundamentally a German patriot. With zeal for the doctrines of the Reformation Dürer inscribed admonitory texts from the Epistles—taken from Luther's translation—on his pair of vigorously painted panels of the Evangelists, given to the council of Nuremberg, his native town, and later transferred to Munich.

Contemporary with Dürer, a lesser, but also celebrated, German master, Lucas Cranach (1472–1553), painted sacred, classical and contemporary scenes in oils on panel. He also executed designs for various wood and copper engravings, but, unlike Dürer, his drawing is somewhat defective ; his chief interest is as a colourist.

Holbein. The next great master produced by Germany was Hans Holbein the Younger (c. 1497–1543). He was born at Augsburg and there instructed by his father, the elder Hans, himself at the time an honoured painter, though later to be eclipsed by his famous son. For a while the younger Holbein worked at Basle, Zürich and Lucerne, and important paintings and drawings by him are in the Museum at Basle. Here he was seriously employed in making designs for wood-engravers, of which art, like Dürer, he was a supreme master. About 1527 he visited England, and subsequently became court painter to Henry VIII. During this period he executed remarkably fine portraits in oil of contemporary personages and also a number of portrait drawings preserved in the Royal Collection at Windsor. His paintings, " The Ambassadors " and the exquisite masterpiece " Queen Christina of Denmark," are in the National Gallery. Darmstadt possesses the curiously interesting " Meier Madonna," so called from its being actually a portrait group of Jacob Meier's family. Holbein's most famous woodcuts of the " Dance of Death " are distributed between London, Paris and Munich. He learned something of his pictorial composition from the Italians—notably Mantegna and Leonardo da Vinci—but his art is characteristically German in its intellectual veracity and attention to the minutest details. His keen observation of human character, together with his unerring technical ability, places him amongst the world's greatest portrait painters.

The Van Eycks. The great commercial activity of Flanders in the 14th and 15th centuries provided a powerful stimulant to the development of art. Although oil painting had been previously practised, Hubert and Jan Van Eyck (the former born about 1366, some twenty years before the latter) perfected the use of this medium, so that the brilliance and finish of their work is unique to-day. The brothers painted in partnership at Ghent for some years ; then Jan was employed at Bruges in the service of Philip the Good of Burgundy. Hubert's great work, " The Adoration of the Lamb," an altar-piece with folding doors for the cathedral of St. Bavon, in Ghent, was completed after his death by his brother Jan. The National Gallery, London, possesses in the portrait-painting of Jean Arnolfini and his wife a masterpiece by Jan Van Eyck in which the homely characters and setting reveal the perfection of his technique. The Van Eycks painted their sacred subjects also, literally and faithfully, from the models they met in their daily lives, the landscapes and the architecture they looked upon, the familiar objects in their homes.

Rogier van der Weyden (1400–64) was rather less literal, a little more emotional in his transcripts from the life. His reputation extended into Germany and France, and he was the moving spirit in the foundation of a school of Flemish realists who, in common with the early German masters, painted zealously the horrors of tortured bodies and the realism of beggars' wretchedness, the effects and ravages of disease. Pieter Brueghel (1525–69) depicted such scenes with forceful composition and good colour. His work has of later years attracted interest and appreciation. He could also paint merry-makings and village scenes with remarkable veracity. Quentin Matsys (c. 1466–1530) linked the Flemish and Dutch schools. He ranks highly as a colourist, his pictures being exquisitely finished.

Rubens. The most famous painter of the Flemish school, Peter Paul Rubens (1577–1640), came under Italian influence, especially that of the Venetian school, early in his career. He may be said to have taken from Italy all that was necessary for the full development of his own robust Flemish art. He was a brilliant colourist. The superabundant vitality of his style expressed itself occasionally in the opulence of his nude figures and in excess of movement, which takes the eye of the spectator out of the picture. He does not equal the gracefulness and dignity of his pupil Van Dyck in aristocratic portraiture, but his range was considerably wider. Though not primarily a religious painter, Rubens rises in some of his religious compositions, notably the Antwerp " Descent from the Cross " (see Volume 1, plate 5), to magnificence. In his landscapes he made clever use of broken colour to convey atmosphere where required.

Court painter to Charles I, Van Dyck (1599–1641) has left us a collection of portraits of the English and Continental royalty and aristocracy of the day. He, like Rubens, learnt his art in Italy, studying the masterpieces of Titian and Veronese, and if as a colourist he was less courageous than Rubens, he was more subtle. In addition to his fine portraiture, he painted religious subjects with distinction and great beauty of form ; he was also a master etcher and executed a series of line portraits of contemporaries, afterwards published as engravings.

Dutch Painters. The Dutch School of the 17th century arose directly out of the Puritanism of the Reformation. North Flanders, or Holland, generally accepted the strictest Protestant doctrines. In the unpretentious new churches there was no room or desire for religious pictures, but the Dutch burghers had grown well-to-do, and demanded small paintings for the decoration of their private houses, not of the sacred or pagan classical subjects of the Renaissance, but landscapes of the country they lived in, and scenes of the daily life of burgher and peasant at work or recreation. The demand was met by painters of landscapes like Hobbema and Cuyp, by seascape painters like Van der Velde, and a host of " little masters," among whom stand out the names of Ruysdael, Vermeer of Delft, Jan Steen, Terburg and Gerard Dou ; the younger Teniers, though a Fleming, may be joined to their number. Technically these men are superb.

Never have cabinet pictures been produced with a keener appreciation of the handling of pigment.

Rising among these excellent " little masters," Hals assumes a great and Rembrandt Van Rijn a gigantic stature. Frans Hals (c. 1580-1666) achieved his greatest triumphs in portraiture, especially in group portraiture, such as the fine series of Burgomasters at Haarlem. Remarkable in their spontaneity are his renderings of the expressions on the faces of his subjects, as seen in his famous works, " The Laughing Cavalier " and " The Lute Player." He founded the Dutch School of figure painting.

Rembrandt. Rembrandt (c. 1607-1669), the first great master of chiaroscuro since Correggio—though neither always so consistent nor so true in this respect as the Italian painter—combined a rich gift of individual characterization with the power of dramatic effect. He was able as a rule to use light and shade in an arbitrary manner to suit his purpose because he understood nature, but occasionally he overstressed his contrasts and thus limited his range of colour. That he could paint in starkly realistic fashion his fine " Anatomy Lesson " at the Hague bears witness. The dramatic intensity of " The Night Watch," and those profoundly human portrait studies of his mother and of himself in old age, reveal his art at its highest. He was a great etcher as well as painter. His life work possesses immense variety, imaginative power and sympathetic insight. Both Hals and Rembrandt have been called impressionists because in their work there is a sense of focus, objects in the centre being more clearly seen than those on the outside of the field of vision.

LESSON 16

Painters of France and Spain

(See plates 16 and 17)

T HE earliest French artist of international interest is Jean Pucelle. In the first half of the 14th century, at his famous atelier in Paris, illuminators, miniaturists and other painters, both native and foreign, worked under his direction. This School of Paris influenced the art of northern Europe, and English painters studied there ; it inspired the three great pieces of medieval painting—the Parement of Narbonne, the portrait of Richard II in Westminster Abbey, and the Wilton Diptych in the National Gallery. The next painter of note whose name emerges from among anonymous primitive masters is Jean Fouquet (c. 1420–c. 1480). He studied in Rome and worked at Tours, was at the court of Charles VII of France and painted a remarkably subtle portrait of the king ; also at about the same period a lovely diptych, the right wing of which is in the Museum at Antwerp and the left at the Museum, Berlin. The latter represents St. Stephen and also has a fine portrait of Etienne Chevalier, minister of finance to Charles, while the right wing represents the Virgin and Child surrounded with blue seraphim and scarlet cherubim. Fouquet also excelled as a miniaturist and book illuminator.

Jean and François Clouet, often called Janet, painted portraits on panel, in oil. (In some cases the medium is not determined.) Jean Clouet came to France from the Netherlands about 1516 and worked in Paris till 1540. François, in Paris 1522–1572, painted many notable persons, including Charles IX.

The Neo-Classicists. In 1530 Primaticcio, a second-rate Italian painter, was summoned to Fontainebleau by Francis I, and his sojourn there led to the foundation of the " School of Fontainebleau," which was mainly a collection of Italian mannerists who produced no great artist from their ranks. These were followed early in the 17th century by the Neo-Classicists, headed by the great painter, Nicolas Poussin (1594–1665), who may be regarded as the founder of a dynasty of painters in the grand, otherwise classical, manner. In the latter half of the 19th century Poussin's work was discredited, but again today the same degree of admiration expressed for it by Sir Joshua Reynolds and Gainsborough is accorded by most critics. Poussin used geometrical and thoroughly architectural shapes in his pictorial compositions. He has been called " the father of the Post-Impressionists," because, like them, he bestowed his attention not on tone, but on that comprehension of form which makes things appear solid. His self-portrait, at the age of 56, reveals strength and intellectual nobility. The finest collection of his works is at the Louvre, but he is represented at the National Gallery and at Dulwich. Gaspard Poussin, his nephew, was a landscape painter of some note, though his pictures have little interest today.

Associated in period with Nicolas Poussin, but widely different in style, is Claude Lorraine (1600–1682). Concerned—as were the Impressionists after him—with light as it affected colour, his achievement may be described briefly as the discovery of sunlight as a governing factor in landscape ; it was this aspect of his art that provoked Turner to victorious emulation and Constable to unbounded admiration. Though Claude never painted a landscape without paying homage to the classic ideal by including classic architecture, the varying effects of sunlight were the real subjects of his pictures, and his trees and clouds and winding rivers ceased to be mere forms conventionally coloured. Both Poussin and Claude influenced decisively the rise of modern landscape painting in England.

The Brothers Le Nain. Working about the same time were the three brothers, Antoine (1588–1648), Louis (1593–1648), and Mathieu Le Nain (1607–1677), renowned for their paintings of French peasant life. These pictures were remarkable in a period when art was mainly devoted to classical subjects and landscapes, or to portraits of great persons, and throw much light on the humbler domestic life during the first half of the reign of Louis XIV. A contemporary Court painter was Le Brun, under whose direction was placed the decoration of the palace of Versailles, as well as the organization of the Gobelins Tapestry factory. He possessed great influence at the time, but his work had little artistic value.

Watteau and his Pupils. With the turn of the century a new epoch in French painting arrived, and the artist who set the fashion for this epoch, Antoine Watteau (1684–1721), though born at Valenciennes, was of Flemish origin. Penniless, he arrived in Paris and at the age of eighteen found employment in various studio-factories. After much hard work he painted his diploma picture in 1717, when he attained full membership of the French Academy of Art, founded by Louis XIV in 1648. This picture, " The Embarkation for Cythera," is now in the Louvre. Subsequently he painted portraits, decorative panels, Court and camp scenes. He made his " fêtes galantes " alive with an atmosphere of charm and humanity. His arcadian scenes—French courtiers and their ladies masquerading as harlequins and shepherdesses in appropriate gardens—held up a faithful mirror to the artificial life of 18th-century society. But his subjects throughout remained free from the coarse suggestiveness introduced by some of his followers. Grace and poetry are manifest in all his work—etchings as well as paintings. His delicate, brilliant colour is inimitable in the latter and so, in both branches of his art, is his fluent drawing.

His pupil, Lancret (1660-1743), was a charming painter, without the genius of Watteau; Boucher (1703-1770) and Fragonard (1732-1806) were much influenced by his style. The former was a fine etcher and decorator, and his portraits of Madame de Pompadour are well known. Fragonard, who studied in Rome and outlived the Revolution, was also a Court painter and an etcher. He decorated the apartments of Madame du Barry with exquisite skill. He was apprenticed to a great artist. Jean Baptiste Simeon Chardin (1699-1779), an exquisite portraitist, also famed for his still life, flower and genre paintings. An artist whose pictures possess delicacy of colour and charm is Jean Baptiste Greuze (1725-1805), but his work is spoilt by pretty sentimentality and somewhat weak draughtsmanship.

French sculptors followed dutifully in the footsteps of a classic fashion that had lost all vitality, until a climax was reached in the domination of Europe by Canova and Thorwaldsen, whose uninspired perfection held sway till the 19th century was well advanced. A few French names have survived, but not gloriously.

The " historical " period of Spanish art dates from the School of Seville towards the end of the 16th century. The first name to stand out is Zurbaran. Francisco Zurbaran (1598-1662) most truly represents the sombreness of the national character at this time : he was pre-eminently the painter of the monks and of the dramatic side of the Catholic Reaction. His is emotional art, indeed, with the emotion pitched in one key ; yet there is a fine sense of form in his work, and he handles his limited palette skilfully.

El Greco and Velazquez. Earlier than Zurbaran was working the celebrated mystic painter, El Greco (1545-1614), who, though born in Crete, became a Spanish master, painting in startling contrast to the school represented by Zurbaran and the greatest of all Spanish artists, Velazquez (1599-1660). El Greco was influenced by the religious mysticism of Ignatius Loyola, the founder of the Jesuit Order. This mysticism is noticeable in all his pictures. In comparing the technique of El Greco with that of Velazquez it is important to note that the latter is always grasping at essential things in the world as he saw it, while the former is always concerned with the world of the spirit. The technique of Velazquez is stronger and more perfect, but he lacks the imagination and creative originality which distinguish the work of El Greco in such a masterpiece as " Christ's Agony in the Garden." On the other hand, El Greco could not render contours and textures as delicately or so truthfully.

In his first years of painting Velazquez followed Zurbaran in colouring. The Spanish school loved warm colours—reds, yellows, orange—and painted their shadows in browns. The effect was heavy and lacking in variety. Velazquez developed his magnificent sense of colour after his visit to Italy. Like Rembrandt, he has been called an Impressionist. His insight into human character may be studied in a long series of portraits of the Bourbons and the men who stood behind them, now scattered throughout the European galleries. One marvels the more at his achievement since the Court to which he was painter held etiquette as hardly second to religion, and every one of its members wore a mask of cold dignity to conceal his inner self from the world. But Velazquez penetrated the masks. Perhaps the greatest and most human of his portrait groups is the famous " Las Meniñas." The National Gallery possesses examples of his work—portraits, historical scenes and the Rokeby Venus—and also, it may be added, works of Zurbaran and El Greco.

Goya. In comparison with El Greco and Velazquez, Murillo (1617–1680) is merely a journeyman painter, though he enjoyed an enormous popularity. Spanish painting remained quiescent and undistinguished till the later part of the 18th century, when Goya (1746–1828) " arrived." A talented artist of immense versatility, Goya was a rebel by nature, and much of his art is keen satire directed against the effete and corrupt Church and State. The vitriolic pungency of his work is expressed in his famous etchings. His portraits are characterized by uncompromising realism. One of the most famous is that of Charles IV for which he was made Court painter. There are examples of his painting in the National Gallery, London, including the well-known portrait of Doña Isabel Corbo de Porcel, of which an illustration will be found in Vol. 1, plate 6.

LESSON 17

English Painters of the Georgian Era

(See plates 17—19)

THREE great foreign artists dominated portraiture in England during the Stuart period—Sir Anthony Van Dyck (1599–1641), Flemish Court painter to Charles I, Sir Peter Lely (1618–1680), Dutch Court painter to Charles II, and the German, Sir Godfrey Kneller (1646–1723). All three had much influence on the magnificent epoch of British painting which immediately succeeded them and continued throughout the reigns of the four Georges. Lely is famous for the series of " Beauties " at Hampton Court, though his masterpieces are his splendidly individualized " Admirals " at Greenwich Hospital. Kneller's popularity as a portraitist was so prodigious that his large output of work is of necessity unequal. Two fine examples, which combine delicacy of modelling with firmness and reveal his skill as a colourist, are the portraits of Sir Christopher Wren and or " The Duke of Monmouth after execution," both in the National Portrait Gallery.

Genre Pictures. Kneller was governor of the first art school in London, situated near Lincoln's Inn Fields. He had, therefore, ample opportunity to affect the technique and style of the rising generation of painters, although amongst them a distinctively English art was forming, while a demand was being created among the well-to-do public for a different type of pictures. Large portraits and vast paintings of classical subjects were suitable for palatial buildings and the stately mansions of the great ; but now the prosperous professional classes and city merchants required smaller pictures to adorn the panelled walls of their Georgian houses, which were being erected by terrace and square in city and town, while sporting squires wished for paintings of hunting scenes and of their horses and dogs The immediate demand, therefore, was for something more after the Dutch type of *genre* pictures, William Hogarth (1697-1764), the first definitely English painter of genius in the 18th century, arose to supply this demand with his extraordinary output of narrative pictures, stage scenes, " moralities " and small " conversation pieces." The last-named type of portrait groups, in which all the members of the family introduced were united in some occupation or interest, were exceedingly popular throughout the century. The painters John Zoffany (1733–1810) and George Stubbs (1725–1806) are particularly noted for their fine work in this style of portraiture. The latter artist also excelled as an animal painter.

Hogarth. Hogarth was born in Smithfield, the son of a schoolmaster, and was an engraver before he began to paint in oils at the age of thirty. His industry was almost as amazing as his gift of memory and the fluent swiftness of his art. He professed much contempt for foreigners, though he derived great benefit from the study of Dutch pictures ; his method of composition by means of light and shade was influenced by Rembrandt. He may also be compared with Hals in the talent which they both possessed of being able to catch to perfection momentary facial expressions. The " Shrimp Girl " in the National Gallery, London, is the finest example of Hogarth's work of this kind, in which he was a pioneer of impressionism. Excellent also in their lifelike characterization, though without unity of composition, are the six heads of his " Servants " in the National Gallery.

Hogarth lived and worked through a troubled period. It was an age of violent contrast between the upper and the lower classes of society, of wild experiments in government and finance, of State lotteries, of the South Sea Bubble, of the most flagrant abuses of power, privilege, and common human decencies. He hated hypocrisy and showed up some of these abuses in such pungent fashion that they were uprooted. The fame of his pictorial series of " moralities "—" Marriage à la Mode," " The Rake's Progress," etc.—is not, however, based only on their moral or narrative interest. The six pictures of the first-mentioned series belong to his most brilliant period, as also does that masterpiece—portraying the contemporary misery and destitution of the poor in France—" Calais Gate," painted 1749, in which he records his arrest while sketching the town.

Mr. Charles Johnson, official lecturer at the National Gallery, London, in his book " English Painting " (Bell, 1932), says of Hogarth :

" His wide sympathy inspired in him a curiosity to investigate every aspect of human life, so that he proved that anything can be interesting and even picturesque. His excitement in noting movement and life naturally led to a swift enjoyable method

of painting figures ; just as his perception of the beauty of light-
ing led to a transparent painting of its gradations. The same
wide sympathy led him to moralise. Whether this was also good
for his art has been doubted. Certainly it often caused him to
overstress his meaning or overcrowd his canvas, and sometimes
to become obscure or even to forget the requirements of a picture
altogether. It has been said that he was at his best as a cool,
detached observer. But sympathy makes complete detachment
impossible ; and without such sympathy with the inner workings
of men's minds he could have never recorded their outward
actions with such vivacity."

Reynolds and Gainsborough. By the time that Hogarth had
arrived at the height of his powers, two younger painters were
coming to the fore. Sir Joshua Reynolds (1723–1792) and Thomas
Gainsborough (1727–1788) were rivals throughout their careers,
and their relative merits have been vigorously contested. Though
the former artist exercised a more lasting influence on portraiture,
Gainsborough was the more versatile painter—he would have
been famous for his landscapes alone—and possessed the deeper
insight. Some of his most exquisite masterpieces are now in
America, notably the lovely painting of Eliza Linley (afterwards
Mrs. Richard Brinsley Sheridan) and her brother ; a most
delightful portrait of a little girl, " Miss Juliet Mott," and the
famous " Blue Boy." In London, his Miss Singleton (Nat. Gal.)
and Mrs. Robinson (Wallace Col.) are beautiful examples of his
genius for painting women.

Gainsborough never laboured his art. He derived an additional
dexterity from the study of the work of the Flemish masters,
Van Dyck and Rubens ; Hogarth also influenced his portraiture,
while in landscape he deeply appreciated and studied the technique
of the French artists Nicolas Poussin and Claude Lorraine.
Gainsborough was great enough to learn from others and yet
evolve his own individual style. Much of his work is painted
thinly with rare beauty of execution and luminous colour. In
Ruskin's opinion he is the greatest colourist since Rubens.

Sir Joshua Reynolds was founder and first president of the
Royal Academy in London (1768). Steeped in the tradition of
the great Italians—and also receiving the mantle of Sir Godfrey
Kneller as his successor in portraiture in the grand manner and
following him in the use of a rich impasto—he painted both
portraits and historical pieces. But whereas he lives through

his portraiture, he was comparatively mediocre in the historical compositions, which he himself believed to be the more important part of his work, painted according to the doctrines which he preached in his famous " Discourses." To some extent his portraiture is also intellectual in character. In his earlier work he was always making experiments and so striving after perfection that his painting lost the freshness which characterizes that of his great rival Gainsborough ; but, in many of Reynolds' portraits the psychological insight is penetrating and sympathetic, showing his wide understanding of humanity. He is usually at his best in his portraits of men, but the exquisite " Nelly O'Brien," painted in 1763 and now in the Wallace Collection, London, is one of his finest masterpieces. In this portrait he has combined spontaneity with the complete finish which he loved.

Romney, Raeburn and Lawrence. George Romney (1734–1802) followed him in the grand manner of portraiture and classical grouping, and also was one of those encouraged by Reynolds' teaching to study historical composition, but he had great individual qualities, especially as a colourist. His work is less even in quality than that of either Gainsborough or Reynolds, but he possessed a strong sense of beauty ; most of his many portraits of Lady Hamilton reveal her feminine loveliness enhanced by exquisite decorative arrangement.

The Scottish artist Sir Henry Raeburn (1756–1823) ranks with Gainsborough and Reynolds. His portraits of lairds and old ladies are superb. Of all British portraitists of his day he had the finest sense of character ; his technique was forceful and brilliant. Many of his finest portraits were painted in the first decade of the 19th century. In England John Hoppner (c. 1758–1810), though not comparable with Raeburn in acute or sympathetic penetration of character, was carrying on the tradition of great painting with quiet distinction. John Opie (1761–1807), of Cornish origin, is at his best as a realistic recorder of country scenes ; his more ambitious historical compositions suffer from theatricality, while his later more sophisticated portraits lack the sincerity of his earlier work.

With Sir Thomas Lawrence (1769–1830) the great Reynolds tradition in portraiture came to an end. Though possessed of extraordinary facility as a capable draughtsman and executant with his brush, this most successful portrait painter during the regency and reign of George IV lacks sincerity in his work.

Blake. Working in London during this wonderful period, but, on account of his imaginative genius, not exactly of it, was the great painter-poet, William Blake (1757–1827). He was influenced by Sir Joshua Reynolds' ideas insomuch as he produced historical compositions (this term included literary or classical subjects not taken from everyday life), the greatness of which Reynolds had always held to be infinitely superior to portraiture. Among other illuminating remarks on Blake, Mr. Johnson says :

"The power to express movement is one of Blake's greatest gifts. Most of the distortions of which his enemies complain—the lengthened limbs or twisted bodies—are introduced for no other purpose. Had Blake avoided them and accurately copied the pose of a moving figure at an instant of time, the effect upon the eye, as in an instantaneous photograph, would have been that of a sudden cessation. For vision is continuous and not instantaneous, and those like Blake, who can make a figure run or swim or fly, always produce their effect by combining what happens at different instants of time."

Experiments in tempera and in illumination led to a medium which Blake used for some of his most impressive designs—his colour-printed drawings. He also painted transparent water-colours, some examples of which are at South Kensington, and a fine collection of his work is at Millbank. His last undertaking was that of engraving a series of designs for Dante's " Divina Commedia," but his finest engravings are perhaps the twenty-one illustrations for the Book of Job (at the British Museum).

LESSON 18

British Landscape from Wilson to Constable

(See plates 20 and 21)

DURING the reigns of the four Georges the art of landscape painting was not neglected in England. The names pre-eminent in this branch, besides Gainsborough—whose beautiful landscape painting is referred to in the preceding Lesson—are Wilson, Girtin, Morland, Crome, Turner and Constable. The Welsh artist, Richard Wilson (1714–1782) studied in London and Rome, and produced a series of excellent landscapes in the grand manner both of subject and treatment. Unity characterizes his work and the effect of his wonderful power of rendering light and space. Thomas Girtin (1775-1802), a Londoner, left behind him, in spite of his short life, works of enduring beauty ; his paintings are of cathedrals and abbeys. George Morland (1763-1804) enjoyed popularity ; he liked to paint rustic scenes and had a good sense of character and colour.

Towards the end of the 18th century a school of landscape painters flourished at Norwich, the leading spirit of which was John Crome (1768-1821). This great painter was nearly forty when he produced his first masterpiece, " Moonrise on the Marshes of the Yare," now in the National Gallery. Crome's eye for colour was subtle and his sense of design exquisitely delicate.

Turner's Art and Artistry. One of the greatest—by some authorities considered the greatest—of English painters and of landscape painters in the world, William Turner (1775-1851), was the son of a barber and born in London. He was apprenticed at the age of thirteen to Thomas Malton, an excellent draughtsman of architecture.

This training brought out Turner's wonderful power for the explanation of structure in his later work, which enabled him to combine in his pictures—more completely than any other artist had been able to do—the solidity of all natural forms introduced, with his understanding of the atmospheric qualities of light and air. Turner learnt much from the best of the older English landscape painters—Wilson, Gainsborough, Girtin and Crome— and greatly admired both Poussin and Claude, paying them all the compliment of some imitation. To the National Gallery, London—to be hung next to two fine examples of Claude's work— Turner bequeathed his " Sun rising through Vapour " and " Dido building Carthage " as an acknowledgment and a challenge. While ready to learn about gradations of light and classical composition from the French master, Turner's genius joined almost mathematical precision of drawing with atmospheric softness, and as a draughtsman of trees he is unsurpassed.

In water-colour Turner achieved the strongest possible contrast between lights and darks. In his earlier landscapes in this medium the colours are subdued and their luminous quality depends on gradations of light and shade. He did not use oil-colour until after he was twenty-one, and the work belonging to his first period of oil-painting was too dark in tone as a whole. He was at his best when painting sea pieces, ships and the men in them. His early boyhood was spent at Margate, and throughout his life he had a sailor's understanding for marine things, an amazing genius for depicting ships, and a complete grasp of wave and cloud formation. " Calais Pier," though it suffers somewhat from the defect of darkness, is one of Turner's finest pictures.

Mr. Charles Johnson, in " English Painting," considers that the spirit of Turner's earlier work—pictures of ruined castles, stormy seas and frowning mountains—is akin to Byron, while, after his continental tour in 1802, his eyes being opened to the beauty of a type of English scenery, hitherto neglected, his mood became Wordsworthian : " though Turner had probably not read Wordsworth's poetry, but rather was inspired, like the poet, by a spirit belonging to the age." " The Sun rising through Vapour " and " Frosty Morning," both at the National Gallery, belong to this Wordsworthian period, and " Windsor " is a beautiful example at the Millbank Gallery. After the Words-worthian mood had passed came the idea of rivalling Claude in classical composition, and it was not till Turner was forty-four that he first visited Italy, and the series of lovely water-colours of Venice resulted, together with some important oil paintings, such as the exquisite " Bay of Baiae."

The year 1829 marks the beginning of the final phase of Turner's career, as he then adopted his individual technique as a colourist. An example of this perfected sense of rich colour is " Ulysses deriding Polyphemus " (National Gallery). Mr. Johnson (ibid.) says of him : " after over forty years of severe discipline as a draughtsman, his hold upon structure has begun to relax ; and he is now absorbed exclusively in problems of rendering colour, light and atmosphere. In all his later work, however, the benefit of his early severity can be seen, in his never failing to give to his pictures space and inward depth." While his use of bright colour occasionally gave rise to his recurring fault of theatricality, he could use the brightest colours to express deep sincerity of feeling. Mr. Johnson places " The Fighting Téméraire " (National Gallery) highest of Turner's achievements ; painted when he was sixty-three, it contains " all the glory of his later colour without any vagueness. It has all his splendour of invention, with all his depth of feeling." The output of Turner's work is vast ; throughout his lifetime from the age of twelve he painted continuously. He pointed a new way in his later work ; with its concentration on the problem of light and its relation to colour, it formed the starting point of French Impressionism.

Constable. Contemporary with Turner was working that other celebrated landscape painter, John Constable (1776–1837), the son of a Suffolk miller. After early apprenticeship in his father's business, Constable became an artist at twenty-three. Technical ability was slow in arrival and his best work was done after the age of forty ; his great ambition was to be a " natural painter." Though greatly inferior to Turner in draughtsmanship, Constable had an exquisite sense of local colour, and after much labour produced a style of his own which won wide appreciation and recognition in France, and he practically became the leader of a new school of realistic landscape painting there.

Constable was supremely able to depict lovely colour in meadow and forest, the movement of foliage in the breeze, of the sea in sunlight, and of clouds in the sky. The " beauties of nature " took on a new significance in his hands. His natural medium was oils, and he handled his paint superbly once he had reached his best stage in technique. Examples of his work at his happiest period are " Flatford Mill" (National Gallery) and the beautiful " Cottage in a Cornfield " and " Lock on the Stour " at the Victoria and Albert Museum, both painted in 1817. In his later work he made lavish use of his palette knife to dab on impasto high lights, which sometimes led him into clumsiness of technique.

In contrasting Constable with Turner, Mr. Johnson says : "They have both been called Impressionists, and were both in many ways pioneers of the movement of that name. For they were both students of light. But while Constable loved to record a fleeting instant of time when light was passing, Turner's peculiar gift lay in representing the gradual increase or decrease of light upon an abiding spacious area. Turner was ultimately always concerned with form. Even when most vague in his drawing he aimed at making the horizon appear immeasurably far away. Turner's accuracy of perception of tone, combined with the system of colour he used in his later works, makes him the forerunner of the scientific Impressionists. Constable's indifference in his sketches to fact and absorption in the momentary effect make him the forerunner of the emotional Impressionists."

Our Course in Art and Architecture is continued in Volume 4.

LESSON 16

Miniature Worlds of the Solar System

ONE of the results of Kepler's study of the heavens was the recognition of what seemed to be an arithmetical relation between the distances of the planets from the sun. This relation was worked out by the astronomer Titius, but it is generally ascribed to the German astronomer, J. E. Bode (1747–1826). As subsequently amplified, it may be arrived at as follows : First write down the numbers 0, 3, 6, 12, 24, 48, 96, 192, 384, and then add 4 to each. We then have 4, 7, 10, 16, 28, 52, 100, 196, 388 ; and these numbers are approximately proportional to the distances from the sun of Mercury, Venus, the earth, Mars, the asteroids, Jupiter, Saturn, Uranus and Neptune. Thus, if 10 be taken as the earth's distance from the sun, then the distance of Mercury is 4, that of Mars is 16, and so on. As a matter of fact, the actual distances, taking the earth as 10, are Mercury 3·9, Venus 7·2, the earth 10, Mars 15·2, the asteroids 27·4, Jupiter 52·9, Saturn 95·4, Uranus 192 and Neptune 300. To this sequence the name of Bode's Law is generally given, although it should be realized that up to the present it is merely an empirical rule.

Discovery of the Asteroids. When it was first framed the existence of the asteroids was unknown, and there was a gap between Mars and Jupiter. It was inferred, therefore, that another planet must exist, corresponding to the number 28, and in 1800 astronomers set to work to locate it.

On the night of January 1, 1801, the Italian astronomer Piazzi, at Palermo, discovered a hitherto unknown star ; this was found to have a planetary orbit and was named Ceres after the mythical divinity of Sicily. Its mean distance from the sun was found to be 257 million miles (28·1 on the Bode scale), and corresponded, therefore, very closely with the missing number. What was almost as amazing was its exceeding smallness, as it was found to be only 477 miles in diameter.

Then on March 28, 1802, another planet was discovered by Olbers, who named it Pallas ; this was found to be at an average distance of about 256 million miles and to be only 304 miles in diameter. On September 2, 1804, Harding discovered Juno, a third small planet, only 120 miles in diameter and at a mean distance of 248 million miles from the sun. Then on March 29, 1807, Olbers discovered yet another, which he named Vesta. This is only about 250 miles in diameter, and at a mean distance of 219 million miles from the sun.

Thus, instead of the solitary planet whose existence had been suspected, there were found instead four little worlds. More were sought after, but not until 1845 was another found—Astraea, discovered by Heneke, in the same group. In 1847 three more were discovered, and since then more have been added every year—all of them much smaller than the first four discovered.

Since the application of photography to astronomical research large numbers of these asteroids have made their existence known by way of small streaks on photographic plates—their motion while the plate was being exposed causing them to be presented in this way instead of dots, as are the " fixed " stars. Telescopically, they appear as small stars ; hence their name asteroids, though planetoids or minor planets are more correct terms.

Altogether over 2,200 have been discovered to date ; of these about 1,400 are permanently followed in recognized orbits. These have received names, chiefly from ancient mythology, together with numbers enclosed and prefixed to the name, thus : " [911] Agamemnon." A large proportion of the more recently discovered and very small planetoids are known at present only by numbers, and will be so known until their identity is definitely established by successive revolutions.

Only about twenty of this host are estimated to possess diameters exceeding 100 miles ; probably about 150 have diameters between 50 and 100 miles ; while the remainder, judging from their relative faintness, are all below 50 miles in diameter. There are, in addition to these known planetoids with assigned orbits, a large number—probably a thousand—whose identities are so involved with one another that they become difficult to follow. Averaging between 5 and 10 miles in diameter, they are very faint, and can be glimpsed only when near opposition ; and perturbations due to Jupiter's attraction still further complicate their orbits. There are certainly many more less than 5 miles in diameter and beyond the range of telescopic photography—the only means by which they may be distinguished from faint stars. Each year sees hundreds added to the list, 218 having been discovered in 1937.

It might be supposed that from such numbers there might be sufficient material to form a planet at least as massive as the earth. This is far from being the case, however, for it is probable that the combined mass of all the planetoids known is between 1/500 and 1/000 of that of our world. At least 8,000 bodies similar to Ceres, the largest planetoid, would be required to constitute a world as massive as the earth.

As the force of gravity and, therefore, the velocity of escape are so low on even the largest of the planetoids, it is certain that they can have no atmospheres such as we are familiar with. Air molecules would speedily fly off into space should any form on their surfaces.

Several planetoids exhibit periodical variations of brightness, indicating that they rotate. It has been found that they take between 1·75 and 13·7 years to complete their revolutions round the sun, both revolutions and rotations (where known) being direct, as in the case of the earth and planets in general. The inclinations of their orbits average within about 9 degrees of the ecliptic, thus conforming to that of the major planets. There are some notable exceptions, however, the chief being Hidalgo, which is 43 degrees, and Pallas, which is nearly 35 degrees removed from the ecliptic.

Distance From the Sun. The eccentricity of their orbits varies considerably, for while some are nearly circular, others are elongated ellipses with eccentricity amounting to 0·65 in the case of Hidalgo, 0·55 for Reinmuth's 1932 planetoid, and 0·54 for Albert. Exceedingly great, therefore, is the range of some of the planetoids' distances from the sun. The distances of about seven-eighths range from between 215 million miles and 310 million miles from the sun. The remainder include Hidalgo, which has an aphelion distance of about 880 million miles—as far as the orbit of Saturn—while its perihelion distance is only about 185 million miles. Its revolution period, the longest of the planetoids, is 13·7 years. On the other hand, Eros, which at aphelion is 165,630,000 miles from the sun, is only 105,230,000 miles distant at perihelion ; hence it may approach to within 13,840,000 miles of the earth, and in January, 1930, actually came within 16,200,000 miles. Eros was then found to be an elongated body, suspected to be almost divided in the centre, irregular in form, while the two sections rotated about $4\frac{1}{2}$ times in the course of a day. Its greatest diameter has been variously estimated to be between 15 and 20 miles ; the period of its revolution is 643 days, but its synodic period is 845 days.

Four other planetoids have since been found to approach the earth still closer. Amor, with an orbit which also crosses that of Mars, was discovered by M. Delporte on March 12, 1932 ; it came within 10,160,000 miles of the earth on March 23, 1932. Amor appears to be only about 3 miles in diameter ; its revolution period is 2·76 years. The minimum distance of Apollo, a tiny planetoid discovered by Herr Reinmuth in 1932, is 3,000,000 miles. Four years later Delporte discovered and named Adonis, which at its nearest is only 1,500,000 miles away. But the smallest planetoid hitherto observed—it is probably less than one mile in diameter—has approached nearer to the earth than any other celestial body except the moon. Now known as Hermes, it was accidentally discovered by Reinmuth on October 28, 1937 ; two days later it was only 485,000 miles away, missing a collision with the earth by $5\frac{1}{2}$ hours. It is possible for this planetoid to approach within 220,000 miles of the earth, which is less than the mean distance of the moon ; its revolution period is rather more than 2 years. At perihelion its orbit will be within that of Venus.

What of the origin of the planetoids ? Are they, as has been suggested, fragments of an exploded world ? Although they occupy such a wide belt between the orbits of Mars and Jupiter —and even beyond—yet it can be shown this could have been produced by the gravitational action of the planets, more particularly Jupiter. A remarkable circumstance is that all their orbits are so involved that it is not possible to disentangle one from the rest without breaking through others. It has been possible to trace back mathematically the perturbations until they are all equidistant from a point on a line which joins the sun with the *centre* of Jupiter's orbit. Thus there is decided evidence for the conclusion that all the planetoids once occupied a certain spot at a certain epoch, and that they are actually parts of a world that met with catastrophe. The alternative theory—that they were formed from nebulous matter which failed to coalesce into a single large planet—leaves the tangle of their orbits and the exceptional eccentricities and inclinations much more of a problem.

LESSON 17

Jupiter and its Many Moons

THE greatest of the planets is Jupiter. Thirteen hundred and twelve times the size of the earth, it has an immense mass—318·4 times that of the earth and more than twice the amount of all the other planets put together. With the exception of Venus it is usually the brightest planet in our sky, and with its nine satellites forms a miniature solar system of its own.

Its mean diameter is given as 85,750 miles, but the planet is so elliptical that its polar diameter is 82,800 miles, while its equatorial diameter is about 88,700. It is thus an oblate spheroid with a great equatorial bulge, and possesses a surface about 120 times greater than that of the earth. Its density is only 0·24 that of our world and 1·34 times that of water ; this indicates that Jupiter is largely composed of gases, which descend doubtless for many thousands of miles below its visible surface as a colossal atmospheric envelope.

While the force of gravity on Jupiter *averages* about 2·65 times that of the earth, it varies considerably between the equator and the poles, the weight of bodies becoming greater as the poles are approached ; therefore, superficial gravity, which is 2·64 at the equator, amounts to 2·67 at the poles of the planet. This is due in part to the polar flattening and in part to the very rapid rotation of the planet's equatorial regions.

Rotation Periods. Jupiter's rotation periods are remarkable. Not only does it rotate faster than any other planet, but also at rates which vary for different latitudes and even for different objects at the same latitude. At the great equatorial belt, averaging about 12,000 miles in width, the speed amounts to a mean of 9 hours 50 minutes to complete a rotation ; this is known as System I. In temperate latitudes the speed averages about 9 hours 55 minutes ; this is System II. In high latitudes the speed of rotation amounts to about 9 hours 57 minutes. Thus there is a difference of 7 minutes, or approximately 1/85th of the entire period ; in the course of 85 revolutions of the planet, therefore, the equatorial regions must gain a complete rotation on the rest of Jupiter's surface. Since the equatorial circumference is about 300,000 miles, objects at or near Jupiter's equator travel at the rate of some 30,000 miles an hour, and 350 miles an hour faster—more or less according to latitude—than in the north and south temperate zones. This may be compared with the speed of nearly 1,000 miles an hour at which bodies travel in terrestrial equatorial regions. Jupiter rotates in an almost upright position, since the inclination of its axis to the plane of its orbit is only 3°; it can have no appreciable seasons.

Jupiter revolves at an average distance from the sun of 5·20 astronomical units, i.e. 483,300,000 miles; but this is subject to wide variation owing to the great eccentricity of the planet's orbit, which amounts to one-twentieth. Therefore, while Jupiter is about 507,000,000 miles from the sun at aphelion, it is only about 460,000,000 miles away at perihelion. This makes a considerable difference in the apparent size and brightness of the planet as seen from the earth; for when Jupiter is in opposition and at perihelion, i.e. in October, it is then only about 367,000,000 miles away and has an apparent diameter of about 50 seconds of arc. When opposition occurs at aphelion, i.e. in April, then Jupiter is about 414,000,000 miles distant and has an apparent diameter of 44 seconds of arc. It takes Jupiter 11 years, 314 days to complete one sidereal revolution; about six years, therefore, intervene between aphelion and perihelion.

Varying Surface Features. The details on Jupiter's disk are varied, distinctly visible, and subject to constant change. Even a small telescope of 2-inch aperture will reveal two or three of the chief belts. The general arrangement of these belts is more or less uniform in character, but they change both in width and depth of tint in the course of Jupiter's long year. With the aid of powerful instruments we may see a mass of detail—the great reddish tropical belts bordering the bright yellowish equatorial band, while greyish and greenish belts indicate the temperate regions. Spots—some very bright, others quite dark—appear on these belts and change their positions relative to one another from time to time.

The most remarkable of these spots is the Great Red Spot, which first became prominent in 1878 below the South Tropical Belt. It was calculated to be about 30,000 miles long, parallel to the belt and 7,000 miles wide. Originally pinkish in tint, it became a deep red by the next year and has continued until the present time, gradually getting fainter and rounder, until now it is scarcely perceptible. But the great bay or hollow, 45,000 miles long, which it occupied still remains a very distinct feature of the South Tropical Belt and one of the most permanent markings on the planet ; it is known as the South Tropical Disturbance. The Great Red Spot cannot be attached to the planet's surface, because it travels at a different rate from that of the adjoining belts and appears to be floating, together with the belts and other details, in the atmosphere of Jupiter. The continual and rapid changes in the other surface details indicate that they are produced by currents and storms in a dense atmosphere, only the upper layers of which are ordinarily observable. These layers have been found by radiometric tests to be at a temperature far below zero. Probably thousands of miles below them is the actual and largely molten surface of the planet, at a terrific heat consistent with its low density and disturbed state. There is no probability of life existing on such a world.

Moons of Jupiter. Jupiter has eleven satellites. The four largest were first discerned by Galileo in January, 1610, and have been known since as the Galilean Moons. They have also individual names, as indicated below, but as a rule they, together with Jupiter's other satellites, are known by Roman numerals. Details of these satellites are as follows :

Satellite	Diameter	Mean distance from Jupiter	Sidereal Period of Revolution		
	miles	miles	days	hours	mins.
V	(about) 100	112,500	–	11	57
I Io	2,109	261,000	1	18	28
II Europa ..	1,865	415,000	3	13	14
III Ganymede	3,273	664,000	7	3	43
XI	—	718,600	–	–	–
IV Callisto ..	3,142	1,167,000	16	16	32
VI	(about) 130	7,113,000	250	14	40
X	—	7,186,000	254	5	0
VII	„ 40	7,390,000	260	1	24
VIII	„ 25	14,600,000	738	21	36
IX	11–17	14,690,000	745	(about)	

The first nine of these satellites revolve direct from west to east, but the motion of the two outermost is retrograde, i.e. clockwise. Until 1892 Jupiter was believed to possess only four moons. No. V was discovered by Barnard at the Lick Observatory in 1892. In 1904 Perrine discovered VI by photography at the same observatory, and VII in 1905. Then VIII was discovered by Melotte in 1908, and IX in 1914 by Nicholson, who also discovered X and XI in 1938.

Very little is known about these small bodies. In view of the great eccentricity of the orbits of the five outermost, their considerable inclination from the plane of Jupiter's orbit, and also of the fact that two of the satellites have a retrograde motion, it seems probable that they are " captured " planetoids.

The four large Galilean moons are of great interest, and would be perceptible to the naked eye were it not for their apparent close proximity to the radiant Jupiter. As it is, Ganymede and Callisto may be observed with good field glasses, appearing, at times, about one-twelfth and one-sixth of a degree respectively either to the right or the left of the planet. (A degree is approximately twice our moon's apparent width.)

Observed through powerful telescopes, these satellites present perceptible disks with distinct markings sufficient to indicate that each satellite keeps the same face turned towards Jupiter. The changes in their relative positions, and, more particularly, their eclipse and transit phenomena, provide a constant fund of entertainment to possessors of smaller telescopes. These changes occur several times a week, the orbits of the satellites being so nearly in the plane of Jupiter's equator that they all, except Callisto, pass through the planet's shadow and are eclipsed or occulted at every revolution. When they pass between us and Jupiter they are seen to travel in transit across the latter's disk.

The times of these occurrences are known today with great precision, but in the seventeenth century it was found that they seldom took place at the expected time—either they were too early, or too late, the difference often amounting to several minutes. Then, in 1675, Roemer, a Danish astronomer, explained the discrepancies as being due to the time light takes to travel across the space between us and the satellites. As we have seen, this distance varies, and Jupiter is, at times, over 200 million miles nearer than at others ; hence, as the distance of Jupiter increases so the satellite phenomena appear delayed, the reverse occurring as Jupiter draws nearer. It is now known that light travels at the rate of 186,325 miles per second, but Roemer's explanation was not accepted for more than fifty years, until it was confirmed by Bradley's discovery of the aberration of light.

LESSON 18

Saturn and its System of Rings

(See plate 22)

SATURN, the second largest of the planets, is the most impressive of them on account of the ring system which encircles the planet ; this is seen from year to year at a different angle, and so provides an ever-varying spectacle. Now, while the sphere of Saturn is 95·2 times more massive than the earth, it is 763 times the size or volume ; this indicates how exceedingly light in density the planet must be. Its density is only 0·12 that of the earth and 0·69 that of water. Assuming Saturn to be of equal density throughout, it would float on water.

The planet's mean diameter is 73,000 miles, but owing to its great oblateness or polar flattening, it is more elliptical than any other planet. This amounts to about 10 per cent, so while its equatorial diameter is 75,100 miles, its polar diameter amounts to only 67,200 miles. As a result of this difference bodies would weigh about 30 per cent less at the equatorial regions of Saturn, as compared with the polar. This oval shape of the planet is very obvious when the rings are presented edgewise, and, therefore, are almost invisible. This equatorial bulge, amounting to nearly 4,000 miles, is due to Saturn's very rapid rotation, which takes only 10 hours 14 minutes 24 seconds at the planet's equatorial regions, but from 20 to 25 minutes longer in the belts to the north and south. In this respect Saturn resembles Jupiter and the sun.

Since the axis of the planet is inclined 26° 45' to the plane of its orbit, it has well defined seasons, but of immense length, the sidereal period of its revolution being 29 years 167 days. A season on Saturn is, therefore, between 7 and 8 of our years in length. Saturn revolves at an average distance from the sun of 9·54 astronomical units, or 886,000,000 miles, but, the eccentricity of its orbit amounting to 0·056, the planet's distance varies between 936,000,000 miles at aphelion and 836,000,000 at perihelion. Therefore, while Saturn may approach the earth to within 745,000,000 at its nearest opposition, it will be about 100 million miles farther off at an aphelion opposition :

consequently, this adds to the great variation in the apparent brightness of Saturn.

The planet's sphere, which, like Jupiter and the sun, appears brightest in the centre and fades off round the edges, has a very high albedo, amounting to 0·42. It is crossed by several belts, faint replicas of those of Jupiter, with the broad equatorial belt a brilliant yellow, the tropical and temperate belts greyish, and the polar caps of a greenish tint. On the belts appear occasionally white or dark spots, together with indistinct shadings, but all very faint at such an immense distance.

These belts represent clouds of vapour in an atmosphere of great depth, doubtless of many thousands of miles, the rapid rotation at different rates spreading the clouds out into belts which rush past one another at great speeds. A difference of over 750 miles an hour exists between the speed of the great equatorial belt and those of more temperate latitudes. It is probable that several thousands of miles beneath this visible surface a hot and possibly molten surface exists.

System of Rings. Saturn's ring system is unique and, when wide open, exhibits a large area of the surfaces of the rings. It adds about one and two-third times to the brilliance of Saturn observed with the naked eye. They were last observed thus in 1929–30, and afterwards gradually closed up, so that in the year 1936 they almost vanished. The successive phases they go through are indicated in the illustration in Plate 22, the dark equatorial band shown in the 1921 picture being the shadow produced by the invisible rings on the planet's surface. At intervals of nearly 15 years the rings go through all their phases, but alternately in the reverse direction presenting the north and then the south side of the rings to our view. At present, 1939, it is the south side that we are observing. When at their maximum they extend a little above the globe of the planet and possess an apparent diameter about one-sixth more than Saturn. Just before vanishing the rings appear as a thin line of light projecting from each side of the planet's disk, but when the rings are presented quite edgewise they entirely vanish, and in their place, as seen with most powerful telescopes, are a string of dots and streaks, indicating that the rings are apparently not more than 50 miles in thickness.

In extent the rings are enormous, resembling vast concentric disks, the outer one with a diameter of 171,500 miles. There are three main divisions of the ring system, known as A, B and C. The outer ring, A, being less bright and distinct, is about 10,000 miles wide. This is separated from B, which is much the brightest ring, by Cassini's division, which is between 2,000 and 3,000 miles in width. The ring B is about 16,000 miles wide, and has a diameter averaging 145,000 miles. These rings vary in width, together with the divisions between them, on account of perturbations caused by Saturn's satellites, to which are doubtless due the additional divisions occasionally seen, the ring A being sometimes divided by what is known as Encke's division.

Inside the bright ring B is a division probably about 1,000 miles wide separating it from the inner ring C, which is very faint and dusky. While permitting the ball of the planet to show through, it does not appear in the illustrations in Plate 22. It is usually known as the "crape ring," and is about 11,000 miles in width, the indistinct inner edge of which is between 6,000 and 7,000 miles from the planet's surface. While the rings produce a distinct shadow upon the planet, the globe of Saturn also casts a very dark shadow over the rings; this is well shown in the illustrations already referred to above.

Composition of the Rings. The rings of Saturn have been proved to be composed of innumerable particles in steady but very rapid rotation round Saturn—"moonlets" as we might say —each with its own orbit and travelling in the same direction, that is, counter-clockwise and almost in the same plane as the chief satellites. A few of these particles may approach 50 miles in diameter, judging by the appearance of the rings when seen edgewise, but the great majority must be of small dimensions, perhaps no larger than golf balls or small shot, because the total mass appears to be less than a quarter the mass of our moon. They revolve round Saturn at about 10 miles a second on the outer edge of the ring system, a particle thus taking nearly 140 hours to complete a revolution round that edge of the system. At the inner edge they attain a speed of about $12\frac{1}{2}$ miles a second, and so complete their revolution on this much smaller circumference in about five hours.

In 1857 Clerk-Maxwell had shown from theoretical considerations that the rings must be composed of separate particles like swarms of meteorites. The fact that the planet and some of Saturn's satellites could be seen through the less dense parts of the rings confirmed this. Then, in 1895, Keeler proved conclusively, by spectroscopic observation, that the inner portions travelled faster than the outer, and exactly as they would if they were composed of particles, their light and other considerations leaving finally no doubt in the matter.

The Planet's Satellites. Saturn's satellites amount to nine, or, if the doubtful Themis be included, to ten. Their chief details are given in the accompanying table.

Satellite	Diameter in miles	Mean Distance from Saturn	Sidereal Period of Revolution		
	(about)	miles	days	hours	min.
Mimas	370	115,300	–	22	37
Enceladus	460	148,000	1	8	53
Tethys	750	184,000	1	21	18
Dione	900	235,000	2	17	41
Rhea	1,150	327,500	4	12	25
Titan	3,550	760,000	15	22	41
Hyperion	300	920,000	21	6	38
Iapetus	1,000	2,220,000	79	7	56
Phoebe	200	7,996,000	550	10	35

Themis, whose supposed discovery was made by W. H. Pickering in 1905, has not been seen since, so its existence is discredited. Titan, first observed by Huygens in 1655, has a diameter greater than that of the planet Mercury, and appears to be the largest satellite in the solar system. It is above ninth magnitude, and can be seen with small telescopes of 2 to 3 inches aperture, while in large instruments it exhibits a disk with periodic variations in brilliance. Its mass is greater in proportion than that of our moon and about 3½ times that of water, so Titan appears to be also the most massive of all the satellites of the solar system, so far as is known.

Tethys, Dione, Rhea and Iapetus were discovered by Cassini in 1700. The densities of the first three are very low, while their albedo is high, suggesting a gaseous condition quite unlike Titan. Mimas and Enceladus, discovered by Sir William Herschel in 1789, are the lightest in density, Mimas being over two thousand times less than the moon ; it, therefore, may be nothing but a mass of cloud. Hyperion was discovered by W. C. Bond in 1848, and has also a very low density. Phoebe was found photographically by W. H. Pickering in 1898, and is remarkable as being the only one with a retrograde motion round Saturn ; this, together with

BOTTICELLI'S 'LA PRIMAVERA' (SPRING). Sandro Botticelli (c. 1444–1510) was famed among the Italian painters for his marked success in conveying the suggestion of open air and for the beauty of his linear compositions.
ART AND ARCHITECTURE 14

Academy, Florence

MICHELANGELO'S 'LAST JUDGEMENT.' This fresco on the vault of the Sistine Chapel was painted by the " mighty seer of the Renaissance " when he was more than sixty years of age. Displayed on Christmas Day, 1541, it is perhaps the most famous single picture in the world, and was the master's final achievement in painting. ART AND ARCHITECTURE 14

Sistine Chapel, Rome

RENAISSANCE SCULPTURE. Above, Michelangelo's "La Pietà," a marble group in St. Peter's, Rome. Left, Benvenuto Cellini's "Perseus with the Head of Medusa," executed in bronze in 1553. ART AND ARCHITECTURE 14

Plate 10

Volume III

ITALIAN PORTRAITURE OF THE RENAISSANCE. Left, Vincenzo Morosini,
by Jacopo Robusti (" Tintoretto," 1518–1594) ; right, Mona Lisa, wife of
Francesco del Giocondo (hence the name of La Gioconda), by Leonardo
da Vinci (1452–1519) ; and above, a Doge of Venice by Tiziano Vecellio
(" Titian," c. 1480–1576).   ART AND ARCHITECTURE 14

Vatican, Rome: National Gallery, London; Louvre, Paris

A RAPHAEL 'HOLY FAMILY.' The Madonnas of Raphael (1483–1520) are generally considered to be the greatest works of their kind in the world. ART AND ARCHITECTURE 14
Prado, Madrid

DÜRER'S NATIVITY TRIPTYCH. This Madonna and Child, with St. Anthony and St. Sebastian, by Albrecht Dürer (1471–1528), is at Dresden.
ART AND ARCHITECTURE 15

Plate 12   *Volume III*

its great eccentricity of 0·166 and very great inclination of about 149° to the planet's equator, points to the satellite being a " captured " planetoid.

The fact that sunlight is 90 times less (1/90) per unit area at the distance of Saturn, as compared with the earth, renders the satellites rather faint objects ; but regular variation in their brightness is perceptible, and from this it appears that they keep the same face toward Saturn as does our moon to the earth.

LESSON 19

The Green Planet of Uranus

(See plate 23)

URANUS, the next planet beyond Saturn, being about twice as far from the earth, presents therefore a much smaller disk and with but little detail perceptible. It is, however, of great interest, because Uranus was the first additional world to be discovered, and it led directly to the finding of Neptune. The discovery of Uranus was made by Sir William Herschel on March 13, 1781, with the 7-inch reflector telescope which he had made himself. At first the new body was regarded as a tailless comet, but by the following year it was found to be a planet moving in an orbit quite unlike that of a comet. Lalande and Continental astronomers gave it the name of Herschel ; then, later, Bode named it Uranus after the father of Saturn in Greek mythology. This gradually displaced the other name.

By referring to old star catalogues and previous observations it was found that Uranus had been recorded many times as a star, including an observation recorded by Flamsteed, the first Astronomer Royal, in 1690. Uranus appears as a star of the sixth magnitude, and is, therefore, just discernible to the naked eye, a good telescope being required to show its planetary disk. It may seem surprising that the keen-eyed ancient astronomers had not noticed Uranus in the clear air of Egypt and Chaldea, but the apparent movements of this planet are so slow, taking 84 years and six days to complete a circuit of the heavens (this being the planet's year), that its daily motion would, therefore, escape notice.

The mean distance of Uranus from the sun is 1,783,000,000 miles, but, the eccentricity of its orbit being 0·047, its actual distance therefore varies between about 1,866,000,000 when at aphelion and 1,698,000,000 at perihelion ; consequently, there is very little difference in its apparent brightness or size as seen from the earth, its angular diameter averaging about 3·75" (seconds of arc) and attaining about 4" when at its nearest.

Uranus is 59 times the size of the earth ; but though so much greater in volume, Uranus is only 14·6 times the mass, consequently its density is only 0·25 that of the earth or 1·36 times that of water. It therefore resembles Saturn and Jupiter in density, and also in possessing a very deep gaseous envelope. The mean diameter of Uranus according to the outer cloud surface of this atmospheric envelope is about 31,900 miles, but, as in the case of Saturn and Jupiter, its polar diameter is much less than the equatorial, amounting to about 1/14. The planet's ellipticity indicates a very rapid rotation, which has been found to amount to only 10 hours, 49 minutes ; this represents the length of a Uranian day, except so far as they are abnormally lengthened by the planet's remarkable arrangement of seasons.

Uranus rotates at the surprising angle of about 98 degrees to the plane of the planet's orbit. At this angle the greater part of the northern hemisphere and, alternately, the southern would remain continuously in the sunlight for 21 years ; this is the length of a season on Uranus, while a winter night of similar length would be experienced. On the other hand, the sun appears at that distance only as a very bright star with a scarcely perceptible disk and with a surface 368 times less, so Uranus must receive 368 times less light and heat than the earth. From this we see that twilight conditions must prevail on Uranus, providing that this feeble sunlight can penetrate the planet's dense cloud canopy. A curious and unexplained circumstance is the greenish tint of the disk of Uranus, a feature which is shared by Neptune. It indicates the presence of an extremely rarefied and unknown gas ; the spectrum of Uranus, while consisting of reflected sunlight, contains absorption bands indicating that pure hydrogen is in the planet's upper atmosphere. The question is whether it is this, subject to great cold, which produces the greenish hue.

The surface of Uranus exhibits belts similar to those of Saturn, but much fainter and tilted at the remarkable angle that is almost perpendicular to the plane of the planet's orbit. This orbit has an inclination of only 46' (minutes of arc) to the plane of the earth's orbit, and is, therefore, about the same. The albedo of Uranus is very high, amounting to 0·60, as would be expected from a cloud-laden atmosphere of great reflecting power.

Satellites. Uranus has four satellites, their chief details being shown in the accompanying table.

Name	Diameter in miles	Mean Distance from Uranus	Sidereal Period of Revolution		
	(about)	miles	days	hours	min.
Ariel	900	120,000	2	12	29
Umbriel	700	167,000	4	3	28
Titania	1,700	273,000	8	16	56
Oberon	1,500	365,000	13	11	7

They are all very faint. Titania and Oberon, appearing about $14\frac{1}{2}$ magnitude, were discovered by Sir William Herschel in 1787. Ariel, about 16 magnitude, and Umbriel, about $16\frac{1}{2}$ magnitude, were discovered by Lassell in 1851. The most remarkable features about these satellites are that they all appear to travel in a retrograde direction round Uranus (that is, clockwise), a motion that is shared by the rotation of the planet itself, which is also retrograde ; also that the orbits of these satellites are at an extreme angle to the plane of the planet's orbit. This amounts apparently to 82° (degrees of arc), but is actually 98°, when theoretically considered.

These point to the conclusion that Uranus at some far-distant epoch turned over to this angle of 98° together with its satellites, or while the whole was in a gaseous state and before the birth of the satellites ; for since the planet rotates in the same plane and direction as the satellites, the inverting process must have been common to both. The most probable cause would appear to have been the near approach of some great body—another sun perhaps—which, by raising great tides on the plastic and possibly half-formed world of Uranus, was thus able to alter its axis of rotation long ages before the satellites came into existence.

Now the south pole of Uranus is actually on a higher level relative to the plane of its orbit than is its north pole as the result of inversion ; thus the effect is produced of the revolution of its moons being retrograde, whereas their motion is in reality direct. If the student experiments with a ball to imitate the rotation of Uranus and its satellites, it will be seen that, whereas normally they will appear to revolve, say, from left to right, if they are inverted they will appear to revolve from right to left, though still continuing in the same rotation.

Uranus is at present between the constellations Aries and Taurus, and remains in the latter for seven years, since the planet's annual motion through the heavens amounts to an average of only 4¼ degrees, though it is actually travelling with a velocity of about 4¼ miles a second.

The physical condition of the planet is generally regarded as being similar to that of Jupiter and Saturn, the actual surface being some thousands of miles below its atmospheric cloud surface and at a great heat—probably molten, more or less—notwithstanding what must be a very frigid exterior. Absorption effects of both water vapour and hydrogen, already referred to, have been found in its spectra, and there seems little doubt that Uranus is a world in the making and in a much earlier stage of existence than our own.

LESSON 20

Discovery of Neptune and Pluto

(See plate 23)

NEPTUNE, for long regarded as the outermost planet of the solar system, is not visible to the naked eye, though it may be glimpsed with powerful field-glasses. Its discovery in 1846 was the result of one of the greatest triumphs of mathematical astronomy. The existence of a world beyond Uranus had been suspected as the cause of certain accelerations and retardations in its orbit, which amounted to nearly two minutes of arc. While Saturn and Jupiter accounted for part of this irregularity, the residue was suggested by the astronomer Bessel as due to a planet beyond Uranus.

Then, in 1845, the English astronomer J C. Adams and, in 1846, the French astronomer Leverrier independently calculated where this supposed planet must be. Though Adams had computed the position first and informed the Astronomer Royal by letter, his communication was neglected, and he thus lost the honour of the discovery. It was not until July 19th, 1846, that Professor Challis, of the Cambridge University Observatory, took up the search at the suggestion of the Astronomer Royal, as Leverrier's results had now been made known.

In August, 1846, Leverrier's elements of the planet's position, which were in accord with those already computed by Adams, were published. Subsequently, Leverrier wrote to the observatory at Berlin, on September 18, asking them to search for a " new planet looking like a star of the ninth magnitude and having a perceptible disk," indicating also where it was to be found. It was discovered within half an hour, and only 52 minutes of arc from the place predicted ; it possessed the apparent disk but was a magnitude brighter. This was a great achievement for Leverrier, and one in which Adams shares the honour, though at the time it caused much controversy, for Professor Challis at Cambridge had actually observed the planet weeks before, but in the absence of good star-charts had failed to identify its presence. G. B. Airy, the Astronomer Royal, received much bitter criticism for his neglect of Adams' request, which lost to him the honour of sole discovery and, at the time, nearly all recognition.

Neptune's mean distance from the sun is 30·06 astronomical units ; from this it departs relatively little, being at aphelion 2,816,000,000 miles, and at perihelion 2,768,000,000 miles from the sun. The eccentricity of Neptune's orbit is, therefore, only 0·0086, and its orbit the most circular of all the planets, except that of Venus. Moreover, the inclination of its orbit to the ecliptic is only 1° 47′.

While the mass of Neptune is 17 times that of the earth, its size or volume is 72 times ; therefore the planet's density is much less, being 0·24 that of the earth or 1·32 that of water. Neptune is, therefore, but little denser than Uranus, and is generally a replica of that planet, except that it exists under much more frigid conditions as regards solar heat. The sun would appear as a very bright star, and to the unaided eye would exhibit no perceptible disk. The heat and light received by Neptune are 900 times less, area for area, than are received by the earth ; although this solar light would far exceed our brightest moon-light, Neptune is a world of twilight.

It rotates very rapidly in about 15 hours 40 minutes on an axis inclined about 61 degrees to the planet's orbit. Since it takes 164 years 280 days to complete a revolution of the same, Neptune has very pronounced seasons of great length, amounting to about 41 of our years.

Telescopically, Neptune's disk appears an average diameter of only 2·3 seconds of arc. From this its real diameter has been variously calculated to be between 31,000 and 34,800 miles in length ; the difference is possibly the result of the planet's polar flattening being presented at different angles in the course of many years. Neptune has the high albedo of 0·52, indicating a cloud-covered surface This, as in the case of Uranus, appears greenish, but without trace of belts or markings, the details so far ascertained being revealed spectroscopically. These indicate a very dense and deep atmosphere, and while its surface may be 220 degrees below zero (Centigrade), yet great heat doubtless exists in its depths, where, however, neither sunlight nor solar heat may ever penetrate.

Neptune's Only Satellite. Triton, the only known satellite of Neptune, revolves in a period of 5 days 21 hours $2\frac{1}{2}$ minutes, at an average distance of 220,000 miles from Neptune's centre, and so almost as far as the moon is from the earth. Its orbit is retrograde and inclined at between 35° and 40° to that of Neptune. It appears to possess the remarkable property of a varying angle of inclination, which has been found to change in the course of many years to the extent of about 10° ; this deflection of the path of the satellite has been ascribed to variations in the plane of Neptune's equator. Triton was discovered by Lassell in 1846. It is very faint, appearing about 13th magnitude, and is, therefore, estimated to be about the same size as our moon.

Since the discovery of Neptune the existence of yet another world beyond this planet has been suspected for many years. Further unaccounted perturbations of Uranus, together with the fact that the aphelia of several comets might, therefore, be accounted for, stimulated the search by methods similar to those used by Adams and Leverrier. The existence of " families " of comets (to be explained later) had long been regarded as indicating worlds beyond Neptune, because, while the comets had the sun at the perihelion end of their very elliptical orbits they had one of the greater planets near the aphelion end. Now, since certain comets had their aphelia far beyond the orbit of Neptune, these were regarded as pointing to Trans-Neptunian planets, but they supplied no data as to where such worlds were to be found.

More definite were the small irregularities in the motion of Uranus, Neptune and even Saturn, which could not otherwise be accounted for. Dr. Percival Lowell, Professor W. H. Pickering and A. Gaillot, in particular, made elaborate mathematical calculations to locate the Trans-Neptunian world which they firmly believed existed. An immense amount of work was involved in these, Percival Lowell publishing his " Memoir on Trans-Neptunian Planet " in 1915. This indicated the region where the body, which he termed " Planet X," would be found. Professor W. H. Pickering also published the approximate position of this unknown world as early as 1919.

Discovery of the Unknown Planet. Though an intermittent search was maintained after Lowell's death in 1916, it was not until January 21, 1930, that it was discovered. It had been the rule at the Lowell Observatory at Flagstaff, Arizona, to photograph those regions in some part of which, according to Lowell's elements, the planet might be situated, and then to scrutinize the plates to find any small dash in place of the multitude of dots which represented the so-called fixed stars. It was thus that the young assistant at the observatory, Clive W. Tombaugh, discovered the world beyond Neptune on one of the photographic plates. Dr. V. M. Slipher, chief of the observatory, closely studied the moving body ; elements were calculated, and then, on March 13, the official announcement was made that the Trans-Neptunian planet was actually discovered only 6 degrees away from the place assigned to it fifteen years earlier by Lowell's elements. It was subsequently found that Professor W. H. Pickering's predicted position was only about 10 degrees from where the planet was found, while some of his figures relating to it were closer than Lowell's.

The new planet was named Pluto at the suggestion of a child, aged eleven, Miss Venetia Burney, of Oxford, the first two letters of Pluto commemorating the initials of Percival Lowell. It has been closely studied since, being well placed for observation in the constellation of Gemini, passing almost overhead in the winter months.

Pluto is estimated from its brightness to be about half the diameter of the earth, or 4,000 miles, the period of its revolution round the sun being 248 years. Its orbit is the most elliptical of all the planets, ranging from about 50 astronomical units in aphelion, that is, 4,650,000,000 miles, to 29·6 units, or 2,753,000,000 miles, at perihelion. Then, it comes within the orbit of Neptune, but at the high inclination of its plane of 17 degrees to the ecliptic, so Neptune and Pluto can never meet.

At present Pluto is at a distance of about 3,700,000,000 miles, and it is gradually coming closer to us each year. Sunlight is there equivalent to our moonlight, while Pluto at present receives about 1,500 times less heat and light from the sun than the earth does.

The possibility of yet another world beyond Pluto is now seriously considered, and Professor W. H. Pickering, at the Mandeville Observatory, Jamaica, has made exhaustive computations by which he hopes with the increasing powers of great telescopes that it may be discovered.

LESSON 21

Comet Visitors to the Solar System

(See plate 24)

THE name comet is derived from the Greek *komētēs*, long-haired, a name that had its origin in the hairy appearance of the luminous mist which surrounds the celestial body known as a comet and which, in many, trails away into space ; this appearance forms the so-called tail, and obtained for comets their old title of *stellae comatae*, that is, " hairy stars." About 950 comets are known, the elements of whose orbits have been computed ; while, on an average, about five new ones are discovered each year. The greatest number observed in one year is fourteen, in 1932 ; of these eight were new comets.

The majority of comets have never been seen without telescopic aid ; as a rule, not more than about one in ten becomes easily visible to the naked eye. Occasionally, a splendid body appears, with a nucleus that may be as bright as Venus and with a tail that stretches half way from the horizon to the sky overhead ; but only about five of these great comets may be expected on an average in a century.

While a comet usually possesses a bright central nucleus or a perceptible condensation surrounded by a more or less spherical mass of fainter luminosity, called the coma, the radiant tail is frequently imperceptible or absent from the smaller comets, or it may develop as the comet approaches the sun. From the orbits of several hundred comets which have been defined the majority are found to be parabolic, a large number elliptical and a few hyperbolic ; but as only a small portion of a comet's orbit —i.e. that which is in the vicinity of the earth and the sun—is observable, it becomes a question as to whether the entire orbit may not be elliptical. If some are hyperbolic it appears certain that these comets, therefore, leave the solar system never to return. The orbits of nearly a hundred comets are definitely known to be elliptical, so that their return to the sun may be predicted ; these are, therefore, an integral part of the solar system, and are known as periodic comets.

Such comets are better known than the others, since in many cases the return of the same comet has been observed several times, as in the case of Halley's famous comet, and of Encke's comet, observed for 33 returns. Thus it becomes possible to note the changes, both in the comet's period and its structure, which have occurred in the intervals of their return. These are very numerous.

Generally, the eccentricity of these cometary orbits is much greater than that of the planets and most planetoids. Therefore, the comet approaches comparatively close to the sun at the perihelion end of its orbit, while the aphelion may be within the orbit of Jupiter or it may be far beyond that of Neptune ; so the period of its return may be anything between $3\frac{1}{2}$ years and 10,000 years. These comets are divided into two classes : (1) the short-period comets ; (2) the long-period comets.

Short-Period Comets. About 50 comets are known with short-period orbits, requiring between three and nine years for the comets to complete a revolution and return to perihelion. These comets are all faint objects, only a few being perceptible to the naked eye. They are usually known by the name of their discoverer, but their full title states also the year of discovery and the order of discovery relative to others, thus : Geddes' comet 1932 *g*, and Faye's comet 1932 *h*, the letters in italics indicating that these comets were the seventh and eighth discovered in 1932. There is another form of nomenclature used by astronomers, based upon the time the comet arrives at perihelion, when it passes closest the sun, and which, therefore, represents the major axis of its orbit. This affords greater precision than the order of discovery, since a comet may overtake another which was found later, and arrive at perihelion first. So in the case of comets discovered before the present year or two, this form of nomenclature is usually adopted ; it is expressed thus : Coggia's comet 1874 III, or Taylor's comet 1916 I. The Roman numerals replace the letters when the perihelion time is established.

All these short-period comets have their aphelion point not far from the orbit of Jupiter—some within it to the extent of about 90,000,000 miles as in the case of Encke's comet, which is the least of all. A few have it about 100,000,000 miles beyond Jupiter's orbit, but, on an average, they are within 22,000,000 miles. A remarkable feature is that the inclination of their orbits to the ecliptic is within 30°, whereas, generally, comets' orbits are at all inclinations from 0° to 90°. Moreover, their motion is direct, that is, they travel round the sun in the same direction as Jupiter and the other planets. These are elements which indicate that these comets are an integral part of the solar system ; also that they are a great family of comets dominated by Jupiter, which somehow has caused them to possess these orbits ; for this reason they are known as the Jovian family of comets.

There are other very similar, though larger comets, which have their aphelia comparatively near to the orbits of the outer planets ; Saturn has thus a " family " of two comets, Uranus three, and Neptune six, while Pluto also appears to possess some. There are also other groups whose aphelion points are several times the distance of Neptune or even Pluto ; this seems to suggest the existence of other undiscovered worlds.

Halley's Comet. The best known member of these families of comets is Halley's, so named because Halley computed its orbit for the first time and, having identified it with several which had previously appeared, predicted its return to perihelion in March, 1759. He did not live to see this verified, for he died the year before its return, but ever since it has been known as Halley's comet ; it returned as predicted, on March 13, and with a tail 50 degrees long, that is, about 100 times the apparent width of the moon. The discovery of Halley's comet is lost in the mists of antiquity. The historical records of its return go back through the years 1682, 1607, 1531, 1456, 1301, 1145, to 1066, the famous historical year commemorated on the Bayeux Tapestry, which depicts Halley's comet. Thence it has been traced to 240 B.C.—with records of every return to 87 B.C.

From the evidence it is found that the comet returns at an average interval of 75 to 76 years, with a variation of about 18 months each way, due to planetary accelerations and retardations, its motion being retrograde. Following Halley's predicted return, it again appeared to time in 1835, but with a tail only 10 degrees in length, which occasioned some anxiety as to the possible condition of the comet at its next return in 1910.

This was predicted with remarkable accuracy by the astronomers Cowell and Crommelin of Greenwich Observatory. The comet returned to perihelion on April 20 and proved the most sensational astronomical event for many years, since it had regained all its old splendour and through coming so close to the earth surpassed itself as a celestial spectacle. The weather and conditions were not very favourable in this country, but the comet was very well observed farther south and in America and the tropics.

It appeared at its best as an early morning object in the early part of May, when its nucleus rivalled the brightest stars and its tail attained a length of 60 degrees. Later, when at its nearest to the earth and only 14,300,000 miles away, the tail had broadened out to a band of luminosity resembling the Milky Way ; it was then about 120 degrees in length and stretched two-thirds across the sky, though the comet's head was not then visible. It is believed that the earth actually passed through the tail on May 21 of that year. This comet may be regarded as typical of this class of periodic comets—and a very good specimen, because it usually approaches close to our world.

Long-Period Comets. The comets of long period, of which there are not many with *known* elliptical orbits, are best exemplified in a well-known group, two of the most famous being the magnificent comets of 1843 and 1882. These are so similar as to be almost identical. Both passed through the sun's corona at perihelion and less than 300,000 miles above its surface, so from the earth they would have appeared less than half the sun's diameter away. In their close approach to the sun they resembled the great long-period comets of 1668, 1880 and 1887. They had another common resemblance in approaching the sun from almost the same point in space—the direction of the brilliant star Sirius—and in possessing almost identical elements of their orbits. It was as if they were various apparitions of the same object, which was, however, impossible. The comets of 1843 and 1882 presented vastly different spectacles owing to the different distances and perspective from which they were viewed.

The comet 1843 I was calculated to have a period of between 400 and 800 years, while that of the comet 1882 III was computed to be between 600 and 900 years. Now, it so happened that the 1882 comet—after its violent ordeal, when it passed so close to the terrific solar furnace—emerged as a " broken comet " and split into four divisions, which gradually parted company and travelled away into the depths of space as four comets along slightly different paths. The astronomer Kreutz has calculated that they will return after a lapse of 664, 769, 875 and 959 years for each portion, when a great comet will be observed, which will be only a fourth part of the original comet 1882 III.

Thus the singular grouping of the five great comets, those of 1668, 1843, 1880, 1882 and 1887, may be accounted for as being due to a still greater comet subdividing, long ages ago, on one of its perilous visits to the sun, as did the 1882 comet. We thus learn something of the birth and disintegration of comets.

Our Course in Astronomy is continued in Volume 4.

LESSON 16

The Chromosomes' Part in Heredity

IN the preceding Lesson it was pointed out that a plant bred true and is homozygous for a certain character only when it received a double dose of that character from its parents. Moreover, in the second generation this double dose may split, so that one dose only goes into each germ cell to form a heterozygote. These facts seem to imply that characters are carried in pairs, but that the pairs may divide. This view is confirmed by an examination of the constitution of the germ cell, or gamete, which is undertaken in this Lesson. Here we find that Mendel, without our present-day knowledge of cell formation, formed a wonderfully correct view of the laws of heredity.

Somatic and Gametic Cells. The reader is advised to read again Lesson 2 (volume I, page 79). In that Lesson the division process was described by which a typical body-building cell, or somatic cell as it is called, multiplied ; the point that must be remembered is, that the chromosomes, after assembling on the spindle, split longitudinally into halves, and the halves of each chromosome then part company. Attracted by some force, whose nature is not yet fully understood, each company of half chromosomes is drawn towards one of the two poles or spindle ends and, after division, occupies separate cells. Thus, whatever the number and contents (and these are all-important) of the chromosomes in the first somatic or body-building cell, the same number and contents are represented in every subsequent cell of the billions of cells in the body. This kind of cell division practised by the somatic cells is called mitosis.

There are, however, cells which are exceptions to this rule. The cells known as gametes, which are involved in reproduction—the cells in the testes and ovaries of animals and in the anthers and ovules of plants—do not exhibit this chromosome splitting.

Since the nucleus of the male gamete will presently fuse with the nucleus of the female gamete, the resulting fertilized egg cell, or zygote, would contain a double number of chromosomes if the gametes themselves contained a complete number, and the next generation of gametes would produce a quadruple zygote, and so on indefinitely. But mitosis does not take place in the formation of gametic cells, and, in consequence, they do not possess the same number of chromosomes as the somatic cells. Instead, as the gametes are being formed, the chromosomes line up *in pairs* across the spindle, and then, before the cell divides, *one whole chromosome* of each pair goes to one pole and the other chromosome to the other pole. Thus, if the original number of chromosomes was six, only three would be found in the gametes. (Compare this reduction division, or meiosis as it is called, with the mitotic division shown in the illustration depicting stages of cell division in volume 1, page 80.) The consequence is that when the male gamete meets and fuses with the female gamete, the resulting zygote will contain the double number (six) of chromosomes once more. Cells in the first stage, that of possessing a single set of chromosomes, are called the *haploid* cells ; those in the second, when the double set of chromosomes is restored, are called *diploid* cells.

Chromosomes and Species. We may note here that every species of plant and animal is distinguished by the number of chromosomes carried by its cells. Some species have a large number of chromosomes, some only a few. There are species of round worms with only two chromosomes in the nucleus of each somatic cell. Some flies have a set of four chromosomes, crayfish over two hundred, mice forty, and men forty-eight in their somatic cells. These somatic cells, in accordance with the preceding argument, may be regarded as bearing a double number of chromosomes, hence the term diploid. It is the male sperm cell, or gamete, and the female gamete, or egg cell, which bear the standard or haploid number of chromosomes, e.g. the human male sperm and the human female ovum each contain twenty-four chromosomes. Beyond this common feature there appears little resemblance between the male gamete and the female gamete—between the paternal element and the maternal element which join to form the offspring.

The male sperm is usually small and active, and in most cases proceeds eagerly to search for the female egg, which is comparatively large and immobile. In the sea urchin, for example, the process of fertilization has been cinematographed, and we see through the microscope the male sperm as a small tadpole-like body moving through the water until it comes in contact with an egg. Directly this contact is made, a little protrusion of protoplasm appears on the surface of the egg, which absorbs the head only of the male sperm, leaving its tail outside to die and drop off. Once inside the egg, the tiny head of the male sperm swells into a nucleus which fuses with the egg nucleus, and the two single sets of chromosomes—a set from the nucleus of each haploid gamete—join to form the diploid zygote, or fertilized cell, from which, by subsequent mitosis, or cell division, the new animal is formed.

Since, then, practically no part of the male gametic cell enters the egg except the nucleus with its chromosomes, it would seem that it is they, and they alone, which transmit the paternal characters to the offspring ; and, as the paternal and maternal contributions to the characters of the offspring are, on the average, equal, it would seem that the chromosomes in the egg nucleus bear the maternal characters to the offspring. That the chromosomes are bearers of heredity becomes more likely still when we remember how they form in pairs, and how, during the union of gametes, either member of a pair may go into the zygote. This gives us exactly the same law as to the probability of the emergence of any parental character in the offspring as Mendel discovered by practical experiment. Thus the Mendelian inheritance, shown in the diagram in volume 2, page 85, may

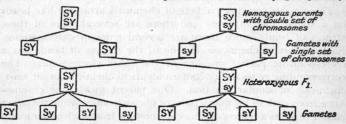

MENDELIAN INHERITANCE AND CHROMOSOMES. If two factors SY and sy are carried by a pair of chromosomes we get the combinations shown here, which will give the dihybrid ratio of 9 : 3 : 3 : 1 in the F_2 generation.

be explained as being due to a cross between parents one of which is homozygous for two dominant characters, smooth yellow (SY), while the other is homozygous for two recessive characters, wrinkled white (sy).

If the two factors, SY and sy, are carried by a pair of chromosomes, we get the combinations shown in the diagram above.

LESSON 17

Chromosomes that Determine Sex

IN the previous Lesson chromosomes were treated as possessed of or carrying one or two unit characters, such as tallness, smoothness, etc. When, however, we think of the thousands of ways in which offspring resemble, or differ from, their parents, it is obvious that the few chromosomes which each parent contributes (24 in Man) must each contain thousands of these unit characters. These unit characters are now called " genes." Under high-powered microscopic examination the tiny thread-like chromosomes are seen to contain numbers of darkly stained granules or genes, and it is these which are now thought to be the bearers of heredity. It should be noted that the human egg cell is $\frac{1}{125}$ inch in diameter. This is an enormous cell compared with the human male gamete or sperm cell. Yet the sperm cell is largely cytoplasm, and it is only a small fraction of the cell—the nucleus—which contains the 24 chromosomes that are so biologically important.

These genes are tiny packets of chemicals arranged like beads on a string, and in every cell there are several pairs of these strings of beads, since there are several pairs of chromosomes. Each packet of chemicals in one of the strings of beads has a corresponding packet or gene in the other chromosome. The corresponding genes either contain identical chemicals or, at least, chemicals of similar reaction. One parent yields one chromosome from each of his many pairs of chromosomes, while the other parent supplies a corresponding chromosome from each of her many pairs, and these contributed chromosomes form a fully equipped cell, which divides up in the usual way to form a new individual. The new cells, and the new individual formed by them, will, however, owing to the fresh arrangement of chromosomes and genes, be different from either of its parents, although it will exhibit some of the characteristics of both.

The reader is reminded here of the description given in Lesson 2 (volume 1, page 79) of the building up of the body by the division of somatic cells. The chromosomes split longitudinally, one half going to the nucleus of one daughter cell, and the other half of the chromosome to the other cell. It is now seen that, by this process, every cell in the new individual gets an equal share of every gene contributed by the parents.

Linkage. In considering Mendel's law of inheritance, we instanced, for the sake of simplicity, one or two unit characters only. The result of many experiments proves, however, that whole groups of characters are transmitted according to Mendel's laws. It is found, moreover, that, in breeding any organism, the number of groups of characters so transmitted agrees with the number of pairs of chromosomes possessed by the organism.

Actual experiments show (*see* Sex Linkage, below) that the presence or absence of a certain group of characters in the individual coincides with the presence or absence of a certain chromosome in the zygote from which the individual developed.

We cannot, then, escape the conclusion that this linkage of characters in groups is due to the fact that each chromosome carries a group of characters, and that each of the hundreds of granules or genes that are ranged along the length of each chromosome represents a single character, or is one of several factors necessary to produce a character. Fortunately for biology, Mendel chose for his experiments characters located in separate chromosomes, so that he discovered the law of segregation of unit characters.

Experiments in Drosophila. Professor T. H. Morgan, of Columbia University, and his co-workers, for some years have been investigating this question of grouping, or linkage of characters, in the banana fly. This tiny fly (*Drosophila melanogaster*), whose four chromosomes have been subjected to such intense scrutiny, bids fair to outrival Mendel's peas in biological fame. It has had this greatness thrust upon it because of its obliging tendency to produce every ten days a family of over two hundred, which live quite happily in a bottle on a piece of banana. In the Columbia laboratory are rows and rows of bottles containing millions of flies of known pedigree, and a record is kept of the particular shuffling and redealing of the chromosomes and genes concerned in their make-up. Flies of unimagined patterns have been bred—flies with white eyes, flies with pink eyes, flies with no eyes, flies with wings and without, and flies of nightmare build with half the body male and the other half female. We shall return to these experiments in the next Lesson, but, first, we must give the clue on which the experiments were based.

Sex Linkage. It has been known since 1902 that in many animals the female has one more chromosome than the male, that is, the male has an unpaired chromosome, known as X, while the female has a pair of X chromosomes. In Man, and in the *Drosophila* fly, the single X chromosome of the male has a rudimentary and largely inactive chromosome paired with it. This dummy chromosome (Y) does not function as a bearer of characteristics from parent to child. Therefore, the female gametes or eggs will all contain one X chromosome, owing to reduction division (*see* Lesson 16, page 109), but the male gametes or sperm will be of two types, (A) those containing an active X chromosome, and (B) those containing only the functionless Y chromosome. If the egg be fertilized by a sperm of the A type, the resulting zygote will have a pair of X chromosomes, and will be a female. If the egg is fertilized, however, by a sperm of B type, the resulting zygote will have only one X chromosome (which was contributed by the *mother*), and one inactive Y chromosome (from the father). It will, therefore, be male. Since, then, this unpaired X chromosome of the male is always passed to the daughter, all the genes or characters in this chromosome will be handed to daughters and not to sons. The sons will show the characters carried by the genes in the X chromosome contributed by the mother only.

Colour-Blindness. It is known, for example, that ordinary colour-blindness in Mankind is due to a gene carried by the X chromosome, and it is, therefore, known as a sex-linked character. As such it follows the rule for sex-linked inheritance. In the diagram (p. 115) all the other 23 pairs of chromosomes are ignored, and only the XX pair of chromosomes of the female and the corresponding XY pair of the male are shown. To indicate that the X chromosome of the father contains a gene for colour-blindness, this X is underlined.

The diagram shows, as will be seen, that a colour-blind woman occurs only when a colour-blind man marries either a *carrier* or a colour-blind woman, and for this reason colour-blindness is far more prevalent in men than it is in women.

It should be noted that this sex-linked type of inheritance is somewhat different from Mendelian inheritance. The genes in the ordinary chromosomes (autosomes as they are sometimes called) are inherited, according to Mendel's laws, because there is a complete pair of autosomes in each sex ; but, as the male (in many species) lacks one of the X chromosomes, the inheritance of the genes in the X chromosomes is sex-linked and is different for each sex.

There is a disease of the blood, haemophilia, which prevents it from clotting, with the result that difficulty is experienced in stopping bleeding from even a slight wound. This defect is inherited in the same way as colour-blindness. Rarely does a woman suffer from it, but the daughters and grand-daughters of a defective male hand the disease on to half their sons. (*See* diagram.) Characters transmitted in this way must be carried in

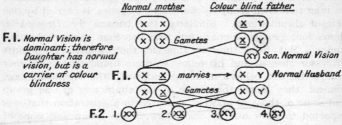

INHERITANCE OF COLOUR-BLINDNESS as a sex-linked character. 1. Daughter of normal vision. 2. Daughter of normal vision, but a carrier of colour-blindness. 3. Son of normal vision. 4. Son colour-blind.

the unpaired X chromosome of the male, and it is by following this clue that the first step towards discovering which chromosome carried a certain gene was made. One result of the breeding experiments with the banana fly has been to locate more than fifty characters in its X chromosome alone.

Sex Determination. Various theories have been held as to the cause of sex. Malnutrition of the mother, such as she might suffer in war-time, has been thought to produce boy babies. Another theory was that gametes from one testis or ovary would form zygotes of the male sex, and that gametes from the other testis or ovary would form females. Age and vigour of the parents have also been thought to be determiners of sex. In the light of the discovery of the X chromosome, none of these theories is tenable any longer. Thousands of breeding experiments dealing with inheritance in many organisms, but especially in the banana fly, prove that the two sexes differ from the beginning in the sense that one sex has one more chromosome than the other. This, as we have seen, is the female sex in Man and insects; it is, however, the male in birds.

LESSON 18

What the Banana Fly has Taught Us in Genetics

IN experimental breeding it is found that characteristics pass on from generation to generation in groups. In peas, for example, eight groups of characters are inherited according to Mendel's laws, and, since peas have eight pairs of chromosomes, we infer that each group of characters, or genes, is carried by one pair of chromosomes. Similarly, the banana fly, *Drosophila*, shows four groups of characters and has four pairs of chromosomes. But from time to time in their many experiments Professor Morgan and his fellow workers found that these four groups did not behave in accordance with the Mendelian law. Instead, they found that some of the characters of one group and some of those of another appeared in a generation that was expected to show all the characters of one group and none of those of the other. It was found that two of the chromosomes, when lying in pairs across the spindle (*see* Lesson 2, volume 1, page 80), had " crossed over," that is to say, one lay across the other; therefore, a breakage had occurred in the chromosomes— one end of chromosome (A) had joined the complementary part of chromosome (B), and a similar junction had been effected by the other two ends, as shown in Fig. 1. The offspring which receive either of these chromosomes will not show the characters expected. Crossing over has taken place.

Locating the Genes. It is obvious that, if there were 100 genes in each chromosome, either the one or the other of the two extreme gene numbers, 1 and 100, would cross over every time a crossing over took place. Thus, if there were 200 crossings, the

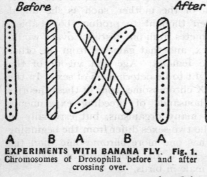

Before　　　　*After*

A　B　A　B　A　B

EXPERIMENTS WITH BANANA FLY. Fig. 1.
Chromosomes of Drosophila before and after crossing over.

expectation that either number 1 or number 100 would cross would be 200, that is 100 in respect of each number. But each of two genes lying close together in the middle of the chromosome, e.g. genes numbered 49 and 50, would be liable to cross over only once in 200 times. It is on these lines that actual charts of the chromosomes of *Drosophila* have been made.

Charting the Chromosomes. The chromosomes of the fly are seen by a high-powered microscope to be of the shape shown in Fig. 2, and, infinitely small though they are, the scientist has

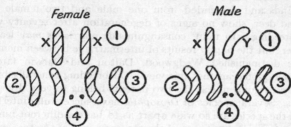

GENE POSITIONS. Fig. 2. Method of charting positions of the genes in the Drosophila chromosomes.

been able, by breeding thousands of generations, to chart the position of over 400 genes along their length. The gene for a vestigial wing, for example, is found to be 67 units distant from the end of number 2 chromosome ; the gene that may cause the offspring to be eyeless lies at a certain point in chromosome 4, and so on. These experiments have shown that sometimes a single gene affects, by its presence or absence, a whole group of characters, while a whole group of genes is sometimes required to produce a single character.

Inbreeding and Outbreeding. Most organisms carry some defective genes, but, since the zygote is diploid—since, that is to say, it is furnished with two sets of genes, one paternal and one maternal—a defect in one set may be made good by a corresponding normal gene in the other set. It is only when the defective genes *coincide*, and the defect is present in a double dose, that it appears. This is what happens in some cases when inbreeding takes place. The nearer the relationship of the parents to a common ancestor, the more likely is it that the defective genes in the chromosomes contributed by each will coincide in the zygote, and an offspring will be produced which is homozygous for, that is, which has received a double dose of, the defect. This defect will appear in the offspring according to Mendel's law (*see* Lesson 15, volume 2, page 82).

No definite law can, however, be laid down as to the general effects of inbreeding. Weismann, inbreeding mice for twenty-nine generations, found that the average fertility dropped from 6·1 to 4·2 per litter as a result. Loss of vigour in plants has again been proved to be the consequence of continued self-fertilization. On the other hand, the deer in Windsor Park, numbering some thousands and descended from one male and two female New Zealand deer, show no signs of degeneration after seventy years of inbreeding. In man, consanguineous marriages *may* lead to disaster, but the happy results of intermarriage between members of the distinguished Wedgwood, Dalton and Darwin families are often quoted against this view. Outbreeding generally brings increased vigour, unless the two parents belong to very divergent species. Several species of *Drosophila* have successfully interbred, but, if the species are so wide apart as to have a different number of sets of chromosomes, or, if the chromosomes of the two species differ widely in size and shape, the young either die or, if they grow, are sterile.

Sterility. The reason for this sterility appears to be that of two widely differing sets of chromosomes combined in the zygote, each will endeavour to reproduce in different directions. If the incompatibility of the genes and chromosomes is not too great, they may achieve a compromise and produce an organism more or less abnormal. Genes from very diverse parents, however, cannot effect even this compromise, and sterility is the result. A familiar example is the ass, which has 64 small chromosomes, mated to a mare, which has 38 large chromosomes. The ass sperm, containing 32 small chromosomes, is able to fertilize the equine ovum, containing 19 large chromosomes, and to produce the vigorous hybrid mule. The unequal sets of chromosomes which the mule inherits cannot pair normally to form germ cells.

Mutation. Of very great importance to the student of biology is the increased knowledge of what is known as mutation, which has been acquired from experiments in breeding during recent years. Changes in the *structure* of the chromosomes have some-times occurred in breeding *Drosophila.* In one case, the two rod-shaped X chromosomes became united and formed a single V-shaped chromosome, and a new type of fly was produced.

Other new types have arisen through some alteration in the *number* of chromosomes. It sometimes happens in cell division that one of the new cells receives all the chromosomes (a double set), and the other none. The latter cell is abortive, but, if the cell with the double set unites in the next generation with one of the usual type, a new individual appears (with three sets of chromosomes), differing in many respects from the original stock.

Many cases of mutation have occurred in the plant world. The wild rose has 7 chromosomes, but there are species with 14, others with 21, 28 and 35 chromosomes. There are different species of chrysanthemums with different multiples of 9 (18, 36, 54—90) chromosomes. The most fundamental and important mutation, however, is that due to an alteration in the nature of the *gene* itself. Little is known of the cause of such alteration in the chemical constituents of a gene, but alterations have been produced by X-rays.

Changes in the gene occur rarely, but in the many thousands of generations of *Drosophila* that have been bred during the last twenty years, some hundreds have occurred. New permanent species of banana fly have thus arisen—wingless species, eyeless species, species with duplicated legs, etc.

Varieties and Species. We shall refer to these mutations in later Lessons, when we come to consider the causes of evolution. The student is asked here to distinguish between the unstable *varieties* (such as wrinkled yellow peas in the diagram in Lesson 15, Volume 2, page 85), produced by ordinary Mendelian breeding, and the permanent new types, or *species*, established by changes in the structure, or number, of chromosomes, and especially those species or mutants caused by change or mutation in the chemical characteristics of the gene.

In this and Lessons 16 and 17 chromosomes and genes have been presented as the sole and all-important factors in the evolution of new types. This view is illusory, and the reader should suspend judgement until the question of heredity and environment has been considered in a later Lesson. The subject of genetics is dealt with very fully in : " Genetics," by H. E. Walter (Macmillan & Co.), pages 300–329 ; and in " The Biological Basis of Human Nature," by H. S. Jennings (Faber & Faber).

LESSON 19

Scientific Classification of the Animal Kingdom

IN several Lessons the term *Species* has been used to denote a group of living organisms which was regarded as distinct from some other group, and in Lesson 14 (volume 2, page 79) the term species is defined as a group of organisms the members of which breed freely with each other but do not breed freely with members of other species or groups. Nature is so variable, however, that no definition can be sufficiently exact to apply to all cases and to every member of a group. As might be expected, if the theory of evolution is valid, there will always be overlapping of groups and always individuals that are on the borderline between two groups. In the preceding Lesson it was related how several species of *Drosophila* interbred to form new species. During the War, the numbers of representatives of separate species of deer which were kept on the Mappin Terraces in the Zoological Gardens were allowed to dwindle, with the result that members of a species which had hitherto mated exclusively within that species began to interbreed with members of other species. Thus it seems that wild species may in certain circumstances interbreed with members of other species.

To enable the reader to appreciate the various theories as to the causes of evolution which will be given in later Lessons, it is necessary to give a preliminary account of the system of classification of animals which is generally adopted by zoologists, and, secondly, to glance at some of the fundamental differences which exist between the great groups, or phyla, in which the immensely varied multitude of living organisms has been classified. To determine to which phylum, class, order, family, genus and species a living organism belongs, various sciences must be consulted. The science of morphology must be invoked to give such particulars as number and structure of limbs, character of skin and hair, and position and form of internal organs. Various parts must be examined microscopically by the histologist, while in modern zoology the embryologist is asked to give his evidence as to the various structural changes that occur in the embryo at different stages of its growth, before the adult can be accurately and certainly labelled a member of this or that group.

By these methods all the members of the animal kingdom have been classified in twelve great groups known as phyla. Let us take at random some common organisms, for example, worms, snakes, fish, dogs, crabs, spiders and snails. Of these, snakes, fish and dogs are distinguished from the others by the possession of a backbone, and for this reason they are called vertebrates and are placed in the phylum Chordata. Of the others, crabs and spiders are built on a different plan from any of the rest. They have jointed bodies with jointed limbs and a kind of skeleton outside their bodies. Their internal organs are also of a different kind from those of the other creatures cited, and in a different position in their bodies. The crab and spider, with other organisms of a similar build, belong to the phylum Arthropoda. Snails, again, have no joints or segments in their bodies, and their shells are quite different from those of the crab or lobster. They are accordingly classified with oysters, mussels, etc., as molluscs, while the worms, which differ from all the rest in having a ringed body, which is not supported by bone or shell, form the great phylum Annulata. Each phylum is subdivided into classes, the classes into orders, the orders into families, the families into genera, and the genera into species.

Single-Celled Organisms. In order that the reader may familiarize himself with this method of classification, it will be well to turn to the humble organism, the Amoeba, which has already been discussed in Lesson 3 (volume 1, page 83). It is there described as an animal the body of which is a single cell. This feature, which it shares with many other organisms, marks it off from the great groups of many-celled organisms. Because it is unicellular, it is grouped with all similar organisms into the lowest of the animal phyla, the phylum Protozoa.

Some one-celled organisms are distinguished by the possession of flagella ; others by the property of sending out threads of protoplasm (cilia, as they are called) which wave rhythmically ; others, again, by being what is called encysted, that is, enclosed in a cell wall, while the amoeba travels, as already described, by projecting false feet or pseudopods. The phylum Protozoa, therefore, is subdivided into classes, and the amoeba is classified as *Rhizopoda* (rootfooted). But this class, Rhizopoda, contains different orders. One order of Rhizopoda has finely branched pseudopods ; another is distinguished by having stiff, radiating pseudopods, and so on. The amoeba described in Lesson 3 protrudes short, blunt, finger-like pseudopods, and is placed, therefore, in the order *Lobosa*.

Again, the particular kind of amoeba which has been described does not possess any shell-like or chitinous covering as do some other members of the order Lobosa, and, therefore, it is placed in the family *Amoebidae*. This family grouping is again divided into genera, and, as the amoeba in Lesson 3 is described as having a nucleus and a contractile vacuole, it is placed in the genus *Amoeba*. Finally, as its pseudopods are comparatively well developed and, when protruded, alter its shape, it belongs to the species *Amoeba proteus*.

The scientific classification, therefore, which identifies the kind of amoeba we have considered from all other unicellular forms is :

Phylum. *Protozoa.*

Class. *Rhizopoda.*

Order. *Lobosa.*

Family. *Amoebidae.*

Genus. *Amoeba.*

Species. *Amoeba proteus.*

The Protozoa foreshadow in their free one-celled existence many of the functions carried out by the specialized cells of higher organisms. In respect of their usual method of multiplication (by fission), the Protozoa exemplify the mitotic division (*see* Lesson 2, volume 1, page 79) of the somatic cells of higher organisms, while their occasional resort to conjugation hints at the evolution of sexual reproduction. This is particularly true of the kind of conjugation practised by the species *Volvox*, in which small, active sperm-like cells fuse with larger inactive cells. The method of conjugation adopted by the *Paramoecium* (Lesson 4, volume 1, page 87) is very suggestive of the action of coition practised by higher organisms.

The *Amoeba proteus*, slowly sliding over its muddy hunting ground and enveloping and absorbing specks of organic débris, is a prototype of the white cells of the blood which maintain the purity of the blood stream in mammals by absorbing bacteria in a very similar fashion. The class Ciliata is, similarly, typical of the ciliated cells in the breathing passages of mammals, while in the colonies of single independent cells formed by many classes of Protozoa, we see the beginnings of the many-celled animal.

The Protozoa are to be found wherever there is moisture. Some groups are marine, others live in fresh water, while others, again, live their lives in the bodies of animals and mankind. The order *Foraminifera* build tiny shells of carbonate of lime, but, when the time comes for division into two daughter cells, the original cell is rejected and sinks slowly to the floor of the ocean. Microscopic though the contribution of each Protozoan is, it is by their agency that huge layers of chalk, such as our North and South Downs, have been deposited. Of the parasitic Protozoa, the flagellate known as *Trypanosoma* is important, since it is the cause of Gambia fever when it enters the blood stream. It is often carried, however, via the lymphatic glands into the fluid of the spinal canal, and the infected person is smitten with the fatal sleeping sickness. For an account of other diseases caused or transmitted by Protozoa the student should read " Outlines of Zoology " (Thomson), Oxford University Press, pp. 145–150.

LESSON 20

More About the Groupings of Animal Life

I N the limited space at our disposal it is impossible to do more than glance at some of the phyla in which the vast variety of living forms has been grouped, and which are treated in some detail in our Course in Zoology. In the previous Lesson we dealt with the group of one-celled organisms, *Protozoa*. All the other organisms (*Metazoa*) are composed of many cells, and the lowest group of Metazoa is the phylum *Porifera*, of which the common sponge is typical. The sponge is a loosely organized community of cells living together and forming a vegetative animal " body." The cells are in some respects differentiated, but can scarcely be said to have become specialized. There are flagellate cells that drive the water through the horny skeleton and abstract nutriment therefrom ; there are other cells that form the horny skeleton, and rudimentary muscle cells that can control the openings through which the water flows ; but there are no definite organs, and there is no body cavity. This phylum appears to be a bypath in evolution, and does not lead to the development of higher forms.

On a slightly higher plane than the sponges are the *Coelenterata*, which include such animals as sea anemones, corals, hydra and jelly-fish. Their bodily structure is all on the same plan—a hollow two-layered tube, or gastrula, with tentacles radiating symmetrically from a common centre. These tentacles have stinging cells, by which the minute prey is numbed or killed. Like the sponges, the Coelenterates reproduce by budding, but they also practise sexual reproduction. In one class—Hydra— self-fertilization, which is a very rare process in the animal kingdom, takes place. In this phylum are found the beginnings of a nervous system ; a network of nervous fibres runs diffusely through the body, but there is no actual nervous centre.

Worms. Grouped under the title of worms are three phyla of unsegmented worms and one of segmented worms. The unsegmented round or flat worms are mainly internal parasites of beast or Man. An example of the latter is the dreaded tapeworm. Among the segmented group (*Annelida*) are the common earthworm and leech. In this worm group we first meet with the " fore and aft " development. Worms move forward with one end always in front, so that, instead of the radial symmetry of the Coelenterates, these worm phyla have a bilateral symmetry with head and tail. Moreover, the end that travels first receives the most stimuli and tends, therefore, to evolve an apparatus for responding to them ; this worm shows the beginning of a head-brain and a ventral nervous system. The earthworm, a member of the phylum *Annelida*, has a body which is ringed into segments, each of which has a rudimentary nerve centre and two excretory tubes, which in some segments are also reproductory ducts. It is also hermaphrodite, possessing two pairs of testes lying between segments 9 and 10 and 10 and 11, and two ovaries lying in the division between segments 12 and 13. Thus, in coition, two worms lie head to tail, and each fertilizes the ova of the other. This peculiar variation of bi-sexual reproduction is limited to some members of this phylum, e g. the earthworm and the leech. The segmented body with its tiny " bristles " attached to each segment appears to link up the *Annelida* with a much higher phylum in the scale, the *Arthropoda*.

MORE ABOUT GROUPINGS OF ANIMAL LIFE

The animals in the phylum *Echinoderma* are possibly an off-shoot of some worm " stock," but they have reverted to radial symmetry, as instanced in the starfish and sea urchin, although in the larval stage they are bilateral, like the worms.

Starfish and Sea Urchins. Like the worm, the starfish, although eyeless, is sensitive to light, and has, in fact, an " eye-spot " at the end of each of its five arms. Its mouth is on the under or ventral side, and from it the starfish extrudes a part of its stomach over small shellfish and begins the process of digesting them where they lie. The partly digested shellfish is then transferred to the interior of the starfish, and the digestive process is finished in the five branch stomachs, one of which is found in each of the five arms. On the under-side of the starfish are rows of " tube feet " arranged along the groove that runs the length of each arm. The starfish is able to extend its tube feet by filling them with water, and then, having obtained a firm grip of the ground with the terminal suckers, it draws the rest of the body along. If it wishes to travel west, the arm pointing that way becomes the " head " for the time being, its eye-spot is raised, its tube feet flooded, and the other arms follow, side-stepping or marching, according to their relative position to the pilot arm. To change the direction of the promenade, there need be no right-about-turn. All that happens is that the arm pointing in the new direction assumes the initiative, and the hydrostatic locomotion is resumed. The pentagonal layout of the body, and the system of locomotion constitute this group a clearly defined phylum.

Molluscs. Although in the phylum *Mollusca* the animals are unsegmented and have no appendages, they show some resemblance to the *Annelida* in virtue of the presence of a nerve ring round the gullet and of the structure of the larva. The bivalves (oysters, mussels, etc.) are built on a simple plan, rather like that of a book The hinged covers of the book correspond to the two shells. These shells are secreted by the " mantle "—a pair of thin folds of flesh which hang down from the back and cover the whole body, more or less after the manner of the first and last pages of a volume. The body creeps along on a muscular flexible " foot," while the gills drive water through a kind of siphon, which passes within the space between the two mantle flaps. All supplies of food and oxygen are taken in this way The genital products of the two sexes are discharged into the water, where the ova are fertilized.

The snail (*Gastropod*) possesses a " foot " somewhat similar to that of the bivalves, but its shell is spiral. Instead of gills, there is a lung cavity formed by the mantle fold, and its blue-tinted blood (peculiar to molluscs and arthropods) is driven round the body by the single ventricle of the heart back to the auricle. The snail is hermaphrodite.

The most active and highly developed molluscs are the *Cephalopoda*, which include the cuttlefish and octopuses. As the name implies, the " stomach-foot " of the snail has in this group become a part of the head. The foot has developed into eight or ten writhing arms, by means of which the animal captures its prey and holds it by the powerful suckers with which the arms are furnished, while the beak-like jaws bite a piece from the victim. The octopus then pours a salivary secretion into the wound, which poisons and digests the victim at the same time ; the semi-liquid mass is finally drawn into the globular stomach, where digestion is completed.

The eyes of the cephalopods are large, and it is chiefly their intent stare that gives the cuttlefish and octopus such an intelligent and malignant appearance. Although the eyes arise from skin cells and are not developed from the fore brain, they bear a strong superficial resemblance to the eyes of vertebrate animals.

Before we pass to the consideration of the higher phyla, arthropods and vertebrates, it is important to emphasize the fact that, although each of the groups already dealt with is marked off from the others by some fundamental differences in structure, there is no sharp line of demarcation ; on the contrary, there are many links between these groups and between them and vertebrates.

Some of these group linkages will be referred to in later Lessons. A very full account of the evolution of phyla is given in " Outlines of General Biology," by Thomson & Geddes (Williams and Norgate), pp. 817–911.

LESSON 21

Biological Account of the Arthropods

THE two remaining phyla, Arthropoda and Vertebrata, present a striking contrast to each other. Two superficial differences are immediately apparent. In the arthropods the soft parts of the body are covered with a chitinous or horny skeleton, to which the muscles are attached. This outside skeleton is a marked contrast to the internal skeleton of the vertebrates. In place of the four limbs possessed by most vertebrates, the arthropods have a large number (varying in different classes) of jointed appendages. Other contrasting features will emerge as we study each phylum. Both groups include classes which show great diversity of form, and the members of each group, in virtue of their increased complexity of structure and greater activity and intelligence, are distinctly in advance of those organisms at which we have already glanced.

The chief classes into which the arthropods are grouped are (1) *Insecta*, including beetles, butterflies, moths, bees, wasps, ants, dragon-flies, etc. (with three pairs of walking legs). (2) *Myriopoda*, or millipedes and centipedes (with many pairs of walking legs, all nearly alike). (3) *Arachnida*—scorpions, spiders, mites and ticks (with four pairs of walking legs). (4) *Crustacea*—lobsters, crabs and shrimps (showing great diversity in the number and arrangement of walking or swimming legs).

Crustacea. As a broad illustration of the general structure of the arthropods, and as a typical crustacean, the lobster is an interesting subject for study. All the *Crustacea* have a segmented body, and each segment bears a pair of appendages, but, in the lobster, five segments are fused together to form the head, which carries five pairs of appendages. This head part, together with the next eight segments, is covered by the carapace—a single stiff sheet of armour—and the whole is called the cephalothorax or head-chest. The rest of the body consists of the so-called abdomen, which has six segments, each furnished with a pair of swimmerets. In swimming, the abdomen is flapped forwards, causing the lobster to travel backwards.

The lobster, like most of the crustaceans, has stiffened the ordinary chitinous skeleton into a " shell " by the addition of carbonate of lime. Unfortunately for the wearer, the covering will not expand, and the animal has to " moult " several times during its growth. When this happens, a soft new covering forms underneath the old one, and the old garment splits in two and is shed. The unprotected crustacean goes into retreat in some rocky cleft until its new armour hardens.

The lobster possesses altogether twenty pairs of appendages, which in the very young lobster are much alike, but which later specialize into the form best fitted to carry out their work. In front of the swimmerets are the five pairs of legs, the front pair of which form the large pincer-claws. These claws are not of the same size. One, the larger (that on the right, in some species of crabs), is used for crushing the shells of the molluscs on which the lobster feeds, while the smaller claw holds

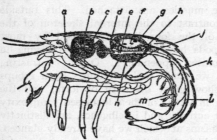

STRUCTURE OF AN ARTHROPOD (LOBSTER). a, cerebral ganglia; b, d, j, m, n, arteries; c, gizzard; e, mid-gut; f, heart; g, pericardium; h, gonads or genital organs; k, superior abdominal artery; l, hind-gut; p, digestive gland.

From Sir J. A. Thomson, " Outlines of Zoology," Oxford University Press

and tears the prey. The remaining appendages of the thorax are three pairs of foot-jaws or maxillipeds. Attached to the head are the stalked compound eyes, two pairs of feelers or antennae, and, near the mouth, three pairs of jaw appendages or mandibles, which help in tearing and shredding the food.

Near the base of the first pair of antennae in many crustaceans are little cavities, lined with feathery hairs, in which are entangled grains of sand. It is proved experimentally that these particles of sand act on the nerve endings in the hairs, much in the same way as the " chalk-balls " (*see* volume 2, page 69) in the semi-circular canals of our ears act upon our nerves and give us the sense of balance.

Internally, the lobster is as queer as it is externally. After its food has been finely divided by the mandibles it passes into a double-chambered stomach, which is lined with chitin and which

FAMOUS 'OLD MASTERS.' Above, Van Dyck's (1599–1641) painting of William II of Orange and Mary Stuart on the occasion of their marriage in 1641. Below, " The Ambassadors," painted by Holbein the Younger (c. 1497 – 1543) in 1533.
ART AND ARCHITECTURE 15
National Gallery

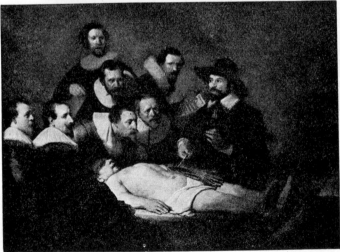

MORE FAMOUS 'OLD MASTERS.' The lower picture is "The Anatomy Lesson," painted by Rembrandt (c. 1607–1669) in 1632. Above is "The Lute Player" of Frans Hals of Haarlem (c. 1580–1666). The model was Adrian Brouwer, a favourite pupil, depicted in the act of serenading the lady of his choice.

ART AND ARCHITECTURE 15

Rijks Museum, Amsterdam, Mauritshuis, the Hague

Plate 14   *Volume III*

LANDSCAPES OF THE DUTCH SCHOOL. Above, the Avenue, Middelharnis, painted in 1689 by Meindert Hobbema (1638–1709), a fine example of the work of one who excelled in the representation of the placid beauties of the Dutch countryside. Hobbema's paintings are now much regarded, but he was little appreciated by the art patrons of his day and died in obscure poverty. Below is the " View of Delft," by Jan Van der Meer (1632–75), more often called Vermeer of Delft.
ART AND ARCHITECTURE 15

National Gallery; Hague Museum

INTERIOR BY LE NAIN. The three brothers Le Nain—Antoine, Louis, and Mathieu—specialized in domestic genre and portraits; a typical specimen is the one shown above, by Louis Le Nain. ART AND ARCHITECTURE 16

The Louvre

EL GRECO'S 'AGONY IN THE GARDEN.' El Greco counts today as the most modern of all Spanish painters. ART AND ARCHITECTURE 16

National Gallery

Plate 16   *Volume III*

is fitted, at the junction of the two chambers, with three teeth. This gastric mill finishes the mastication of the food, which is now bathed in secretions from the liver. These secretions are the equivalent of our salivary, gastric and pancreatic juices. The lobster's heart is a small organ placed near the middle of the back. It drives the bluish-coloured blood through the body by ill-defined and sinuous passages. On its way back to the heart the blood passes through the gills—two brush-like pieces of apparatus which lie under the carapace. It is here that the blood becomes oxygenized from the water.

Close to the heart lie the gonads or genital organs. The sperm from the male is transferred, via the openings in the basal segments of the last pair of legs, to the " sperm receptacle " on the underside of the female's thorax.

Insecta. This class is unique among the backboneless animals in that it has taken to the air. Like the birds, which occupy a similar position in the phylum *Vertebrata*, insects are very active, with well aerated and brightly coloured bodies. Their nervous and respiratory organs are well developed, and, again as in the case of birds, there is often considerable difference in the appearance of the two sexes, while both in birds and insects there is a vast variety of species.

The body of the adult insect is marked off into three divisions—head, thorax and abdomen. The head carries a pair of feelers, or antennae, and three pairs of mouth appendages. Since the food of different species of insects differs widely (some living on nectar, others on animal juices, etc.), the shape and structure of the mouth appendages in one species may be very different from those of the mouth appendages of another species.

The thorax bears, in addition to the two pairs of wings, three pairs of walking legs. When walking the insect advances the first and third leg on the one side simultaneously with the middle leg on the other side ; thus the body is borne along on two tripods, which advance alternately.

Internally, the insect is built on broadly the same structural plan as is found in the crustaceans. The cockroach, for example, possesses a double ventral chain of nerve ganglia, which are connected with the pair of nerve ganglia, or " brain," in the head. Its mouth cavity, gullet, crop and gizzard are lined with chitinous cuticle, which in the gizzard is modified to form six hard teeth, and, as in the case of the *Crustacea*, this chitinous lining is cast, together with the outside skeleton, every time moulting occurs. In such species of insects as undergo metamorphosis, moulting occurs in all species before the wings appear.

The respiratory system of insects—and, indeed, of all land arthropods—shows a marked contrast to that of the *Crustacea*. Insects breathe by means of air tubes (trachea), which ramify among the internal organs all over the insect's body. These elastic tubes (spirally strengthened like a fire hose) are compressed and relaxed rhythmically by the insect's muscles, and, if we watch a bee as it is extracting nectar from a flower, we can see the rhythmic respiratory movement of its abdomen.

Myriopoda. Although both centipedes and millipedes have a somewhat worm-like appearance, their nervous system, heart, excretory tubules and tracheal breathing are like those of insects.

Arachnida. Spiders, scorpions, mites, ticks, etc., differ from insects in the following particulars : 1. The head and thorax are fused. 2. They have no antennae. 3. They have more than three pairs of walking legs. 4. They develop directly from the egg, and do not undergo metamorphosis.

Books on the subject include " Life of the Crustacea," by Catman (Methuen) ; " The Science of Life," Bk II, pp. 128–132 (Wells, Huxley, and Wells) ; and, for insect communal life, " The Social Insects," Wheeler ; "Social Life in the Insect World,' J. H. Fabre ; "The Honey Bee," Langstroth and Dadant.

LESSON 22

Distinguishing Features of the Vertebrates

I N Lessons 5–10 in this Course the chief functions ot the vertebrate body were described. Here those features in the structure of vertebrates are emphasized that are found in no other phyla. (1) Gill slits open from the sides of the pharynx to the exterior. In fish and young amphibians these are used in respiration. In higher forms, e.g. mammals, they either disappear after the embryo stage, or they are modified into other structures. (2) The heart is always in a ventral position. (3) The eye is formed by an outgrowth of the brain. (4) The nervous system runs along the back (contrast this with the ventral nerve cord in Arthropoda). (5) An internal backbone: in the embryo of the vertebrates the backbone is preceded by a supporting elastic rod known as the notochord. For this reason the naturalist classes all vertebrates in the phylum *Chordata*, and he includes in this phylum such lowly creatures as: (a) *Balanoglossus*, a worm-like creature that burrows in the sea mud; it possesses gill-clefts, and the front part of its body, which it uses for boring, is perforated along its length by a tube which is suggestive of a notochord; (b) Lancelet, a sluglike burrower in sand, which has numerous gill-clefts in the throat: beneath the spinal cord and running the length of the body is the stiff elastic notochord, which is retained throughout life; (c) *Tunicata*, another strange class of the phylum *Chordata*, a typical member of which is the common sea squirt. When hatched from the egg, the sea squirt has a tadpole-like appearance; the little creature

STRUCTURE OF A VERTEBRATE. a, ureter; b, kidney; c, posterior air-sac; d, lung attached to ribs; e, cerebellum; f, cerebral hemisphere; g, ear opening; h, gullet; j, windpipe; k, crop; l, proventriculus; m, heart; n, liver; o, keel of sternum; p, gizzard; q, small intestine; r, large intestine; s, cloaca.

From Sir J. A. Thomson, "Outlines of Zoology," Oxford University Press

swims somewhat like a fish by means of its strong tail, which contains a notochord; moreover, this larval sea squirt has gill-slits, a dorsal nerve cord, and an eye developing from the brain; but on reaching the adult stage, it undergoes a strange degeneration, fastening itself upside down to a rock, where, after losing tail, nerve cord, notochord and eye, it remains for the rest of its life, looking now something like a small jar with two narrow spouts; water passes slowly in through one spout and out of the other, and the animal lives on the food which it filters from the water, showing animation only when disturbed; it then squeezes out the water in two strong jets, and relapses for a time into a gelatinous mass.

Above these groups of semi-vertebrates are the fish, which have permanent gills and, with the exception of the cartilaginous fish, have a vertebrated backbone. It has been suggested that fish developed in running water, and that the " stream-line " body, strong muscles and backbone have been evolved in order to maintain a position against a current and to force the body up-stream. The fish's heart is furnished with a single auricle and ventricle.

Amphibians. The transition from water to land animals is marked by the amphibians. In this class, to which frogs, newts, etc., belong, lungs, a voice and five digital extremities appear. The heart has two auricles and one ventricle. In the reptiles (snakes, lizards, tortoises) the heart is further developed. There are two auricles, and the ventricle is also partly (in crocodiles completely) divided into two. Two characteristics are found in the egg of the reptile belonging only to the three highest classes of vertebrates : (1) the *amnion*, which is a membrane enfolding the embryo ; (2) the *allantois*—a hollow outgrowth from the ventral side of the embryo, which extends enormously and by means of which respiration is accomplished through the porous shell.

In mammals, the allantois becomes connected with the folds of the uterus of the mother, so that the foetus is nourished by the mother's blood and waste products are removed by the same means. The structure which is thus formed is called the placenta, and is a distinguishing feature of mammalian embryonic life only.

Birds. Next to mammals, birds take the highest place in the phylum *Chordata*. With the mammals they are distinguished from all other organisms by the possession of warm blood. The bodily temperature of birds is from two to fourteen degrees above that of mammals. This is due to the presence of numerous air sacs in the body. At each inspiration a large quantity of air rushes through the lungs into the air sacs, and as there is hardly any exchange of gases in the air sacs, the air has still some oxygen to give up in its passage back through the lungs. Thus the blood in the lung capillaries is oxygenated twice at each respiration. This high temperature is conserved by the feather covering and also by the rapid beat (amounting to over 120 per minute) of the relatively large four-chambered heart.

The lungs do not expand and contract as in other vertebrates, but are fixed to the ribs. The air sacs normally remain expanded, and muscular effort is needed to *expel* the air—a process which is the reverse of mammalian breathing. Like mammals, however, birds probably had a reptilian ancestor. The scales on birds' legs are very similar to the scales of reptiles, and the feathers are merely highly developed scales with the outer edges frayed into barbs. The skin, moreover, is reptilian in character, for it has no glands, except one oil-gland at the base of the tail, from which the bird oils its beak when preening.

Mammals. This class is superior to birds in at least two respects : (a) higher brain development ; (b) the long period of gestation, which demands care and sacrifice from the mother. The following characteristics : (1) mammary glands, by which the female suckles her young ; (2) a muscular diaphragm, which divides the bodily cavity into chest and abdomen ; and (3) the furry or woolly covering, are also exclusively mammalian features.

The first and lowest grade of mammals is to be found only in Tasmania and Australia. One member of this group—the duck mole—feeds on slugs and snails, and is oviparous, that is to say, the female lays eggs, as the reptiles do, but, unlike them, suckles her young after they are hatched. Its low blood temperature and some peculiarities of the duck mole's skeleton strongly suggest reptilian ancestry. Another member of the same grade is the spiny ant-eater, which carries its eggs and hatches them in a belly pouch.

The marsupials, such as the kangaroos of Australia and opossums of America, form the next grade. The young of this group are born in an extremely helpless and undeveloped condition, and are carried and nourished for some time in the mother's pouch.

The third grade, the *placental* mammals, includes all the other known warm-blooded animals. This grade is distinguished by the fact that the embryo, as already mentioned, is wrapped in and nourished through a placenta, and the young are thus born in a well-developed condition. In this class, however, the brain is " wrinkled with thought," showing those convolutions of the cerebrum which indicate high mental capacity. There are, altogether, fifteen orders of placental mammals, which may be assembled in four groups.

(1) *Cetaceans*, which have returned to the water from the land, e.g. whales, porpoises, etc. (2) *Ungulates*, or hoofed mammals—a vegetarian group, which includes horse, elephant, camel,

etc. (3) *Unguiculates*, or clawed animals, including the rodents, insect eaters, bats, carnivores or flesh eaters, sloths. (4) *Primates* (monkeys, apes, Man), which have, with few exceptions, five digits on hands and feet and, instead of claws or hoofs, flat nails on the digits. The thumbs are opposable, that is, the hand is suitable for climbing and for picking up things to be eaten or to be examined.

Man is distinguished from the rest of the order by the following characteristics : (a) he walks on the sole of his foot ; (b) his big toe is usually longer than the other digits of the foot, and is not opposable ; (c) the S-shaped curves of the vertebral column and the shape of the pelvic girdle enable him, despite his heavy brain, to walk upright ; (d) the brain is relatively heavy, highly convoluted, and large. (The average weight of the human brain is 48½ oz. and occupies about 56 cubic in. The ape's brain is never more than 20 oz. and occupies about 27½ cubic in.)

Our Course in Biology is continued in Volume 4.

LESSON 16

Influential Factors in Plant Growth

PART of the energy set free in respiration is employed in the process of growth, during which some of the food materials produced in the course of nutrition are used in building up new tissues. There are three distinct phases of growth : first, the formation of new cells by the division of pre-existing cells in the growing points ; secondly, the enlargement of the new cells ; and thirdly, their modification to perform the different functions which they fulfil in the life of the plant. The second phase is the only one visible externally, and constitutes " growth " in its popular sense.

The growing points, which are found at the extreme tips of the shoot and immediately behind the caps in the root, consist of numerous small cells which undergo repeated divisions. Some of the cells thus formed become gradually changed into mature cells ; others retain their power of division and persist as the growing point. Apart from growing points at the tips of roots and stems, some plants—for example, grasses and pinks—have similar " growing point tissue " situated along their mature stems near the nodes. These are spoken of as *intercalary* growing points, as distinct from the *apical* growing points. These intercalary growing points help the plants to raise their shoots when they have been flattened down by rain or wind.

This restriction of growth to definite regions constitutes a marked point of contrast between the growth of plants and of higher animals. Another distinction is the continual formation of new organs from the growing point of plants, whereas in animals the number of organs remains constant after the embryo stage is passed.

Rate of Growth. By marking roots and plumules with Indian ink (as described in Lesson 8, volume 1, page 139), we see that the region of elongation in roots is restricted to a very short portion just behind the tip, whilst in stems it is spread over a much greater length. In both we see that the rate of growth of different parts of the elongating zone is not uniform. The intervals near the tip of the root will have elongated very slightly, but as we pass farther from the apex the intervals become wider and wider, until they reach a maximum; after this they show gradual decrease up to the mature zone where no elongation has occurred. We therefore, conclude that newly formed cells elongate but slightly at first, grow in length more rapidly as they get older, until, when they approach maturity, their rate of elongation again decreases. This gradual rise and fall in the rate of elongation are spoken of as the *grand period of growth*, and are also well seen in the growing plumules of seedlings.

By means of different experiments it has been established that growth in length is greater by night than by day, provided the temperature remains approximately uniform. This is well illustrated by seedlings or sprouting potato tubers which are allowed to grow in the dark. The plants become etiolated ; that is, have no chlorophyll, very small leaves, but exceptionally long internodes. Many herbaceous plants exhibit longer internodes when grown in shady places than when grown in the open, or on the shady as compared with the sunny side of a hedge. The acceleration of growth in darkness is of great advantage in Nature, as it enables plants rapidly to reach the light. In plants growing from a rhizome or a root-stock the absence of light causes great elongation of the petioles.

As well as influencing the rate of growth, the intensity of light may also affect the extent of development of plant organs. The buds which are entirely shaded in a large tree usually fail to develop, whereas the majority of those at the margin give rise to branches. Flowers are rarely produced on the yellow dead nettle if growing in the deep shade of a wood, but flowering is profuse when the wood is coppiced. In many plants leaf development is affected by light intensity, " sun leaves " being smaller and thicker than " shade leaves."

Temperature has a marked effect on growth, as on all other vital processes. Plants grow slowly at a low temperature, the rate of elongation increasing as the temperature rises, until a degree of heat is attained which is unfavourable to further existence. Since at night the temperature is usually lower than in the day, the tendency to more rapid growth at night is not obvious in Nature. Apart from light and temperature, the most important factor influencing growth is the supply of oxygen for breathing. Other essentials are moisture and nutritive materials.

Injury to any living tissue of a plant causes the surrounding cells to undergo rapid division, and thus the wounded surface becomes covered up with a new growth. Injury due to insects or fungus pests is a similar stimulation to growth, and leads to the formation of galls, such as the well-known " oak-apple." " Witch's brooms," seen on birch, cherry and elm, are the result of excessive branching due to invasion by fungal pests.

Influence of Light. It is natural to ask why the majority of plants constantly assume the erect position in Nature, and the question is answered by considering the effect of light on direction of growth. If an erect plant is placed near a window, so that it receives one-sided illumination, the shoot will soon be found to have curved towards the light. If the plant is now turned through a right angle, it will be found later that the shoot has again bent over to the light. Thus the erect growth of the stem is dependent on its being exposed to equal illumination on all sides, and one-sided light causes bending until this condition is attained. The influence of light on the direction of growth of a plant is spoken of as *heliotropism*, and stems which curve towards the light are *positively heliotropic*. The aerial roots of the ivy are common examples of *negative heliotropism*, always growing away from the light ; a few subterranean roots—for example, those of mustard—react negatively to one-sided light, though the majority of roots are unaffected.

Influences other than light play a part in determining the erect position of the shoot. If a potted plant is placed horizontally in the dark for some hours the tip of the shoot gradually curves upwards till it again assumes a vertical direction. Evidently some agency other than light is responsible ; this is the force of gravity, which in stems causes growth in a direction opposite to that in which gravity acts. The influence of the force of gravity on the direction of growth of the plant is spoken of as *geotropism*, and stems are *negatively geotropic*. Main roots, which always grow downwards, are *positively geotropic ;* lateral roots, which grow obliquely from the main axis, are not so strongly influenced by gravity, while this force has no influence on the finer ramifications of the root system—these spread through the soil in search of water.

If a seedling with plumule and radicle marked with ink is placed horizontally in a dark box, it will be found after twenty-four hours that the geotropic curvature has occurred in the region of maximum elongation. It has, however, been shown that the region of curvature is not the region in which the influence of gravity is first felt. The " perceptive " region is at the extreme tip, and in experiments with roots whose tips are cut off no curvature results. The stimulus which is received at the tip of a root or shoot must, therefore, be transferred by some means or other to the zone of elongation. In the case of heliotropic curvature the bending also takes place in the region of elongation, though the perceptive power is localized elsewhere. There must, therefore, again be conduction of the stimulus to the region where bending occurs.

Effect of Moisture. The distribution of moisture markedly influences the direction of growth of roots, especially of finer branches of the root system. This influence of one-sided moisture on the direction of growth of roots is known as *hydrotropism*, and roots which grow towards the moisture are *positively hydrotropic*.

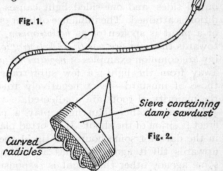

Fig. 1.

Sieve containing damp sawdust

Curved radicles

Fig. 2.

Negative hydrotropism is a much rarer phenomenon and has not been observed in the higher plants.

The curvature of roots towards water is easily shown by growing some cress seeds in damp sawdust in a fine wire sieve. The sieve should be tilted at an angle of 45°. When the radicles of the seedlings emerge

ROOT GROWTH. Fig. 1. Experiment to show the region of geotropic curvature in the radicle and plumule of a pea seedling placed horizontally. **Fig. 2.** Experiment showing hydrotropism in roots.

into the air at the bottom of the sieve they then turn through a right angle to reach the damp sawdust which lies on one side of them. The influence of moisture is stronger than the influence of gravity. If a similar sieve be hung up horizontally there is no such hydrotropic curvature; this is due to the fact that all sides of the radicles are stimulated by the moisture in an equal degree.

Those students who care to supplement their reading with practical work may (1) place potted plants in a window and notice curvature of the shoots towards the light ; (2) soak some pea or bean seeds, allow them to germinate until the radicles have emerged, place them in damp sawdust with the radicles pointing in different directions and, after a few days, notice the downward curvature of all the radicles ; (3) show the positive curvature of roots towards moisture as described above.

LESSON 17

Insectivorous and Parasitic Plants

(See plate 25)

WE have already considered the way in which the ordinary green plant builds up its body from simple chemical compounds obtained directly from the soil and the air. There are plants, however, which, like members of the animal world, are dependent upon elaborated food substances, and can only thrive when these are available in the form of either living or dead organic material. In such plants the leaves are always small and frequently without chlorophyll. When some or all of the food is obtained from another living organism, the plant is called a *parasite* and the organism which feeds it the *host*. When the source of nourishment is dead organic matter, the plant living on it is known as a *saprophyte*.

Parasitic Plants. Some parasites are only partly dependent upon their hosts and are described as *semi-parasites*. Their leaves, though relatively small, are often green, and consequently the plants can grow independently, though in these conditions growth is not vigorous. Common examples are found among our meadow plants in the yellow rattle, cow-wheat and eyebright, which are parasitic on the roots of other plants, particularly grasses. The roots of the parasite are attached at certain points to those of the host by minute suckers, which appear as slight swellings. These penetrate into the roots of the host as far as the central conducting tissues, and thus absorb nourishment.

Complete parasites are comparatively rare amongst British flowering plants ; the best examples are the dodder, the tooth-wort and the broom rapes. The dodder (plate 25) is parasitic chiefly on gorse and heather. The fine reddish-coloured stems entwine the stems of the host, penetrating it with small suckers, through which nourishment is absorbed. The stems bear minute scale-like leaves completely devoid of chlorophyll, and rosettes of pink flowers which produce an enormous amount of seed. This feature of extensive seed production is common among parasites, as it minimizes the risk of a host not being near one or other of the numerous offspring. When the dodder plant is mature it has no roots; it is exceptional among British parasites in being attached to the stem of its host.

The toothwort and broom rapes (neither genus is common) are root parasites, that is, they attach themselves by suckers to the roots of a suitable host. The toothwort, an early spring plant with pinkish flowers on a pale brown shoot, usually grows at the foot of hazels or elms. The species of broom rape, which are somewhat similar to toothwort in their overground organs, are usually parasitic on clover. In common with all parasites these plants show a much reduced leaf surface and extensive seed production.

Owing to reduced transpiring surface, parasites may receive too much water from their hosts, hence many are provided with special water-exuding glands.

The reduction of the vegetative parts is well seen in a small family of parasites found in tropical forests, some of them remarkable for their enormous flowers, which are the only conspicuous part of the plant outside the host. The strangest species in this respect, *Rafflesia arnoldi* (plate 25), is native to Sumatra, where it grows upon the roots of wild vines, and bears gigantic flowers over a yard in diameter. The mistletoe is a parasite which grows on apple, oak and poplar. It resembles the semi-parasites in having green leaves, and sends its suckers deep into the branches of the host.

Saprophytes. These are rare amongst British flowering plants, the commonest being the bird's-nest orchid, which grows amongst the humus (decaying organic matter) in dense beech woods. Although the parasitic and saprophytic habits are rare amongst flowering plants, a large number of the more lowly members of the plant kingdom adopt these methods of nutrition. Everyone is familiar with the fact that organic substances such as bread, jam and fruit soon become mouldy in a state of decay. These moulds are saprophytic fungi with thread-like bodies, through which they obtain nourishment from the decaying matter. Similarly, many other fungi, such as mushrooms, toadstools and puffballs, live as saprophytes on the humus of woodlands, where they abound in the autumn. Many other fungi are parasites and cause serious diseases to plants of economic importance, and occasionally also to animals. The bacteria also are parasitic or saprophytic plants of simple structure, the former being responsible for many virulent diseases, while the latter are frequently very beneficial in furthering processes of decay in Nature.

All the higher plants which are saprophytes are unable to utilize the humus directly, but require the help of fungi, which live in the soil intimately associated with the saprophyte. Such an association with fungi is not confined to saprophytic plants, but occurs in many other forms, such as beech, conifers, and heaths.

The surrounding or penetrating fungus is spoken of as *mycorhiza*, and possibly helps in water absorption by the roots as well as in the taking up of organic matter from the humus. This association is one of mutual benefit to both organisms (symbiosis), such as the association of nitrogen-fixing bacteria with roots of members of the pea family, already described in Lesson 14 (volume 2, page 103).

Carnivorous Plants. One other special method of nutrition remains to be considered, viz. that of the flesh-eating or carnivorous plants, which have adopted the habit of feeding upon small insects and are thus frequently termed *insectivorous plants*. One of the most familiar of these is the sundew, which grows in peaty bogs. The plant consists of a small rosette of reddish leaves, which have relatively long petioles expanding into a round or oval blade. The upper surface and edges of the leaf blade are studded with reddish tentacles, whose swollen ends glisten with a sticky fluid. This attracts insects, which alight on the leaf and get held by the sticky substance. The more distant tentacles then curve in to come in contact with the insect's body, and digestive juices are exuded which convert the softer parts of the insect's body into a soluble form suitable for absorption by the plant. Later only the undigested hard portions of the insect remain, and the tentacles are ready again for another victim.

The butterwort also grows in peaty bogs, in association with sundew. It captures and digests its prey in a similar manner, by means of numerous sticky glands on the upper surfaces of the flattened radical leaves. Another example is the bladderwort (plate 25), a submerged water-plant which bears numerous little bladders on its deeply divided leaves. Each bladder has a narrow aperture closed by a little trap-door, which only opens inwards ; hence minute water-insects which find their way into the trap remain imprisoned there till they ultimately die, when the products of their decay are absorbed by the plant.

The Venus's fly-trap (plate 25) is a North American relative of the sundew, possessing leaves specialized to capture insects. Each half of the leaf-blade is fringed with long spines and also bears sensitive hairs. If an insect touches one of these the leaf rapidly folds up, the two sets of spines interlocking so as to render escape impossible. A digestive fluid is then poured out from other minute hairs on the surface of the leaf.

In the well-known pitcher plants, of which numerous species inhabit the warmer parts of the globe, the blade of the leaf is modified to form the pitcher in which many insects meet their death. The inner walls of the pitcher are very slippery and covered with downwardly directed scales ; any insects which venture on to the inner walls are unable to retain a foothold and, having fallen in, are imprisoned till they ultimately die and become digested.

LESSON 18

Analysis of Flower and Fruit

(See plate 26)

SOME of the branches of the stem of a flowering plant, instead of giving rise only to ordinary foliage leaves, bear one or more flowers, into the nature and use of which we must now inquire. Generally the flowers appear towards the end of seasonal activities. In an annual they herald the termination of its life-cycle and provide for the formation of fruits and seeds, which are all that remain through the winter to perpetuate the race. In some cases flowers appear early in the season and before the leaves, as in many trees, e.g. hazel, and in several herbaceous plants, e.g. wood anemone and coltsfoot. Whether early or late, however, the chief object of the flower is to produce fruits containing seeds, which may produce a new generation.

An idea of the nature and use of the different parts of a flower may be gained by considering a " pattern flower," which answers to the general plan of which all flowers are variations.

The flower is, in reality, a greatly specialized shoot, concerned with the production of healthy seeds, capable of growing into fresh plants. Like all shoots, it is a stem bearing leaves, though these differ more or less from ordinary foliage leaves, in accordance with their different use. It is borne on a flower-stalk, which may also bear simplified and often scale-like leaves known as bracts.

Parts of the Flower. The central stem part, the receptacle, is very short, owing to the suppression of its internodes, so that the different flower leaves which it bears are crowded together, much in the same way as are the foliage leaves in the rosettes of the dandelion and daisy. The flower leaves are of four kinds, arranged in two sets, (a) the perianth or covering leaves externally, and (b) the essential or reproductive leaves internally.

The two sets of leaves of which the perianth is composed are an external circlet or whorl of five sepals—collectively termed the calyx—and an internal whorl of five petals—the corolla—alternating with the sepals.

The sepals are firm and green, being more like foliage leaves than their associates. They protect the delicate internal parts of the flower, and especially do they afford protection in the bud. The petals are larger in size and are more delicate in texture than the sepals, and they are brightly coloured. They

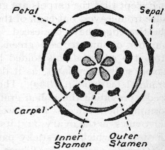

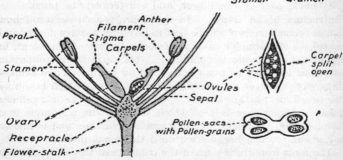

PATTERN FLOWER. Sections of a typical flower; cross-section of anther at A.

help to protect the essential leaves, but their chief use is to make the flowers conspicuous, in order to attract insects.

In the essential or reproductive leaves, again, we have two sets of structures—i.e. two whorls of stamens, five in each whorl, and a whorl of five carpels. The members of each whorl alternate with those of the preceding one.

The stamens, which are to be regarded as the male part of the flower, differ greatly in appearance from the petals and sepals. Each of them is like a thread with a thickened end, the two regions being the filament and anther respectively. In the latter is produced the flower dust, or pollen, which probably everybody has noticed in a lily or tulip. If a young anther is cut across and examined under the microscope, it will be found to contain four pollen sacs, in which the particles of this yellow dust, the pollen grains, are formed. They are essential to the formation of the seed, as we shall presently see, and are liberated by the splitting of the anthers.

Except that the carpels are green, they differ widely in appearance from leaves, but each of them is really a folded leaf, of which the two edges have coalesced. Sheltered within the cavity are a number of minute pale green bodies (ovules), which grow out from the edges of this folded leaf, as will be realised when the carpel splits open later, as it does, e.g. in larkspur (*Delphinium*) or marsh marigold (*Caltha*). The ovules are destined to become the seeds, providing the pollen grains are allowed the chance of performing their office. The lower part of a carpel, which contains the ovules, is the ovary, and its narrow upper end is the style, on the top of which is a sticky patch, the stigma. The carpels are the female part of the flower, and are termed the pistil.

Structure of an Ovule. In order clearly to understand how ovules become seeds it will be best to leave our pattern flower, and consider a still simpler case, where only one carpel is present, in which but one ovule is contained. Microscopical examination will show us that this ovule is covered by two protective skins—imperfect, however, at one place, the *micropyle*, which is simply the Greek for " little gateway." Within these skins is a cellular mass (*nucellus*), one cell of which, close to the micropyle, has developed into a relatively conspicuous structure, and is known as the embryo sac, because within it the young plant is formed.

The most important part of the contents of this sac is the egg apparatus, a group of three small cells next the micropyle. One of them, which is much larger than the others, is the egg cell, or *ovum* (the female gamete), from which the young plant originates when it is fertilized—i.e. when an infinitesimal amount of what may be called male protoplasm fuses with it. It is the office of the pollen grain to supply this. And here it may be stated, once for all, that sexual reproduction in plants and animals alike essentially consists in the coalescence of two minute masses of living matter, or protoplasm, one male and the other female. We do not at present precisely know why fertilization should be necessary, or exactly how it makes it possible for the egg cell to develop.

A pollen grain is a small mass of protoplasm containing two *nuclei* when ripe, and covered by two skins, of which the inner one is very delicate. It may be regarded as consisting of two cells—

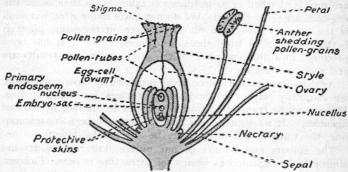

SECTION OF A SIMPLE FLOWER, in which only one carpel is present, containing a single ovule.

as indicated by the two nuclei—though in the higher seed plants these are not separated from each other by a party-wall. The first step towards the attainment of fertilization is the transfer of pollen grains to the stigma. This is pollination.

Fertilization. Supposing this transfer to have been accomplished, the pollen grain germinates in the sticky fluid of the stigma, and sends out a delicate pollen tube (*see* plate 26), which grows down through the style into the ovary, where its tip passes through the micropyle. Meanwhile, both of the nuclei of the pollen grain have passed into the pollen tube ; one nucleus here divides into two, which are the all-important male nuclei or male gametes. The tip of the pollen tube is ruptured and one male nucleus enters the ovum, with the nucleus of which it fuses, and thus effects fertilization. The other male element fuses with a nucleus (primary endosperm nucleus) which lies centrally in the embryo sac, and causes the development of endosperm, a nutritive tissue, which nourishes the developing embryo. In some plants this tissue is present in the ripe seeds, which are then described as albuminous.

Supposing that the pollen grain of our simple flower has been transferred to the stigma of the *same* flower, it will be a case of self-pollination, followed by self-fertilization. But if the pollen grains on the stigma have come from a flower on another plant we have cross-pollination, followed by cross-fertilization.

As a result of very numerous observations and experiments it has been clearly proved that healthier and more vigorous seeds are produced when cross-fertilization takes place than when the egg-cells are self-fertilized. We do not quite know why, but such is the case. Pollen from another flower on the same plant is better than pollen from the same flower, while if it has been produced in a different plant of the same species the results are still more favourable.

As cross-fertilization is necessarily preceded by cross-pollination, we naturally expect to find many devices for securing this. Pollen may be transferred from one flower to another by various agencies. If we suppose our simple flower to be a conspicuous one, the transfer will most likely be effected by insects.

The colours and odours of our native flowering plants are simply to be regarded as means for attracting insects. Flowers, however, do more than merely attract insects by suitable colours and odours. They provide them with what may be called flower food, upon which, indeed, some of their guests are entirely dependent. This partly consists of the pollen itself, which is produced in abundance, and partly of the sweet fluid known as nectar. The latter oozes out from little swellings—nectaries—situated deep down in the flower, and varying also a good deal in number, character, and exact position.

The fertilized ovum divides again and again to produce a small mass of cells, which enlarges and increases to form a minute plantlet, outside or within which is a store of food in the form of starch and albuminous matter, or possibly other nutritive substances, which render growth possible until such time as the young plant is able to draw on the supplies of the outside world. The delicate investments of the ovule become tough seed coats.

Formation of Fruit. While the seeds are ripening the ovary enlarges and becomes the fruit. This may be hard and dry, as in buttercup, poppy, and sunflower, or fleshy and succulent, as in plum, orange, and grape. Other parts besides the ovary may undergo changes, and contribute to the formation of what is then termed a " false fruit." The red pulp of a strawberry, for instance, is formed by the enlargement of the stem part of the flower—i.e. the receptacle. The brown pips are the real fruits—in this case dry, and each formed from an ovary.

The diverse characters of seeds and fruits are often associated with the necessity for giving the young plants a chance of finding some suitable spot in which to grow up, and for preventing them from competing too vigorously with their parents. There are, in fact, all sorts of arrangements by which the scattering or dispersal of seeds is facilitated.

LESSON 19

Sexual Aspect of Plant Life

(See plate 26)

THE transference of pollen from the stamens to the stigma is essential for the production of seeds. If the egg-cells of a flower are fertilized by the agency of pollen from the same flower, or from another flower of the same plant, they are said to be self-fertilized ; if by pollen from a flower of a different individual, cross-fertilized. Experiments have proved that in many plants a greater number of seeds and frequently more healthy offspring are produced from cross-fertilization, and, therefore, it is not surprising to find that, in the course of evolution, innumerable devices have come into existence by which self-fertilization is hindered and cross-fertilization promoted. Such devices are connected with the transference of pollen to the stigma, i.e. with pollination, the process preceding fertilization.

Most flowers contain both stamens and ovaries and are described as hermaphrodite. In these, the male and female organs rarely ripen at the same time. In the Canterbury Bell, for example, the stamens ripen first and discharge their pollen before the stigmas are capable of receiving it ; in the plantain, on the other hand, the stigmas in each flower wither before the stamens appear. In this latter plant the small flowers grow closely together in a dense spike, and ripening of ovaries and stamens occurs in the basal flowers first. The top of the spike may, therefore, bear ripe ovaries, while at the bottom the stamens have begun to ripen. Since, however, the flowers in the female stage are always above those in the male, the falling pollen cannot effect pollination (*see* plate 26).

Some flowers are spoken of as " self-sterile," such as many members of the pea family. In these cases the pollen has no effect at all on the female organs of flowers of the same individual plant. In other cases we find that stamens and ovaries occur in distinct flowers, which are then said to be unisexual. The flowers of different sexes may be found on the same individual, as in hazel, or on different individuals, as in dog's mercury and willow. In the latter case self-pollination is out of the question. Unisexual flowers probably arise from the hermaphrodite condition by suppression of the organs of one sex. Quite commonly the remains of the other essential organ can be recognized.

The modes of distribution of male, female and hermaphrodite flowers are very varied. Quite a number of plants have unisexual and hermaphrodite flowers side by side. Thus in the daisy the outermost flowers (popularly, but erroneously, known as the " petals ") are female, while the central yellow flowers are hermaphrodite. In the campion male, female, and hermaphrodite flowers occur on distinct plants, whilst the ash bears all three types on the same individual.

Since pollen-grains are not themselves capable of movement, they must, to secure crossing, be transferred by some outside agency from the anthers of one flower to the stigma of another. The commonest agencies for conveying the pollen are wind, insects, and, more rarely, water.

Wind-Pollination This is common among many herbs with inconspicuous flowers, and among most of the ordinary trees of temperate regions. It is evident that this method of pollination depends largely on chance, and, therefore, to ensure success, an enormous amount of pollen must be produced. This is brought about in various ways ; either the flowers

GRASS FLOWER. Single grass flower, showing the large anthers and feathery stigmas (magnified × 2).

contain many stamens (e.g. poplar and elm), or the anthers are very large (e.g. sedges and grasses), or the number of male flowers greatly exceeds that of the female (e.g. Scots pine and hazel). The grasses further ensure successful pollination by possessing a richly branched and feathery stigma, by which the pollen is easily caught.

Wind-pollinated trees open their flowers in early spring before the new leaves have unfolded, and when, therefore, the pollen-grains are most likely to reach the stigmas. It is essential that

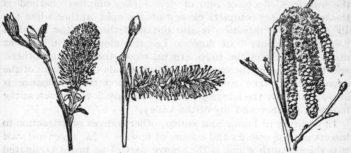

WILLOW AND HAZEL. Left, male and female catkins of Salix caprea. Right, catkins of the hazel; the female catkins are like leaf buds but have a tiny tuft of crimson filaments at their apex.

the pollen should be readily shaken out of the flowers by the wind, and related to this is the frequent occurrence of loose hanging catkins (a familiar example being the yellow lambs' tails of the hazel), or of anthers which swing freely on long filaments, as in the grasses and plantain. The pollen itself is dry and powdery, and thus wide distribution is facilitated.

Insect-Pollinated. The vast majority of conspicuous flowers are cross-pollinated by the agency of insects, and in the course of evolution an immense number of mutual adaptations have arisen between them. The first features to be noticed in insect-pollinated flowers are the devices which induce insects to visit them, and foremost among these are the nectaries or glands which produce honey. Nectaries vary greatly in size and shape in different flowers, and may be situated on almost any part of the flower, generally near its base. Quite commonly dark streaks or spots, known as " honey-guides," occur on the petals converging to the point where the nectary is situated. These may be seen in the pansy and several members of the pea family, and have been thought to indicate the position of the nectary to the pollinating insect.

Some insect-pollinated flowers, however, produce no honey and offer only pollen to their visitors. The poppy and broom are common examples of such "pollen-flowers" and, in common with their type, possess a large number of stamens, so that pollen is produced in sufficient quantity both for pollination and to serve as food for the insect.

Many plants are able to protect their pollen and honey from the injurious effects of rain or dew. The simplest method is the more or less complete closing of the split anther when the air is damp. Protection is also obtained through the so-called "sleep-movements" of flowers, i.e. the closing of flowers at night, as occurs in the tulip, crocus, wood anemone and others, and the closing of the compound flower-heads of members of the daisy family. The same end of protection from moisture is also attained by the hanging position of many flowers, such as the harebell, heather and lily-of-the-valley.

In addition to honey and pollen, other sources of attraction to insects are the colours and odours of flowers. As a general rule it is the perianth which is the showy part of an insect-pollinated flower, but occasionally other parts, such as stamens or bracts, may become expanded and brightly coloured. Different insects are attracted by different colours. Pale tints or white are characteristic of flowers which open in the evening and are pollinated by moths, for they render them as conspicuous as possible. Flowers of small size are rendered conspicuous by being massed together in large numbers to form a conspicuous flower-head, as in the daisy and the guelder rose (*see* plate 26).

Since pollination is almost a certainty in insect-pollinated flowers, a relatively small number of stamens is usually formed. The pollen itself has a rough or sticky coat, to adhere the more easily to the insect's body, whilst the stigma is not richly branched as in wind-pollinated forms, but has a very sticky receptive surface.

The insects which most often serve as pollinating agents are the various types of bees and bumble-bees, butterflies, moths, flies, and beetles. All these, except beetles, have a special sucking organ, the tongue or "proboscis," of very diverse length, short in flies and very long in butterflies and moths. Flowers whose petals form a long corolla-tube with a nectary at the base are only visited by long-tongued insects, whilst wide-open flowers provide honey to both long and short-tongued insects.

In the majority of cases the insect alights on the perianth of the flower it is visiting, with the result that some part of its body becomes dusted with pollen. Sooner or later the stamens and stigma in an insect-pollinated flower occupy the same positions within the perianth, and, therefore, the pollen taken from one flower will probably get rubbed off on the stigma of another.

LESSON 20

Insect and Other Means of Flower Pollination

(See plate 27)

IN certain aquatic plants the movements of the surrounding water bear the pollen to its destination. The best example is probably that of *Vallisneria* (eel grass), commonly grown in aquaria in this country. Self-pollination is entirely prevented by a method which is adopted by many other forms. The stamens and carpels are developed in different flowers, borne by separate plants. The female flower is placed at the end of a spiral stalk, which uncoils, and brings it to the surface.

Meanwhile, the ripe male flowers have broken off their stalks, and float about like so many little boats, being drifted here and there by the wind. Their perianths expand and the stamens project, lifting up their anthers so that the pollen is kept dry. Should one of them be driven against a female flower, some of the pollen is likely to adhere to the sticky surface of one or other of the three projecting stigmas, and thus cross-pollination is brought about. When the egg-cells are fertilized, the stalk of the female flower coils up again, and the seeds mature in a sheltered situation.

In the case of land plants pollen may occasionally be transferred by mammals, birds, snails and slugs, but the vast majority of conspicuous flowers are cross-pollinated by the agency of insects. In a large number of small regular flowers, mostly of white or yellow colour, which cater for a miscellaneous crowd of short-tongued insects, the nectar is fully exposed to view. We find this state of things in most members of the parsnip and carrot order and in some saxifrages. Not unlike these, but somewhat more specialized, are flowers which partly conceal their nectar, and lay themselves out for a rather more select circle of guests with somewhat more elongated mouth parts. Such are most members of the wallflower order, buttercups, stitchworts and their allies, barberry and cinquefoil. Lastly, we have flowers which completely conceal their nectar in deep recesses or long spurs, and attract the most intelligent and highly specialized insects, such as bees and butterflies, in which the mouth parts are drawn out into a long proboscis, which forms a very efficient sucking organ. Many such flowers are irregular, and adapted to the shapes of particular guests ; while red, blue, and violet are the favoured, though not the only, colours. Here belong foxglove, honeysuckle, larkspur, monkshood, and the orchids.

Methods of Cross-Pollination. Many members of the pea and bean order are adapted for visits of bees or humble-bees, and possess a special mechanism by which transfer of pollen is secured.

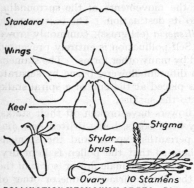

The butterfly-shaped flowers of our native species possess five petals—namely, an upright standard, two wings, and two lower petals united into a " keel," which shelters ten stamens surrounding the simple pistil. There are four chief kinds of mechanism by which cross-pollination is furthered : (*a*) In clover there is a simple valvular arrangement. Should a bee alight on the flower and probe for nectar, its weight causes the stamens and stigma to

POLLINATION MECHANISM OF PEA. Dissected flower of sweet pea, showing the five petals, and left, ten stamens (one free and nine united). Bottom right, position of essential organs when these are released from the keel.

project from the keel and touch its under surface. The former dust the insect with pollen, while the latter is likely to receive pollen grains brought from another flower. (*b*) A piston device is possessed by such forms as bird's-foot trefoil and lupine. Here the pollen accumulates in the tip of the keel, and is pushed forward by the thickened ends of the filaments as the result of pressure. (c) In vetches, pea, broad bean, and scarlet runner the style bears a brush of hairs which, on the application of pressure, sweeps out pollen against the body of the visitor. (d) The flowers of gorse and broom are in a state of tension, and explode from the pressure brought to bear by the insect visitor. In gorse the under, and in broom the upper, side of the insect is dusted with pollen and touches the stigma.

Pollination by Bees. The dead-nettle order contains many forms which are cross-pollinated by bees. In white dead-nettle, for instance, the irregular corolla possesses a convenient platform on which a large bee can alight, and while it is probing for the nectar secreted near the base of the ovary, the four anthers and the forked stigma—which are sheltered under a hood—come into contact with the upper side of its body. Meadow sage and scarlet sage possess but two stamens, of which the anthers are modified into a sort of curved swinging apparatus. Should a bee settle upon one of the younger flowers it presses against the lower ends of these anthers, and the upper parts of them, containing the pollen, swing down and dust its back. In older flowers the forked stigma bends down so as to touch the back of a visitor and take up any pollen sticking to it.

The foxglove can be cross-pollinated only by humble-bees. The four stamens and the stigma lie along the upper side of the bell-shaped corolla, the former maturing first. If a humble-bee creeps into a young blossom its back is dusted with pollen, and some of this is likely to be received by the stigma of the next older flower it may chance to visit. A somewhat similar arrangement is found in snapdragon, but here the humble-bee has to force open the curiously shaped corolla in order to secure the nectar which lies within.

The more specialized members of the buttercup order are also bee-flowers. One of the most interesting examples is afforded by monkshood, in which the two upper petals are modified into tubular nectaries, which can only be rifled by a humble-bee. The stamens mature first, and after them the stigmas, these successively occupying a position in front of the flower which has the effect of bringing them into contact with the under side of a visitor.

As a last example of a bee-flower, we will take the spotted orchis, of which the purple spikes are often seen in meadows from May to July. The three sepals and three petals are all brightly coloured, and one of the latter expands into a large lip, which serves as an alighting platform for guests. It is drawn out into a long spur, the delicate inner wall of which is perforated by bees to get the honey. Facing the entrance to the spur is a broad stigma, above which is a sticky knob, the *rostellum*. Only one stamen is present, united to the top of the pistil, and devoid of filament. Its anther contains two cavities, the pollen in each of which is bound together into a club-shaped mass (*pollinium*), possessing a slender stalk, which runs down to the rostellum. If now a humble-bee alights upon the flower and probes for sap it will strike against the rostellum, and, on withdrawal, will carry off the two pollinia on the top of its head. These quickly bend forward, and adhere in whole or part to the stigma of the next flower visited (*see* plate 27).

Butterfly-flowers are mostly of red colour, and very fragrant. Pinks afford a typical example. Nectar is secreted at the bottom of the long, narrow tube formed by the stalks of the petals, and is only accessible to the slender proboscis of a butterfly.

There are also flowers reserved for moths. These are white or pale in colour, and conspicuous in the dusk, at which time they usually add to their attractions by exhaling a fragrant odour. Honeysuckle is pollinated by hawk-moths, which possess a very long proboscis, and suck nectar while on the wing. In accordance with this, the corolla is drawn out into a nectar-containing tube, and there is no alighting platform. The stamens first mature, and project from the blossom in such a way that some of their pollen is readily shaken on to the visitor, which will be likely to transfer some of it to the stigma of an older flower that occupies the position taken up by the stamens in an earlier stage.

The primrose and dog-violet are visited chiefly by bees and butterflies. The former flower is of great interest, because it possesses two kinds of blossom. In one (" thrum-eyed ") the five anthers occupy the mouth of the corolla tube, and the rounded stigma is borne upon a short style. In the other kind (" pin-eyed ") the anthers are deep down in the tube, while the stigma is on a long style and occupies its entrance. It naturally follows that the pollen from one kind of flower is likely to be transferred to the stigma of the other.

The pollination mechanism in the daisy family is quite different from those we have already considered. Usually only the hermaphrodite flowers produce seed. The five stamens of these flowers are united to form a tube, inside which the pollen is shed. The stigma grows up as a straight rod through this pollen, which is caught up on the hairy style below the stigma. When mature, the stigma opens out into a Y shape, and the inner receptive surfaces await cross-pollination. If this fails to occur, the stigma lobes, when old, curl right back till they come in contact with the style bearing entangled pollen grains, and thus self-pollination is ensured if cross-pollination fails.

SECTION OF DAISY, showing mechanism of pollination. Bottom right, old stigma curling back to ensure self-pollination.

Flowers as Fly-traps. A number of flowers possess traps by which small flies are caught and held prisoner until they have done the work required of them. Our common wild arum presents us with a striking arrangement of the kind. The flowers are enclosed in a chamber formed by the lower part of a large green bract (*spathe*), which opens to display a thickened purple stem (*spadix*), upon the base of which these flowers are arranged in two crowded sets, of which the lower ones are female and the upper ones male.

Above the latter are a number of downwardly directed traphairs. These are no other than modified male flowers which have lost their original function. Small flies are attracted by the dull purple colour of the spadix and by an ammoniacal odour which is exhaled. Creeping down the spadix or inner side of the spathe, they easily make their way past the trap-hairs, and find themselves prisoners in the chamber containing the flowers. At this time the stigmas are mature, and should any arum pollen be sticking to the bodies of insect visitors, they are likely to receive some of it (*see* plate 27).

When this takes place the stigmas wither, and each of them exudes a drop of nectar as payment for services rendered. The stamens next shed their pollen, and some of this is likely to stick to the guests, which are at last allowed to escape, because the trap-hairs wither. The pollen is carried by them to another arum in a certain proportion of cases.

LESSON 21

Classification of Fruits

THE ovary and the ovules contained in it undergo great changes as a result of fertilization. The union of the two elements, a nucleus from the pollen-grain and the nucleus of the egg-cell, results in a stimulus to growth, which is the starting point in the life history of a new plant. The ovary enlarges while the character of the ovary wall becomes changed, and at maturity the structure is known as the fruit. The fertilized ovules within the changing ovary become the mature seeds. A seed can always be distinguished from a fruit by the fact that it only exhibits one scar, the hilum, whereas the fruit shows two, one marking the former attachment to the flower stalk, and the other the remains of the style.

According to the changes undergone by the ovary wall after fertilization, fruits may be classified as " dry " or " succulent." Some plants produce what are known as " false fruits," for in them some part of the flower other than the ovary has contributed to fruit formation. If the ovary consists of only one carpel (e.g. pea), or of more than one carpel united (e.g. lily), the fruit is spoken of as simple, but if the ovary consists of several separate carpels the resulting fruit is compound (e.g. buttercup).

Dry Fruits. Two types of dry fruits may be distinguished : one usually remains attached to the parent plant and splits open to liberate the contained seeds ; the other type does not split open, but the fruit wall merely decays away after the fruits reach the ground. These types are described as " dehiscent " and " indehiscent " respectively. Common examples of dry dehiscent fruits are the pods of pea, gorse and broom, the pod-like follicles of columbine and monkshood, the flattened fruits (*siliquas*) of honesty and wallflower, and the globular fruits (*capsules*) of lily, bluebell, iris, campion, violet, poppy and pimpernel. Many different modes of dehiscence are seen among the capsule fruits, some opening by simple splits, some by teeth, others by valves, pores or a complete lid.

Good examples of dry indehiscent fruits are furnished by nuts, such as hazel, sweet chestnut, beech and acorn. Of the same type are the fruits of members of the daisy family (e.g. sunflower and dandelion), the grasses and the buttercups. Fruits of the indehiscent type usually contain but one seed. The reason for this is to avoid overcrowding and competition among many seedlings germinating in one spot. The seeds usually have a thin seed coat, in contrast to the thick covering of seeds which

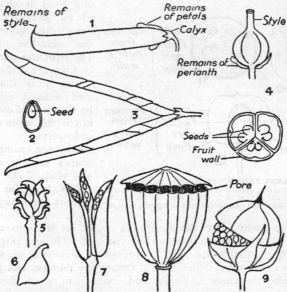

DRY FRUITS. 1. Pod of pea (simple fruit), formed from one carpel. **2.** Transverse section of pea. **3.** Dehisced pod of pea ; the ripe fruits are in a state of tension and the sudden dehiscence of the pod along both edges scatters the seeds. **4.** Capsule of lily formed from three carpels united ; below, transverse section. **5.** Compound fruit of buttercup : it is formed from many separate carpels. **6.** One carpel (an achene). **7.** Compound fruit of columbine, composed of several follicles which split along their inner edges. **8.** Capsule of poppy opening by pores. **9.** Capsule of pimpernel opening by lid.

are liberated from fruits and are thus without the protection of the fruit wall.

Succulent Fruits. There are two chief kinds of fleshy fruits, known respectively as " drupes " and " berries," both types being indehiscent. Examples of berries are found in currant, gooseberry, tomato and cucumber—the characteristic feature of this type of fruit being that the wall is fleshy throughout and forms all the succulent portion. The seeds are held within the fleshy middle region. Other examples of berries are orange, lemon, grape, banana, vegetable marrow, melon and date. In the case of the orange and lemon the ovary wall forms the coloured outer skin, the underlying white skin and the membranous skin round the fleshy sections. The fleshy part consists of a great development of juice-containing hairs, which grow from the skin-like lining. The structure commonly known as the date "stone" is the true seed rendered very hard by the store of cellulose in the cell walls of the endosperm.

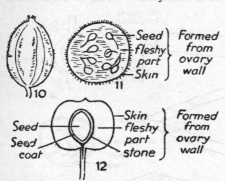

SUCCULENT FRUITS. 10. Fruit of the gooseberry.
11. Transverse section of a berry, showing the seeds.
12. Vertical section of a stone fruit or drupe; the seed is closed in a thin brown coat within the "stone."

Common examples of drupes are the cherry and plum. The drupe differs from the berry in that the ovary wall does not become entirely fleshy, but the innermost region of it forms a hard stony layer in which the seed is enclosed. On cracking open the stone, the white seed is revealed, contained in a thin brown seed-coat. Other typical drupes are damson and peach, etc., also the almond, walnut and coconut, in which, however, the layers outside the "stone" are generally removed before they are placed on the market. The raspberry and blackberry furnish instances of compound fruits composed of several small drupes.

False Fruits. In some plants the fruit is not composed of the ovary alone, but other parts of the flower (especially the flower-stalk) take part in its formation. When this is the case we speak of the resulting structure as a "false fruit." Thus, in the strawberry the true fruit is compound, consisting of a number of minute dry fruits (technically called achenes), borne on the much enlarged and fleshy flower-stalk, which is the actual edible part. In the apple and pear (fruits known as pomes) the flesh is formed by the flower-stalk, in which the ovary is embedded, the ovary wall forming the core. The rose hip is another false fruit, in which the coloured flask-shaped portion is formed from the flower-stalk and the true fruit is constituted by the dry achenes within.

Complex Fruits. The fruits of fig, pineapple, mulberry and hop differ from those we have already considered because a complex fruit is formed from a whole inflorescence, i.e. from a group of flowers. The fig is really a swollen stalk bearing numerous small male and female flowers on its inner surface. The female flowers produce minute fruits, popularly regarded as seeds. The composite fruit of the pineapple is formed from a spike of flowers.

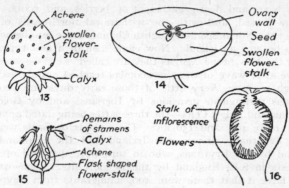

FALSE AND COMPLEX FRUITS. 13. Fruit of the strawberry; it consists of a number of tiny dry fruits (achenes). **14.** Apple in transverse section. **15.** Vertical section of a rose hip; the true fruit is contained within. The three foregoing are called false fruits. **16.** Vertical section of a fig, a complex fruit.

the fleshy flower-stalk and flowers all fusing together. The areas on the surface of the fruit represent the flowers. Above the flowers the stalk produces a number of leaves forming the "crown." The mulberry is also formed from a spike of flowers whose perianth members become fleshy and enclose the true fruits, which are achenes. The fruit of the hop (the cone) is formed from an inflorescence whose stalk bears numerous membranous scales.

In all cases the object of fruit formation is the production of seeds containing a young plantlet capable of growth, and in Lesson 22 we consider how the ripe seeds are scattered and dispersed.

Our Course in Botany is continued in Volume 4.

LESSON 1

When the English Came to England

(See plates 28 and 29)

MANY thousands of years ago Britain formed part of the continental mainland, and the Thames was a tributary of the Rhine. Through its forests and across its downs passed the Men of the Old Stone Age, hunters of bison and mammoths, bears and deer ; gatherers of berries and roots. The Ice Age passed, and with the withdrawal northwards of the ice sheet the North Sea and English Channel came into being and Britain became an island. Now came men of a new type, the Men of the New Stone Age, as they are called.

Wave after wave of these newcomers reached our shores, and although we know very little of those early days and peoples, historians distinguish invasions by Iberians, and by Goidelic, Brythonic and Belgic Celts—the three latter being dated approximately 1000, 400, and 150 B.C. The Goidels or Gaels were, it seems, eventually driven into Ireland and the Highlands of Scotland by the Brythons, who in turn were deprived of their conquests in S.E. England by the Belgic Celts. Some writers would have it that there were, too, immigrants from Egypt, or at least immigrants acquainted with its civilization ; but whether this be so or not, it is certain that many centuries before Britain made its first appearance in history its people were practising the primary arts of civilization—agriculture and the keeping of domesticated animals, pottery and weaving and metal-working.

Three hundred years or so before the beginning of our era Greek traders visited Cornwall in search of tin, and there is a possibility that they were preceded by Phoenician merchants on the same errand. But Britain came definitely within the orbit of the civilized world as the result of the visit by Julius Caesar, who passed over from Gaul (the modern France) in 55 B.C., inspired by the desire to see whether it were worth while attempting to incorporate the land within the Roman dominions. In the next year he paid a second visit, made what he reported to Rome was a conquest, and then dropped the whole thing, having more pressing business elsewhere.

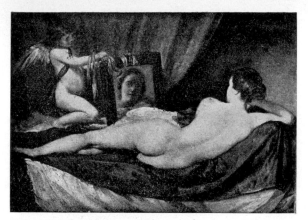

THE 'ROKEBY VENUS.' This Venus and Cupid by Velazquez was painted for Philip IV of Spain and is an excellent example of the great master's realism and modernity. ART AND ARCHITECTURE 16

HOGARTH'S 'CALAIS GATE.' William Hogarth's (1697–1764) powers of composition and atmosphere are well evinced in this rendering of an incident that occurred during his visit to France in 1748. ART AND ARCHITECTURE 17

National Gallery

SOME BRITISH PORTRAITS. Left : Miss Nelly O'Brien (died 1768), a famous beauty of her time, painted by Sir Joshua Reynolds in 1763. Centre : Miss Elizabeth Singleton, daughter of Col. Singleton of Deans Lease, Dorset, painted by Thomas Gainsborough about 1769. Right : Sir Henry Raeburn's portrait of Sir John Sinclair, Laird of Ulbster (1754–1835), one-time M.P. for Caithness, and a financial and agricultural reformer.   ART AND ARCHITECTURE 17

Wallace Collection; National Gallery; National Portrait Gallery

Plate 18

Volume III

When the morning Stars sang together, & all the Sons of God shouted for joy

London. Published as the Act directs March 8 1893 by Will Blake N 3 Fountain Court Strand

A BLAKE DRAWING. William Blake (1757-1827), the son of a London hosier, was an engraver and kept a print-shop before exhibiting at the Royal Academy in 1784. Thenceforth, oftentimes miserably poor, he poured out a stream of highly individual poems and paintings, in all of which his mystical philosophy found expression. The illustration shown above is one drawn by him for John Linnell's edition of the Book of Job, and on the right is a portrait of the artist himself. ART AND ARCHITECTURE 17

'**WINDSOR.**' Painted in 1808, this picture of the great castle in its pastoral setting is a product of Turner's "Wordsworthian mood," when he was intent on depicting the beauties of the English landscape. He first exhibited at the Royal Academy in 1790 and in the course of his long life executed hundreds of paintings and nearly 20,000 drawings. Many of the finest of the former, including the one reproduced above, are in the Tate Gallery, Millbank.

ART AND ARCHITECTURE 18

'**ON THE WYE.**' Richard Wilson (1714–82) studied portrait-painting but soon turned to landscape. He won fame with his "Niobe" in 1760 and was one of the original Academicians in 1768. "On the Wye" is one of nine of his paintings in the National Gallery. ART AND ARCHITECTURE 18

Plate 20   *Volume III*

WHEN THE ENGLISH CAME TO ENGLAND

Britain under the Romans. By A.D. 43 the Roman empire had been established, and the emperor Claudius decided to add Britain to it as a province. In about thirty years the conquest was completed as far north as the Tyne on the east and the Solway on the west, and a chain of forts, connected by what we know as Hadrian's Wall, was built across. This constituted the effective boundary of the Roman dominion, though Roman armies made victorious expeditions and planted another chain of forts across Scotland from the Forth to the Clyde to overawe the tribes of the Highlands.

Until the beginning of the fifth century the Romans kept a great garrison in Britain, which guarded it from the incursions of the northern tribes of Caledonia, while a sort of Channel fleet protected the shores against pirates from the North Sea. Great military roads radiated north and west from the Thames, and the Roman peace reigned over the land. But the Celtic peoples, whether they were the Gaels of the north or the Brythons of the south, never became latinised like the Gauls across the Channel, though superficially they became Romans. The old Druidic religion had been suppressed by the conquerors as too barbaric ; and when the Roman empire adopted Christianity as the leading officially recognized religion, the Britons accepted it.

At the beginning of the fifth century the Roman empire was threatened with a general break up by the hosts of barbarians from beyond its borders who were flooding through the barriers, and by the ambitions of successful soldiers who dreamed of making themselves emperors. So in the first ten years the Roman troops, the legionaries, were withdrawn, and Britain lapsed from the hold of Rome.

Chaos ensued. The whole machinery of the Roman government went to pieces ; there was no supreme controlling authority anywhere. The Britons fell to fighting each other ; the Picts and Scots, hitherto bridled by the garrisons on and beyond the Wall, broke through on the north ; pirates swooped on the now undefended coasts on the east and south and even from Ireland on the west ; and before another century had passed bands of rovers from over sea had made themselves masters of much of the eastern half of the land.

Invaders from Over the Sea. In this area it is a much disputed question how far the Britons were exterminated and how far they were enslaved or absorbed ; the invaders certainly did not

F3

drive their way into Cumberland, Wales and Damnonia (Devon and Cornwall) ; but there was a broad intervening belt which neither invaders nor invaded could hold. In the Briton tradition the attack was held up by the leader whom legend has named King Arthur, who is said to have won a great victory at Mount Badon (probably in the south) and gave his name to Arthur's Seat by Edinburgh in the north. The English tradition names, as the conquerors from over the sea, the Jutes Hengist and Horsa in Kent, the Saxon Aella in Sussex, and the Angle Ida between the Trent and the Forth ; but no doubt there is more imagination than fact in the legends of those early times.

There was a pause in the conquest ; but in the sixth century came fresh swarms, sometimes quarrelling, sometimes combining, with those who were already settled—west Saxons in the south ; more Angles in the north, who pushed into the midlands, Mercia, the marches between the English and the Welsh Britons, and along Wessex to the Bristol channel ; so that before the close of the century the Britons were cooped up in three separated sections—Damnonia, which was often called West Wales ; Wales itself ; and Cumbria from the Dee to the Solway and on to Clyde-mouth. Three great battles are to be noted : Deorham, which cut off Wales from the south in 577 ; Dawston, which broke an attack by the Celtic Scots of the north (603) ; and Chester (613), which drove a wedge between Wales and Cumbria. Until after Deorham, the English remained solidly pagan, though the Britons held to the Celtic Christian Church which had some differences from that of Rome, and Celtic Christianity had been introduced to the Scots from Ireland by disciples of Columba.

Conversion to Christianity. The conquering chiefs were made kings of the conquered lands by their followers as they settled down on the soil in the villages or townships (which meant farm-buildings with the cultivable land lying round them). The king was the war-lord, the judge, and a person of general authority. There was a king in Northumbria ; another in Kent ; others in East Anglia, Wessex, Sussex, and Mercia. The strongest and most respected of them at the close of the sixth century was Ethelbert of Kent, whose wife was sister of the king of the Franks across the Channel. In 596 the great Pope Gregory I sent a band of missionaries, headed by Augustine, to convert the English.

As the Frankish queen of Kent was already a Christian, the mission was received with honour, after a short time Ethelbert was converted and baptized, the leading men followed his example, and Augustine became the first English bishop of Canterbury. A few years later Kent had given place to Northumbria under Edwin as the most powerful of the kingdoms. Edwin was in turn converted, Northumbria following suit. Half England was now Christian, at least in name ; Wessex followed the example of Kent and Northumbria. But Penda of Mercia would have none of it : he defeated and killed first Edwin, then his successor Oswald ; and the victory of Christianity was only secured when Oswald's successor Oswy killed Penda himself. Oswy is of special importance because it was he who settled at the Synod of Whitby in 664 that the Church in England was to be not after the Celtic pattern but after the Roman, in the obedience of the Pope, like the rest of the countries of western Europe.

Northumbria remained the most powerful of the seven kingdoms which are counted (Essex being the seventh) after the death of Penda of Mercia. Numerous monasteries grew up, and did an immense amount of extremely useful work ; but they or rather the zeal for entering the religious life had one unfortunate result. Kings who were really good and just rulers had a way of retiring into monasteries when their kingdoms were very much in need of their secular services, so that lawlessness broke loose.

First King of England. Of course there was fighting between the kings, though as yet none of the petty rulers claimed that he was king of all England ; but one, Ine of Wessex, is notable for having put the customs of Wessex into a code of laws which were to be generally observed. This was in the first quarter of the eighth century ; and then in the century's second half there arose in Mercia a king, Offa, who did make himself the overlord of all the other kings. But in the next generation, that is, the first quarter of the ninth century, the supremacy passed from Mercia to Wessex under its king Egbert, generally reckoned as the first king of England, and founder of the House whose blood runs in the veins of our royal family.

LESSON 2

When Dane and Saxon Fought
for England

(See plate 30)

EGBERT became king of Wessex in 802, when he returned to England after a sojourn at the court of Charles the Great, king of the Franks, who had just been crowned emperor at Rome. While there he had no doubt profited much from personal contact not only with that great ruler but also with one of the most remarkable Englishmen of the day, Alcuin, the intimate counsellor and friend of Charles and the pupil of the Venerable Bede, the finest scholar and one of the most attractive personalities of the eighth century. These two names, with that of the English Winfrith or Boniface, the Apostle of the Germans, earlier in the century, illustrate the very high standard of religion and scholarship attained during that period in the cloisters of English monasteries.

Wessex had not been prospering of late owing to disputed successions and other troubles. For some twenty years after his accession Egbert was engaged in setting his own kingdom in order ; and he did it so effectively that when the king of Mercia, still reputed the most powerful, attacked him, he not only defeated the Mercian, but successfully aided one after another of the southern kings to break free from the Mercian yoke. The result was that by 825 all of them " took him for father and lord "— that is, they all voluntarily accepted Egbert's supremacy. The power of Mercia was finally broken : and from that time, though the sub-kingdoms did not at once disappear, the general overlordship of Wessex was not disputed by English rivals.

Incursions of the Danes. The first raiding long ships of the Northmen, Vikings, or Danes as they are commonly called in the English history books, had appeared on the Northumbrian coast before the eighth century was ended. Now they began to come as the English themselves had come in the old days ; and not only to England but to every river-mouth on the northern and western shores of Europe, raiding, spoiling, slaying, carrying off booty and captives, but not at first seeking to settle. Once before his death in 839 Egbert smote them in a great fight at Charmouth on the Dorset coast. In the reign of his amiable and pious but not very effective son Ethelwulf, more and larger fleets came year by year. Before his death in 866 they had camped through a whole winter on the Isle of Sheppey. Then for five years of his son Ethelred's reign they left the south alone, but made good their footing on the east from the Thames to the Tyne. Only then began the really desperate seven years' struggle (871–8) for Wessex between the Danes and first Ethelred and then his brother Alfred, who was made king after him.

Alfred the Great. The fortunes of war swung now to one, now to the other. Alfred did not win decisively till 878, when the contest was ended by the treaty of Wedmore, which, so far from expelling the Danes, really left them masters of half England—East Anglia, Northumbria, and part of Mercia—known as the Danelaw, although they acknowledged Alfred's overlordship and accepted Christianity in place of their old worship of Odin and Thor. Alfred had peace for the rest of his life, and devoted his time to educating his people, promoting their welfare in every possible way, and earning an unqualified right to the title which the English have bestowed on him alone among all their rulers —" the Great." Not the least of the debts they owe to him was his codification of the various laws of the English so as to bring them, outside the Danelaw, into some sort of uniformity.

It was very shortly after his death that one of the great Norse captains, Hrolf or Rollo, became the " man " of the French king, and duke of what was thenceforth known as Normandy.

Alfred, learning from the enemy, created a fleet which could meet invaders on the open sea and prevent a landing, and fortified towns or burgs to be a centre of resistance to attacks. Such precautions were most necessary, for though there were no more invasions from across the sea for a century, Alfred's children and grandchildren had much ado to bring the whole country under central control, the chiefs in the Danelaw not being at all accustomed to obey any superior authority. This effective control was finally won by Athelstan's great victory at Brunanburh in the north, in 937, over a coalition of the Northumbrian Danes, the Scots, and Northmen from Ireland, where they had recently established colonies. Athelstan's nephew, Edgar the Peaceful (959–75), was able to claim that all kings between the Forth and the Channel had acknowledged themselves his vassals. For the undoubted success of his rule he was probably largely indebted—for he was only thirty-three when he died—to the abilities of his chief adviser, Archbishop Dunstan, about whose name many legends have gathered.

The Danish Conquest. But after Edgar came a period of disaster. His elder son was assassinated by his stepmother, who wanted the crown for his younger half-brother, her own child Ethelred, who grew up to be known as the Redeless, " the lacking in counsel," for the counsellors he chose were evil and gave him the worst possible advice. The Danes began raiding again, and instead of fighting them Ethelred bought them off, imposing on the people for the purpose a heavy tax called the Danegeld (Dane-money). This only incited the Danes to come again with fresh demands, and enraged his own subjects. Then he plotted a massacre of the Danes living in England, on St. Brice's day, which brought the Danish king Swegen down upon the country with forces bent on revenge and conquest. As the English would not fight for him, Ethelred had to take flight to Normandy, and Swegen's son, Knut or Canute, became in 1016 king of England as well as of Denmark.

For twenty years Knut ruled mightily and well, and the chroniclers have nothing but praise for his government. But England was for him only a part, albeit the main part, of the Scandinavian empire which he wished to create. He had no sub-kings in England, but he divided it into five great provinces or governorships called earldoms, the earls holding office from the king. As he chose good men whom he could trust to be loyal, all went well. But on his death his empire broke up and England was separated from Denmark. His sons were very bad rulers, and when they were both dead, leaving no certain heir, the English recalled from Normandy the pious son of Ethelred, Edward, called for his virtues " the Confessor."

Knut, taking no interest in Scotland, had handed over to its king Malcolm II—on terms—the eastern part of the Lowlands, which in former days had formed part sometimes of Northumbria, sometimes of the Scottish kingdom. During Edward's reign, Malcolm III, nicknamed Canmore (Big-head), deposed and killed the usurper Macbeth and founded the royal dynasty of Scotland, which, when it had become the House of Stuart, succeeded to the throne of England in 1603.

Edward the Confessor. Edward was king for 24 years; his heart, however, was in a Norman cloister, not in the English council chamber. He married the daughter of the mighty earl Godwin of Wessex, but there were no children and no heir with an indisputable claim—in fact, there was no established law of succession. It was usually a matter of course that when a king died a son should follow him on the throne, but the last word lay with the council of state, known as the Witan. The Witan had elected Knut, and Knut's sons, and finally Edward himself. As time went on, there was no member even of the royal house to claim the succession except a great-nephew, Edgar the Atheling (a title given to princes born in England).

There were three great earls when Edward became king: Siward, who was practically an independent prince in the north, Leofric in Mercia, and Godwin in Wessex. Godwin's sons held lesser earldoms, while his daughter was queen, and between the houses of Leofric and Godwin there was intense jealousy. Godwin stood for what might be called the national party in the state, against the influence of the king's Norman and clerical friends. After long conflicts, Godwin became the most powerful man in the kingdom, and on his death his son Harold, a wise statesman and a great soldier, succeeded to that position, winning deservedly the confidence of Edward himself : and because he was obviously the one fit man, the Witan elected Harold king on Edward's death in 1066.

LESSON 3

New Masters in Old England

(See Colour Frontispiece)

WHEN Harold was elected king, he was beyond question the one man in England whose proved capacity as a statesman and soldier fitted him for the office ; but it was only in the south that he could rely on loyal support. The only other Englishman with a shadow of a claim was the boy Edgar Atheling. But abroad, Swegen of Denmark might claim as the heir of Knut, and could count on the backing of half the Danelaw if he chose to come forward, and a still more dangerous candidate—though one whom no Englishman could favour—was the very powerful and practically independent prince, William, duke of Normandy, the great-nephew of Edward's mother.

William vowed that Edward had promised him the succession (though having no power to do so), and Harold had been trapped into taking a particularly solemn oath that he would support William's candidature—the breaking of that oath being regarded as a terrible sacrilege. Swegen made no move ; but William at once claimed the crown, gathered an army of adventurers who expected to be handsomely rewarded with great estates in England, and procured from the Pope a blessing on his banner as the Church's champion against the perjured Harold. While Harold was drawn to the north to meet and crush an invasion by the Norse king, Harald Hardrada, William landed his army in Sussex ; and Harold, returning in haste, was slain, and his Wessex army shattered at the battle of Hastings or Senlac, Oct. 14, 1066. The forces from Mercia which should have joined the king were not yet on the march.

The Norman Conquest. William marched on London, cutting off the Mercians. Resistance was impossible. The Witan elected Edgar ; then thought better of it, and offered the crown to William as the lawfully-elected king. He promised to rule according to the laws of England, and was crowned in Westminster Abbey on Christmas Day. But the obvious fact remained that he was king by right of conquest and nothing else ; the election was no more than a formal farce. The estates of all the rebels who had actively supported the usurper, Harold, were forfeited and bestowed upon William's Norman, Fleming, or Breton followers.

The crown had been won because the English had failed to stand together, but for five years there were repeated risings in various areas. After each rising there were fresh forfeitures, the penalty of rebellion. The last revolt was long and fierce, and was crushed with a devastating ruthlessness. When it was finished, Normans instead of Englishmen were lords of half the manors in the country, and many of them individually were lords of several manors in different districts. But after 1071 there were no more risings of the English against William, though Normans occasionally rose in revolt. It was not the Norman king so much as the Norman lords who oppressed the people.

What in fact did the Conquest entail ? William would have said without hesitation that he kept his promise to rule by the laws of Edward—but by those laws as they were understood and interpreted not by English custom but by his Norman lawyers. He ruled with the advice—though he was not bound to take it—of the council or Witan ; but the character of the great council was changed because most of its members, lay or clerical, were not English, but Normans, with Norman ideas and habits of government ; and the authority of lords over their tenants was much greater in Normandy than it had been heretofore in England. And all the time, whatever professions anyone might make, the fact was always very much in evidence that the lords were foreign conquerors who treated the English as a conquered people.

Community of the Manor. We have spoken of lords and manors and tenants. Manor was the Norman name for the old agricultural settlements, the tons, hams, wicks and so on, into which the country had been divided—very nearly what from the ecclesiastical point of view were the parishes. Each manor formed a community which grew its own crops, pastured its own sheep and cattle, and provided its own fighting men for the shire levy when there was a common enemy to be fought. Every man worked on the soil, and owned the produce of the strips of land which belonged to him. There were no large farms, but in most big manors there was one person who had a good deal more land than the rest, who, for the most part, though not by any means always, were bound to give him a certain amount of service on his land. These persons had come to be recognised as lords of the manor, the rest being their tenants, holding their plots of land from them on fixed conditions from generation to generation.

But now half the old lords were dispossessed, and their places taken by Norman lords, who only wanted to extort everything they could get out of their tenants. So it came about that great numbers of those who had been free tenants, merely bound to render some services in return for their land, became serfs, or " villeins," bound for ever to the service, often cruelly humiliating, of the lord.

In the old days the serfs had been few ; now the number of freemen diminished, while the villeins multiplied ; because when the lord claimed that a tenant held his land in villeinage, it was very difficult for the latter to prove his case. And in any case, the tenants who had been on terms at least of good will with their old lords looked on their new lords as enemies and robbers.

Growth of Feudalism. Again, the Norman conquest established feudalism, which had perhaps begun to find a footing before. The basis of it was that all land is the king's property, but that he has granted estates to individuals conditionally on their undertaking to render him certain military and other services ; they are his " men," vassals. barons who do him " homage." They may in turn bestow the land or part of it on other people who become their men, holding the land from them ; but in the system set up by the Conqueror, these sub-vassals owe homage to the king first and to the immediate overlord only after him ; they must serve the king if need be against his vassal, not the vassal against the king. Otherwise a vassal with many vassals of his own might become a menace to the king himself.

Another safeguard of the crown was that the richest of the barons did not have all their estates close together, but scattered through the country. Still it was very difficult for a king who had to spend a great deal of his time in Normandy controlling his vassals there, to maintain, too, a strong control over his powerful vassals in England. William and his two sons, Rufus and Henry I, however, were very strong men who, if great barons combined to rebel, always crushed them very thoroughly.

Henry I (1100–35), in particular, established law and justice, not so much because he was virtuous as because he was shrewd enough to know that a king can be prosperous only by giving prosperity to the land he rules, and that the land in which lawlessness reigns cannot be prosperous. Therefore he came to terms with Anselm, archbishop of Canterbury, with whom Rufus had quarrelled ; protected the weak by sending to every part of the country his own ministers, whose authority no one would dare to gainsay for fear of the king's strong hand ; and improved the system under which the king's revenues were collected, so that men called him the Lion of Justice. But all he had done went to pieces when, on his death in 1135, his nephew Stephen snatched the crown from his daughter Maud. Stephen promised many reforms, but the barons proved too strong for him.

LESSON 4

When the Barons Warred Against the Crown

(See plate 31)

SHEER exhaustion brought comparative peace in the last days of Stephen. In 1154 he was succeeded by Henry Plantagenet, count of Anjou, the son of Henry I's daughter, Matilda or Maud, and her second husband, Geoffrey, count of Anjou. Through his mother he was duke of Normandy ; through his wife, Eleanor of Aquitaine, he was duke, or count, of so many provinces that he was lord of half France, though he held those provinces as vassal of the French king ; his English kingdom was wholly independent of France. For centuries to come the foreign policy of the kings of England was determined by the fact that they were at once the rivals and the vassals of the kings of France.

Henry was just the man England needed—one with a genius for organization in a land where only the foundations of organization survived, one to whom disorder was intolerable ; utterly fearless and utterly self-confident ; shrewd and swift of judgement and still swifter of action. The country was sick of lawlessness, ready to give whole-hearted support to anyone who would restore order and justice. Before two years were over he had crushed the most turbulent, overawed the rest, and won over all the order-loving elements in the community. He pulled down castles that lawless barons had built for themselves in the days of the anarchy. He revived the royal courts of justice that his grandfather had set up. He reorganized the shire levies, so that every man who was called up by the sheriff (shire-reeve, the king's officer who was appointed for this and other administrative purposes in each shire) was bound to appear in arms according to his means.

Henry even tried to bring the clergy, subject only to the Church's laws, into the jurisdiction of the king's courts ; this involved him in a long struggle with Thomas Becket, ending with the latter's murder by some of the king's knights. This was the last thing that he intended, but the murderers made it their justification that they had acted upon some words Henry spoke in a moment of frenzied anger, and it was the dead arch-bishop who won the victory. The king succeeded in setting up in Ireland a sort of English government, but his rule did not in fact extend outside a district known as the English pale ; and he also made William the Lion, king of Scots, who was taken prisoner while raiding across the border, acknowledge him overlord.

Richard I. The close of Henry's reign was greatly troubled by quarrels with his turbulent sons with whom he was actually at war when he died in 1189. Richard I (Coeur-de-Lion), who succeeded him, cared little for England, much for Aquitaine, and most for Palestine, where Saladin had just captured Jerusalem. He went on crusade, was captured on his way home, and spent less than six months of his ten years' reign (1189–99) in England, where matters were generally well and wisely man-aged for him by the minister Hubert Walter. Richard is a great figure in romance, but England has cause to be grateful to him mainly for absenting himself and putting Walter in control. He was killed while fighting a recalcitrant vassal in Normandy, and the barons recognized as king his brother John (1199–1216) instead of his nephew, Arthur of Brittany, whose title, according to modern ideas, was the better.

King John and Magna Carta. John has been described as the worst king who ever ruled in England. He had brilliant abilities, which he occasionally brought into play in brief spasms of energy, but he was the slave of his own passions and inordinate vices. He was a tyrant and a murderer, faithless, reckless, vindictive, and cruel ; but, oddly enough, England was the gainer. For he made himself so generally detested that all the best elements in the country united in opposing his oppression and forcing him to seal, in 1215, the Great Charter (Magna Carta), which proclaimed the fundamental principle that no man, high or low, king or noble, gentle or simple, may override or break the law of the land with impunity, and that none has power to change the law without the general assent.

The Separation from Normandy. This, however, was only when John had already been king for sixteen years. Long before that he had lost Normandy and most of the French fiefs which had come to the Plantagenets with his mother. Disgust at the king's misrule, and especially at the murder of his nephew, Arthur of Brittany, made the barons of England refuse to fight for him when the barons of Normandy sided against him with his overlord—as concerned Normandy—Philip II, king of France, who declared the dukedom to be forfeited. No one after this in effect held baronies both in England and in Normandy, so that the barons of Norman blood in England were very soon looking upon themselves as Englishmen and on England as their country. Though, to be rid of John, half the barons were trying in the last year of his life to make Louis, the crown prince or dauphin of France, king in his place, he was no sooner dead than they rallied to support his young son, Henry III (1216–72).

Henry III and Simon de Montfort. After John's death the country settled down into reasonable order and progress under William Marshal, and then Hubert de Burgh (who had both been loyal to John without upholding his crimes), the new king being too young to act for himself. But when he grew up Henry, being extremely pious, fell under the influence of an ambitious bishop, who surrounded him with foreign favourites. Then he married Eleanor of Savoy, who brought over a number of her kinsmen, and so matters went from bad to worse. Curiously enough, the leadership of the opposition to the foreigners passed to Simon de Montfort, who was a foreigner himself.

At last Simon seemed to have got the upper hand, and called, not the ordinary great council, attended only by barons and ecclesiastics, but one which included elected burgesses from some of the towns. He had not really won, however. After a time some of the nobles who had been his followers left him for the king, and he was killed at the battle of Evesham, fighting against a royal army commanded by the king's son Edward, later Edward I.

LESSON 5

England in the Reign of Edward I

(See plate 32)

IN 1216 Henry III began to reign, and he was on the throne for nearly sixty years. This was not, as we are apt to imagine, a period of constant civil war. Nearly fifty years of it had passed before Montfort took up arms against Henry in 1264, and there was no real resistance to the king after the earl's death in 1265. For the people it was a time of prosperity. When the king died in 1272 his son Edward was away on a crusade, but the government went on quite quietly. Norman and Saxon were fused, England was at last England again, and Edward, bearing an old English name, might fairly be counted the first English king since the Conquest. In his reign he united Wales, but failed to unite Scotland, to England ; he put the law into clear shape ; and he transformed the council into Parliament.

Edward's aims as a lawmaker were to make certain what was uncertain in the law, and, in doing so, to fix upon it the interpretation which would best strengthen the crown against turbulent barons. As Henry II had used the council to express what thereafter no one could refuse to recognize as common consent to his measures, so Edward used Parliament ; and therefore he gave Parliament a shape which made it represent a much wider body of public opinion than the old council, which in practice had consisted mainly of a few great barons, bishops and superior abbots, and some of the lesser barons called knights of the shire, two of whom were selected from each shire by the sheriff—not elected by vote. Montfort had, for the first time, added two burgesses elected by certain boroughs, boroughs being the larger towns which had charters of self-government ; Edward made this innovation permanent, and also his knights of the shire were not chosen by the sheriff, but were elected.

The Model Parliament. The first Parliament in which this was worked out completely was called in 1295, and is known as the Model Parliament, because the model remained unchanged for five hundred years. These elected representatives were called collectively the Commons. The greater barons had been summoned by a personal letter from the king, and this summons now became a distinctive right passing from generation to generation. Those so summoned were the lords or peers, and early in the reign of Edward III the custom was established of the Lords and Commons sitting and voting in separate chambers. The clergy, too, separated from Parliament as a body and sat in Convocation to legislate for the Church and settle their own contributions to the royal exchequer, though bishops and certain abbots still sat with the lords. Whatever laws were passed in Parliament and confirmed by the king became thenceforth the law of the land, which could only be altered by another Act of Parliament.

Edward's legislation was mainly concerned with fixing the laws about the succession, inheritance and alienation of land, and the claims the king might lawfully enforce as a matter of course for money to be paid to the royal exchequer, out of which all the expenses of government had to be paid. This being settled, if he found himself in need of more, for whatever purpose, as he was quite sure to do, he must ask for it from Parliament; which presently had the effect that if Parliaments were dissatisfied with the way in which the money was being spent they could refuse his request. Parliament learnt that, as against the king, it possessed " the power of the purse."

Legislation and the building up of Parliament were not accomplished at a stroke; they were going on all through the reign. But Edward also wanted to unite the whole island into one dominion. Welsh princes and Scottish kings had sometimes admitted, but more often refused to admit, some sort of English overlordship. Edward succeeded in forcing the Welsh to submission, though only by hard fighting; and planted great garrisoned castles at strategic points to overawe them.

Scotland was a bigger country and a bigger task, and it was harder to find a legal excuse. He found his chance when the Scots nobles, many of whom had estates in England in respect of which they were already his vassals, appealed to him to arbitrate between rival claimants to the succession to the throne on the death, first, of Alexander III. and then of Alexander's little daughter Margaret.

Origin of the Scottish Kingdom. Now we must throw back a glance at the history of Scotland. The Scots kingdom had grown out of the union of Dalriada, the first Celtic Scots kingdom, with the Pictish (probably Celtic) kingdom in the Highlands. The English had never absorbed the Celts north of Solway; and though the eastern lowlands formed part of Northumbria the Scots kingdom had drawn them in, so that in the time of Knut the Tweed had become the boundary between England and Scotland. Malcolm Canmore, as we saw, secured the crown a little before the Norman Conquest. He married Edgar Atheling's sister, who did much to Anglicize the lowlands; but the Highlands would have remained entirely Celtic if a number of Vikings had not established themselves in the western isles and far north. The kings of Scots never had exercised a real authority beyond the Highland line, but they did rule in the lowlands. Malcolm's daughter was the wife of Henry I and grandmother of Henry II; and his third son, David I, was a powerful, enlightened, and successful prince, to whose benefactions the Church in Scotland owed much. But, by way of civilizing the country, he bestowed large estates on Norman barons from England, so that the lowlands were to a great extent Normanized as well as Anglicized. His direct descendant, Alexander III, who was reigning when Edward became king of England, was far too strong to be attacked ; but when Alexander's line died out there was none nearer the throne than John Baliol, Robert Bruce, and John Comyn, all Norman barons of England as well as Scotland, and all three descended from daughters of the younger brother of Alexander's grandfather, William the Lion.

Attempted Conquest of Scotland. Edward then agreed to arbitrate between the claimants but definitely as suzerain ; the successful candidate must hold the Scots crown as a vassal of the king of England, earlier kings of Scots having done homage to kings of England. The Scots agreed, regarding the claim as a mere formality. The award fell, rightly enough, to John Baliol. Then, to their surprise, the Scots found that for Edward the claim was not a formality, but a very real acceptance of his authority. Baliol revolted ; the revolt was crushed, and Edward resumed the crown which his vassal's rebellion had forfeited. The estates of Baliol's supporters were forfeited ; English officers and garrisons were sent to Scotland, and behaved very much like the Normans when they conquered England.

There was no king to lead the Scots, but they found a leader in William Wallace, who gathered followers, attacked the English, and for a time drove them out. Edward vowed, and took, vengeance. Wallace's levies were overwhelmed by the English archers at Falkirk and he himself was captured and taken to England to die the ignominious death of a traitor. Leaderless Scotland was ground under the heel of her English master, till Robert Bruce, grandson of the first claimant, having committed a murderous offence for which he could not hope to be pardoned, raised the standard of revolt, claimed the crown forfeited by John Baliol, and renewed the war of liberation. The old king gathered a great host to crush the rebel once for all ; but before he could reach Scotland he died.

On Edward's death the army of conquest was disbanded. For six years Edward II was fully occupied in quarrels with his barons, while king Robert in Scotland was gathering adherents and capturing one by one the English strongholds till Stirling only was left. Then Edward II gathered the largest English army that had ever taken the field, marched into Scotland, and was utterly defeated at Bannockburn (1314). The independence of Scotland was won, though fifteen more years passed before England admitted the truth by signing the treaty of Northampton (1329).

LESSON 6

Edward III and the French War

A FTER one of the ablest of English kings, Edward I, came one of the most incapable. Edward II (1307–27), though a man of some culture, was feeble, obstinate, and vacillating, with no sense of responsibility as a ruler, though he had apparently no wish to play the tyrant. Throughout his reign he was the tool of unworthy favourites. Barons who had feared and respected his father had neither fear nor respect for the king or his chosen advisers, and tried to substitute the misrule of a self-seeking clique for that of king or Parliament.

Edward's ceaseless quarrels enabled Bruce to secure Scottish independence ; when the barons got the upper hand their rule was no better than his ; when he got the upper hand his favourites ruled no better than they. In a final revolt, in which his own wife, Isabella of France, joined Roger Mortimer, the most ambitious, turbulent and unprincipled of the barons, he was taken prisoner and forced to abdicate in favour of his sixteen-year-old son, who was proclaimed king as Edward III. Mortimer and Isabella ruled in his name ; but their rule, beginning with the murder of Edward II, was the worst of all. At length the young king and his friends, by a sudden coup d'état, captured Mortimer and hanged him. As more than once before, barons and people alike were sick of civil war and misrule, and Edward III (1327–77) began his real rule with the whole country at his back.

The French wars are the most spectacular feature of the long reign of Edward III—wars which for twenty years brought repeated triumphs and then drifted away in futility and doleful failure. They are typical of the romance and glitter of medieval warfare ; but there was a serious purpose behind them, which should be understood.

Though the great French possessions of the first Plantagenet kings had dwindled under John and Henry III, Edward I had still been lord of Guienne and Gascony. French kings had worked on a consistent policy of annexing their vassals' fiefs on every available pretext. Edward I had held his own against them ; but something had been lost under Edward II.

In 1328 died Charles IV, the last male of the reigning house of Capet. The French decided that the succession lay in his cousin, Philip of Valois, but it was just possible for Edward, as the son of a sister of Charles IV, to claim that he was the heir. The claim was put in, but not pressed. Philip VI became king, and continued the old policy. Edward would have to fight or he would lose his French possessions, which from a commercial point of view were of value to England, so he advanced his claim to the French throne, and in 1337 began what is known as the Hundred Years' War.

A naval victory at Sluys (1340) gave the English command of the Channel. Six years later Edward led a great raid into France. The gathering of a huge French force caused him to retreat hastily towards Flanders ; but he was overtaken at Crécy, near the Somme, where he turned to bay and inflicted on the French a tremendous defeat (1346). This was mainly due to the English archers—in effect, a form of artillery.

Surrender of Calais. The capture of Calais next year gave England a foothold in France, and a great market for her commerce, which she retained for two hundred years. In this siege cannon were used, although they were not particularly effective. Calais was starved into surrender. Although Edward eventually spared the lives of the six chief burghers, condemned to death, he drove all the French out of the town and occupied it with his English subjects. In 1356 Edward's son, the Black Prince, won an almost incredible victory over an enormously superior French force at Poitiers. This led to the peace of Brétigny, whereby Edward acquired his fiefs in full sovereignty.

In 1369 war broke out again, each side claiming that the other had broken the treaty. But the tale of English victories was over. The mental powers of Edward and the physical powers of the Black Prince had broken down. Every campaign was a failure, and when Edward died in premature dotage his possessions in France—except for Calais—were no greater than they had been when the war began.

Economic Developments. During his long reign there were many economic developments. At first the French wars, by employing many men abroad and reducing available labour at home, brought economic prosperity to the country. In addition, Edward aimed at building up sound trading conditions, particularly with regard to the woollen industry. Though as early as the 12th century there were weavers' guilds in England, cloth-working had declined, and so the king took measures to revive the manufacture. He invited excellent weavers from Flanders, many of whom settled in Winchester, Bristol, London, and other centres, and forbade the importation of foreign wool. At this time England was practically the only country supplying wool to western Europe. The wool staple was transferred from Bruges to England, though afterwards placed at Calais. The object of a staple town was that all exported wool should pass through it so that the king's revenue on it could be secured.

The prosperity of this period, however, was checked by the terrible pestilence of the Black Death (1348). The plague, in addition to an enormous death roll, had far-reaching economic results. At least one-third of the population in England is said to have perished. There was accordingly an unprecedented scarcity of labour, and wages rose—for men as much as 50 per cent and for women 100 per cent. The small freeholder was able to buy his land from his lord because the latter could not afford to pay labourers to work it. On the other hand, the lord valued services more highly and was less willing to commute them, which roused bitter discontent in the villeins, who, unable to pay rent for their holdings, deserted them and migrated to the towns. From this arose the real danger that the country might suffer by the land going out of cultivation. The discontent was, therefore, widespread at the end of Edward's reign.

Richard II. His successor was Richard II (1377–99), a boy of ten, son of the Black Prince. His uncles and other nobles quarrelled for control of the government. The discontent came to a head and there was a great rising of the peasantry, headed by Wat Tyler and Jack Straw. The insurgents marched on London ; but the boy king boldly rode up to them and persuaded them to disperse by making promises which were never kept, and the unfortunate peasants were severely punished.

Richard chafed under the control of his uncles, and, like Edward II, put his trust in favourites—with somewhat similar results, since he antagonized most of the nobles. However, without open war, he managed to get the upper hand and for a time used his power with moderation. Then there came a sudden change. He turned on his uncle, Thomas, duke of Gloucester, charged him with treason committed in the earlier part of the reign, and arrested him. While in custody Gloucester was murdered. The nobles took alarm ; two of Richard's former opponents charged each other with treason. One of these was his cousin, Henry, earl of Hereford and Derby, the son of Edward III's oldest surviving son, John, duke of Lancaster, and the other was Thomas Mowbray, duke of Norfolk.

Richard seized the opportunity to banish both. When they were gone he imagined that he was too strong to be resisted. John of Gaunt, duke of Lancaster, died, and Richard seized the inheritance, which should have gone to the exiled Henry of Hereford, and departed to Ireland. This was too much for the nobles. Henry returned, avowedly to claim his inheritance and no more. But when Richard got back to England he found himself practically deserted. Henry's demands had risen ; he insisted upon helping his cousin to rule better. Richard surrendered to him, was taken—obviously a prisoner—to London and was there forced to sign a deed of abdication. Henry then claimed the succession as the grandson of Edward III ; Parliament accepted his claim, and he became king as Henry IV.

Our Course in British History is continued in Volume 4.

CHEMISTRY

Chemical Aspect of Electricity

IN Lesson 20 (volume 2, page 151) we discussed the element carbon, and now proceed to consideration of the most important carbonates. These are sodium carbonate (washing soda), sodium bicarbonate (baking soda) and calcium carbonate, which is used in one form or another in the production of cement and for making lime, which is a component in preparations of whitewash, lime paints and mortar. The solution of carbon dioxide in water has a feebly acid reaction, presumably through the formation of the acid, carbonic acid, according to the equation :

$$H_2O + CO_2 \rightleftharpoons H_2CO_3$$

Owing to the readiness with which carbonic acid decomposes into carbon dioxide and water, it has not been isolated in the pure state ; but it gives rise to comparatively stable salts called carbonates. The acid is dibasic, both hydrogen atoms being replaceable. Thus with caustic soda :

$$NaOH + H_2CO_3 \rightleftharpoons NaHCO_3 + H_2O$$
(sod. bicarbonate)
(or acid carbonate)

$$2NaOH + H_2CO_3 \rightleftharpoons Na_2CO_3 + 2H_2O$$
(sod. carbonate)

These salts are slowly hydrolysed in solution and give an alkaline reaction to litmus owing to the formation of sodium hydroxide.

All carbonates, with the exception of those of sodium, potassium and ammonium, are insoluble in water. If carbon dioxide is bubbled through lime-water—a solution of slaked lime (calcium hydroxide)—calcium carbonate is formed as a milky-white precipitate :

$$Ca(OH)_2 + CO_2 \longrightarrow CaCO_3 + H_2O$$

This reaction is used as a test for carbon dioxide.

Combustion and Flame. It has been mentioned in Lesson 2 (volume 1, page 148) that combustion is merely a process of oxidation accompanied by the development of light and heat, and that in many cases it is necessary to heat the materials up to

a certain temperature before the phenomenon of combustion actually starts. This temperature is called the " ignition point " or " flash point " of the substance ; once combustion has started the heat evolved by the burning substance is sufficient to keep the

CONTROL OF COMBUSTION. Fig. 1. Flame may be prevented by cooling gas below its ignition point by means of a wire gauze.

temperature considerably above the ignition point and the process goes on continuously. If, on the other hand, the substance is cooled sufficiently, the combustion may be made to stop. This can be shown in a very simple way (*see* Fig. 1).

If a wire gauze is held about an inch and a half above an open gas burner, and a light applied to the gas above the gauze, it is found that the flame burns *above the gauze only*. This is because the gauze conducts the heat away so quickly that the temperature of the gas below the gauze is kept below the ignition point. Only when the wire becomes quite hot does the flame spread to the mouth of the burner. This is the principle of the miner's safety lamp invented by Sir Humphry Davy, shown in Fig. 2. All the air holes to the flame are protected by wire gauze, and although the combustible gases can pass in and burn inside the lamp, the flame cannot pass through the gauze and be communicated to the explosive mixture of " fire-damp " and air present in the mine.

Silica and Silicates. The element silicon belongs to the fourth group of the periodic table and comes immediately after carbon, to which it bears a very close chemical resemblance. This is especially noticeable in the case of the oxides—SiO_2 (silicon dioxide or silica) and CO_2. Thus, like CO_2, which is found widely distributed as carbonates of calcium and sodium, SiO_2 occurs abundantly in the form of silicates of calcium, sodium, potassium and aluminium.

Silica also occurs in the free state as flint, opal, amethyst and quartz or rock crystal. The last is a constituent of granite which contains in addition mica and felspar. Under the action of water, frost and carbon dioxide—a process which is called the "weathering of rocks"—the granite is broken down into its constituent substances. Felspar is a compound of potassium oxide, aluminium oxide, or "alumina," and silica ; carbon dioxide reacts with potassium oxide to form potassium carbonate, and the alumina and silica are set free in a finely divided form called china clay. The quartz is further disintegrated and ultimately reduced to sand, which is a fairly pure form of silica.

Silica is comparatively unreactive chemically ; it is weakly acidic in character, and when boiled with strong bases, e.g. the caustic alkalis, it forms silicates. Because of its non-volatile character it is able to displace most of the other acidic oxides from their salts. An example of this was given in the preparation of phos-

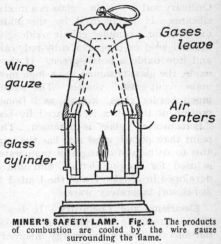

MINER'S SAFETY LAMP. Fig. 2. The products of combustion are cooled by the wire gauze surrounding the flame.

phorus (*see* Lesson 18, volume 2, page 141) ; a similar reaction takes place with the alkali carbonates, thus :

$$Na_2CO_3 + SiO_2 \longrightarrow Na_2SiO_3 + CO_2$$
$$\text{(sodium silicate)}$$

Sodium silicate is known commercially as "water-glass" and on treatment with a dilute acid it forms a gelatinous precipitate of silicic acid, thus :

$$Na_2SiO_3 + 2HCl \longrightarrow 2NaCl + H_2SiO_3$$
$$\text{(silicic acid)}$$

Silicic acid gradually sets into a hard, glassy substance which is a hydrated form of silica ; hence the use of water-glass as an egg preservative, for finishing off concrete work and for adhesives. If a solution of sodium silicate is poured slowly into concentrated hydrochloric acid, the silicic acid does not separate out, but remains in " colloidal " solution in the hydrosol form (*see* Lesson 8, volume 1, page 173, on colloids).

Glass is a complex silicate made by fusing together such bases as lime, lead oxide, sodium or potassium oxide with sand or silica. Ordinary soft or " soda " glass is a mixture of sodium and calcium silicates. It is coloured by the addition of various metallic oxides ; for example, cobalt oxide gives a blue colour, finely-divided gold or copper a ruby-red, calcium phosphate a white, and iron oxide a bottle-green. If the lime is replaced by lead oxide, the glass obtained has a high metallic lustre and is used to make " cut-glass " vessels. The addition of a potash gives a much harder glass, known as " Bohemian " glass, while if a portion of the silica is replaced by boric oxide, the very hard " borosilicate " glass is obtained. This has a higher melting point than potash glass and has the important property of being able to withstand changes of temperature without cracking. It is used for making lenses, and under trade names has been developed in England and the United States for making baking dishes and laboratory ware.

Electricity and Chemistry. It has been mentioned that a chemical reaction involves a transformation not only of the form but also of some of the energy inherent in the substances taking part. As we have seen in Lesson 13 (volume 2, page 119) on the heat of chemical reactions, this inherent or " chemical " energy is, in general, transformed into heat energy ; under certain conditions, however, the energy which is transformed or released in a chemical reaction may take another form, viz. electrical energy. This was first observed at the end of the eighteenth century by the Italian chemist, Volta, who found that whenever two metals were combined with certain liquids to make a circuit, an electric current was produced. Using strips of copper and zinc and a solution of sulphuric acid—an arrangement now known as the voltaic cell, in honour of its discoverer (Fig. 3)—Volta was able to obtain a continuous current of electricity. The zinc gradually dissolves in the sulphuric acid ; a chemical reaction is, therefore, continually taking place, and chemical energy is being continuously transformed into electrical energy.

CHEMICAL ASPECT OF ELECTRICITY

In such a cell the two metal plates are called "poles" or "electrodes," the one from which the electricity flows outside the cell—viz. the copper—being the positive pole or anode, and the other—the zinc—the negative pole or cathode. Just as the flow of water in a pipe depends on the pressure or head of water and the dimensions of the pipe, so the flow of an electric current depends on the electrical pressure — the electromotive force or E.M.F. of the cell — and the resistance which the wire sets up to the flow of current. Various other types of voltaic cell have been constructed, one of the best known being the

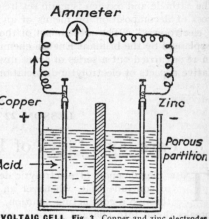

VOLTAIC CELL. Fig. 3. Copper and zinc electrodes are dipped into sulphuric acid.

Daniell cell, in which copper and zinc electrodes are immersed in a solution of copper sulphate. The chemical reaction which takes place is represented by the equation :

zinc + copper sulphate ⟶ zinc sulphate + copper.

Electrolysis. If the ends of two wires which are connected to an electric circuit are placed in a vessel containing pure distilled water or a solution of sugar in water it is found that no current flows in the circuit ; these liquids do not conduct an electric current. If, however, the sugar solution is replaced by a dilute solution of sulphuric acid, the flow of electricity is no longer interrupted. Substances which dissolve in water may, therefore, be divided into two groups—those, like sulphuric acid, which conduct an electric current, and those, like sugar, which do not. The former are called "electrolytes" and include all acids, many bases and inorganic salts ; the latter are called non-electrolytes and include many organic substances, such as glycerin, alcohol, etc. When an electric current is passed through the solution of an electrolyte, some chemical decomposition of the conducting solution takes place. For example, with a dilute solution of sulphuric acid bubbles of hydrogen gas appear at the cathode, and oxygen is liberated at the anode, while if a solution of copper sulphate is taken, a deposit of bright metallic copper forms on the cathode and oxygen is again set free at the anode. This process of decomposition by means of an electric current is called " electrolysis." The mechanism of the process was successfully explained by the brilliant English chemist, Michael Faraday, who in 1834 carried out a series of exact investigations of the quantitative aspects of electrolytic dissociation.

LESSON 22

Faraday's Laws of Electrolysis

THE phenomenon of electrolytic decomposition led Faraday to conclude that, whenever an electric current is passed through a conducting solution, the substance in solution breaks down into charged particles which migrate towards one or other of the electrodes and thus act as carriers of the current. These electrically-charged moving particles he called ions (Greek, meaning " wanderers "). Those which were positively charged and were, therefore, attracted to the oppositely charged cathode were called " cations "; those which were negatively charged and moved towards the anode, " anions." The decomposition of sulphuric acid was then explained according to the equation:

$$H_2SO_4 \rightleftharpoons H^+ + HSO_4^- \rightleftharpoons 2H^+ + SO_4^=$$

The hydrogen ions are discharged on the surface of the cathode and set free as elementary hydrogen; the sulphate ions have their charge neutralized by the anode and immediately react with water thus:

$$2SO_4 + 2H_2O \longrightarrow 2H_2SO_4 + O_2$$

The net result of the electrolysis of sulphuric acid, therefore, is that hydrogen is liberated at the cathode, oxygen at the anode, and sulphuric acid gradually accumulates round the anode.

With copper sulphate a similar process takes place. The positively charged copper ions migrate to the cathode, where they are discharged and deposited as fine particles of metallic copper;

the negatively charged sulphate ions are discharged at the anode and react with water to give free oxygen and sulphuric acid as before. In general, it may be said, therefore, that in the electrolysis of a dissolved salt the metal ion migrates to the cathode, the acid ion to the anode. Whether the metal will be deposited on the cathode depends on its tendency to react with water after it has passed from the ionic to the atomic state. For example, in the electrolysis of a sodium salt, metallic sodium is not deposited on the cathode ; it immediately reacts with water thus :

$$2Na + 2H_2O \longrightarrow 2NaOH + H_2\nearrow$$

and hydrogen gas is set free at the cathode. These are the principles underlying the electrolytic refinement of metals, electroplating, and so on ; numerous examples of their application will occur in the Lessons on the preparation of the metals.

Faraday showed that in the process of electrolysis the amount of substance liberated at either one of the electrodes is strictly proportional to the total quantity of electricity which has been passed through the cell.

It is independent of the temperature and concentration of the solution, and also of the area of the electrodes exposed in the solution. Moreover, if the same current is allowed to pass through a series of solutions, as shown in Fig. 1, the

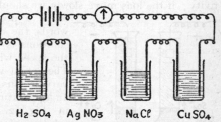

H_2SO_4 $AgNO_3$ $NaCl$ $CuSO_4$

Fig. 1. Chemically equivalent quantities of substances set free by passing the same amount of electricity through their solutions.

amount of substances liberated at the electrodes in each cell is proportional to the chemical equivalent of the element. For example, the quantity of electricity which liberates 1·008 grams of hydrogen from dilute sulphuric acid, also liberates 23 grams of sodium from sodium chloride solution, 107·88 grams of silver from silver nitrate solution, 63·6/2 = 31·8 grams of copper from copper sulphate solution, and so on.

Faraday found that the quantity of electricity required to liberate one gram equivalent, that is, the equivalent weight expressed in grams, of an element is equal to 96,540 coulombs ; a coulomb, the unit quantity of electricity, corresponds to the passage of 1 ampere of current for 1 second. Comparatively recently, Faraday's figure has been corrected to 96,490 coulombs ; and this amount of electricity is generally known as the " faraday," and is usually denoted by the symbols $+$ or $-$. Since the equivalent weight of a univalent element is the same as the atomic weight, each ion in such a case, e.g. Na^+, carries with it one faraday of electricity ; similarly, a divalent ion carries two, e.g. Cu^{++}, a trivalent ion, three, e.g. Fe^{+++}, and so on. Faraday's laws, therefore, afford an excellent method of determining the chemical equivalent of an element—sometimes called the electro-chemical equivalent in this case. The quantity of electricity actually used in such determinations is estimated by weighing accurately the amount of silver or copper deposited in a specially designed cell called a " voltameter."

Migration of the Ions. The tendency of solutions of electrolytes to conduct an electric current has been shown to be due to the motion of the ions. If the ions move very rapidly we should expect the electrolyte concerned to have a high conductivity ; if the ions move slowly we should expect the electrolyte to be a poor conductor. In other words, the electrical conductivity of solutions is somewhat dependent on the speed with which the ions move. The actual velocities of migration of various ions have been measured in an apparatus similar to that shown in Fig. 2. A moderately dilute solution of some coloured salt, such as copper sulphate, potassium chromate, cobalt nitrate, etc., is introduced, together with some gelatin, into the lower portions of the U-tube. When the jelly has set, a dilute solution of a colourless salt, e.g. potassium sulphate, is added to each limb and, the positions of the coloured boundary having been marked, the terminals are connected to a battery. The jelly prevents diffusion currents but permits the migration of the ions, as is shown in the case of copper sulphate by the movement of the blue boundary towards the cathode, and in the case of salts such as potassium chromate, potassium permanganate, etc., by the

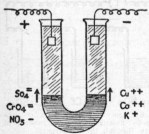

Fig. 2. Migration of coloured ions towards oppositely charged electrode. Coloured substance made into jelly with gelatin in the bottom of the U-tube.

movement of the coloured boundary towards the anode. By comparing the distances which the boundaries moved in a given time, it was possible to determine the relative speeds of migration of the ions. By this method it was found that the hydrogen (H^+) and hydroxyl (OH^-) ions move considerably faster than any others, the H^+ ion being about twice as fast as the OH^- and about five times as fast as most others, e.g. Na^+ and Cl^-.

The Ionic Theory. In putting forward his laws of electrolysis Faraday assumed that it is the electric current which causes the molecules to dissociate into ions. If this were so, a certain minimum amount of electricity would be necessary before electrolysis could begin. In no case was this found to be so, the merest trace of current being sufficient to start the decomposition. In 1887, the Swedish physicist, Svante Arrhenius, put forward the theory that the molecules of an electrolyte when dissolved in water break up or *ionize of their own accord*, and that the positively and negatively charged ions exist quite independently of each other in the solution and have their own specific properties. On this assumption Arrhenius was able to account for the abnormal values of osmotic pressure, depression of freezing point, etc., which all electrolytes appeared to show (*see* Lesson 9, volume 1, page 177). Since these properties are dependent on the total number of particles present in the solution (whether undissociated molecules or ions), the splitting up of the molecules into ions would obviously cause an increased effect upon the osmotic pressure, etc. Careful investigations of the degree of this ionic dissociation—that is, the proportions of dissolved molecules which ionize in solution—have shown that the abnormalities of osmotic pressure can be almost exactly accounted for on this basis, and the ionic theory of Arrhenius has now been accepted as the correct explanation. The mechanism of this dissociation is indicated in the following equations :

$$NaCl \rightleftharpoons Na^+ + Cl^-$$
$$AlCl_3 \rightleftharpoons Al^{+++} + 3Cl^-$$
$$Na_2CO_3 \rightleftharpoons 2Na^+ + CO_3^=$$
$$H_2SO_4 \rightleftharpoons H^+ + HSO_4^- \rightleftharpoons 2H^+ + SO_4^=$$
$$NaOH \rightleftharpoons Na^+ + OH^-$$

All acids in solution give the H^+ ion, all bases the OH^- ion ;

the common properties of all acids and of all bases are due to the presence in their solutions of these ions. It must be remembered that the ions of elements have specific properties which are quite different from those of their atoms. Thus copper metal has a reddish colour, while the cupric ion is blue ; chlorine gas is yellowish-green and very poisonous, while the chlorine ion is colourless, and solutions containing such ions, e.g. NaCl, are in general non-poisonous.

Chemical Reactions between Ions. When an electrolyte is dissolved in water an equilibrium is at once set up between the undissociated molecules and the ions. For example, with hydrochloric acid :

$$HCl \rightleftharpoons H^+ + Cl^-$$

In such a case the proportion of dissolved molecules which dissociate into ions is called the " degree of dissociation," and the concentration of ions present can be calculated by application of the Law of Mass Action. If the degree of dissociation is large, the solution will contain a large number of ions, and since its ability to conduct an electric current depends on the production of charged ions, solutions which are good conductors are also highly ionized. This is particularly so in the case of acids and bases owing to the high velocity with which the H^+ and OH^- ions migrate. These facts offer a convenient method of comparing the relative strengths of acids and bases by the measurement of their electrical conductivities.

Applying the ionic theory to reactions in solutions, it is apparent that such reactions are actually reactions between ions. Thus in the neutralization of an acid by a base, e.g. HCl and NaOH, the reaction may be written :

$$HCl \rightleftharpoons H^+ + Cl^-$$

$$NaOH \rightleftharpoons Na^+ + OH^-$$

$$H^+ + OH^- \rightleftharpoons H_2O$$

$$\text{hence } HCl + NaOH \rightleftharpoons Na^+ + Cl^- + H_2O$$

Similarly, the hydrolysis of a weak salt—that is, a salt of a weak base or a weak acid, e.g. aluminium chloride—may be written :

$$AlCl_3 + 3H_2O \rightleftharpoons Al(OH)_3 + 3HCl$$

$$HCl \rightleftharpoons H^+ + Cl^-$$

and since $Al(OH)_3$ is only slightly ionized in solution, and, in fact, is slowly precipitated as a white gelatinous solid, a solution of $AlCl_3$ contains H^+ ions and shows an acid reaction to litmus. For further treatment of this subject the student is advised to consult the chapters on Ionic Theory in any text-book.

LESSON 23

Alkali Metals and Their Compounds

THE metals lithium, sodium, potassium, rubidium and caesium—known as the caustic alkali metals because of the vigorously caustic properties of their hydroxides— occur in group 1 of the periodic table (*see* Lesson 4, volume 1, page 160). These elements afford a good example of the gradation of physical and chemical properties which was shown by Mendeléeff to be associated with a gradual increase in atomic weight. Thus lithium, the lightest of the five, forms the weakest base, caesium the strongest ; also, with the exception of lithium, which in some respects resembles the alkaline earth metals, calcium, strontium and barium, the order of increasing solubility of the salts is the same as that of decreasing atomic weight of the elements. For example, sodium salts are in general more soluble than potassium salts, and so on.

Sodium and Potassium. Of these five metals, sodium and potassium are much the most important ; both occur widely distributed in Nature, sodium chiefly in the sea, as rock-salt $(NaCl)$ and as Chile saltpetre $(NaNO_3)$, while potassium occurs as sylvine (KCl) and as carnallite $(KCl, MgCl_2, 6H_2O)$. The metals were first isolated in 1807 by Sir Humphry Davy, who found that, when an electric current is passed through molten sodium or potassium hydroxide, small globules of metal separate out at the negative pole. This is the basis of the modern Castner process for the preparation of these metals ; the hydroxide is kept at a temperature of about 320° C., care being taken to prevent the oxygen, which escapes at the anode, from coming into contact with the metal. Both are soft, white, lustrous metals that float on water. They are readily oxidized by the air, and react violently with water according to the equations :

$$2Na + 2H_2O \longrightarrow 2NaOH + H_2 \nearrow$$

$$2K + 2H_2O \longrightarrow 2KOH + H_2 \nearrow$$

The heat generated in these reactions is usually sufficient to make the hydrogen explode; they must, therefore, be carried out with great care. Sodium and potassium also react readily with sulphur and the halogens.

Hydroxides. Sodium and potassium hydroxides—known as caustic soda and caustic potash—find an important commercial use in the manufacture of soaps. They are prepared by two methods; if calcium hydroxide (slaked lime) suspended in water is run into a boiling solution of the carbonate, insoluble calcium carbonate is precipitated and the hydroxide is formed. In the case of potassium hydroxide the reaction may be written:

$$Ca(OH)_2 + K_2CO_3 \longrightarrow CaCO_3 + 2KOH$$
(slaked lime)

This process is rapidly being superseded—at any rate, in the manufacture of caustic soda—by the method based on the electrolysis of the aqueous solution of the chloride. The first stage of the process is the electrolytic dissociation of the chloride according to the equation:

$$NaCl \rightleftharpoons Na^+ + Cl^-$$

The sodium ions then migrate to the cathode, where they are discharged, and the sodium metal immediately reacts with water thus:

$$2Na + 2H_2O \longrightarrow 2NaOH + H_2 \nearrow$$

while the chlorine ions are discharged at the anode. Owing to the tendency of chlorine to react with sodium hydroxide to form the hypochlorite and chlorate (*see* Lesson 10, volume 1, page 181), care must be taken to prevent the gas from diffusing back into the cathodic liquors. This is done in some cells by enclosing the anodes in cement boxes, which act as diaphragms. In the Solvay cell—*see* diagram, page 193—a layer of mercury, flowing slowly across the bottom of the cell, acts as the cathode, and the sodium which dissolves in the mercury to form an amalgam is carried out of the cell before any reaction can take place. The amalgam is then treated with water, which immediately reacts with the sodium to produce sodium hydroxide. Chlorine, which

'MOONRISE ON THE MARSHES OF THE YARE.' John Crome (1768–1821) was born in Norwich, and many of his most famous paintings, including the one shown here, are of scenes in the Norfolk countryside. He was the leading spirit of the Norwich Society of landscape painters, and to their exhibitions he contributed nearly 300 works. ART AND ARCHITECTURE 18

National Gallery

'LOCK ON THE STOUR.' Painted in 1811 by John Constable (1776–1837), this Suffolk landscape demonstrates his remarkable gift for the expression of atmosphere and movement of the wind in sky and trees. Constable was a native of East Bergholt, in Suffolk, and he was never so much at home as in his pictures of the East Anglian flats. ART AND ARCHITECTURE 18

Victoria and Albert Museum, S. Kensington

1909

1912

1911

1916

1915

1917

1921

SATURN AND ITS RINGS. Discovered by Galileo in 1610, the ring system of Saturn was thought, until the middle of the 19th century, to be a solid body or bodies, but it is now held to be composed of an aggregation of small moonlets revolving about the planet with great rapidity. Details of the system are fully discussed in the text. ASTRONOMY 18

Plate 22   *Volume III*

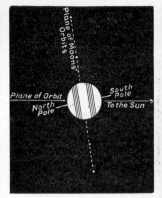

SYSTEM OF URANUS, showing the singular angles of the equatorial belts, planes of orbits and position of poles.   ASTRONOMY 19

DISCOVERY OF PLUTO (right). It was by means of this 24-inch telescope at the Lowell Observatory, Arizona, that Pluto was proved to exist.   ASTRONOMY 20

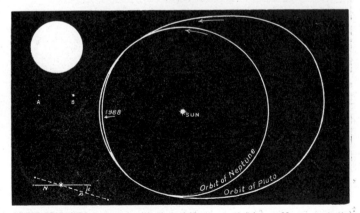

ORBIT OF PLUTO compared with that of Neptune; the date 1988 represents the next perihelion of Pluto.   Top left, the sun as seen from the earth; A, sun as seen from Pluto at aphelion; B, at perihelion.   In the diagram, bottom left: N, diameter of Neptune's orbit; P, greatest diameter of Pluto's orbit; I, inclination of Pluto's orbit to Neptune's.   ASTRONOMY 20

HALLEY'S COMET. This photograph shows the famous comet in relation to the planet Venus. A periodic comet, returning at intervals of 75 to 76 years, it has been observed for more than two thousand years. The diagram below shows its orbit
ASTRONOMY 21

Photo, Union Observatory, Johannesburg

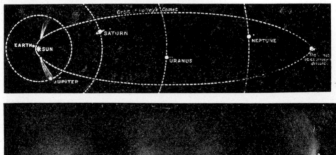

ENCKE'S COMET. Discovered by J. L. Pons of Marseilles in 1818, this short period comet is named after the German astronomer, J. F. Encke (1791–1865), who first determined its orbit and demonstrated that it had been previously observed in 1786, 1795 and 1805. The period of its recurrence or revolution about the sun is approximately 1,200 days. It is one of the Jovian family of comets its orbit approaching near to that of Jupiter. ASTRONOMY 21

Plate 24   *Volume III*

is liberated at the anode in this process, forms a very important by-product.

Carbonates and Bicarbonates. Sodium carbonate occurs in Nature as a deposit from certain salt lakes in Egypt and Kenya; it was also found to be present in the ash obtained

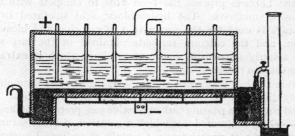

PREPARATION OF SODIUM HYDROXIDE by the electrolysis of a solution of sodium chloride.

from plants growing on the sea-shore. Potassium carbonate—called " potash "—was obtained in the same way from the ash of wood used to heat pots; hence its name. As a result of the increasing importance of these carbonates in such industries as the manufacture of glass and soaps, the natural sources were soon found to be inadequate. The first commercial method of preparation was invented by the French chemist Leblanc in 1791, and was awarded a prize offered by the Academy of Paris for the best process of converting common salt (sodium chloride) into sodium carbonate. In the first stage of the process, sodium chloride is heated with strong sulphuric acid, sodium sulphate and hydrochloric acid being formed according to the equations :

$$NaCl + H_2SO_4 \longrightarrow NaHSO_4 + HCl$$

$$NaHSO_4 + NaCl \longrightarrow Na_2SO_4 + HCl$$

The sodium sulphate—known as " salt-cake "—is then mixed with limestone and coke and heated more strongly, when these reactions take place :

$$Na_2SO_4 + 2C \longrightarrow Na_2S + 2CO_2$$

$$Na_2S + CaCO_3 \longrightarrow Na_2CO_3 + CaS$$

The residual black mass—called " black ash "—containing sodium carbonate and calcium sulphide together with various

G3

impurities, is washed with water ; the carbonate dissolves and is readily obtained from the solution by recrystallization. In this process considerable importance attaches to the utilization of the by-products, since they would otherwise be an obvious source of waste ; in fact, it is only by eliminating this waste that the Leblanc process has been able to compete with more economical methods. The hydrochloric acid liberated in the first stage is used for the production of chlorine and bleaching powder, and the calcium sulphide obtained in the last stage forms a fairly important source of sulphur, which is extracted by the Chance process.

Within the last fifty years the Leblanc process has been almost entirely displaced by the ammonia-soda or Solvay process. This method consists in passing carbon dioxide gas, prepared by heating limestone, up a tower down which a solution of brine saturated with ammonia is percolating. Crystals of sodium bicarbonate are deposited on the baffle plates in the tower. The solid bicarbonate is sold as such or converted into the carbonate (soda) by heating. The reactions taking place in this process may be written :

$$NH_4OH + CO_2 \rightleftharpoons NH_4HCO_3$$
$$\text{(ammonium bicarbonate)}$$
$$NH_4HCO_3 + NaCl \longrightarrow NH_4Cl + NaHCO_3$$

If carbonate is required :

$$2NaHCO_3 \longrightarrow Na_2CO_3 + H_2O + CO_2$$

and the CO_2 is available for a further cycle. Also the ammonium chloride, when heated with lime (from the limestone), yields ammonia gas, which is then put through the plant again, so that there are no wasteful by-products in this method.

The process cannot, however, be used for the potassium salt, since potassium bicarbonate is comparatively soluble in water and is, therefore, not precipitated at the first stage. Potassium carbonate is prepared by the Leblanc process or by passing carbon dioxide into the hydroxide.

In solution, sodium carbonate—washing soda—tends to hydrolyse according to the equation :

$$Na_2CO_3 + H_2O \rightleftharpoons H_2CO_3 + 2NaOH$$

The solution always shows an alkaline reaction owing to the presence of free sodium hydroxide, and it is the detergent action of this free caustic soda which gives to washing soda its cleansing properties.

Sodium bicarbonate readily loses carbon dioxide on heating or on treatment with even weak acids, such as tartaric or citric acid. Baking soda is a mixture of the bicarbonate and what is called " cream of tartar " (acid potassium tartrate), which in solution yields a certain amount of free acid. The process of baking, therefore, involves the evolution of carbon dioxide, which forms small bubbles in the dough and causes the pastry to " rise."

Copper, Silver and Gold. In the periodic table (volume 1, page 160) it will be seen that these elements are connected to sodium by a dotted line, indicating a vague chemical resemblance to the alkali metals. Their weakly basic character and inactivity to oxygen. however, stand in sharp contrast to the alkali metals, and the similarity exists only in so far as they give rise to a series of univalent salts, e.g. CuCl, AgCl, etc.

Copper occurs in Nature as oxide, carbonate and sulphide ; the metal is prepared from oxide and carbonate ores simply by heating with carbon (coke). Sulphide ores present more difficulty owing to the affinity of copper for sulphur. Part of the ore is oxidized in a blast furnace ; the air is then shut off and the copper oxide allowed to react with some more sulphide. The reactions may be written :

$$2Cu_2S + 3O_2 \longrightarrow 2Cu_2O + 2SO_2$$
$$Cu_2S + 2Cu_2O \longrightarrow 6Cu + SO_2$$

This crude copper—called " blister copper "—is refined electrolytically ; copper sulphate forms the electrolyte, " blister " copper the anodes, and thin sheets of pure electrolytic copper the cathodes. During the electrolysis copper dissolves from the anode and precipitates on the cathode.

Silver occurs usually associated with copper and lead as sulphide, and as chloride ; it is recovered in the process of refinement of these metals.

Gold occurs in the free state in Nature either in quartz veins or in the gravel of river-beds. It is obtained from the ore mechanically—that is, by washing the gravel in a cradle, or chemically, by converting it into a soluble cyanide or chloride. In the cyanide process it is converted into a complex gold sodium cyanide—$NaAu(CN)_2$—by treatment with sodium cyanide ; the gold is recovered by precipitation with zinc or by electrolysis.

In the chlorination process the ore is treated with chlorine and the soluble auric chloride, $AuCl_3$, reduced to metallic gold by means of ferrous sulphate.

Chemistry of Photography. When a silver halide is exposed to light it rapidly darkens owing to the formation of metallic silver. In the case of the chloride the reaction may be written :

$$2AgCl \longrightarrow 2Ag + Cl_2$$

This property is made use of in the photographic plate, which consists of a thin film of gelatin containing a fine emulsion of silver bromide. On exposure to light, metallic silver is deposited in thicknesses which depend on the strength of the light. The plate is then treated with a developer which is a reducing agent, such as pyrogallol or potassium ferrous oxalate, and which increases the precipitation of silver in those portions where the reduction has already been started by the light. When the development is sufficiently dense, the plate is immersed in a " fixing " bath containing " hypo," which dissolves out the residual silver bromide, leaving a deposit of silver of varying thickness scattered throughout the gelatin film. The process of printing is exactly similar, the darkest portions of the film (the negative) appearing lightest on the print.

LESSON 24

Alkaline Earth Metals

THE metals calcium, strontium and barium show distinct resemblances to the metals of the alkali group, the chief difference being that they are less reactive. Thus the hydroxides of all three metals are soluble in water and their solutions have fairly strong basic properties. For this reason, and because they are found so widely scattered over the earth in the form of naturally occurring carbonate and sulphates, they are called the alkaline earth metals. As is the case with the alkali metals, the hydroxides of calcium, strontium and barium show a steady increase in basicity with increasing atomic weight. In contrast to the metals of group I, however, the alkaline earth metals form many insoluble salts ; the commonest examples are the carbonates, phosphates and barium sulphate.

Moreover, the action of heat on the nitrate is different in the two cases. Sodium and potassium nitrate, when heated, liberate oxygen and form the nitrite; the nitrates of the alkaline earth metals, on the other hand, break down into the oxide, giving off nitrogen peroxide as well as oxygen, a reaction which brings them into line with the nitrates of the heavy metals.

Preparation of the Metals. The metals were first isolated by Davy by the method used for the preparation of the alkali metals, viz. the electrolysis of the solid hydroxide. It was found, however, that the chloride is more readily fusible than the hydroxide, and it therefore forms the electrolyte in the modern processes. Of the three elements, calcium is the only one which has any commercial application, and even in this case it is very limited. In the preparation of calcium, the chloride is kept molten at a temperature of about 780° C., and the metal solidifies on the end of an iron electrode (the cathode) which is slowly raised from the surface of the molten electrolyte.

The metals are silvery-white in appearance, react vigorously with water and dilute acids, from which they liberate hydrogen, and on heating combine with hydrogen to form hydrides, nitrogen to form nitrides, the halogens to form halides, sulphur to form sulphides, and carbon to form carbides. The nitrides and carbides are interesting; on treatment with water they liberate ammonia and acetylene according to the equations:

$$Ca_3N_2 + 6H_2O \longrightarrow 3Ca(OH)_2 + 2NH_3$$
$$CaC_2 + 2H_2O \longrightarrow Ca(OH)_2 + C_2H_2$$
$$\text{(acetylene)}$$

The metals also act as reducing agents, and reduce fuming sulphuric acid ($H_2SO_4 . SO_3$) to sulphur and concentrated sulphuric acid (H_2SO_4) to hydrogen sulphide.

Oxides and Hydroxides. On exposure to air or oxygen the metals rapidly tarnish, owing to the formation of a film of oxide. The oxides are also formed when the carbonates are decomposed by heat; in the case of calcium carbonate the reaction is written:

$$CaCO_3 \underset{}{\overset{}{\rightleftarrows}} CaO + CO_2$$
$$\text{(limestone)} \qquad \text{(quicklime)}$$

and since the reverse reaction is favoured by an increase in pressure (principle of Le Châtelier), the gas must be removed as rapidly as possible. The kilns in which limestone is burnt are, therefore, arranged so that a steady draught of air blows through the charge. These oxides are white amorphous powders which melt only at extremely high temperatures and dissolve in water to give the hydroxide. The formation of calcium hydroxide (slaked lime) from quicklime is written :

$$CaO + 2H_2O \longrightarrow Ca(OH)_2$$

The hydroxides are strongly basic ; they turn red litmus blue and react with acids to form salts and water. A solution of slaked lime in water is called " limewater " ; in the presence of carbon dioxide it turns milky, owing to the formation of the insoluble carbonate, a reaction which is used as a test for carbon dioxide.

Carbonates. Of the three, calcium carbonate is by far the most important. It occurs widely distributed in Nature as amorphous chalk, which is a deposit consisting of the calcareous remains of marine organisms and shells, as irregularly crystalline limestone and marble, and in the definitely crystalline forms known as calcite and aragonite. Calcite, which is found as large, transparent crystals of the hexagonal system, exhibits the phenomenon of double refraction and is used for polarizing light. Limestone and marble find considerable industrial use as a flux in metallurgical processes and in the production of lime used for making mortar and cement.

If carbon dioxide is passed through a solution containing suspended calcium carbonate, the carbonate gradually passes into solution according to the equation :

$$CaCO_3 + CO_2 + H_2O \rightleftharpoons Ca(HCO_3)_2$$
$$\text{(calcium bicarbonate)}$$

The evaporation of the bicarbonate solution leads to the reverse reaction ; carbon dioxide is set free and calcium carbonate reprecipitated. These are the reactions which are responsible for the formation of caves and gorges in limestone districts and also for the deposition of limestone in the form of stalactites and stalagmites. The erosion is caused by the continued solvent action over periods of thousands of years of water charged with carbon dioxide ; the stalactites and stalagmites are the result of the slow dripping and evaporation of the bicarbonate solution from the roof of the cavern. An illustration showing the stalactites in Cox's Cave, Cheddar, appears in volume 2, plate 43.

Hard Water and Water Softeners. Water containing dissolved salts of calcium and magnesium feels " hard " to the skin when used for washing, and does not form a lather with soap at all readily. Such water is called hard water. Soap is a sodium or potassium salt of certain fatty acids such as stearic acid ; its reaction with hard water leads to the formation of an insoluble calcium or magnesium salt, which is thrown out in the form of a scum. The equation is written :

sodium stearate + calcium bicarbonate
(soap)

$$\longrightarrow$$

sodium bicarbonate + calcium stearate
(scum)

and since the soap does not lather until all the calcium bicarbonate has been removed as insoluble scum, washing with hard water is very wasteful. Hard water also causes the " furring " of kettles, and, if used in boilers for industrial purposes or for central heating, may lead to the deposition of a thick scale which considerably reduces the efficiency of the boiler. It is, therefore, a matter of some importance to remove " hardness " from water.

When the hardness is due to the presence of dissolved calcium bicarbonate, it can be readily removed by boiling, which liberates carbon dioxide and forms a precipitate of calcium carbonate ; it is then known as " temporary " hardness. Temporarily hard water can also be softened by the addition of slaked lime, which reacts according to the equation :

$$Ca(HCO_3)_2 + Ca(OH)_2 \longrightarrow 2CaCO_3 + 2H_2O \downarrow$$

and the insoluble carbonate can be removed.

If, however, calcium or magnesium sulphate is present, these methods are not effective, and the water is said to be " permanently " hard. One method of removing permanent hardness is to add sodium carbonate ("washing-soda"), the lime or magnesia being again precipitated as carbonates according to the reaction :

$$CaSO_4 + Na_2CO_3 \longrightarrow CaCO_3 + Na_2SO_4 \downarrow$$

hence the use of washing soda in the laundry.

Another important modern method of softening water is effected by means of an apparatus, and is based on the use of permutite, a complex sodium aluminium silicate belonging to a group of minerals called zeolites When hard water is filtered through coarse lumps of permutite, the calcium and magnesium salts are converted into insoluble silicates and the water is thereby softened. When the permutite becomes ineffective, it can be regenerated by passing a weak solution of sodium chloride through the calcium permutite ; the sodium compound is reformed, and the calcium washed away in the form of highly soluble calcium chloride.

Mortar and Cement. Mortar is made by mixing slaked lime and sand to a thick paste, with water. The setting is due to the reaction between the lime and the carbon dioxide of the air, which results in the formation of a rigid mass of calcium carbonate. Cement is made by heating a mixture of limestone, clay and sand until it sinters. The mass is then pulverized, and, when mixed with water, it sets to a hard, stone-like mass, due doubtless to the formation of calcium aluminium silicates.

Plaster of Paris. Calcium sulphate is found in Nature in the form $CaSO_4 . 2H_2O$, known as gypsum. When gypsum is heated to about $120°$ C., most of the water of crystallization is driven off, and if the dried solid, which is called plaster of Paris, is moistened with water and allowed to dry, it sets into a firm, alabaster-like mass. Plaster of Paris is frequently used for obtaining casts of statues, etc., as well as for giving support in various surgical operations.

Barium sulphate is practically insoluble in water and dilute acids ; it is used as a means of detecting a sulphate in qualitative analysis, the procedure being to add barium chloride solution to a solution of the substance suspected of containing sulphate. A white precipitate of barium sulphate is produced.

Magnesium. Magnesium follows beryllium in group 2 and stands immediately before calcium strontium and barium, to which it shows distinct similarities. Like them, it is a brilliant white metal, which tarnishes in air, liberates hydrogen from water and acids, reduces carbon dioxide to carbon, is divalent in its compounds and reacts with the elements to form a nitride, carbide, sulphide, chloride and so on.

Unlike the hydroxides of calcium, strontium and barium, however, magnesium hydroxide is comparatively insoluble in water and is only feebly basic. For this reason many magnesium salts are hydrolysed by water, e.g. $MgCl_2$, which, on warming in contact with moist air, is completely decomposed into the oxide.

The most important salts of magnesium are the sulphate $MgSO_4 . 7H_2O$, called Epsom salts, and used as a purgative, and the complex ammonium phosphate $MgNH_4 . PO_4$, which is insoluble in water and is used as a means of estimating magnesium.

LESSON 25

Mercury and Related Metallic Elements

THOUGH also occupying a position in group 2 of the periodic table in volume 1, page 160, zinc, cadmium and mercury show only a vague chemical similarity to magnesium and the alkaline earth metals. Thus, while the valency of all three metals in their soluble compounds is 2, their oxides are only very weakly basic ; zinc oxide, in fact, is amphoteric. Also, unlike calcium, strontium and barium, the metals are comparatively stable to oxygen and water.

Zinc occurs in Nature as oxide, carbonate and sulphide (zinc blende, ZnS), the latter two of which usually contain small amounts of cadmium ; the ore is first converted into oxide by roasting in the presence of air, and the oxide is subsequently mixed with powdered coke and heated in specially designed retorts. The zinc, which distils over, is condensed in receivers and purified by re-distillation or by electrolytic deposition. Cadmium is obtained as a by-product in the extraction of zinc ; being more volatile than zinc, it collects in the first fractions which distil from the retorts.

Mercury is found in Nature as cinnabar (HgS), and is extracted from the ore by roasting in air or sometimes by heating with lime. The metal distils over and condenses as a liquid ; it is purified by washing with dilute nitric acid or by distillation in vacuo.

Both these metals react vigorously with mineral acids ; the use of zinc and hydrochloric acid in the preparation of hydrogen has been described (see Lesson 6, volume 1, page 165). Contact with a more electropositive (noble) metal, e.g. copper or platinum, in the presence of an acid causes the zinc to dissolve freely, hydrogen being liberated on the surface of the noble metal. It is on this property that the use of zinc in galvanic cells is based ; the scheme may be represented :

Zinc / acid / copper or platinum

→

and the current flows through the acid in the direction of the arrow. The use of zinc to protect iron from corrosion is due to a similar cause ; the more noble iron is "galvanized" with a thin layer of zinc, which on exposure to air forms a protective coating of oxide. Zinc is also used in the manufacture of batteries and in alloys such as brass (with copper).

The chemistry of the salts of zinc is largely determined by the behaviour of the oxide or hydroxide towards acids and bases. In this respect the hydroxide exhibits amphoteric properties; with acids it acts as a base, while with strong bases it reacts as an acid ; thus with caustic soda this reaction takes place :

$$2NaOH + Zn(OH)_2 \rightleftharpoons Na_2ZnO_2 + 2H_2O$$
(sodium zincate)

Because of the weakness of the hydroxide in its reactions both as an acid and as a base, zinc salts are somewhat unstable and tend to hydrolyse in the presence of water. Dehydration of zinc chloride, for example, leads to the formation of the oxychloride and the liberation of hydrogen chloride, a reaction which accounts for its use as a flux in soldering. The hydrogen chloride dissolves the film of oxide from the metal and keeps the surfaces clean. Pure dry zinc chloride can only be prepared by dehydrating the wet salt in a stream of dried hydrogen chloride.

Mercury and its Salts. Mercury is the only metal which is liquid at room temperature ; it is silvery-white in appearance, very heavy (about 14 times as heavy as water), and a very good conductor of heat and electricity. It is stable to air and oxygen, but is rapidly attacked by ozone, the halogens and nitric acid. It also dissolves certain metals, e.g. sodium, potassium, zinc, etc., to give what is called an amalgam.

Mercury gives two series of salts—mercurous, which correspond to the oxide, Hg_2O, and mercuric, which correspond to HgO. It was previously thought that in mercurous salts the valency of mercury was 1 ; this has recently been shown not to be the case, the ions present in a solution of a mercurous salt being diatomic and divalent, viz. Hg_2^{++}. The chemistry of mercury salts depends on the reaction :

$$Hg^{++} + Hg \rightleftharpoons Hg_2^{++}$$

which indicates that, in the presence of metallic mercury, mercuric salts are reduced to mercurous. Thus if mercuric chloride (corrosive sublimate), prepared by subliming mercuric sulphate with sodium chloride, is heated with metallic mercury, mercurous chloride (calomel) is obtained. This reaction is written :

$$HgCl_2 + Hg \rightleftharpoons Hg_2Cl_2 \text{ (calomel)}$$

Calomel is a white, amorphous solid, insoluble in water and extensively used for medicinal purposes.

Boron and Aluminium. These elements stand at the head of group 3, and are intermediate in position between the metallic and non-metallic elements of the two short periods. It is to be expected, therefore, that they would show the properties of both metals and non-metals ; boron, in fact, resembles carbon more closely than it does the metals, and is usually classed as a metalloid. Its non-metallic character is shown by the fact that it forms a stable hydride (cf. nitrogen and sulphur) and very stable salts called borates, which are analogous to sulphates and phosphates. On the other hand, boron oxide, B_2O_3, which exhibits acidic properties in boric acid and borates, also behaves as a very weak base, forming unstable salts of the type BCl_3.

Aluminium is considerably more basic in its reactions, as is to be expected with increase in atomic weight. Its oxide does, however, exhibit mildly acidic properties (cf. zinc), and is, therefore, amphoteric. Both elements are trivalent in their compounds.

Boron occurs as boric acid (H_3BO_3) and in the form of borates, usually of sodium, potassium and calcium. Boric—or " boracic " —acid, which is the hydrate of B_2O_3, occurs in lagoons surrounding the outlets of natural hot springs in Tuscany. The acid crystallizes out as leafy crystals, which are soapy to the touch, slightly soluble in water, and are only weakly acid to litmus. The aqueous solution is a mild antiseptic and is used as an eye lotion ; when boric acid is heated it loses water, forming tetraboric acid according to the equation :

$$4H_3BO_3 - 5H_2O \longrightarrow H_2B_4O_7$$

and on further heating, boron oxide is formed as a glassy mass which is very resistant to heat, thus :

$$2H_3BO_3 - 3H_2O \longrightarrow B_2O_3$$

Borax. Borax—the sodium salt of tetraboric acid $Na_2B_4O_7$— occurs naturally as tincal, from which it is recovered by recrystallization. Aqueous solutions of borax show a strongly alkaline reaction owing to hydrolysis, which leads to the formation of sodium hydroxide (strong base) and tetraboric acid (weak acid) ; this reaction is written :

$$Na_2B_4O_7 + H_2O \rightleftharpoons 2NaOH + H_2B_4O_7$$

When heated, borax behaves in a similar manner to boric acid,

CHEMISTRY 25

producing a certain amount of free boron oxide, which forms a glass-like bead, and if a trace of metallic oxide is fused with it, a complex borate having a characteristic colour is formed. It is upon this reaction that are based the uses of borax in borax-bead testing and also in soldering.

Aluminium. Owing to its lightness and durability aluminium is finding increasingly important industrial and domestic uses. It is one of the most abundant of the elements, and occurs extensively in the form of oxide, halide, aluminate and silicate. In the pure form, the oxide, Al_2O_3, occurs as ruby, sapphire and corundum ; in the hydrated form it is found chiefly as bauxite $Al_2O_3 . 2H_2O$. The metal is obtained by the electrolysis of a solution of purified bauxite in molten cryolite (a double fluoride of aluminium and sodium, Na_3AlF_6). The cell, shown in diagram, consists of an iron box lined with carbon plates, which act as

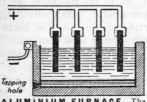

ALUMINIUM FURNACE. The oxide (bauxite), dissolved in molten cryolite, is reduced by electrolysis in a furnace of the Héroult type. The electrical resistance of the ore produces the necessary heat.

the cathode ; the anodes are formed by carbon rods, which dip into the molten electrolyte. When the current is passed, aluminium metal collects in the liquid form at the bottom of the bath, whence it is run off at intervals, and carbon dioxide escapes at the anodes.

Aluminium is very light, its density being 2·7 as compared with 7·9 for iron ; it has a great tensile strength, fairly high melting point, is a good conductor of heat and electricity and is only slightly attacked by oxygen.

In a finely divided form aluminium is an energetic reducing agent, and since a very large amount of heat is evolved in the reduction of some metallic oxides, it is often used in this way to produce the high temperatures necessary for the isolation of certain metals and also for welding " in situ." The method—called the " thermite " process—is to mix aluminium powder, a small amount of barium peroxide and the oxide of the metal required, e.g. Fe_2O_3 ; the mass is then ignited by means of a piece of magnesium wire, and the heat generated is sufficient to cause the iron to melt.

Aluminium hydroxide—$Al(OH)_3$—is formed as a glassy, flocculent precipitate when caustic soda is added to a solution of an aluminium salt. It is amphoteric in nature and dissolves in excess of caustic soda to form sodium aluminate. Aluminium hydroxide finds an important use in the dye industry ; it is what is called a " mordant," and is used to precipitate the particles of dye and hold them fast in the fabric.

Alums. If a strong solution of aluminium sulphate is treated with potassium sulphate and the mixture recrystallized, well-defined crystals of a compound called potash alum, and having the formula $K_2SO_4 . Al_2(SO_4)_3 . 24H_2O$, are formed. Quite a number of similarly constituted salts have been prepared, in which potassium is replaced by sodium or ammonium and aluminium by a trivalent metal such as iron, manganese or chromium. All of these alums are isomorphous—that is, they have the same crystalline form and in aqueous solution give all the characteristic reactions of both the univalent and trivalent metals.

Ceramic Clays. It has been mentioned (Lesson 21, page 181) that china clay—an aluminium silicate—is left behind together with quartz sand when granite or felspar is broken down by the process of " weathering." This clay—called kaolin—sinters into a hard, porous mass when heated carefully in an oven. For this reason it is used in the manufacture of bricks, tiles, pottery and porcelain. Bricks and tiles are made from a poor grade of clay containing iron which gives a reddish oxide ; finer pottery is made from purer clays, which may be coloured by the addition of certain metallic oxides and glazed by the simple process of throwing salt into the furnace. Porcelain is made from the purest form of kaolin ; it is clear and white, and the baking is carried almost to the point of fusion.

LESSON 26

Tin and Lead

REFERENCE to the periodic table, in volume 1, page 160, will show that the elements carbon and silicon, which occur in group 4, are connected, on the one hand, to titanium, zirconium, cerium and thorium, and, on the other, to germanium, tin and lead. Except that they all exhibit a maximum valency of 4—the typical group oxide being MO_2 and the chloride MCl_4—there does not appear to be much chemical similarity between the non-metallic elements at the head of the group and the well-defined metals which follow. It has been mentioned, however, that an *increase in atomic weight in any group* of the table leads to a gradual development of basic—that is, metallic—properties, and this is well exemplified in group 4. Thus germanium (atomic weight, 72), though a metal, has many properties which are suggestive of carbon and silicon ; both of its oxides, for example, are amphoteric, while tin (119) and lead (207) show increasingly pronounced basic properties. Thoria, the oxide of thorium (atomic weight, 232), is purely basic in its reactions.

C
|
Si
/   \
Ti   Ge
| |
Zr   Sn
| |
Ce   Pb
|
Th

Extraction of Tin. Tin occurs in Nature as cassiterite—SnO_2—which is found in Cornwall, the Malay Peninsula, Australia, the East Indies and Germany. The ore is first roasted, to oxidize the sulphides of iron with which it is frequently associated and to remove arsenic. It is sometimes freed from iron and tungsten in a magnetic separator, and then mixed with carbon (coal) and heated strongly in a reverberatory furnace. The oxide is reduced to the metal, which is run off and cast into ingots, called " block tin."

Tin is a lustrous, white metal intermediate in hardness between zinc and lead ; it is very ductile and malleable and can be beaten into thin foil, which is widely used under the name " silver paper " for wrapping cigarettes, confectionery, etc. Because of its resistance to corrosion, it is in great demand for the manufacture of tinplate articles, which are made of steel or copper dipped in molten tin. Many alloys of tin are used commercially—for example, bronze (tin, zinc, copper and lead), pewter (tin and lead), gunmetal and bell-metal ; most alloys with low melting points, e.g. solder and linotype metal, contain tin and lead in varying proportions.

Like carbon, tin exists in three allotropic modifications, two of which—the rhombic and tetragonal forms—are crystalline and the third—called grey tin—amorphous. The latter is obtained by cooling the crystalline forms well below 18° C. The crystalline structure of the metal at ordinary temperatures is more or less apparent to the eye ; the curious sound emitted when a bar of tin is bent—called " tin cry "—is now supposed to be due to the crystals rubbing against one another.

Compounds of Tin. Tin has two valencies, two and four, and gives rise to two well-defined series of salts. The divalent or stannous compounds are generally salt-like in character, and since in solution they tend to pass over into the quadrivalent stannic form, they are fairly strong reducing agents. Stannous chloride and sulphate, both of which are white crystalline solids, are prepared by the action on tin of hydrochloric and hot sulphuric acid respectively. These reactions may be written

$$Sn + 2HCl \longrightarrow SnCl_2 + H_2$$
$$Sn + 2H_2SO_4 \longrightarrow SnSO_4 + SO_2 + 2H_2O$$

Stannous chloride is extensively used in solution as a reducing agent. It precipitates silver and gold from solutions of their salts, reduces chromates to chromic salts and mercuric chloride, first, to mercurous chloride and, finally, if present in excess, to metallic mercury. This latter reaction is important, and is used in qualitative analysis as a test for tin and for mercury. The equations are written

$$SnCl_2 + 2HgCl_2 \longrightarrow SnCl_4 + Hg_2Cl_2$$
$$SnCl_2 + Hg_2Cl_2 \longrightarrow SnCl_4 + 2Hg$$

Stannic salts tend to hydrolyse in the presence of water, and in general cannot be prepared in solution. The chloride—$SnCl_4$—is obtained as a fuming liquid (boiling point, 114°C.) when dry chlorine is passed over heated tin or stannous chloride. Both series of salts react with an alkali to give a precipitate of the appropriate hydroxide. As is the case with aluminium and zinc, these hydroxides are amphoteric and dissolve in excess of

caustic alkali to form stannites (stannous) and stannates (stannic).
The reaction in the latter case is written.

$$Sn(OH)_4 + 2NaOH \longrightarrow Na_2SnO_3 + 3H_2O$$
$$\text{(sodium stannate)}$$

Stannates, therefore, appear to be the salts of H_2SnO_3—meta-stannic acid—which is obtained by the partial dehydration of $Sn(OH)_4$. Meta-stannic acid is also formed when tin dissolves in hot concentrated nitric acid, thus

$$Sn + 4HNO_3 \longrightarrow SnO_2 . H_2O + 4NO_2 + H_2O$$

When strongly heated, the acid is completely dehydrated, giving finally a white powdery residue of stannic oxide—SnO_2.

Sulphides of Tin. Both sulphides are prepared by the direct union of tin and sulphur or by passing sulphuretted hydrogen through a solution of the appropriate salt. Stannic sulphide —which is bright yellow in colour—dissolves readily in caustic soda or ammonium sulphide solution ; the reaction, written

$$SnS_2 + (NH_4)_2S \longrightarrow (NH_4)_2SnS_3$$
$$\text{(ammonium thiostannate)}$$

is similar in nature to that which occurs when the oxide dissolves in caustic soda. It is used in qualitative analysis as a means of separating tin from the other metals.

Lead and its Compounds. This metal occurs in Nature chiefly as galena, an impure form of lead sulphide, which often contains small traces of silver. The ore is roasted until the sulphide has been converted into oxide or sulphate, and then mixed with more galena and heated with the air shut off. Sulphur dioxide is liberated, and the lead which collects at the bottom of the furnace is run off and purified.

Lead is a soft, dense, bluish-grey metal, which tarnishes rapidly in air owing to the formation of a film of oxide, but is otherwise comparatively unreactive. It has a low melting point ($326°$ C.), is very malleable and ductile and, because of the ease with which it can be manipulated, is widely used, in the form of sheets, for lining reaction chambers, e.g. in the sulphuric acid process, and in the construction of water pipes, etc. Alloys of lead are also of considerable importance, and include pewter, type-metal and solder ; rifle bullets are made of lead and nickel.

Lead compounds are poisonous, and since they remain in the body when taken in small amounts, workers in lead mines and in factories where lead is continually used, e.g. in the manufacture of paints, frequently suffer from the cumulative effect of lead poisoning. It is dangerous to drink aerated water which has passed through lead pipes, since, in the presence of oxygen and carbon dioxide, small amounts of lead pass into solution.

Like tin, lead has valencies of 2 and 4, and forms two series of salts corresponding to the oxides PbO and PbO_2. Lead monoxide, or litharge, is formed as a buff-coloured or yellowish-red powder when the metal is heated in air ; it is also obtained by the action of heat on lead nitrate or carbonate, and by boiling white lead hydroxide, which is precipitated when an alkali is added to the solution of a lead salt. Lead hydroxide —$Pb(OH)_2$—is a stronger base than stannous hydroxide, although it still exhibits mildly amphoteric properties and dissolves in caustic soda to form an unstable plumbite, thus :

$$Pb(OH)_2 + 2NaOH \rightleftharpoons Na_2PbO_2$$

Litharge dissolves fairly readily in acids, giving rise to divalent lead salts ; when heated in air to about $400°$–$500°$ C., it turns red, owing to the formation of the oxide—Pb_3O_4—called red lead, which is extensively used in the manufacture of flint and pottery glasses and as a paint.

Lead dioxide—PbO_2—is prepared by the action of strong oxidizing agents, e.g. the halogens, on an alkaline solution of lead hydroxide. It is also prepared by anodic oxidation in the electrolysis of lead salts. It is insoluble in water, is a strong oxidizing agent and reacts with caustic soda to form a meta-plumbate (cf. meta-stannates). As with tin, the quadrivalent compounds of lead are un-saltlike in appearance, and in the presence of water hydrolyse completely to form lead dioxide.

Lead differs from tin in the insolubility of its halides and sulphate, and also in the fact that divalent lead compounds have no reducing properties.

White Lead. When sodium carbonate is added to the solution of a lead salt, a heavy white precipitate of *basic lead carbonate* is formed. This substance, which is known as " white lead " and has the formula $2PbCO_3 . Pb(OH)_2$, is in great demand as a pigment. In the old Dutch stack process of manufacture, still sometimes used, sheets of lead are placed on earthenware pots containing dilute acetic acid. These pots are arranged in tiers on spent tan bark, which furnishes the heat and carbon dioxide necessary for the reaction. After three or four months the white lead is removed and crushed into powder. In the more modern and quicker process—which, however, does not give the same covering power to the lead—sheets of lead are hung from the ceiling of a room, kept at a temperature of about 70° C., into which carbon dioxide and acetic acid vapour are admitted.

Chemistry of Storage Batteries. When dilute sulphuric acid is electrolysed between lead electrodes, the oxygen which is set free by the discharge of SO_4 ions oxidizes the anodic lead to lead dioxide, which forms a dark brown spongy deposit on the anode. If now the electrolysis is stopped, it is found that the cell so formed:

$$Pb \ \big/ \ H_2SO_4 \ \big/ \ PbO_2$$

produces a steady and fairly strong electric current. This is the basis of the lead accumulator or storage battery ; the mechanism of the discharge process is indicated by the equations :

$$Pb + SO_4 = \longrightarrow PbSO_4 + 2\ominus$$
$$PbO_2 + 4H^+ + SO_4 = \longrightarrow PbSO_4 + 2H_2O + 2\oplus$$

The lead acts as the cathode, the lead dioxide as the anode, and the current passes through the cell in the direction indicated by the arrow above. While the cell is discharging, both plates become gradually coated with lead sulphate and the flow of current ultimately ceases. The system may then be recharged by passing a current through the cell in the opposite direction, when the lead/lead dioxide plates are re-formed. The whole process, which is thus seen to be a reversible one, is summarized in the following equations :

$$Pb \ \big/ \ H_2SO_4 \ \big/ \ PbO_2 \ \rightleftharpoons \ PbSO_4 \ \Big/ \ \begin{array}{c} H_2O \\ + \\ H_2SO_4 \end{array} \ \Big/ \ PbSO_4$$

$$\xrightarrow{\text{discharge}} \qquad \xleftarrow{\text{recharge}}$$

Thorium and Gas Mantles. The elements cerium and thorium are comparatively rare, but their oxides—ceria and thoria—have a very important use in the manufacture of incandescent gas mantles and in some catalytic reactions. Their use in gas mantles is due to the discovery of von Welsbach (1885), who found that a maximum incandescence is obtained if the fabric of the mantle is first saturated with a mixture containing 99 per cent of thoria and 1 per cent of ceria.

Our Course in Chemistry is continued in Volume 4

Perspective of Plans and Elevations

I N the direct method, or architect's perspective, no measuring points or distance points are required. It is called the direct method because lines (to represent rays of light) are drawn direct to the eye. The architect is able to make one plan do for any view he may wish to represent, whether it be a front, back, end, three-quarter, or other view, because he draws the plan on one piece of paper or on tracing cloth, which he can turn about for any view, and the perspective drawing is made on another paper. The architect should first consider :

(1) Where is the building to be situated—on high, or low, or level ground ? If on high ground, then the H.L. should be low : if on low ground, then place the H.L. high ; and if on level ground, then place the H.L. at the normal level of 5 feet above the ground plane. Otherwise a wrong impression will be given of what the building will appear like when completed. (2) Whether the view is a front, or end, or back, or three-quarter view. (3) How far the spectator is from the building. The least distance must not be less than twice the greatest dimension of the building ; three or four times would be better. The view should show the whole building within a visual angle of 30° or 40°.

The accompanying figures, of problems 3, 4 and 5, owing to their small size, do not fulfil the above-mentioned considerations. The student should work out the problems on large pieces of paper (at least 30″ by 20″), and place the eye at the proper distance from the building. He should also work out three or four perspective drawings of the same building with the H.L. placed at different heights, to find out the effects of appearance at the various eye-levels.

Problems 1 and 2 concern perspective representations of superimposed objects. It is usual to put the plan into perspective first and then build up from it.

Problem 1. Draw in perspective the object of which plan and elevation are given. The sides make equal angles with the P.P. Nearest corner is 5′ to the left and 1′ within the picture.

First find nearest corner *A* in the usual way, and complete the square base *ABCD*. Through *A* draw a diagonal to C.V. On this diagonal measure (by means of the D.P.1) distances to find the points 1, 2, 3. Point 4 is found by drawing the horizontal diagonal through *D*. Now imagine a vertical plane to cut diagonally through *A* and *C*, and on its I.L. (used as Ht.L.) measure the respective heights of plinth, shaft, and top, from *b* to *e* for plinth, *e* to *f* for shaft, and *f* to *g* for top. From *e*, *f*, and *g* draw lines to C.V. Then vertical lines to meet them from points 1, 2, and 3 will give the nearest corners of the different parts. It will be noticed that the lengths of the sides which vanish 45° right and

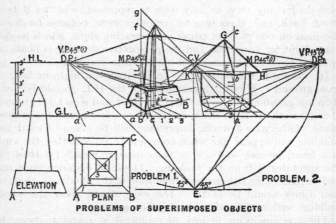

PROBLEMS OF SUPERIMPOSED OBJECTS

left are measured by merely drawing horizontal diagonals through the central points on the vertical axis of the objects, thus saving a good many construction lines.

Problem 2. Draw in perspective a cylinder with axis 4′ long and diameter 6′, standing on a circular end, with its centre 4′ to the right and 4′ within the picture. On top of this place centrally a square pyramid 4′ high. Its sides make equal angles with P.P., and its nearest corner touches the P.P. Point 3 is 4′ to the right and 1′ behind the P.P., because the centre E is to be 4′ behind the P.P., and the radius of the circle is 3′. Complete the lower end. For a Ht.L. use the I.L. of the vertical plane passing through the axis of the two objects. From *a* measure *ab* on this I.L. for the height of cylinder : then *EF* is the apparent length

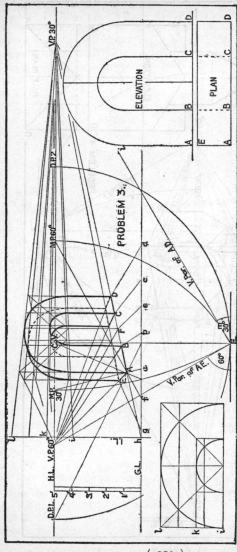

of its axis, and point *F* is the centre of upper end of cylinder as well as centre of base of pyramid. The upper ellipse is not shown, in order to avoid confusion of lines, and it would not be visible. The line from C.V. through F meeting I.L. in *b* gives *b* as the nearest corner of the pyramid touching the P.P. From *b* draw lines to V.P. 45° (1) and (2). The horizontal diagonal through *F* cuts these lines at points *K* and *H*, which are two more corners of the base of the pyramid. On I.L. measure *bc* for the height of the pyramid. From *c* draw a line to C.V. cutting *EF* produced at *G*, the apex of the pyramid. Join *GK*, *Gb*, and *GH*, thus completing the pyramid. The back edges are not shown.

Problem 3. Draw the perspective representation of an arch, of which the plan and elevation are given. The front

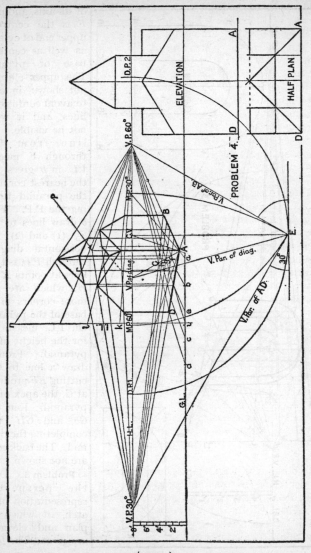

ELEVATION

HALF PLAN

PROBLEM 4.

of it recedes to the right at 30° with the P.P. Point A is 4′ to the left and 2′ behind the P.P. Scale ½″ to 1′. E. is 5′ above G.P., and 10′ in front of P.P. Find point A, draw from it a line to V.P. 30°. On this line measure the lengths AB, BC, CD; also on it find point F vertically under the centre of the arch. From A draw a line to V.P. 60°, and measure on it the depth of arch AE. From E draw a line to V.P. 30°, and another from D to V.P. 60°. Draw lines to V.P. 60° from points A, B, F, C, and D, which give corresponding points on back line. We now have the plan drawn in perspective.

Bring on the line from V.P. 30° through front points to meet G.L. in h, where must be drawn the I.L. of vertical plane of the front of arch. On this I.L. (used as Ht.L.) find the points i, k, and l for heights of various parts obtained from the elevation, and construction lines around the semicircles. From these points draw lines to V.P. 30°. From A, B, F, C, and D draw verticals to meet the former lines to V.P. 30°. Complete front of arch. The rest of the work can be easily understood.

Problem 4. The elevation and half-plan are given of a building standing on the ground plane. Put this into perspective, its nearest edge to be 2′ to the left of the spectator and 2 within the picture, and one side receding to the left at 30° with the P.P. The E. is 24′ in front of the P.P. and 8′ above the G.P. Scale, ¼″ to 1′. Find point A the nearest corner on G.P. Draw AB to V.P. 60°, and AD to V.P. 30°. On AD measure the four divisions as per plan by means of the lines drawn from points a, b, e, c, d to M.P. 30°. From the points thus obtained on AD draw lines to V.P. 60°. Find the V.P. of the diagonal of the square base of the building. This V.P. is often very useful in saving work, and is found by bisecting the right angle between the V. Par. of AD and the V. Par of AB.

From A draw a line to V.P. of diagonal cutting the lines drawn to V.P. 60° in points f, g, h, and C. Through these four points draw lines to V.P. 30°, thus completing the construction lines of the plan.

To obtain the heights, imagine a vertical plane to pass through the centre of the building through the point g, and receding to V.P. 60°. This vertical plane intersects the G.L. at point i, through which draw the I.L., and on it find the points k, l, m, and n for the heights of the various parts of the building (*see* elevation). Draw lines to V.P. 60°, and erect vertical lines from

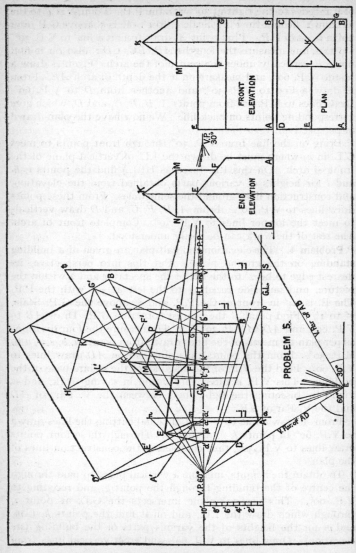

the proper points in plan, thus obtaining the heights. Complete as shown. Notice how the height of the other gable is found from point p, and of upper corners of tower from point r.

Problem 5. The plan with front and side elevations of a building are given. Put this into perspective with the line AB receding to the right at 30° with the P.P. The point A is to be 6′ to the left of the spectator and 2′ behind the P.P. The E. is 10′ above the G.P. and 24′ in front of the P.P. Scale ½″ to 1′.

First draw the plan and so place it that the long edges are 30° and the end 60° with the horizontal ; also draw a line to represent the plan of the P.P. two feet in front of the point A', and fix the C.V. 6 feet to the right of A'.

Owing to considerations of space, the H.L. is doing double duty, for it represents not only the eye-level, but also the plan of the P.P. The architect would keep these two lines separate, and use the line representing the plan of the P.P. on one piece of paper ; then, when he has obtained the points d', e', b', etc., where the plan of the rays of light direct to the eye cut this line (plan of P.P.), he would transfer the points to the paper on which he is to make the perspective. Sometimes he transfers these points to the edge of a strip of paper, which he can then place in any position on the other paper for the perspective, being careful, of course, to keep these points in their proper respective positions in relation to the C.V.

After drawing the plan of the P.P. and fixing the C.V., determine the position of the E. 24′ from C.V. and draw through the E. lines parallel to $A'B'$ and $A'D'$ to meet the plan of P.P. at V.P. 30° and V.P. 60°, which are respectively the vanishing points of long and short sides.

Next draw lines to represent the plan of rays of light direct to the E. It is not necessary to show these lines all the way to the eye, but let them finish on the line which represents the plan of the P.P. at the points d', e', a', h', f', etc.

It is now required to find the nearest corner A in perspective. To do this, produce the line $D'A'$ (in plan) to meet the plan of P.P. at point a'', and through a'' draw a vertical line (which really represents the I.L. of the plane containing the gable end of the building) to meet the G.L. at point a. From a draw a line to V.P. 60°. Now draw a vertical line through a' to meet the line from a to V.P. 60° in point A, the nearest point required. From A draw a line to V.P. 30°, on which determine the point

B by drawing a vertical through b'; also fix point D on the other line which vanishes to V.P. 60° by a vertical through d', intersecting AD at point D. Thus AD is the perspective length of lower edge of the gable end, and AB is similarly the apparent length of lower edge of front of building.

Next obtain the height of the gable end by measuring full scale the heights $a\ m$ and $m\ n$ on the I.L. of gable end, and from m and n draw lines to V.P. 60°. The vertical lines through a' and d', meeting the line from m to V.P. 60°, determine the corners of the eaves and the vertical line through e', meeting the line from n at point E, gives the highest point of the gable. The eave and ridge lines will vanish to V.P. 30°.

To obtain the representation of the tower, first produce $H'\ F'$ (in plan) to meet plan of P.P. at point u, and through u draw the I.L. of near vertical wall of the tower, and intersecting the G.L. at point o. Measure full scale on the I.L. the heights $o\ p$ and $p\ r$. From o, p, and r draw lines to V.P. 60°, and through h' and f' draw verticals to intersect these lines at N and M (the upper corners), and at F, the point where the nearest vertical edge of the tower intersects the roof. Another vertical line through l' intersecting the ridge gives point L where the ridge meets the vertical wall of the tower. Join FL, which is the intersection line between roof and vertical wall of the tower. From F and M draw lines to V.P. 30°, and through g' draw a vertical to intersect them, thus finding points G and P.

To find the apex of the tower it is necessary to find the I.L. of a vertical plane which contains the apex. There are definite ways of placing this vertical plane, but we will suppose one through the apex and parallel to the gable ends. Therefore, through K' (in plan) draw a line parallel to $D'A'$ or $B'C'$ to meet the plan of P.P. at point v. Through v draw the I.L. and on it measure st full scale the height of apex from the ground. From s and t draw lines to V.P. 60°, and through k' draw the vertical to intersect the line from t at point k. Join KM, KN, and KP.

LESSON 17

Planes and Traces in Perspective Drawing

THE student must have noticed that all V.P.'s (*see* Lesson 11, volume 2, page 158, for abbreviations) used in the preceding problems were placed on the H.L., but sometimes the V.P. may come above or below the H.L. In such cases it is called an *accidental vanishing point* (A.V.P.).

It should be remembered that the only lines which have their V.P.'s on the H.L. are those which recede and are in reality parallel to the G.P. All others have their V.P.'s either above or below the H.L., but they will always be on the V.L. of the plane which contains the receding line or lines.

Definitions of Planes. In order to know how to find and use these A.V.P.'s, the student must first learn to distinguish the various kinds of planes used in perspective, and their relative positions with regard to the P.P. and G.P.

The planes are (i) Horizontal. (ii) Vertical—1, parallel to the P.P. ; 2, perpendicular to the P.P. ; and 3, inclined to the P.P. (iii) Inclined. (iv) Ascending and descending. (v) Oblique— 1, ascending ; and 2, descending.

(i) A horizontal plane is one which is parallel to the G.P.

(ii) A vertical plane is upright—that is, perpendicular to the G.P.—but it may also be either parallel to the P.P., as *ABCD* (Fig. 1), or perpendicular to the P.P., as *EFGH*, or inclined to the P.P., as *GJKL*.

(iii) An inclined plane is one which is inclined to the G.P., but is perpendicular to the P.P., as *ABCD* (Fig. 2).

This plane must be carefully distinguished from a vertical inclined plane, which is perpendicular to the G.P., but inclined to the P.P. [Compare Figs. 1 and 2.]

(iv) An ascending plane is one which goes directly upwards from the P.P., as *ABCD* (Fig. 3). A descending plane is one which goes directly downwards from the P.P., as *ABCD* (Fig. 4).

(v) An oblique plane is inclined to both the P.P. and G.P. It may be either oblique ascending, as *EFGH* (Fig. 5), or oblique descending, as *KLMN* (Fig. 6).

Traces The intersection of any one of these planes with the G.P. is called its *horizontal trace* (H.T.), but its intersection with

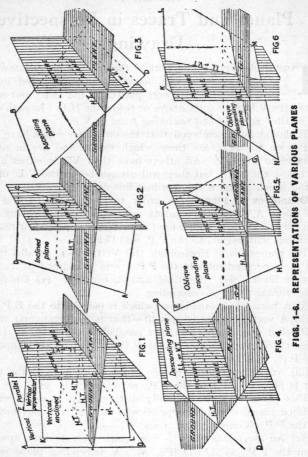

FIGS. 1–6. REPRESENTATIONS OF VARIOUS PLANES

the P.P. is named its *vertical trace* (V.T.), or more generally, its *intersecting line* (I.L.). [*See* Figs. 1-6 above.]

Order of Procedure. (i) Prepare the diagram of the P.P., etc., and find the starting point. (ii) Find the H.T. of the plane in which the line lies. (iii) Find the V.L. and I.L. of the same plane. (iv) Find the C.V.L. and new representation of the E. (v) Find the A.V.P. and A.M.P. of the line whose representation is required. (vi) Draw and measure the said line.

NOTE. By the rules of geometry it is possible to prove that a vertical plane may always be found to contain any given straight line.

Problem in Vertical Planes. Give the perspective representation of a line *AB*, which is 9 feet long, lying in a vertical plane inclined at 50° to the left. The line is inclined to the G.P. at an angle of 40°, and recedes upwards from a point *A* on the ground, 3′ to the right, and 4′ behind the P.P. The eye is 5′ above the ground and 10′ in front of the P.P. Scale, $\frac{1}{2}″=1′$.

NOTE. The plane which contains this line is similar to *GJKL*.

(i) Prepare the diagram of the P.P., etc., and find point *A* on the G.P. as in elementary perspective.

(ii) Find the H.T. of the vertical plane. As the latter is inclined towards the left at 50° with the P.P., therefore its H.T. also recedes at 50° towards the left. At the E., measure the angle of 50° and draw the V.Par. of the H.T. to find V.P. 50° (V.P. of direction). Through *A* to V.P. 50° draw the H.T. (represented

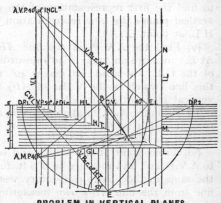

PROBLEM IN VERTICAL PLANES

by a dot-and-dash line), and bring it forward to meet the G.L. at point L. It should be noticed that V.P. 50° is the farther end of the H.T. (and this end is in reality a great distance away—in fact, miles away on the horizon), while point L. is its near end on the P.P.

(iii) Through V.P. 50° draw a vertical line to represent the V.L. of the vertical plane, and through L another vertical line to represent the I.L. of the vertical plane.

NOTE. The V.L. and I.L. of any plane are always parallel to each other.

In this case they are vertical, because they belong to a vertical plane.

(iv) Find the C.V.L. (that is, centre of the vanishing line of the vertical plane). This is always done by drawing from the C.V. a line at right angles to the new V.L. In this case the C.V.L. happens to come just where V.P. 50° is. The C.V.L. is somewhat similar to C.V., which is merely the centre of the H.L., which is the V.L. of all horizontal planes.

We now require the new representation of the true or real position of the eye. To do this we must first find the distance from the eye to the C.V.L. This distance is the length of the V.Par. from E. to V.P. 50°. With C.V.L. as centre, revolve this distance on to a line always perpendicular to the V.L., just as in elementary work we take C.V. as centre, and the distance from it to the E. as radius, and revolve it downwards (or upwards) to find the first representation of the eye. In this problem in vertical planes the new representation of the eye comes on the H.L. at point E.1.

(v) Find the A.V.P. of the line *AB*—that is, 40° upwards. At E.1 measure an angle of 40° upwards from the H.L. (the V.L. of the G.P.), because *AB* makes 40° with the G.P. Continue this line (which is the V.Par of *AB*) to meet the V.L. of the vertical plane at point A.V.P. 40°.

To obtain the A.M.P. take the A.V.P. as centre and the distance from it to E.1 as radius, and measure it off on the V.L. of the vertical plane at point A.M.P. 40°.

(vi) From point *A* (already found on the G.P.) draw a line to A.V.P. 40°, and measure on it 9 ft. for the length of *AB* (using the same method as in elementary work)—that is, first draw a line from the line *AB*'s own measuring point (i.e. A.M.P. 40°) through *A*, and bring it forward to the I.L. of the vertical plane at point *M*. From *M* measure *MN* 9 ft. (full scale). From *N* draw a line back to A.M.P. 40°, cutting the line from *A* to A.V.P. 40° at point *B*. Then *AB* is the perspective length required.

NOTE. In the drawing for this problem the upright and horizontal shading lines are only put in to indicate the planes more clearly.

LESSON 18

Finding the Proper Perspective
of Shadows

SHADOWS are of two kinds—namely, those projected from natural light, as the sun or moon, and those from some artificial light. As regards the rays of light from the sun, although they radiate in all directions in the sky, yet those which reach our earth are held to be parallel (Fig. 1). The rays from an artificial source are said to radiate in all directions.

To determine the size and shape of any shadow, we must know the position of the light, the position and kind of surface on which the shadow falls, and the position, shape and size of the object causing the shadow. Also, to obtain the perspective representation of shadows it is necessary (1) to imagine a vertical plane to pass through the source of light and the point whose shadow is required ; (2) to determine the intersection of this vertical plane with the plane or surface of shadow ; (3) to draw a line (to represent the

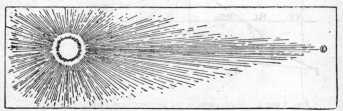

Fig. 1. Light rays from the sun to the earth appear to be parallel.

ray of light) from the source of light through the point of the object, to meet the intersection on the plane or surface of shadow. This intersection is the shadow of the point.

Thus in Fig. 2 there are two vertical rods, AB and CD, standing on the G.P., with an artificial light (A.L.) at A.L. vertically over a point R.S.1 (on the G.P.). In order to find the shadows of these two rods, we must imagine one vertical plane to contain the A.L. and the rod AB, and another vertical plane to contain the A.L. and the rod CD. The intersection of the first vertical plane with the plane of shadow (the G.P. in this case) is the line from

(223)

R.S.1 through *A* to *b*, and of the second vertical plane with the plane of shadow is the line from R.S.1 through *C* to *d*. The ray of light from A.L. through *B* to *b* gives *b* as the shadow of *B*. Join *Ab*, which is the shadow of the rod *AB*. Similarly, *Cd* is the shadow of *CD*.

The principles are the same, whether we are finding the shadows projected from artificial or natural light, as may be seen from the right-hand portion of Fig. 2, in which the sun (S) is substituted for the artificial light (A.L.).

The point R.S. is called the *point of radiation of shadow*. When such a point is found by drawing a line from the light perpendicular

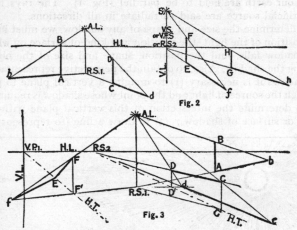

Fig. 2

Fig. 3

Figs. 2 and 3. Illustrations of the perspective of various shadows.

to the plane of shadow, the point is called the *seat of light*. The V.S. or V.P.S. is the *vanishing point of shadow*, and this name is generally used when finding shadows from natural light. It really answers the same purpose as the R.S.

Shadows cast by artificial light are explained in Fig. 3. There are three lines: (1) a vertical line *AB* standing on the G.P.; (2) a horizontal line *CD* receding to R.S.2, and above the G.P. in a vertical plane whose H.T. also recedes to R.S.2; and (3) an oblique line *EF*, which is receding downwards in a vertical plane whose H.T. recedes to V.P.1. There is also an artificial light at A.L. vertically over the point R.S.1. Find their shadows.

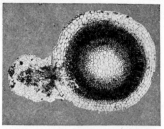

PARASITIC PLANTS. Left, dodder parasitic on small furze. Top right, micro-photograph of dodder on clover. Bottom right, gigantic flower of Rafflesia arnoldi. a tropical parasite which grows on wild vines. BOTANY 17
Microphotograph, H S. Cheavin

CARNIVOROUS PLANTS. Top left, Venus's fly-trap, which closes the blades of its leaves upon insects. Bottom left, pitcher plant, the curiously formed leaves being adapted for entrapping insects. Above, greater bladderwort. which imprisons and ingests water insects; magnification 8 times. BOTANY 17

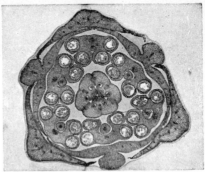

FERTILIZATION SHOWN IN PHOTOMICROGRAPHS Left, pollen grains on stigma of evening primrose developing their penetrating tubes. Right, transverse section of lily flower bud, showing outer and inner perianth, anthers with pollen sacs and central ovary. BOTANY 18

Left photo, J. J. Ward; right, H. S. Cheavin

HERMAPHRODITE FLOWERS. Left, plantain; each flower of the dense spike contains both male and female elements. Above, right, daisy, in which the outermost flowers are female and the central yellow ones hermaphrodite. Bottom right, guelder rose, showing an outer ring of sexless flowers surrounding the complete ones. BOTANY 19

Photo of plantain, H. S. Cheavin; of guelder rose, John J. Ward

Plate 26 *Volume III*

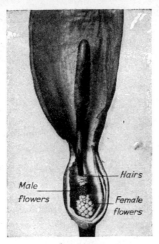

WILD ARUM. Section of interior
of spathe showing the male and
female flowers, and the hairs above
them which serve to imprison insects
until pollination has taken place.
BOTANY 20

John J. Ward

INSECT POLLINATION OF ORCHIS. Left, spotted orchis (O. maculata) with
bristle, representing the tongue of an insect, being inserted into the tube of
the nectary. Right, bristle withdrawn bearing two tiny club-shaped masses
of pollen ; these will adhere to the stigma of the next flower visited. BOTANY 20

John J. Ward

Plate 28

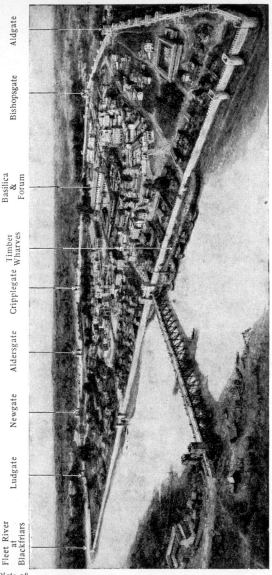

Fleet River at Blackfriars   Ludgate   Newgate   Aldersgate   Cripplegate   Timber Wharves   Basilica & Forum   Bishopsgate   Aldgate

London Museum

WHEN LONDON WAS A ROMAN CITY. Based upon material supplied by the Royal Commission on Historical Monuments, this drawing by Mr. A. Forestier gives a careful, albeit largely conjectural, reconstruction of the London that arose on the ashes of the city destroyed by the British Queen Boadicea in A.D. 61. As will be seen, it was enclosed by a high wall and the river was spanned by a "London Bridge" somewhat farther downstream than the structure of today.   BRITISH HISTORY 1

PERSPECTIVE OF SHADOWS

The shadow of *AB* is found as explained in Fig. 2, but to get the shadow of *CD* we must first find the plane of *C* and *D* (the ends of this line) on the G.P. (the plane of shadow) by drawing a perpendicular from *C* and *D* to meet the H.T. at *C'* and *D'* respectively. We then proceed as in finding the shadow of *AB*, that is, to find the shadows of the vertical construction lines *CC'* and *DD'*. The shadow of *CC'* is *C'c*, and that of *DD'* is *D'd*. Join *cd*, which is the shadow of *CD*. Again, to find the shadow of the oblique line *EF*, find the plane of *F* on the G.P. by means of the perpendicular from *F* to meet the H.T. of the vertical plane (which contains *EF*) at *F'*; then find the shadow of the vertical line *FF'*. The latter's shadow is *F'f*. Join *Ef*, which is the shadow of *EF*.

The student should remember the following rules :

1. When a line (as *CD* in Fig. 3) is parallel to the plane of shadow, then both the line and its shadow have the same V.P.

2. To find R.S. from the A.L., draw a line to meet the plane of shadow parallel to the line whose shadow is required. The intersecting point is the R.S.

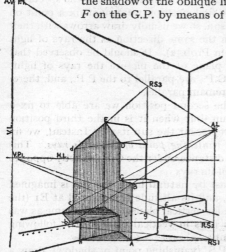

Problem 1. Shadows cast by artificial light.

Problem 1. Given the perspective representation of a buttress standing on the G.P. against a vertical wall, at the foot of which is a rectangular step ; A.L. an artificial light, and R.S.1 a point vertically beneath it on the G.P. ; trace the shadow of the buttress on the ground, step and wall. Most of the processes used in solving this problem can easily be understood on reference to the drawing. We shall here only call attention to one or two steps in the procedure. R.S.2 must be the same height perspectively from R.S.1 as the height of the step. R.S.2 is used from which to draw the line through *m* to *b*. R.S.3 is obtained by drawing from A.L.

parallel to *DE* to A.V.P.1 (which is the V.P. of *DE*), and from R.S.1 draw a line perpendicular to the left-hand wall, that is, draw it to V.P.1. This line cuts the dotted base of the wall at *g*, through which draw the vertical line cutting the one from A.L. to A.V.P.1 at R.S.3.

For shadows cast by natural light, the sun may be in three different positions with relation to the Picture Plane : (1) in the plane of the picture ; (2) behind the P.P.—that is, in front of the spectator ; (3) in front of the P.P.—that is, behind the spectator.

When the sun is in the first position we cannot fix a point on the paper to indicate the sun, so we usually draw arrows with their shafts slanting exactly in the same direction as the rays of light from the sun (as shown in Prob. 2). It should be observed that when the sun is in the plane of the picture the rays of light, although inclined to the G.P., are parallel to the P.P., and, therefore, do not vanish, but remain parallel.

When the sun is in the second position we are able to fix a point to represent the sun, but when it is in the third position again we are unable to represent the sun itself. Instead, we fix a point to represent the *vanishing point of the sun's rays*. This point is in reality a great distance under the G.P., exactly opposite the sun in the direction of its rays.

To find the shadows cast by natural light, the sun is imagined to be in a vertical plane, and its altitude is measured at E1 (the representation of the eye for vertical planes), just the same as was used in the problems on lines in vertical planes. The following rule should now be learnt :

To find the V.S. or V.P.S. (vanishing point of shadow), draw a line through the sun (or the V.P.S.R.) and the V.P. of the line whose shadow is required. Where this line cuts the V.L. of the plane of shadow is the V.P.S.

Problem 2. The perspective representation is given of a vertical rod *GH*, a square slab, a rectangular hut with a pyramidal roof, and a vertical wall perpendicular to the P.P., all standing on the G.P. It is required to find their shadows when the sun is in the P.P. on the spectator's left at an altitude of 30°. As the sun is in the P.P., all the intersections (H.T.s) of the vertical planes through the various points whose shadows are required will be parallel to the P.P., whether they cut the G.P. or plane of the wall. To find the shadow of the edge *AD*, draw the intersection line *Aa* on the G.P. and the intersection line *ad* on the wall, both parallel

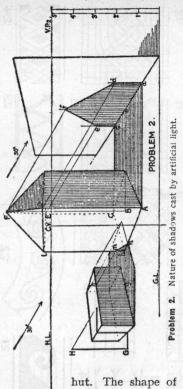

PROBLEM 2.

Problem 2. Nature of shadows cast by artificial light.

to the P.P.; then through D draw a line Dd (to represent a ray of light from the sun) parallel to the direction of the sun's rays, that is, parallel to the direction of the shaft of the arrow at 30° inclination to the G.P. Where the line Dd cuts the wall at d is the shadow of point D, and the lines Aa on the G.P. and ad on the wall are the shadow of AD. To find the shadow of point F, imagine a vertical plane to contain the axis BF, and from B draw the intersection lines Bo and of. Then through F draw a line (as a ray of light), Ff cutting of at f, which is the shadow of point F. Join fd to represent the shadow of FD. Find the shadows of the other edges of the hut; also those of the square slab and the rod in a similar way.

It will be noticed in the drawing that a part of the shadow of the slab falls on the hut. The shape of this portion of the shadow is found by imagining a vertical plane to contain the upright edge bL of the hut, and to cut the G.P. along bg and the slab at gh; then through h draw a ray of light hm as usual to cut bL at m. Join mn, which is a part of the shadow of the upper edge of the slab.

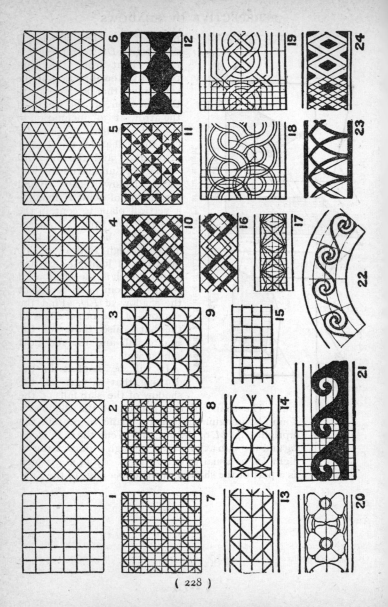

LESSON 19

Ornamental Forms in Geometrical Design

ALTHOUGH geometrical ornament is more abstract than that founded on natural forms, yet it is the oldest, as is shown by the primitive art of savage races of past and present times. No doubt this is so because geometrical ornament is easier and requires less artistic skill than conventional arrangements of natural forms. Probably sewing with a thread suggested the zigzag line, and the wave the wavy line ; woven work may have suggested reticulated patterns, and plaited hair the plaited band. The revolution of a fork gave the circle ; the combination of dots at regular intervals suggested the polygons or pointed stars. The gradual development of these original geometrical forms led, finally, to such forms as are seen in Moorish panelled ceilings, in Gothic tracery, and in the guilloche.

A knowledge of the principles of geometrical design is essential if the student contemplates taking up commercial design. He should always carry his sketch-book in readiness to note a characteristic piece of design or a beautiful detail of ornament ; also he should be on the alert for new industrial materials and processes.

Geometrical ornament may be generally divided into three groups : first when the ornament is in bands or borders, as in 13 ; secondly, when it is repeated in patterns over an unlimited space, as in diapers (7) ; and thirdly, when the ornament fills an enclosed space, as in panels of various shapes.

The designs here given are not by any means exhaustive, but are suggestive of the many variations that can be made in geometrical forms. The student, after copying them as exercises, should test his skill by endeavouring to design suitable variations in order to develop his ingenuity and taste.

Explanation of Terms. A succession of the same form is known as *repetition*. This becomes monotonous if not varied, and for this reason the curves are introduced among the interlacing straight lines in 19. In 17 the nailhead shape is *repeated*. When the same shape is repeated in an opposite direction, it is said to be *reversed* or *contrasted*, as in 12, where the left-hand half of the repeat is reversed in the right-hand half of the same repeat. *Symmetry* is the repetition of any form on its axis, as in 12, where the central vertical line in each repeat is the axis. This principle of symmetry is one of the most important in producing ornament. The *unit of design*, or *unit of repetition*, is the whole ornament in each repeat, as in 17, where each nailhead is the unit of design.

Kinds of Network. The construction lines used in setting out geometrical patterns are arranged to form a *network* in order to secure accuracy of construction and repetition. This network is of various kinds. The most frequent is quadrangular reticulation, as in Figs. 1 to 4, in which 2 is the *diamond* or *lozenge* net, and 4 is a combination of the square and diamond, while Figs. 5 and 6 illustrate the equilateral triangular network.

It will be seen that the square net has been used in 7, the diamond in 10 and 11, and the triangular net in 24. These different nets may be easily and accurately constructed by means of the T-square and set-squares of 45 deg. and 60 deg. It is essential that the network should be accurately made; otherwise patterns will not repeat and fit properly.

In 7 and 8 are shown examples of *all-over* patterns, as they are sometimes called. These designs may form construction lines for richer patterns for carpets, tapestry, ceilings, etc. Figs. 10 and 11 suggest arrangements for parquet flooring. Figs. 8 and 9 are similar to tiling arrangements for roofs, and are *scale* designs. In 12 the black and white forms are the *ogee* pattern.

Bands or borders with square net foundations are not limited with regard to length and are generally narrow, ribbon-like ornament. The principal patterns in this group are: the fret, as in 15; chain, as in 16; interlaced patterns, as in 14 and 19; the guilloche, as in 18; foliated bands in the forms of rosette, as in 20; the Greek wave scroll, as in 21; the leaf, and the egg and tongue pattern.

Application of Borders. The proper application of bands is to the enclosing of ceiling, walls, floors, panels, on certain architectural constructions, on the abacus and plinth of columns, and as a running ornament round the shaft of the latter. They are also used as the hem or border of garments, carpets and other textiles, on the rims of plates, in typography, etc.

The fret is specifically Greek ornament, and no doubt of textile origin. Greek vase-painting and architecture gave rise to the variations of the pattern. Among the Romans the fret was used for mosaics on floors. In the Middle Ages this pattern was seldom used, but the Renaissance revived it in its ancient application, and made new combinations.

The Greek wave *scroll*, or the evolute-spiral band, is shown in 21 and 22. The line of this pattern divides the surface of the border into two parts, which in flat ornament are coloured

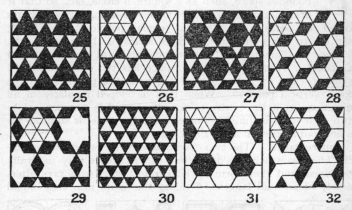

differently. In plastic work the lower part projects. This border is suitable for shields, plates, friezes, cornices, tablets in architecture, etc. Examples of borders drawn on an equilateral triangular foundation are shown in Figs. 23 and 24.

A triangular net foundation is easily constructed with the 60-degree set-square and T-square, and may be arranged in two ways, as in 5 and 6. Many different shapes, such as the triangle, the rhombus or diamond, the hexagon, etc., all make perfectly fitting diapers upon this net, as shown in 25 to 32. Many designs for parquetry and marquetry may be founded on these lines.

LESSON 20

Some Geometrical Designs for Panels

ENCLOSED ornament is a decoration designed to fill a definite bounded space, such as a square, a circle, etc., so that it fits exactly into the space alone. The space is sometimes called a "panel." Besides the regular polygons, the ellipse, the lunette (or semicircle), various forms of the spandrel, the lozenge (or diamond) and the triangle are most commonly used as panels. When the enclosed space has the design arranged symmetrically on both sides of one axis, the panel is suitable for a vertical position. When it is developed regularly in all directions from the centre of the shape, and is symmetrical to two or more axes (multi-symmetrical), the panel is suitable for a horizontal position as in Figs. 1–4.

Square Panels. The two diagonals and the two diameters are the lines on which the decoration of the square may naturally be based, and they form an eight-rayed star, with rays alternately of unequal lengths, dividing the figure into eight equal

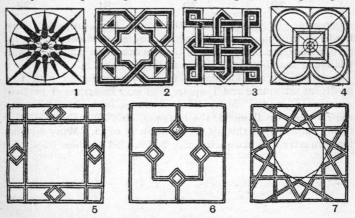

spaces. The design shown in Fig. 1 is the uraniscus, an ornament used in the coffers of Greek ceilings ; the rays were gold on a blue ground. The patterns in Figs. 2 and 3 are examples of inlaid work of the fourteenth and fifteenth centuries, while Fig. 4 is the planning out for a tile design used in medieval times, but trifoliated forms were in some instances added to this linework.

Another decoration for squares is that in which the square is subdivided into separate spaces, as in Figs. 5, 6 and 7, and each space may receive independent ornament. It will be noticed that these are much used for

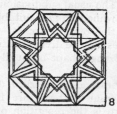

panels in ceilings. The panelling in Fig. 7 is constructed by dividing the square into sixteen smaller squares, and then drawing lines from the middle points of the sides of the large square at an angle of 60 degrees.

Octagonal Panels. These may be easily constructed within the square as shown in Fig. 8, or within a circle. The diagonals and diameters intersecting again give a great variety of sub-divisions.

Hexagonal Panels. These are best constructed within a circle, and may be subdivided in a similar manner to the octagon. Many variations of the six-pointed star may thus be obtained.

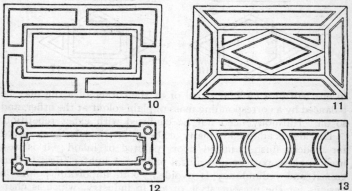

Circular Panels A circular shape is usually subdivided into 3, 4, 5, 6, 8, 10, 12, or 16 similar parts, by lines radiating from the centre ; or it may be divided into zones, with each belt-like band decorated independently. The subdivision formed by means of arcs, as in Fig. 9, is very suitable for this shape, especially when required for tracery.

Oblong Panels. The usual subdivisions of this shape are shown in Figs. 10 and 11, while Fig. 12 is suitable for a tablet, and Fig. 13 for door panels or the soffits of arches.

Trapezium shapes may be divided as indicated in Figs. 14 or 15. The rhombus or lozenge shape is usually subdivided as shown in Figs. 16 and 17.

In modern decorative geometrical designs for textiles, etc., fragments of different patterns are frequently used. Every geometrical pattern is the repetition of two halves, the second reversed. Any of the designs here given, if cut in two, will suggest its other half. A feeling of novelty is introduced if, instead of repetition of the first half, it is replaced with an equivalent, not an imitation, of the second. Thus a block of geometrical design

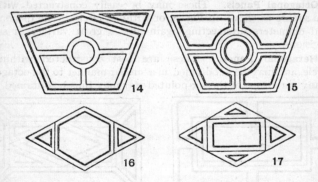

in one half of a circular panel or at the corner of a rug may be balanced by a corresponding mass of plain colour at the other, and so on. Harmony need not be confused with exact repetition.

This idea is adapted in many of the geometrical designs evolved for modern flush panelled doors painted or inlaid ; it is also used in glass, pottery and mural panels. A lighter effect is thus gained and redundancy is avoided—both important points in designs for the present style of art in industry, which is characterized by simplicity, clean line and absence of superfluous detail.

LESSON 21

Geometrical Design in Architecture

THE Gothic style in architecture evolved and brought to perfection a characteristic decoration known as tracery. This was used to decorate the windows, which in Early English Gothic became an important feature. They had pointed arches, and, being grouped in twos or threes, the space contained in an enclosing arch above the windows was ornamented with geometrical perforated designs. Later, in the Decorated Gothic, more florid and flowing forms were introduced into the tracery. The earlier designs in particular possess the charm and balance associated with fine geometrical patterns, and tracery is chiefly used now for architectural panels and for furniture, being applied to stone or wood. The designs, however, may be adapted for various purposes by the modern decorative artist.

The necessary construction for Fig. 2, a design for a square panel in tracery, is shown in Fig. 1. Three foliations for a circle are seen in Fig. 3, while Fig. 4 is the planning for a rose window or for a circular panel. Fig. 5 is the foundation for Fig. 6, a curvilinear triangle, and Fig. 7 is a design for tracery for an equilateral triangle ; all these patterns are suitable for woodwork or stone. In Fig. 8 is given the construction for Fig. 9, tracery which might be used for window or screen. Fig. 10 gives the foundation line for a simple but beautiful head of a four-light window, shown in Fig. 11. Many other fine designs in tracery can be seen in good textbooks on architecture and building.

Forms of Arches. In building, arches are subjects of geometrical design. The earliest shape of the arch was semicircular, as shown in Fig. 12, in which are given the names of the separate components of an arch. The segmental arch may be struck from one centre, as in Fig. 13, or from two centres as in Fig. 14 ; Fig. 15 is one form of the horseshoe or Moorish arch. Equilateral (Fig. 16), lancet (Fig. 17) and obtuse arches (Fig. 18) are common in Gothic architecture.

The *three-centred* arch given in Fig. 19 is constructed by first determining the height and the span ; then make AC, BC, and DE all equal. Join EC and bisect in F. The intersection C of

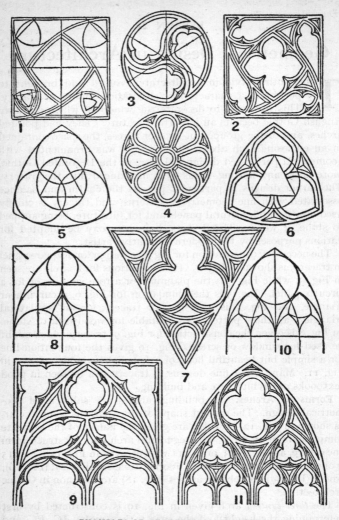

EXAMPLES OF GEOMETRICAL TRACERY

the bisecting line *FC* with *DE* produced is the third centre. Describe arcs from *C, C, C,* as centres.

The depressed Tudor arch (Fig. 20) is described from four centres. The *ogee* arch, or so-called ass's back, has either three (Fig. 21) or four centres (Fig. 22). The *pointed trefoil* opening has the centre placed as shown in Fig. 23. The parabola and ellipse may also be used for arch forms.

Mouldings. In architecture mouldings form a constituent part of an order, and were used in eight forms by the Romans

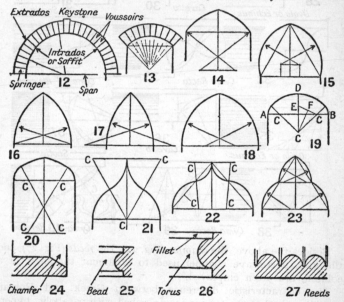

and the Greeks. These forms are named : the *fillet*, a narrow, flat band used to separate and combine curved mouldings ; the *astragal* or *bead*, a narrow or small convex cylindrical moulding (Fig. 25) ; the *torus* (Fig. 26), which is really a large form of the astragal, and is often used at the base of columns ; the *ovolo* (meaning " egg-shaped "), or *echinus*, a convex moulding (Figs. 28, 29) which appears to have originated in the capital of the Doric column : the *cavetto* (Fig. 30), which is the reverse of the ovolo : the *scotia* (Fig. 31), a concave moulding which gives a deep shadow on itself and is very effective when used on bases of columns; the *cyma recta* (Figs. 32, 33), a moulding with the concave above the convex portion; and the *cyma reversa* (Fig. 34), which has the convex part uppermost.

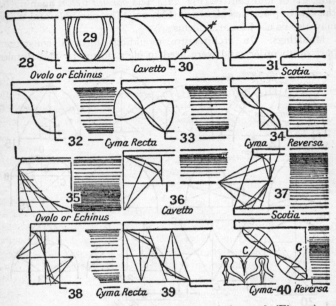

Besides the above, the *chamfer* (Fig. 24), the *reeds* (Fig. 27), and the *flute*, a concave channel used to ornament the shaft of a column, are often employed.

The characteristic difference between Greek and Roman mouldings is that the former are described with parabolic, hyperbolic, and elliptical curves, and the latter with arcs of a circle. Figs. 28–34 are the Roman versions of the *ovolo, cavetto, scotia, cyma recta, and cyma reversa* mouldings, while 35–40 are the Greek.

Our Course in Drawing and Design is continued in Volume 4.

ECONOMIC GEOGRAPHY

Highways and Seaways of the World

(See plate 33)

ECONOMIC Geography is concerned with the earth as the scene of Man's economic or " business " activities. It treats of the influence of geographical features on commerce ; of climate and soil, as they affect Man's food and drink, clothing and shelter ; of the products on which human life depends ; of the methods by which these products are transferred from where they are produced to where they are " consumed." Winds and ocean currents, cotton and coal and copra, the rocks of the Rand and the loess of China, railways and aeroplanes, motor-vans and camels, mammoth liners and flimsy canoes, human porters and dog-sleighs—come within its scope.

As is generally known, although some countries, e.g. India and China, enjoying a tropical or sub-tropical climate and possessed of highly fertile alluvial plains, are enabled to maintain a vast population on the produce of their own lands, other areas—most of Europe and the eastern states of North America, for instance—are largely dependent upon supplies from overseas to feed and clothe their people. Thus vast quantities of goods have to be transferred, and on the proper functioning of the transport system the lives of millions depend.

On the sketch map of the world on page 240 there are marked : (1) the areas in which primitive methods of land transport are still the rule ; (2) areas in which mechanical transport preponderates ; (3) the railways that have penetrated into the less civilized—or shall we say, less industrialized—regions ; (4) the main routes of oversea trade.

Primitive Transport. Primitive methods of land transport are found in various parts of the world, and, being based on physical and climatic conditions, are today practically what they were many centuries ago. They have not wholly disappeared even from the areas in which mechanical transport preponderates. The greatest contrast is provided by the sledge (dog or reindeer) in the extreme north of America and Asia, on the one hand, and the camel, assisted by the horse, in the great mid-world deserts (Sahara, Arabia, and Iran), on the other. It will be seen that the camel appears in parts of Australia,

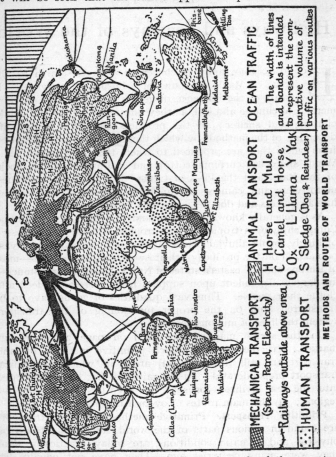

METHODS AND ROUTES OF WORLD TRANSPORT

OCEAN TRAFFIC

The width of lines and bands is intended to represent the comparative volume of traffic on various routes

ANIMAL TRANSPORT

H Horse and Mule
C Camel and Horse
O Ox   L Llama Y Yak
S Sledge (Dog & Reindeer)

MECHANICAL TRANSPORT
(Steam, Petrol, Electricity)

---- Railways outside above area

HUMAN TRANSPORT

where, on account of the arid nature of much of the country, it operates with considerable success. The farther away we get from the desert the more we find the horse and the mule in use. The horse, in fact, must be regarded as the most widely spread beast of burden. Originally confined to the Old World, it was introduced into America by the Spaniards under Cortes, early in the 16th century. In parts of both North and South America it is today well nigh indispensable.

The ox is fairly widespread. India, which produces almost as much cattle as all the rest of the world put together, naturally employs oxen largely as beasts of burden ; as do also the cattle-raising countries of South America. Two beasts of burden peculiar to comparatively restricted areas are the yak in Tibet, and the llama of the central Andes, both being well suited to a region presenting peculiar difficulties in the matter of transport.

Human transport belongs mainly to the tropics, especially where dense forests make anything in the way of roads impossible. This applies to most of equatorial Africa and to the interior of New Guinea. The blank space in central Africa represents the densest portion of the Congo rain-forest, where the rivers are practically the only means of communication. For the same reason, the basin of the Amazon river is left blank.

Railway Areas. What we may, for the sake of simplicity, call the railway area covers all the more populated regions of the globe, and includes three of the chief centres of population, namely, Europe, U.S.A., and India. In North America the railway area includes a narrow strip of Canadian territory along the U.S. border, extending from the Atlantic coast into the prairie provinces. In South America the largest railway area corresponds to the chief cattle-raising district of the central Argentine. Within that area the railway mileage exceeds that of the British Isles. The manner in which the lines converge on Buenos Aires illustrates clearly the purpose for which they were built, viz. to provide direct access for the produce of the central Argentine to the harbours of the River Plate, the chief outlet for oversea trade in this part of the continent. We are reminded of the way in which the railways of Saskatchewan and Manitoba converge on Winnipeg, collecting the produce of the wheat-growing region, for conveyance to Port Arthur on Lake Superior, and thence oversea to the markets of the world.

The peculiar formation of the Chilean state is easily recognisable on the map. Its extent from north to south is well over two thousand miles, while its width between the Andes and the Pacific coast hardly anywhere exceeds a hundred miles. Fifteen hundred miles of its length are traversed by a trunk line.

There remain three of our self-governing dominions : the Union of South Africa, New Zealand, and Australia. Of these, the last-named deserves special mention, because the position and extent of the two railway areas illustrate clearly the peculiar distribution of Australia's population. The south-western corner, round Perth and its harbour, Fremantle, is separated by a desert region from the largest settled area, extending along the coast from Adelaide to beyond Brisbane.

India, of course, owes her great railway system (more than double the mileage of all the British railways) to a far-seeing administration. It will be readily understood, however, that in such an extensive region railways are actually few and far between, so that millions of the natives never see a train, and the ox is still the chief carrier of burdens, as it has been for many centuries.

We have spoken of a " railway area," but it should be understood that the term includes the motor car, by means of which railway routes can be easily and cheaply continued and linked up as required.

Pioneer Railways. In one of the later Lessons of this Course we shall have something to say about the great transcontinental railways. In dealing with the third group of facts shown on our map, we are, however, concerned with a rather different aspect of railway development—the lines which in various parts of the world from a coast town or from some point on the outskirts of the railway area have been pushed forward into less civilized regions. The term " pioneer railways " perhaps best describes their nature and purpose.

The term is certainly applicable to African railways outside the Union territory. Owing to the fact that most African rivers are interrupted by cataracts at a short distance from the sea, river navigation is possible only when the plateau level has been reached. Some form of land transport is, therefore, indispensable.

British Africa is particularly well served in this respect, as there is not one among our African dominions which is not furnished with direct access to the sea by rail. The interior of British East Africa has three such lines, two of which, from Mombasa and Dar-es-Salaam, reach the shores of Lakes Victoria and Tanganyika, while the Nigerian railway runs inland for nearly 700 miles to its terminus at Kano, the chief trade-centre of this part of the Sudan. Rhodesia, besides its railway connexion with

Capetown, has a much shorter line connecting it through Portuguese territory with the east coast port of Beira. The Nile valley railway, interrupted by a stretch of river navigation between the first and second cataracts, not only connects Khartum with Cairo and Alexandria, but also gives the Anglo-Egyptian Sudan access by the Berber-Port Sudan railway to the Red Sea, which is today, as it has been from time immemorial, one of the world's great ocean highways.

The North American railways, being transcontinental lines, will be dealt with elsewhere ; but mention must be made here of the railway from Prince Albert in Saskatchewan to Churchill on the Hudson Bay. It was designed to give the wheat-growing prairie provinces direct access to the sea, if only for a few months of the year, by a cheaper route than that by the great lakes and the St. Lawrence to Quebec.

South America has only one direct transcontinental railway— from Buenos Aires to Valparaiso ; but the Argentine railways are continued north through Bolivia to the plateau of the central Andes, and finally to the Pacific coast at Africa.

Australia has several lines running inland from the two settled coast districts, themselves connected by the Perth-Adelaide railway, running through the Coolgardie goldfield, but they will be further discussed in connexion with shipping.

For the sake of completeness we have shown on the map the chief ocean routes in such a way as to bring out their relative importance in world trade.

LESSON 2

Ships and Shipping Through the Ages

(See plate 34)

THE previous Lesson dealt first with those primitive methods of land transport which have been in use for many centuries. We saw how mechanical transport (steam, petrol, electricity) has come to predominate in the more civilized regions, and how, from those regions, or from some point on the sea-coast, it has penetrated into less civilized countries. Finally, the main shipping routes were shown on the map in such a way as to give some idea of their relative importance, and the relative amounts of traffic they carry.

The Egyptians, as long ago as 4000 B.C., built ships capable of carrying 50 passengers, mainly for use on the Nile, though later on they shared, with Greeks, Phoenicians and Romans, in the trading voyages to all parts of the Mediterranean. For centuries nothing which could be called an ocean voyage was undertaken, with the result that, till the time of Columbus, hardly any ships more than 100 feet long were built.

During the next 300 years but little progress was made in the matter of size. The Great Harry, the first English two-decker, built by Henry VIII in 1514, had a tonnage of only 1,000. The Ark Royal, flagship of the English fleet against the Armada, was smaller by 200 tons. Nelson's Victory, built in 1765, is only 226 feet long, less than one quarter the length of some modern liners.

As early as 1775, a paddle steamer carried passengers on the Saône river for a period of several months, and the early years of the 19th century saw other successful experiments in this direction, by Symington on the Forth-Clyde canal (1801), by Fulton on the Hudson river (1807), and by Stevens on the Delaware (1809). The Sirius, and the Great Western, which in 1838 crossed the Atlantic in 15–17 days, were paddle boats, the screw propeller not coming into general use till 1860. The Great Eastern, which made her first voyage to New York in 1860, employed paddles and screw, supplemented by sails.

But marine engineering was then in its infancy, and this giant's only real success was the laying of the Atlantic cable in 1866. Even in the matter of speed, the sailing ships for long held their own. One of the clipper ships, built for the China tea-trade, crossed the Atlantic in 13 days.

How completely steam has now beaten sail as a means of world communication is shown by the fact that in 1938 the percentage of steamships in the world was 76·11, of motor-ships 22·45, and the sail percentage no more than 1·44.

Voyages of Discovery. Voyages out of sight of land, except for short distances, were almost unknown till the invention of the mariner's compass, about 1300, so that even in the Mediterranean the regular trade routes were coastwise. Till the end of the 15th century, trade between Europe and the Far East was carried out by Venetian and Genoese galleys, which took on board at Alexandria, or some Syrian port, eastern produce brought by Arab sea traders to Basra or Suez, and thence carried overland. Meanwhile the Portuguese, inspired by Prince Henry the Navigator, had been feeling their way along the west African coast. In 1487 Bartholomew Diaz rounded the Cape, and ten years later Vasco da Gama, crossing the Indian Ocean from near Zanzibar to Calicut, showed the way to what was to remain for nearly 400 years one of the world's great ocean trade routes. Incidentally his discovery ruined the Italian merchant cities. St. Helena, Capetown and Mauritius came to be important as stations on this long voyage, and consequently play a considerable part in the history of the British Empire.

Suez Canal. The opening of the Suez Canal (1869) made a great change, and brings us to the conditions existing at the present day, as shown on the map in page 240. It was preceded by a revival of the overland route, mentioned above in connexion with the Italian merchant cities. To meet the need of more rapid communication with India after the Mutiny, Lieutenant Waghorn arranged to convey passengers and goods by caravan between Alexandria and Suez, in connexion with ships running between the latter port and Bombay.

As our map shows, the opening of the Suez Canal made possible regular traffic on one of the world's greatest ocean highways, serving, as it does, not only India, but a long stretch of the East African coast, as well as the Far East and Australian waters.

Triangles of Trade. From the time of Prince Henry the Navigator, the Guinea trade, as it was called, was, apart from its primary object of exploration, one of the chief direct ocean trade routes. It soon developed into that terrible so-called triangle of trade, first established by Sir John Hawkins in the 16th century, and over it sailed ship after ship carrying slaves from West Africa to the West Indies, receiving there the produce of slave labour (tobacco, molasses, raw cotton) for transport to Bristol, and returning to the African coast to buy more slaves in return for the rum and cotton goods into which that produce had been worked up. Our map shows the West African trade as in some sort a coasting trade, ships going out from home, calling at various ports for cargo, and returning. As the country's resources are developed, and as certain ports become more important, or as the coast comes to be better supplied with good harbours rendering the surf boat unnecessary, trade with this part of the world will become more and more a matter of direct voyages of larger vessels to a few ports, such as Lagos or the new harbour of Takoradi on the Gold Coast, with subsidiary coasting lines.

Panama Canal. Another change of far-reaching influence followed the opening of the Panama Canal. This was practically completed by 1914, and actually in use, though not formally opened till 1920. It affected practically the whole of the Pacific sea board, especially those portions of it nearest to the canal, say the North American coast to Vancouver, and the South American coast to Iquique. It has led to a revival, with the difference of a shorter route, of the old inter-coastal trade between eastern and western United States, in opposition to the railways, thus replacing the old sailing route round Cape Horn. A recent development is a round-the-world cargo service as follows : North Pacific—East Indies—India. Thence to New York through the Suez Canal, and to the Pacific coast by way of Panama.

Recent developments, keen competition, and the necessity of reducing the cost of transport, have led to the establishment of other triangles which form admirable illustrations of the working of world trade. A small instance is the Mediterranean tramp-steamers which carried coal to Italy (it has none of its own), went on to Odessa in ballast, and returned home with Russian grain.

Early in the 20th century there was a considerable development of the so-called " west-about " route. Ships carried general cargo from the eastern United States to Australia through the Panama Canal, then coal from Australia to South American ports, returning through the straits of Magellan with nitrates.

Another triangle shows us Vasco da Gama's route to India still in use, as follows : Europe to the Cape with general cargo, especially railway material and machinery, then to India in ballast, and home by Suez with jute for the Dundee mills.

In distinguishing between the relative importance of the various routes, our map takes account rather of amount of tonnage than mere numbers. It was to be expected that, from this point of view, the North Atlantic ferry, with its enormous liners, and connecting as it does the world's two greatest industrial regions, should stand out before all other routes.

The recent economic development of South America, especially the Argentine, is well illustrated by the next widest band of shipping shown on the map, namely to Pernambuco in Brazil, continuing to the river Plate for Buenos Aires.

LESSON 3

Historic Railroads of Commerce

FROM earliest times, direct communication by land from Europe had been possible only with Asia, and practically only with the south-western area of that continent. Distance, as well as the nature and climatic conditions of central Asia, made direct trade with India and the Far East so difficult as not to be a paying proposition.

The discoveries of Columbus, Vasco da Gama, Magellan, and Captain Cook gave us knowledge of the extent and shape of the oceans, and showed European seamen the routes by which they might reach, at any rate, those countries which touched the sea. These discoveries, however, at the same time, made it plain that land and sea are distributed in such a way as to put very considerable difficulties in the way of world trade by sea only.

America and Asia extend so far into the Arctic regions that a north-west or north-east passage cannot be considered as a practicable proposition. The broad mass of Africa separates the Atlantic and Indian oceans, so that the northern portion of the latter can be reached only by a sea voyage nearly twice the length of the direct distance. The island world between Asia and Australia does, it is true, allow passage by a variety of routes, but these routes bristle with dangers to shipping. As for South America, if that continent extended only 500 miles farther south it would cut off Pacific and Atlantic from each other as effectively in the south as North America does in the north.

That the need for modifying these natural conditions by artificial means was recognized in very early times is shown by the fact that de Lesseps' idea of a Suez Canal had been anticipated by over 2,000 years, when an Egyptian king caused a canal to be dug from the head of the Red Sea to an arm of the Nile delta. The object in each case was the same, namely, to shorten the route to a part of the world which could be reached otherwise only overland through difficult country.

In the first Lesson of this Course (page 239) we showed how, in certain areas, mechanical transport had become predominant, and how, either from those areas, or from points on the coast elsewhere, railways had been pushed forward into less civilized regions. Strictly speaking, however, such railways have little more than local significance. All they can do is to bring the products of the interior to the coast. So far as these products are to become staple commodities of world trade, they are still entirely dependent on shipping.

The invention of the steam engine, and its application to the railway, provided Man with a means of communication much more rapid than the ship, even the steamship. The result has been the construction of a number of transcontinental railways, designed to play a real part in international commerce.

The United States. The first crossing of the North American continent, within the limits of what is now United States territory, was made by Clark and Lewis (1804–6). In 1845–7 the Mormons established themselves in what is now the state of Utah, but it was not till the following year (1848) that Spain finally abandoned her shadowy claim to all territory north of the Mexican border, so that the United States definitely extended from sea to sea. The same year saw the first Californian gold discoveries, to be followed immediately by an enormous increase of population. As an illustration, we need only mention that the population of San Francisco, which in 1846 was only 600, had increased to over 300,000 by 1852.

West of Mississippi and Missouri, the whole territory, except a narrow strip on the Pacific coast, was occupied, or rather ranged over, by savage Indian tribes. Regular communication between east and west was possible only by sea. The " Pony Express," established in 1860, served the need for more rapid conveyance of letters. But it was expensive, the postage of a letter costing 5 dollars. The dangerous nature of the service is shown by the fact that the riders were paid 1,200 dollars a month. It was abandoned when the first transcontinental telegraph line was opened (1863), and in 1869 the first railway crossing the continent was completed. This was the Central Pacific, connecting New York and San Francisco (3,300 miles) by way of Chicago and Salt Lake City in Utah.

During the eighties of the 19th century, three further transcontinental lines were built, the Northern Pacific from Chicago to what is now the state of Oregon, the Southern Pacific by way of New Orleans to Los Angeles, and the Atchison, Topeka and Santa Fé railway between the latter and the Pacific.

Central America. No fewer than seven railways cross this, the narrow waist of the continent, from sea to sea. The earliest was that across the isthmus of Panama. Its construction (1850–55) may be taken to have been the direct result of the increased economic importance given to California by the gold discoveries of 1848 ; and, until the opening of the Central Pacific in 1869, it formed a link in the quickest means of travel between the eastern and western states. Of the remaining six lines, two are on Mexican territory, and the other four on that of one or other of the small Central American states. They can, however, hardly claim to be regarded as routes of world trade.

Canada. In 1867 the British North America Act established the Dominion of Canada, comprising at first only Ontario, Quebec, New Brunswick, and Nova Scotia. Two years later, however, when the Hudson Bay Company was bought out and its vast territories taken over, the way was clear for building up British North America into a great Dominion stretching from ocean to ocean, and secured by our command of the sea at each end of its long southern frontier.

At that time Canada's chief wheat growing area was southern Ontario. The men who formed the Canadian Pacific Railway Company (1881), in the face of gloomy prophecies of failure, found their courage justified when the opening up of the prairie provinces (Manitoba, Saskatchewan and Alberta) showed that Canada possessed some of the finest wheat growing country in the world. Since the completion of the C.P.R. main line to Vancouver (1885), the railway system of these three provinces has been considerably developed, and the manner in which numerous lines converge on Winnipeg illustrates clearly the purpose for which they were built, namely, the collecting of the produce of the wheat lands for conveyance to Port Arthur on Lake Superior, for shipment overseas.

A second transcontinental line runs from Quebec to Winnipeg. It serves the mining areas of northern Ontario, and is continued beyond Edmonton to Prince Rupert, a port on the Pacific 500 miles north of Vancouver.

Asia. The Siberian railway, the longest direct line in the world, was begun at several points in 1892. Regarded from an economic point of view, it might be looked upon as designed to connect those areas of Siberia which are the most valuable by reason of their mineral resources and their agricultural possibilities, but political, and especially military, considerations played a part in the working out of the scheme. The length of the line, from the Ural mountains, where it connects with the Russian railways, to Vladivostok on the Pacific, and to Port Arthur on the Manchukuan coast, is in each case about 5,500 miles. It was completed in 1902, and part is now double-track. There is also a branch, the Turk-Sib, to Soviet Turkestan.

Africa. Cecil Rhodes's dream of a Cape to Cairo railway, with branches to the coast on British territory, seemed to come nearer realization when German East Africa became linked with the British Empire. Recent developments, however, point rather to a combination of railway with steamers on the Nile and the east African lakes, certain gaps (where railway construction would be costly) being filled by air transport.

Australia. The scheme of a transcontinental railway, following the line of the telegraph from Adelaide to Port Darwin, was seriously discussed as long ago as 1880, and the Australian Handbook of 1883 stated definitely that the contractor had undertaken to complete it in $7\frac{1}{2}$ years. Today the terminus is Alice Springs, about 1,000 miles from Adelaide, leaving 600 miles still to be constructed.

It appears, moreover, that the route from Colombo by sea to Fremantle, Western Australia, and thence by the recently opened Trans-Australian railway to Adelaide, has a slight advantage in distance over the sea voyage to Port Darwin and a possible railway across the continent. As a glance at the map will show, this so-called Trans-Australian line is not transcontinental at all. Looked at from a geographical point of view, however, it appears to be much better adapted to the real requirements of Australian internal communications. The regrettable differences of gauge on the railways of some of the states are, it is true, a great drawback, but at least there is now railway communication available between all five state capitals of the Australian continent.

LESSON 4

The World's Inland Waterways

WHEN civilization had advanced beyond the stages of the huntsman, the nomad herdsman, and the primitive agriculturist, there arose the need for a method of transporting commodities for the purpose of trade. Water transport was the easiest, and consequently the earliest form to be adopted, whether by river or by sea. Some of the oldest of the world's great cities are situated either on the banks of important rivers or on the sea coast. Examples are Babylon, Bagdad, Alexandria, London, Marseilles, and Cologne. Water transport was in a highly developed and well organized condition on such rivers as the Nile, Tigris, Euphrates, Ganges and Yangtze before a start had been made with the construction of roads.

A map of the world showing the navigable rivers would tell us that, as might be expected, it is only in the world's great lowlands that rivers are deep and slow enough to be of real use for commercial purposes. Modern developments in transport, however, have greatly reduced their importance, although in the basins of the Amazon and the Congo, covered as they are by dense, almost impassable, tropical forest, the rivers are really the only practicable means of travel.

The First Canals. Agriculture being the oldest human industry, it is likely that the earliest attempts at canal making had irrigation in view. But there is evidence that even the Egyptians and Assyrians used some of their canals for navigation. The Chinese imperial canal, constructed in the 13th century, which runs north from the Yangtze river at Nanking, crosses the Hwang-ho at Tsi-nan, and goes on to join the Pei-ho at Tientsin, was certainly intended for that purpose, while in Italy canals were in use as early as the 11th century.

The above are lowland canals, in level country, and without locks. The invention of the lock, which made it possible to carry canals through hilly country, has been claimed by both Holland and Italy, and the construction, in 1487, of six locks connecting the Milan canals is ascribed to Leonardo da Vinci. A canal connecting Eskilstuna, near Stockholm, with Lake Mälar, was completed in 1606, but the Canal du Midi, opened in 1681, must be regarded as marking the beginning of modern canal making. It runs from Toulouse to Narbonne, thus connecting the rivers Garonne and Aude, and providing communication by water between the bay of Biscay and the Mediterranean.

English Canals. The oldest English canal is the Foss Dyke, a relic of the Roman occupation, which runs from Lincoln to Torksey on the Trent, and is a continuation of the Caer Dyke (Peterborough–Lincoln), also a Roman canal.

The industrial revolution of the 18th century gave a great impetus to the construction of canals in great Britain. The Bridgewater Canal (Worsley–Manchester–Runcorn) was constructed by James Brindley, 1761–1765, partly at the expense of the duke of Bridgewater, who wanted cheap transport to the manufacturing centres for the produce of his collieries. It is still in use, and is carried over the Manchester Ship Canal by a swing bridge. Britain's canal system is principally in the midland area of England, between the Humber and Thames, although there is in Yorkshire and Lancashire a useful system, the Aire and Calder navigation, that links the east and west coasts. Today there are about 3,000 miles of canal in the British Isles.

Locks, and such devices as inclines and lifts have, it is true, made it possible to carry canals into hilly country, but they are expensive to construct, and waste time in navigation. We must, therefore, expect canals to be most numerous in lowland countries such as Holland and Belgium. Besides providing means of communication between towns, canals are often continued into the towns themselves, where they serve the double purpose of freight carriers and harbours. Amsterdam, Utrecht, and Dordrecht are examples of this, as are Copenhagen and Hamburg.

Outside Europe, we find canals in the lowland areas of China, Japan, and the Philippine Islands. The Batavia Canal in Java shows that the Dutch, long ago, found the advantage of reproducing in their oversea dominions this feature of their homeland. In the lowland districts of Siam canals have been used from earliest times, while there is a modern canal near Bangkok. Of canals in hilly country, Norway and Sweden afford good examples, both countries having numerous streams and rivers from which the necessary supply of water for the locks can be taken.

Canada's extensive system of inland navigation consists mainly of lakes and rivers, with canals where it is necessary to circumvent obstacles. Thus the Welland Canal from Port Colborne on Lake Erie to Port Dalhousie on Lake Ontario, which was enlarged and reopened in 1932 (27 miles with 26 locks), avoids the difficulties of the Niagara river with its falls and rapids. The two Sault Ste. Marie (" Soo ") Canals connect Lakes Superior and Huron. The Americans built a canal here in 1855, but the Canadian canal was not opened till 40 years later.

Germany is carrying out an extensive scheme of inland waterways, which includes the Mittel-Land canal, designed to connect the middle Elbe with the Ruhr district and the Rhine. The Main-Danube canal, which involves a rebuilding of the old Ludwigs-Kanal, passing near Nuremberg, will ultimately allow craft carrying loads of 600 tons to pass from the Rhine to the Danube and the Black Sea.

Sea Canals. Sea canals, or, as they are generally called, ship canals, are of two kinds : those which have the sea at both ends, and those which have the sea at one end only. Of the former, which are in the nature of short cuts, the best-known are the Suez Canal, which has no locks, and the Panama Canal, which has to overcome a rise of 85 feet. The Kiel Canal, which connects the North Sea and the Baltic, runs from the Elbe estuary, below Hamburg, to the mouth of Kiel harbour, a distance of 61 miles, with huge tidal locks at each end. Begun in 1887, it was opened in 1895, with a depth of 30 feet and a surface width of 215 feet. These dimensions were later increased to 36 and 330 feet respectively, the work being completed in the summer of 1914. The canal reduces from 600 to 120 miles the passage between Kiel and Wilhelmshafen, before the World War Germany's two chief naval stations. Further widening was decided upon in 1939.

In Scotland the Crinan Canal, by cutting off Kintyre from the mainland, shortens considerably the passage from the Clyde to the Western Isles. It was constructed 1793–1801, and has 15 locks in its length of 9 miles. The original survey for the Caledonian Canal, which connects Fort William and Inverness, was made in 1773 by James Watt, but the canal was not opened till 1847. It has 28 locks in its 22 miles of artificial waterway, the remaining 33 miles being accounted for by Ness, Lochy and other lochs.

Comparatively modern are ship canals constructed with the object of giving some great industrial town or district better access to the sea. The most important of these is the Manchester

Ship Canal. Begun in 1887, it was opened in 1894. The cost was £15,000,000, but the canal has made Manchester the third port of the kingdom. It is 35 miles long, and has a minimum depth of 28 feet. The passage, which can be made by 12,000-ton ships, occupies seven hours. Other similar ship canals are the Berlin-Stettin canal, the Elbe-Trave canal, the Dortmund-Ems canal, the eight-mile long Zeebrugge-Bruges ship canal, and the great New Russian canals—the White Sea-Baltic, Moscow-Volga, and Volga-Don.

LESSON 5

Airways of the Empire

THE first commercial passenger-carrying plane on the London-Paris route left Hounslow aerodrome on August 25, 1919. It was a small machine that had been converted from military uses, and its cabin had just room for two passengers, with the pilot in a cockpit forward. A few weeks later the Post Office entered into a contract for the carrying of London-Paris mail by air. In 1920 the London airport was transferred from Hounslow to Croydon, and four years later came the combining of several air companies into the one state-aided enterprise of Imperial Airways, Ltd. In 1939 that company and British Airways were merged into British Overseas Airways, a public corporation.

A few figures will best illustrate this development.

MILEAGE FLOWN.

1924	1928	1937
699,900	911,300	5,700,800

NUMBER OF PASSENGERS CARRIED.

1924	1928	1937
10,321	27,303	64,629

The experience in the matter of aircraft, general equipment, and organization of traffic gained on European routes enabled Imperial Airways to proceed with the establishment of Empire air routes. The first of these was the Croydon-Cairo-Bagdad-Basra line, opened in 1927. Two years later it was extended to India, and by 1934 it had reached Australia. This service was extended in 1939 across the Tasman Sea to New Zealand.

In February, 1931, the first air mail was carried from Croydon to East Africa; and since January, 1932, a regular service between England and South Africa has been running, the

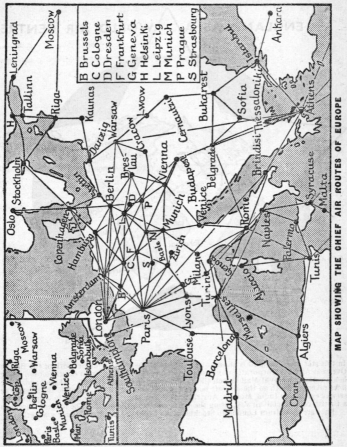

time of transit now being 4½ days, as against the 14 days of land and sea transit. A great advance was made with the introduction in 1937 of flying boats over revised routes. Southampton became the English terminus, with other main termini at Durban and

Sydney. Branch services from Khartoum to West Africa and from Bangkok to Hong Kong were inaugurated, in addition to subsidiary landplane services (notably in Africa). The "all-up"

ENGLAND AS A WORLD AIR CENTRE

In this star map England is shown as the centre of the world-wide network of the British Overseas Airways Corporation and companies in association. From Southampton flying boats carry the Royal Mail out on the 22,000 miles of Empire routes. At Alexandria the lines diverge; south go the aircraft bound for East and South Africa, while to the east the service extends to India, Malaya, Australia, New Zealand. The Atlantic is now spanned by a British commercial airway, using the bases shown in the map. The longest European lines are those from London to Stockholm via Hamburg, and to Warsaw via Berlin.

air-mail scheme for the carriage of all first-class mail without extra surcharge was another big step forward.

The map in page 255 shows some of the chief air lines of Europe. On a map of this scale it is impossible to show any-

SAXONS IN SUSSEX. Sompting church
has a four-gabled tower of a type
almost unique in England but found
in the invaders' homeland.
BRITISH HISTORY 1

WHERE ROME'S EMPIRE ENDED. A portion of the Roman Wall built
A.D. 120–127 by order of the Emperor Hadrian. Stretching for 73 miles from
Wallsend to Bowness it was designed as a barrier against the raiding Picts
and Scots. Forts were distributed along its length, one of them (Borcovicus)
being situated near the clump of trees shown in the mid-landscape.
BRITISH HISTORY 1

Photo, Felton

EDWARD THE CONFESSOR
portrayed on his Great Seal
British Museum

DANISH KING WHO RULED OVER ENGLAND.
From 1016 to 1035 Canute, King of Denmark, was also
King of England. Here he is seen with his wife,
placing a cross upon the altar of a church.
BRITISH HISTORY 2

British Museum. Stowe MSS.

Plate 30

Volume III

MURDER OF BECKET. This early 13th century painting shows the Archbishop assailed by Henry's knights in Canterbury Cathedral, Dec. 29, 1170.
British Museum, Harleian MSS.

COEUR-DE-LION'S STRONGHOLD. Ruins of Château Gaillard ("Saucy Castle") at Petit Andelys on the Seine, built in 1196 by Richard I to protect Normandy from the French. It was captured, however, by the latter in 1204. BRITISH HISTORY 4
Photo, Levy-Neuerdein

EDWARD I AND PARLIAMENT. Here is depicted Edward I, accompanied by the Prince of Wales and Alexander III, king of Scotland, presiding over a session of the royal Council. BRITISH HISTORY 5

From Pinkerton, "Iconographia Scotica"

Plate 32   *Volume III*

thing like all the routes in regular operation, but it will be clear that communication by air between the chief towns is amply provided for.

By means of the small map in the top corner an attempt is made to give some idea of the extent to which air traffic has been able to accelerate travel within the European area, although anything like exact comparison is impossible. On certain routes, where geographical obstacles prevent the railway from taking the shortest way, surface transport is at a disadvantage ; while on others, various reasons, generally of a technical nature, do not allow air transport to make full use of its advantage in actual speed.

It may, however, be taken as a fairly accurate representation of the facts if we say that, in order to make possible surface transport to the various parts of the area shown in the time actually occupied by air traffic, central Europe would have to be smaller than it is by the difference between the scales of the large map and the small inset map.

On the "star" map (page 256) England is shown as the centre of the earth's land surface. It must be noted, however, that the

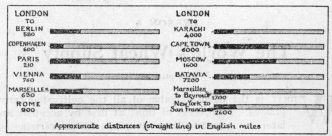

LONDON TO		LONDON TO	
BERLIN 580		KARACHI 4000	
COPENHAGEN 600		CAPE TOWN 6000	
PARIS 210		MOSCOW 1600	
VIENNA 760		BATAVIA 7200	
MARSEILLES 630		Marseilles to Beyrout 1700	
ROME 900		New York to San Francisco 2600	

Approximate distances (straight line) in English miles

projection on which this map is drawn does not allow of measurements being taken except along actual radii of circles drawn round London. If British territory were marked on this map, it would be seen that the only part of the British Empire which does not fall wholly within the body of the star, or one of the five rays, is New Zealand.

The British Overseas Airways and associated companies' routes to South Africa and Australia are shown, but not the proposed extension of the latter to Auckland, New Zealand.

Other lines are under investigation by this company. These

include the crossing of the North Atlantic by way of Eire and Newfoundland, connecting on the east with the Empire services (at Southampton) and on the west with the trans-Canada airway. The Pan-American Airways system, which has operated a trans-Pacific service (San Francisco-Hong Kong) for some years, is collaborating with the British services across the North Atlantic. A more southerly route via the Azores, Lisbon and Marseilles is favoured. There is a British service between the U.S.A. and Bermuda, and a line is projected to West Africa and across the South Atlantic to South America. This has already been pioneered by French and German air-liners and Zeppelin airships.

The diagram given in page 257 is intended to show how air and surface transport compare in the matter of speed on certain representative routes. The bands showing the time occupied by surface travel are all drawn the same length, with the relative time taken by air (including airport to city transport) shown in proportion in black.

LESSON 6

The World's Wheat Supply

(See plate 35)

WHEAT is the most valuable of all the cultivated cereal grasses. In process of time, at first by accident and later by scientific care in propagation, varieties of wheat suited to all manner of climates and purposes have been produced. Some years ago scientists averred that the growth in population was outstripping the world's increase of wheat production, with the probable consequence that by 1933 there would be a universal wheat famine. Since then the adoption of more scientific methods in wheat farming has resulted in such increased yields in many countries that the world has now not a famine but a glut in wheat.

Wheat is an annual grown from seed. From each seed cultivation produces four to eight or more stems, on each of which is a head with many kernels—the grain or corn of commerce. From the kernels the miller obtains flour and bran. The simpler wheats of little commercial value are spelt varieties, grown on dry land in Europe and largely used for food for animals. Emmer, a hard, two-grained spelt, is also unimportant commercially. Club wheat, which has short, stout straw stems and holds its kernels long after they are ripe, is grown in Turkistan, China, Chile, and western North America. Among wheats proper, durum, a hard wheat grown for macaroni, is widely

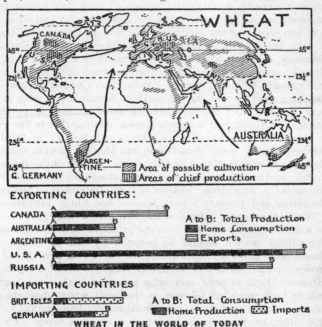

WHEAT IN THE WORLD OF TODAY

cultivated in southern Europe, northern Africa and also in the United States. The most obvious distinction between the different kinds of wheat is that between red and white. The red varieties are somewhat hardier but the grain is inferior to the white. Among strong red wheats may be mentioned Russian and the best Manitoba.

Winter wheat is sown as soon as the ground has been ploughed in autumn, and is reaped the following year ; spring wheat is

(259)

sown on ground ploughed in the autumn, directly the winter frost has thawed out of it, and is reaped the same year as it is sown. Where the summer is short, sowing may not be completed before the middle of May. During the early growing period, when the plants are tender, drought and hail are dreaded equally with the various pests ; the ripening period requires dry sunny weather.

Wheat is the most widespread of the world's cereals ; somewhere somebody is harvesting wheat on each day in the year. In June the harvest is reaped in the United States and along the northern shores of the Mediterranean Sea, in France and Italy ; in July the crop is gathered north of these areas, in England, Germany, southern Russia and in the north of France and of the United States ; in August the reapers are busy still farther north, in England, Belgium, central Russia, and Canada. These are the three chief months for the northern hemisphere ; later in the year, in September and October, wheat is gathered in northern Canada, Scotland, and northern Russia, while earlier in the year, in May, it is reaped in Algeria, China, and Japan ; in April, in northern Egypt, India, Asia Minor, and Mexico ; and in southern Egypt and India in March and February. South of the Equator, in the southern summer, the crop dates are : South Africa, November ; Argentina, November and December ; Australia, December and January ; New Zealand and Chile, January.

Where the farmer cultivates his own ground and grows wheat on a small scale for his own uses the principal limits are climatic ; the annual rainfall should lie between 15 and 30 inches, and should occur generally least during the harvesting period, and the growing period should be relatively long. Where cultivation is extensive, both in area over large tracts of fairly level country and in bulk intended for sale in the great wheat markets, the principal limits tend to be commercial rather than climatic. The crop must, on the average, pay over a series of years. To this end wheat production has been mechanized, all the operations— ploughing, drilling, harvesting, threshing, and transporting to storehouses—being done more cheaply by machines which reduce the number of hands employed. Consequently, the three main limits are suitability of the land to the use of machines, nearness to markets to reduce the cost of transport, and adequate supplies of human labour at a wage which makes its employment commercially practicable. The great revolution in wheat production during recent years, which is responsible for the existing glut, is due to greater suitability of the seed to climate, and freer use of increasingly improved machinery to cheapen production. Everywhere the yield of grain in bushels per acre tends to increase ; everywhere on the prairie lands greater skill and better seeds tend to enlarge the area where payable production is possible.

Wheat is graded for sale as spring or winter wheat according to its sowing time, as hard or soft, red or white, and as choice, No. 1, No. 2, No. 3 according to its weight (62, 60, 59, 57 lb.) per bushel.

A modern mill is a complicated flour factory ; as many as 23 different machines may be installed on different floors, and through these in turn the produce passes, to emerge finally as packed flour ; the grain is separated, washed, dried, ground, freed from dust, purified and re-ground. Between the floors the produce is lifted mechanically by elevating hoppers, and drops by its own weight from one machine to the next, passing from the bottom of the factory to the top and down again three times.

Centres of Wheat Production. The by-products of wheat are straw, used for cattle feed and for straw plait ; shorts and bran, both valuable food for stock ; and for human consumption, macaroni and patent preparations, *e.g.*, shredded wheat. The great wheat-growing countries are shown on the map (page 259). Canada grows wheat chiefly in the middle of the country in the prairies. The somewhat scanty rainfall occurs chiefly during the growing season. The high latitudes give 16 hours of sunshine per day during the ripening period, and growth is rapid during a shortish summer. Hard spring wheats are most common. Trade in wheat is so important that it has produced cities such as Winnipeg, notable as a wheat inspection and collecting centre. Most of the railway lines of the area and such a density of population would have been impossible but for the production of this staple. It has also resulted in the development of the canal system of the Great Lakes, new transcontinental railway lines, and a port on Hudson Bay.

Australia grows wheat in the south-east, where the rainfall is at least 20 inches annually. The ground is never frost-bitten as in Canada. The farms are large, machinery is used, labour tends to be scarce, and the climate is uncertain, so that the yield per acre and the total yield for the area fluctuate. The great advantage is the fact that the harvest comes in December and January.

In India wheat is mainly grown in the Punjab. It is a so-called winter crop, sown when the monsoon rains are over in September or October, and harvested early the following year, before the really hot season begins. During the growing period it is cool and dry with sunny days, which are, of course, short. The necessary water is supplied by irrigation canals fed from the large rivers from the Himalayas. The methods of cultivation are not mechanical and the farms are small ; transport is inadequate in equipment and crude in method.

In the United States the chief area is the wheat belt, roughly halved by the upper Mississippi. West of this river the crop is mainly grown for consumption elsewhere ; south of the line from Chicago to Omaha winter wheat tends to be more frequent than spring wheat. Chicago wheat market, the famous " Pit," is the most important in the world. Transport is by numerous railways and the Great Lakes waterways. In Argentina wheat is grown west of Buenos Aires ; from the 30° S. parallel, where durum wheat is cropped, south through areas of semi-soft wheat suitable for bread-making and for export, to semi-hard wheat near the 40° S. parallel, is the range of an extensive production, much of which is exported.

Consumption of Wheat. Wheat consumption is limited to the countries of production and, in the main, western Europe. Britain and Germany are the chief customers, for France usually produces what is needed with the help of her African colonies ; Hungary, Rumania, and Russia have surpluses for export. In round figures the percentages of the world's crop for the principal countries—consumption first, production second—are the following : British Isles, 6-1, imports 5 ; Canada 1-10, exports 9 ; Australia 1-3, exports 2 ; India 5-7, exports 2 ; United States 12-20, exports 8 ; Argentina 1-6, exports 5 ; Italy 5-5 ; France 6-6 ; Germany 5-3. imports 2 ; Russia ?-18, exports ?

Maize and its Uses. One of the most important of cereal foods is maize. It is sometimes known in England as Indian corn, in America as corn or sweet corn, and in Africa as mealies. Maize is used for human food as a vegetable in the form of sweet corn, as cornflour and hominy ; also as tortillas, polenta, mamaliga, and kukurus. The chief use of the plant, which is a native of America, is as food for stock. Maize requires a longer, hotter and wetter summer than wheat, without frosts, and the soil should not become saturated with water. It grows, therefore, in the warmer lands where winter wheat is also grown. In the United States, where two-thirds of the world's production is cultivated, it is mainly grown in the corn belt south of the spring wheat belt, and is fed to stock. The next producer is Argentina, which yields

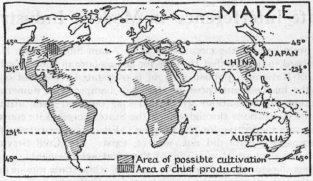

WORLD DISTRIBUTION OF MAIZE

about one-tenth of the U.S. crop. In central Europe and Italy the total yields are relatively small.

Oats and Barley. Oats are hardier than wheat. The producers of this cereal are the United States, Russia, Canada, Germany, France. The British crop, important as it is to British farmers, is but half that of France, a third of that of Canada and Germany, and a tenth of that of the United States.

The hardiest of cereals is barley. Its production is scattered throughout the wheat-growing areas. Barley bread was formerly in use, but today the main purpose of the crop is to obtain malt for brewing, especially in Britain and Germany, where neither wines nor cider are extensively produced. Rye is the bread plant of eastern Europe. Its production is definitely localised in Russia and the neighbouring states in Europe. It can be grown on poorer soils and in more inclement climates than any other cereal.

Our Course in Economic Geography is continued in **Volume 4.**

State Interference in Modern Industry

IF we allow for the circumstances of Adam Smith's day, it is hard to believe that the case for laissez-faire in the " Wealth of Nations " (published 1776) is overstated. For not only was the business enterprise of that day hampered in numerous directions by regulations which had long outlived their utility, but the institutions through which the State exercised its control were quite ineffective for the purpose. Effective institutions for government control did not, in fact, exist. The Civil Service, the creation of which was one of the great achievements of the nineteenth century, had yet to be built up, while trade unions and organizations of employers, which today greatly facilitate the work of government control, did not emerge in this modern form until well on in the nineteenth century. Moreover, the business unit was as yet too small to be effectively controlled. Thus the State had slowly to feel its way forward before it could become an effective instrument of control.

In this Lesson and the next we shall concern ourselves with the deficiencies of the price mechanism which create the need for State interference. It is, of course, possible to hold the view that the mechanism of prices is so defective in its function of regulating production and distribution that, to attain a tolerable economic system, it is necessary to supersede the whole structure of capitalism. This view is held, in fact, by the Communists, who desire to see the complete supersession of individualism and private enterprise by various forms of public enterprise and control. It, however, cannot be discussed here, since it is based on certain tenets, such as the inevitability of the class struggle and the competence of public enterprise, which are outside the scope of Economics.

These tenets are, in fact, derived not from a criticism of the mechanism of prices, but from a denial of certain assumptions, such as that private enterprise can be made reasonably effective, that the competition among capitalists is on the whole beneficial to the community, and so on. These assumptions may or may not be valid. It is, however, convenient to assume their validity for our present inquiry, for we are thus enabled to analyse the mechanism of prices under ideal conditions, thereby following the scientific method of isolating, as far as possible, the question under consideration.

We shall not, therefore, be here concerned with the problem of monopoly, or that of the mobility of the factors of production. We shall, that is to say, continue to assume that competition is sufficiently free for prices to correspond to the cost of production, and that capital and labour are sufficiently mobile to transfer themselves to the parts of the economic system where they can be most profitably employed. Nor shall we question the adequacy of the profit motive in stimulating efficient management.

Defects of Price Mechanism. The defects of the mechanism of prices may be divided into two categories : (1) those cases in which the individual and public interest do not coincide ; (2) those cases in which, though there is a coincidence of interest, the individual through lack of knowledge, enterprise, intelligence, or money, is unable to pursue his best interest.

In the first place, the production of a commodity may incidentally inflict a loss on the community which is not borne by its producer. The development of a particular industry, for example, may involve a wholesale destruction of the amenities of the locality. The development of the coalfields and the Black Country eloquently testify to this danger. Besides the destruction of amenities, the production of a commodity may be detrimental to public health owing to the pollution of the atmosphere which it entails. Moreover, the pollution of the atmosphere involves damage to buildings as well as increased washing bills. Thus the community has realized, as a result of bitter experience, the necessity of laying down regulations governing the setting up and the running of industrial establishments. These regulations do not go far enough, but the destruction of amenities in the towns which took place in the last century cannot be repeated.

While the amenities of the towns are to a large extent protected from industrial development, the amenities of the countryside are still exposed to this danger. As the trend of industrial development is taking the factory into the country, the danger is a very real one. The situation has been admirably summed up by Mr. J. L. Hammond, the historian :

" If this generation continues to bungle the second industrial revolution now in progress, it will complete the havoc of the first. Wordsworth said a century ago that the discovery of steam power saved the country because the industrial revolution, after beginning on the banks of streams, was thereby diverted to the towns. The towns suffered, but, for the moment, the country was saved. This was not quite true, even in Wordsworth's day, but now, of course, the truth is just the opposite. The forces that took factories and populations into the towns are spreading the towns over the country. Indeed, it looks as if our fathers, having ruined the towns by their efforts, are to ruin the country by their example."

Clash of Interests. A clear example of a present-day clash of interest between the individual and the community is to be seen in " ribbon development." To the builder sites along the new main roads are eminently suitable, as they save him the expense of laying down roads, and he is thus enabled to build houses at a lower price. From the point of view of the community, however, this ribbon development has not only resulted in a loss of amenity, but also in a loss of public money. For it is more expensive to provide such services as gas, electricity, water, drains, and so on to a locality in which the houses are spread over a large area ; and this burden is largely thrown on the rates.

Thus the rise of new industries in hitherto unindustrialized districts, the enormous extension of housing to relieve the congestion of the towns, the great expansion in road construction to meet the requirements of modern road transport—all this new development which has been proceeding at a great rate since the war must be subjected to social control, if the public interest is to be protected.

An example of the clash between the individual and the public interest, which Mr. Bernard Shaw has frequently cited, is the sale of intoxicating liquor. It is the State and not the publicans and brewers, as Mr. Shaw points out, which has to bear the expense of extra policemen and the enlargement of the prisons necessitated by excessive drinking. This example, however, has lost some of its force with the post-War decline of drunkenness.

LESSON 22

Laissez-Faire in the World of Today

THERE is, as we saw in the last Lesson, a divergence between the interests of the individual and of the community in those cases in which the enterprise of the individual inflicts an incidental loss on the community. Such incidental loss, as we have seen, frequently arises when industrial and housing development takes place in a haphazard and uncontrolled manner. The most important divergence of interest, however, arises out of the use of processes which are liable to injure the workers who participate in them. If a worker is injured or killed, his employer suffers no pecuniary loss, since the burden of supporting the man while he is incapacitated, or, in case of his death, the widow and children he leaves behind him, falls on the State. Thus the first breach that was made in the citadel of laissez-faire was the series of statutes which laid down regulations enforcing the fencing of machinery, safety measures to be taken in mines and the payment of workmen's compensation.

Necessary Government Enterprise. There is, however, another field of equal importance in which Government action is made necessary by a divergence of private and public interest. According to Mr. J. M. Keynes :

" The most important Agenda of the State (i.e. the most important field of Government activity) relate not to those activities which private individuals are already fulfilling, but to those functions which fall outside the sphere of the individual. . . . The important thing for Government is not to do things which individuals are doing already, and to do them a little better or a little worse ; but to do those things which at present are not done at all."

The divergence between the individual and the public interest is, in other words, not confined to those cases in which the enterprise of the individual inflicts an incidental loss on the community. There are certain enterprises which, while they are unprofitable to private enterprise, are highly profitable to the community. Lighthouses perform a function of incalculable value. Why, then, are they not a profitable business proposition ? The answer is that a private company could not collect payment from the ships that made use of them. Thus, in order that adequate provision should be made for those needs for which payment cannot be expected in the normal way, Government enterprise is necessary.

Another example of this kind of need is the supply of information in regard to the activity of trades. The Balfour Committee, which published its final report on the state of British industry and trade in 1929, lays great stress on this point :

" The only real remedy for the irrational aberrations of judgement which are at the root of the psychological factor in trade cycles is the provision of more complete and accurate information and the cultivation by the community of the habit of systematic uses of such data in arriving at practical conclusions."

Inadequacy of the Individual. The exceptions to laissez-faire are not exhausted by those cases in which there is a divergence in the interest of the public and of the individual. It not infrequently occurs that the individual fails to pursue his best interest through ignorance, lack of initiative, or by following some irrational motive. For example, a worker may be earning less money in the occupation in which he is employed than he could earn in some other occupation, but owing to slackness or stupidity he may not make the change. The factor of ignorance in these days of universal education, Employment Exchanges, and newspaper advertisements is far less common than it used to be, but is still operative. Inertia, too, plays some part, especially where a change of occupation involves moving from one part of the country to another. That these factors are operative is shown by the fact that over long periods wages for the same grade of labour in different occupations vary to a considerable extent in different parts of the country. Thus throughout the 19th century, and also in the 20th century, wages in agriculture lagged behind the wages in towns—a phenomenon which is mainly attributable to inertia and ignorance.

Such differences in wages, however, may have another explanation. Movements from one locality to another can sometimes be effected only at considerable pecuniary loss and inconvenience. As Adam Smith pointed out, of all kinds of luggage the human being is the most difficult to transport. Not only has the worker to take with him his furniture and other personal effects ; he may own his house, or be unable to find suitable housing accommodation in the district to which he wishes to go. Moreover, the worker has not only his work to consider. There are also the occupations of his children, if they have left school, and perhaps also of his wife. It is not surprising, therefore, that a cotton operative in Lancashire is earning a good deal less than, say, a transport worker in London.

Irrationality in Business. Perhaps the most important cases from the point of view of the community which fall within this category are those in which individuals, actuated by some irrational motive, prefer to follow a line of action opposed to their pecuniary interest. For example, an owner of a business may prefer to sink his last penny in it before he will be willing to close down, even though he could earn much more in some other business. Or, again, it may be greatly to the interest of many firms in an industry to amalgamate and thereby facilitate a process of rationalization. But owing to such motives as pride and rivalry, they may fail to do so.

An eminent example of this sort of irrationality is provided by the coal industry. The Samuel Report on the Coal Industry states :

"We have arrived at the definite conclusion that the size of the undertakings usual in the coal industry in Great Britain is not economically the best ; and that there are great advantages in large scale production which are not being realized. If nothing more were done than to leave economic forces to work themselves out, it would probably be found, 20 years from now, that over the large proportion of the area the same conditions as those of today would still be prevailing . . . Those who are charged with the care of the public interest have the duty to take such measures as will obviate these eventualities."

The reasons advanced to support these conclusions are instructive. The Samuel Report points out that when the question of the formation of new combinations arises there is the difficulty of deciding which of the old concerns is to be predominant. Moreover, new combinations involve the displacement of directors and managers, as well as the thorny question of the valuation of the individual concerns. To crown these formidable obstacles to progress there is the *vis inertiae* which hampers new developments in all old-established industries.

LESSON 23

Value and Price

I F we glance through the chapters of a text-book on Economics, we shall find that the greater part of it is taken up with the question of " value." The principles which determine the value of commodities and of the various factors of production will be found to comprise the bulk of the theoretical parts of the book. Why is this problem of value so important ? We pointed out in Lesson 3 (volume 1, page 215) that the fundamental principle of the economic organization is specialization. Now, specialization implies that production takes place not for direct consumption, but for exchange. The goods and services which we supply directly to ourselves are very unimportant in comparison with those which we obtain by exchange. Hence arises the importance of " value." For production for exchange instead of for direct use gives rise to two problems. In the first place it gives rise to the problem of the determination of the rates at which the various commodities exchange for one another ; why, for example, does an ounce of gold exchange for a greater number of ounces of iron, or a bushel of wheat exchange for a greater amount of money than a bushel of oats ?

Problem of Distribution. In the second place, specialization gives rise to the problem of distribution. For specialization implies co-operation ; the production of a motor-car, for example, requires the co-operation of many kinds of labour, as well as of capital and land. But on what principles shall the value of the motor-car be divided amongst the various factors of production which have co-operated in producing it ? What proportion of the total value shall be reckoned as interest on the capital, how much shall be set aside for rent for the land, how much as wages for the skilled labour, and how much for the unskilled ?

The problem of distribution consists in ascertaining the principles on which the product of industry is to be divided among the co-operating factors of production. Now, the share which a factor receives is, from another point of view, the value of that factor. Thus the wage which a worker receives is from his point of view his share of the value of the products he has helped to produce ; but from the employer's point of view the wage which he pays is the price or value of the services which he obtains from the worker. And the same considerations apply to interest, which is the distributive share of capital, and to rent, which is the distributive share of land. Thus the problem of distribution is one aspect of the problem of value.

Before proceeding farther with our analysis it is necessary to ascertain what we mean by value. The term value as it is used in Economics means value in exchange. Thus the value of a commodity is the power which it possesses when it is exchanged for other commodities. The value of wheat, for example, is the power which it possesses to obtain other commodities. Wheat rises in value when the amounts of other commodities which can be obtained for a given amount of it increase, and vice versa. Thus values express ratios : the ratios in which things exchange for one another. If a loaf of bread costs 3d., and a lb. of tea costs 2s. 6d., then a loaf of bread exchanges for a lb. of tea at the ratio of 3d. to 2s. 6d., i.e. 1 : 10.

Values and Prices. As commodities are not exchanged directly against one another, but through the medium of money, all values are expressed in prices. The expression of values in prices enormously facilitates the comparison of the values of commodities, since we are thereby saved the trouble of comparing the ratio in which each commodity exchanges for every other commodity. Prices represent generalized purchasing power, so that when we know the price of, say, a bicycle, we not only know the ratio in which it will exchange for any particular commodity of which the price is known, but also the ratio in which it will exchange for things in general. Instead of values, then, we may speak of prices. How are prices determined ?

The kinds of things that are priced may be divided into two categories. There are the goods and services which directly satisfy our wants, and there are the things with which these goods and services are produced. The former are the commodities, goods and services which are available for consumption ; the latter are the land, labour and capital which are available for production. The prices of these two categories of things are determined in very much the same way, but as certain complicating considerations must be taken into account in the second category, it is necessary to deal with each separately.

Prices of Commodities. The influences which determine the price of a commodity are of two kinds—the influences which lie behind demand and those which lie behind supply. The sum of the influences behind demand and supply determines prices. The problem of the determination of prices resolves itself, therefore, into an analysis of the influences which underlie supply and demand. Now, we have already ascertained two characteristics of the price of a commodity. In our analysis of demand we saw that the price of a commodity must equal its marginal utility to the purchaser. In our analysis of the price mechanism we also saw that the price of a commodity must equal in the long run its cost of production. These two characteristics of prices indicate the direction of our inquiry ; we must, that is to say, investigate respectively the influence of cost of production and utility on the prices of commodities.

Costs of Production. In order that a supply of a particular commodity may be forthcoming certain costs have to be incurred. What are costs ? The answer depends on which of the three possible points of view it is decided to take. There is the point of view of the employer who is running a business, that of the individual who co-operates in production, and, finally, the point of view of the community as a whole. From the point of view of the employer costs consist of the money outlays that he has to make in order to place a supply of goods on the market. He has to hire various kinds of labour, to borrow capital from the banks or from the public, and to rent land. These outlays, together with his own remuneration, make up his cost of production. In the long run, these costs must equal the price he obtains for his product, for otherwise he would have no incentive to carry on his business.

To say, however, that the price of a commodity in the long run must equal the sum of the money outlays involved in its production does not tell us very much. It merely pushes our analysis one step forward. What determines the amount of these money outlays ? As all money costs of production resolve themselves into wages, interest, rent and profit, we have next to inquire what determines the rate of wages, the rate of interest, the rent of land, and the profit of the entrepreneur, subjects which are dealt with in the next three Lessons.

LESSON 24

"Real Costs"

THE analysis of costs from the point of view of the employer (or entrepreneur, as he is usually called in Economics), which we undertook in the previous Lesson, does not take us very far. We want to get behind the money costs to the underlying " real costs " of production. Now, the term cost suggests sacrifice. We speak of a thing as costing us so much trouble or effort or time, and in doing so we imply that the getting or doing of a thing involves a sacrifice. This manner of speaking is especially appropriate to getting one's living, which involves the sacrifice of trouble, effort and time. Here, then, is one of the elements in the " real costs " which underlie the money costs, namely, the " real costs " involved in any kind of work.

In addition to the expenditure of effort, however, production also involves the use of capital. Are there also " real costs " underlying the supply of capital ? Capital is, of course, the outcome of saving, and saving involves sacrifice. It involves sacrificing the present to the future. The older economists used to talk of " the sacrifice of abstinence " involved in the supply of capital. Although this phrase is strictly correct, for saving obviously involves abstaining from spending, nevertheless it is too provocative of mirth to be satisfactory. The idea that the rich, who supply the bulk of the savings of the community, are undergoing abstinence in order to make available their contribution to the supply of capital is, in its obvious sense, ridiculous. Professor Alfred Marshall, therefore, substituted the colourless term " waiting."

Labour and Sacrifice. The fact that a good deal of saving takes place without any sacrifice does not invalidate the view that there are real costs underlying interest, which is the money cost of capital. It is equally true that much work is done without any sacrifice, but this does not invalidate the view that there are real costs underlying the wages of labour. Much of the work of artists, craftsmen, and professional men, far from exacting any sacrifice from those who perform it, is the source of perhaps the most profound satisfaction known to man. Such workers, it is true, are the exception ; but even the mass of men, the men who perform the typical work of the community, are probably far happier with their work than they would be without it. It is, in many cases, only the last hour or two in the day's labour which is positively unpleasant to the average man or woman. These considerations, however, do not imply that there are no real costs underlying the performance of labour. The unpleasantness of that last hour of work, the irksomeness, monotony, and danger involved in many occupations, even the sacrifice of leisure pursuits, are " real " costs of a very substantial nature.

Can we say, then, that money costs measure " real " costs ? That is to say, if one commodity costs 10s. and another 20s. to produce, can we say that the latter involves twice as much sacrifice on the part of those who have contributed to its production as the former ? A moment's reflection will show that we certainly cannot. In the first place, we have no means of comparing different individual experiences. How, for example, can we compare the pain or sacrifice involved in the day's work of an agricultural labourer with that involved in the day's work of a miner ? All that we can say is that, in so far as the workers have free choice, they will sort themselves out among the various occupations according to their individual preferences, after making due allowance for the rates of pay and the conditions prevalent in each occupation. In the second place, money cost has no necessary connexion with pain cost. The fact that a lawyer earns ten or twenty times as much as a miner does not signify that he undergoes ten or twenty times as much pain in the performance of his work. The better paid work—it is a platitude—is usually the more congenial. Moreover, the pain involved in work is not the only real cost involved in production. There is also the sacrifice involved in the supply of capital. If it is difficult to compare the sacrifice or pain involved in different kinds of labour, it is impossible to compare the sacrifice of the worker with the sacrifice of the saver. How, then, can we compare the pain involved in the production of commodity A, which is the product of a units of capital and b units of labour, with commodity B, which is the product of b units of capital and a units of labour ?

" Costs " Under Communism. The truth is that we can make no scientific statement about the pain costs involved in production. Is it impossible, then, to go behind money costs ? Must we take the money cost of a commodity as an ultimate fact which is incapable of further analysis. In order to answer this question let us shift our point of view from that of the individual and regard costs from the standpoint of the community. Suppose that the Russian Supreme Economic Council was contemplating an increase in the supply of houses. Having considered the urgency of the demand for houses, it would next consider the cost involved in increasing the supply by the number contemplated. But how would it compute the cost ? Not in terms of money, for the supersession of the free play of supply and demand by authoritarian control has almost destroyed the mechanism of prices. Nor yet, again, would it endeavour to compute the pain involved in the work of producing the houses. The cost of the houses would be reckoned in terms of those other things the production of which would have to be forgone, in order that the necessary labour and capital might be transferred to housing. The production of more houses would obviously involve the sacrifice of other forms of wealth. Other opportunities of production, that is to say, would have to be forgone in order to produce more houses. This is the cost—" opportunity cost " as it is called—which the Supreme Economic Council of Russia would take into consideration.

Thus, the real cost of any commodity which underlies its money cost of production is opportunity cost. That is to say, the real cost of a commodity consists in the alternative commodities which the community has to go without in order to obtain the commodity in question. And in countries where the mechanism of prices functions freely, i.e. in capitalist countries, the opportunity cost of a commodity is measured by its money cost of production. This correspondence between opportunity cost and money cost is dealt with in the next Lesson.

LESSON 25

Cost of Production and the Problem of Value

As we have seen, the cost of producing a commodity can be regarded from three points of view. In the first place, there is the point of view of the business man. From his point of view the cost of producing a particular commodity consists in the money outlays he has to make to obtain the necessary labour, capital, land and materials. The aggregate of these outlays comprises the money costs of production. We may take as an example a motor-car which has cost the manufacturer, say, £450 to produce. This £450 might be made up of, say, £180 for wages, £20 for interest on the capital employed, £30 for rent, £200 for materials and components, and £20 for depreciation of plant. Now, all these outlays in the final analysis consist of payments to the original factors of production, labour, capital and land. The first three items are direct, the last two items indirect payments to these original factors, for the costs of materials and machinery are ultimately resolvable into payments for land, labour and capital. We are thus brought to the second point of view—that of the individuals who supply the original factors of production. What cost does the worker undergo in rendering his services, the capitalist in supplying his savings, and the landowner in making available his land ?

We have seen that cost to the worker consists in the irksomeness, monotony, danger, and the sacrifice of leisure which his work involves. This is the subjective or " real " cost of the work to him. Cost to the capitalist consists in the postponement of consumption, or, in other words, the " waiting " which is involved in saving. These " real " costs, as we shall see later, influence money costs, for they tend to restrict the supply of the factors of production. But as they are not proportional to money costs—a fact which is illustrated by the low remuneration for dirty and disagreeable work—" real " costs cannot be an adequate explanation of money costs.

Social Aspect of Cost. Finally, there is cost from the social point of view. What is the " real " cost to the community involved in the production of a £450 motor-car ? In one sense, of course, the social " real " cost consists in the sum of the sacrifices made by the members of the community who have cooperated in producing it. To compute this cost is, however, clearly impossible. The only scientific conception of cost from the social point of view is what is known as opportunity cost, which consists in the sacrifice of displaced alternatives. Thus, the social cost of producing a £450 motor-car consists in the sacrifice of those commodities which could have been produced by the factors of production which, in fact, produced the motor-car. That is to say, if the car had not been produced it would have been possible to produce other commodities to the value of £450. Thus, opportunity cost not only underlies money cost, but is also proportionate to it.

Having analysed money costs and the ultimate facts which underlie them, we are now in a position to return to the problem of value. The problem of value, it will be remembered, is that of ascertaining the causes which determine the ratios in which commodities exchange for one another ; and these ratios, as we have seen, are expressed in prices. What, then, are the causes which determine the relative prices of commodities ?

Theory of Value. In the nineteenth century there were two principal schools of thought on this subject, namely, the cost theory of value and the utility theory of value. Until the seventies the cost theory of value, which was developed by Ricardo, McCulloch, Senior, and J. S. Mill, held the field as the only explanation of value. According to this theory value is determined by costs. The reasons for this view were mainly these. First, there is no connexion between the utility of a commodity and its value ; bread is of great utility, but of small value, while diamonds are of small utility, but high value. Secondly, there is a close correspondence between the cost of a commodity and its value ; producers would cease to supply any commodity the value of which continued to be below the cost of producing it, while they would increase the supply of it, if the value of the commodity was above its cost. In other words, competition among producers regulates the supply of commodities, so that in the long run cost of production and price always coincide.

The cost theory of value, however, was not entirely satisfactory, for the economists who held this view were unable to find an adequate explanation of costs. As we have seen in our recent analysis, we cannot accept the money costs of production as final facts ; it is necessary to explain the causes which determine money costs. This school of economists, therefore, were driven back to the " real " costs which underlie money costs, and by making assumptions which have no correspondence with reality they endeavoured to show that the money cost of a commodity is determined by the " pain " cost of the workers and the " abstinence " cost of the capitalists who produced it.

Influence of " Pain " Cost. The cost theory of value, however, did contain an important kernel of truth. For, while the " pain " cost of the workers and the " abstinence " cost of the capitalists do not determine value, they, nevertheless, exert an important influence on it. If, for example, saving could be effected without the sacrifice involved in postponing consumption, then the supply of capital would be enormously greater than it is. Moreover, an increase in the supply of capital would have an important influence on the prices of commodities ; for example, the prices of all those goods and services the production of which requires comparatively large amounts of capital would fall relatively to the price of those goods and services the production of which requires comparatively small amounts of capital. To take an extreme example, the price of the services rendered by the railways would fall relatively to the price of the services of domestic servants. Similarly, the " pain " cost of labour exerts an important influence on value. Let us suppose that in the next hundred years inventions will have rendered all occupations equally agreeable, so that the work of the miner is no less agreeable than the work of a farm labourer. Clearly, such a revolution in the processes of production would have an important influence on the relative prices of commodities. It would no longer be necessary, as it is at present, to offer a higher wage than is offered to men of a similar grade in order to induce them to take up the occupation of a miner. Or suppose the imaginations of men were captured by a new religion, which taught the value of work as an end itself. What would be the effect on the value of goods and services if men were thus to become more willing to work ? Clearly, the prices of those goods and services which require a relatively large amount of labour would fall compared with the others. The price of domestic services, for example, would fall relatively to the price of the services rendered by the railways.

These examples illustrate the element of truth contained in the cost theory of value, and this truth can be conveniently summed up in the following generalization : *Any influence which limits the supply of a commodity tends to raise its price.* Where the cost theory of value was wrong was : first, in suggesting that the " pain " cost of labour and the " abstinence " cost of saving were the sole influences limiting supply ; secondly, in suggesting that demand had no influence on value.

LESSON 26

Theories of Value

I N the preceding Lesson we saw how, until the eighteen-seventies, economists were unanimous in interpreting " value " in terms of the cost theory. While differing as to the relative importance of the constituents of cost, they were agreed that value was determined exclusively by the supply side of the equation. How could the other side of the equation, the side of " utility," have anything to do with value ? Iron, it was pointed out, was of much greater utility than gold, and at the same time was of much lower value. Moreover, gold was more valuable than iron in the same proportion as its costs of production were higher. Thus, it was held, there is a strict correspondence between the cost of a commodity and its value, while utility is not commensurate with either.

It was presently realized, however, that the cost theory of value had its limitations. How, for example, could one explain or estimate the value of a work of art ? It was of little use referring to the costs of producing Botticelli's Birth of Venus. It was argued, therefore, that a different theory applied to all those things which it is not possible to reproduce. The value of works of art, it was said, was determined by their scarcity in relation to the intensity of the demand for them. And this apparent deficiency of the cost theory, it was argued, was not serious, since we are mainly interested in the value of those goods which are freely reproducible.

Even in the case of freely reproducible goods, however, the theory soon proved unsatisfactory. How, for example, could it account for the fact that a gallon of French burgundy is more valuable than a gallon of Australian burgundy ? The labour involved in the production of the French burgundy is less highly paid than the Australian labour, and the expenses of the fixed and circulating capital are approximately the same in both cases. The explanation is, of course, that the land comprising the French vineyards is more valuable than the corresponding land in Australia ; the French vinegrower, therefore, has to pay more rent. But the higher rent of the French vineyards cannot be accounted for by any theory of costs. Land cannot be produced like machines.

In 1871 Jevons startled the economists by putting forward his marginal utility theory of value ; this theory asserted that utility and not cost is the fundamental cause of value. The error of previous theories, said Jevons, is due to the fact that economists have paid attention to only one aspect of utility, namely, the *total* utility of a commodity. But, once we recognize the distinction between the total utility and the utility of a small unit of any commodity (i.e. the marginal utility), the fundamental influence of utility on value will be admitted. As we have seen in Lesson 14 (volume 2, page 184), Jevons stated that we could theoretically divide our supply of any commodity, say food, during any period of time into a number of portions. The utility of the first portion, if we were deprived of the other nine portions, would be infinitely great ; the second portion would have a slightly smaller utility, and so on, until we arrive at the last or marginal portion, which would have the least utility of all. According to this theory it is the " *final utility*," as Jevons called it, or " the marginal utility," as we call it today, that determines value. " Value," said Jevons, " depends solely on the final degree of utility," since the utility of the marginal unit of any commodity determines the value of all the other units. For example, the first portion or unit of our food supply is obtained at the same price as the marginal unit, and the price of the marginal unit is equal to its marginal utility. This coincidence of marginal utility and price is obtained, as we saw in Lesson 14, by the action of consumers who endeavour to spend their incomes to the best advantage.

Jevons, however, was as one-sided and inadequate in his explanation of value as were the economists who upheld the cost theory. To show that marginal utility coincides with price is one thing, to show that marginal utility *determines* price quite another ; the cost theory had been equally successful in showing that the cost of a commodity coincides with its price. Nevertheless, the marginal utility theory was an important step forward in the development of Economics. By introducing the conception of the margin, it laid the foundation stone of the modern developments of economic theory. And one of the most important of these developments has been the emergence of a sound and comprehensive theory of value. In the modern theory, cost is no longer regarded as independent of utility, as in the cost theories ; a single cause is no longer given as a sole determinant of value, as in the marginal utility theory. On the contrary, it is now seen that costs cannot be explained without reference to utility, and utility cannot be explained without reference to costs.

Determination of Value. Value, as Professor Pareto has said, arises from the contrast between tastes and obstacles. On the one hand, there is the material environment in which man lives, as well as his ability and reluctance to utilize it. On the other hand, there are the multifarious ends of man which give rise to his desire for wealth. The interaction of man's tastes and the obstacles that he encounters in satisfying them determine the ratio in which things exchange for one another. Let us take an illustration. Why are Paris gowns more expensive than gowns made elsewhere ? The Parisians, possessed of superior taste and skill in dress designing, produce gowns which women regard as superior to other gowns. But the number of Parisians who possess this superior taste and skill are few in relation to the demand for their services. This scarcity of highly skilled labour causes keen competition for its use, thereby forcing up its price, and the high price of the labour raises the cost of Parisian gowns.

Any attempt to explain value, therefore, solely on the cost side of the equation or on the side of utility is doomed to failure. Costs cannot be explained without reference to utility. As we saw in the case of burgundy, the requisite land is scarce, and is, therefore, of high value, but this scarcity is due as much to the tastes of consumers as it is to the limited supply of suitable land. Nor can utility be explained without reference to the obstacles encountered in production. For the extent of these obstacles determines the extent to which a particular desire can be satisfied. And this latter circumstance determines marginal utility.

LESSON 27

On the Problem of Distribution

IN our previous four Lessons in Economics we have inquired into the causes which determine the values or relative prices of commodities. We now turn to the other aspect of the problem of value, viz. the problem of distribution. The question which arises for discussion is : What determines the value of the services of labour, capital and land ? Now, as in the case of commodities, the values of labour, capital and land are obviously determined by the interaction of the influences underlying the demand for and the supply of the various factors of production. In our analysis of distribution, however, we shall not deal with the influences underlying the supply of these factors. We shall take the supply as given. This omission is made partly for the sake of simplicity and partly because the supply of labour and capital is determined by influences which do not lend themselves to economic analysis.

The supply of labour, for example, does not depend on the price offered for the services of labour, as the supply of motor-cars depends on the price offered for motor-cars. It depends partly on the size of the population and partly on the number of hours which each individual works. Now, the size of the population depends on such factors as the status of women, the dissemination of information on birth control, the popularity of motor-cars, and so on—all of which are factors outside the scope of Economics. Even the length of the working day is determined by custom and by authoritarian control. The supply of capital is also largely determined by non-economic factors. Perhaps the most important of these factors is the attitude of business men to the firms they control, which in many cases they regard as ends in themselves. This attitude results in business men putting back profits into their businesses without balancing the sacrifice involved against the possible gain. Thus the supply of labour and the supply of capital are determined by influences which do not easily lend themselves to economic analysis, while the supply of the remaining factor land, does not give rise to a problem at all, as it is fixed for all times. For these reasons we may safely assume that the supply of the factors of production does not respond in any predictable way to the prices offered for them.

Influences Underlying Demand. Our problem, therefore, of ascertaining the principles on which the national income is shared among the three factors which cooperate in its production, consists in analysing the influences underlying demand. Now, as far as demand is concerned, the principles which determine the value of land, labour and capital are precisely the same as those which determine the value of commodities. For the entrepreneur stands in the same relation to the factors of production as the consumer stands to consumable commodities. It is the entrepreneur who purchases the services of the factors of production, and he—like the consumer—endeavours to obtain the maximum return from his expenditure. His constant endeavour is to combine land, labour, and capital in such proportions as to leave the widest possible margin between the expenses he incurs and the price he gets for his product. If, for example, the entrepreneur is a farmer he will endeavour to hire just so much land, just so much capital and just so much labour as will make the most economic combination. Similarly, the consumer purchases just so much food, clothing, house room, etc., as will yield him the maximum return in satisfaction.

Law of Price. Thus the problem for the entrepreneur is essentially the same as that for the consumer, namely, the economic administration of resources. Now, as we saw in Lessons 13 and 14 (volume 2, pages 181 and 184), two fundamental principles must be observed if resources are to be administered to the best advantage—the Law of Price and the Law of Diminishing Utility, and it was pointed out how the consumer does, in fact, spend his income in accordance with these laws. The consumer observes the Law of Price by expending his income according to the terms on which the various goods and services are available, that is to say, according to their prices. The housewife, for example, who is confronted with a rise in the price of tea will transfer a part of her expenditure on that commodity to coffee or cocoa. Similarly, the entrepreneur who is confronted with a rise in the price of labour will transfer a part of his expenditure on labour to capital or land. For, just as the housewife can substitute at the margin coffee or cocoa for tea, so the entrepreneur, while he is unable to do without labour altogether, can substitute at the margin capital or land for labour. This capacity of the factors of production to act as substitutes for one another is of great importance, and will engage our attention at a later stage of our discussion of distribution.

Law of Diminishing Utility. If the entrepreneur, however, is to obtain the maximum return from his expenditure on land, labour and capital, he must also observe the Law of Diminishing Utility. This law, it will be remembered, in its application to the expenditure of consumers, is to the effect that the utility to us of a commodity diminishes with every addition to our stock of it. The consumer observes this law by purchasing just that quantity of each commodity as will cause its marginal utility to him exactly to coincide with its price. Thus, in expending his income, the consumer takes no account of the total utility to him of the various commodities.

Similarly, the entrepreneur, in expending his resources, takes no account of the total utility of land, labour or capital. Some land, some labour, some capital are indispensable to him, but this attribute of indispensability has no influence on the price he is prepared to pay for them. Land, for example, while it is an indispensable factor of production, may, in some circumstances, such as those prevailing in new countries like Australia, be had for a very small payment. As in the case of commodities, it is the marginal utility of a factor of production which tends to coincide with its price. How this works out in practice we shall see in a later Lesson.

Utility and Productivity. An important distinction, however, should be noticed between the utility of a consumable commodity and the utility of a factor of production. The utility of a consumable commodity depends upon its capacity to satisfy human desires ; the utility of a factor of production depends on its capacity to produce commodities, or, as we say in Economics, on its productivity. Thus the utility of bread depends upon its capacity to satisfy the wants of our stomachs, but the utility of a plough or an agricultural labourer depends on its or his capacity to contribute towards the production of food. Instead of speaking, therefore, of the utility of labour, capital or land, we speak of their productivity.

LESSON 28

Marginal Analysis of the Problem of Distribution

IN order that the problem of distribution of the national income may be solved on settled principles, it is necessary that the contribution of the various factors of production should be ascertainable. If it is not possible to ascertain the specific contribution of each factor to the finished product, then, clearly, the share of each contributing element cannot be determined on scientific lines.

Several prominent writers are of the opinion that the problem of determining the specific contribution of each factor of production is an insoluble one. Thus, Mr. G. Bernard Shaw asserts, in page 21 of " The Intelligent Woman's Guide to Socialism," that :

" When a farmer and his labourers sow and reap a field of wheat, nobody on earth can say how much of the wheat each of them has grown."

Earl Russell, in " Prospects of Industrial Civilization," page 146, maintains a similar view in the following passage :

" In an industrial civilization a man never makes the whole of anything but makes the 1,000th part of a million things. Under these circumstances it is totally absurd to say that a man has a right to the produce of his own labour. Consider a porter on a railway whose business it is to shunt trains ; what proportion of the goods carried can be said to represent the produce of his labour ? The question is wholly insoluble."

If we accept this view as correct, then the process of distributing the product of industry is merely a scramble between the various cooperating factors to obtain as large a portion for themselves as possible. The process of distribution, according to this view, is merely a question of bargaining power. Capital and labour confront one another from two hostile camps, each endeavouring to increase its strength by organization and financial power. And the more successful either of them is in this objective, the greater will be its share of the product of industry. If we wish to see a rise in the standard of living of the workers, then—according to this view—we must work to increase the bargaining power of the trade unions. On the other hand, if we wish to keep labour in its place, we must work for the weakening of the trade unions and the strengthening of the capitalists.

Use of Marginal Analysis. The problem of determining the contribution of each factor to the income of the community is only insoluble to those who are unfamiliar with marginal analysis. With the aid of marginal analysis, however, the problem assumes manageable proportions. Just as the consumer is able to regulate his expenditure according to the utility of commodities by estimating their value to him at the margin, so the employer is able to distribute his resources according to the utility to him of the various factors of production by estimating at the margin their contributions to the total product of his firm.

The Principle of Substitution. We shall return to this problem of determining the specific contribution of the various factors in Lesson 29. Meanwhile, it is necessary for us to become familiar with the principle of substitution on which the marginal analysis of distribution is based. The meaning of this principle has been clearly put by Professor Marshall in the following passage :

" He (the employer) is continually comparing the efficiency and the cost of different ways of obtaining his object. He is always looking for new suggestions, watching the experiments of others and trying experiments himself, so as to hit upon the combination (of land, labour and capital) which will yield the largest incomings in proportion to any given outlay ; or, in other words. he is ceaselessly occupied with the principle of substitution."

Clearly, however, this principle of substitution depends on the interchangeability of the various factors of production. That is to say, it must be possible, within limits, to get any one factor to achieve the same results as either of the others. To take an extreme example, a farmer can till his land by employing a large number of labourers and setting them to dig, or by using a tractor plough with one man to drive it. Similarly, capital can be substituted for land. The Underground is an example of the possibility of substituting capital for land, for the capital sunk in the tunnels is virtually a substitute for the land which would have been necessary if the railway had been built overhead.

Competitive Factors of Production. Thus land, labour and capital compete with one another for employment. In order that we may see how this competition works in practice, let us suppose that an entrepreneur is setting up a shoe factory. How will he set about it ? He knows that he will have to hire some land, to borrow some capital, and to employ some labour. The questions he has to solve are—how much land, how much capital, and how much labour ? since, as we have seen, they can be substituted for one another, not in totality, but at the margin. For example, when he is deciding on the size of the factory he will erect, he has the alternative of buying a relatively large area of land, and building thereon a one-storey factory. In this case he will spend more on land by economizing on capital. On the other hand, he may decide to erect a high building on a relatively small area of land. In this case he will economize on land by erecting a more expensive building, requiring deeper foundations and stronger walls.

When he has erected his factory, he will next have to decide on the machines and the various labour-saving devices to be installed, as well as on the number of his employees. Here, again, he will find that the factors of production compete with one another. He can install relatively more labour-saving machinery, thereby dispensing with a certain amount of labour ; or he can decide on a relatively large staff, and economize on machinery.

On what principles will he determine the amount of the total available resources which he will expend on land, labour and capital respectively ? The principles are the same as those which operate in the case of the business man and in the case of the housewife, namely the Law of Price and the Law of Diminishing Utility. As regards the Law of Price, the entrepreneur will obviously devote more of his resources to labour if wages are low than if they are high ; and more to capital if he can borrow money cheaply than he will if the rate of interest is high. This point we dealt with at the end of Lesson 27 (page 284).

The other factor which will determine his decision is the relative utility—or, rather, productivity—of labour and capital for the purposes he has in view. But just as in the case of commodities it is the marginal utility that is significant, so in the case of the factors of production it is the marginal productivity which influences the demand of business men.

Our Course in Economics is continued in Volume 4.

LESSON 16

Modern Methods of Steam Generation

(See plate 36)

WHEN water is heated its temperature rises until the boiling point is reached; the temperature then remains constant while evaporation takes place, that is, while the water is being converted into steam. If the vessel in which the water is contained is open to the atmosphere, as in the ordinary domestic kettle, the temperature at which the water boils is 100 degrees Centigrade, or 212 degrees Fahrenheit, and this temperature is maintained until the water is all boiled away. If the water is contained in a closed vessel, and is under pressure, the temperature at which the water evaporates is no longer 100 degrees Centigrade, but depends upon the pressure. At a pressure of 100 lb./sq. in., for example, the temperature is about 164 degrees Centigrade, and at 200 lb./sq. in. it is 194 degrees Centigrade. This temperature at which steam is formed is called the " saturation temperature," and steam at this temperature is called " saturated steam."

When water is heated in a closed vessel under a definite pressure, a certain amount of heat, depending upon the pressure, is required to raise the temperature to the saturation temperature. This heat is known as the liquid heat, being the heat given to the water in its liquid state. After the saturation temperature has been reached, more heat is required to convert the water to steam while the temperature remains constant ; this heat is called the latent heat of the steam. When all the water has been evaporated, and more heat is added, the temperature of the steam then begins to rise again; the steam is then said to be superheated. In a modern steam power plant a generator is required to convert water to superheated steam at a comparatively high pressure, for use in the steam engine or turbine. The most important part in the steam generator is the boiler.

Parts of a Boiler. There are three essential parts in the ordinary boiler, viz. the furnace, in which the fuel is burnt and heat generated ; the heating surface, through which the heat of combustion passes to the water ; and, finally, a vessel to contain

PRIMITIVE METHODS OF TRANSPORT. West African natives carrying rice
across a stream, and (above) dogs in the Arctic drawing a well-loaded sledge.
ECONOMIC GEOGRAPHY 1

Percival

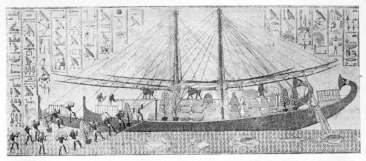

SHIPS THROUGH THE AGES. Above, two ships of the fleet sent by Queen Hatshepsut of Egypt (c. 1500 B.C.) to Punt, at the southern end of the Red Sea, to fetch rare and fragrant woods, resins, balms, etc. Centre, Roman merchantmen such as brought corn and wine to the imperial city. Below, the Homeric (34,351 tons) in the floating dock at Southampton. The Olympic and Aquitania are on the left.

ECONOMIC GEOGRAPHY 2

Egypt Exploration Society; Ny Carlsberg Museum, Copenhagen; The Times

Plate 34   Volume III

ONE OF CANADA'S GIANT ELEVATORS. This great silo or grain elevator, with a capacity of 1,150,000 bushels, is maintained by the Saskatchewan wheat pool for the weighing, cleaning, storing and eventual discharging of the grain raised by its members. The smaller photograph shows the interior of a grain elevator. ECONOMIC GEOGRAPHY 6 with a belt conveyor in operation.

Courtesy of the Canadian Government

STEAM GENERATION. Fig. 2. Cylindrical boiler,
fitted with oil fuel sprayers under a system of forced
draught. ENGINEERING 16

Thornycroft & Co., Ltd., Southampton

STEAM BOILERS. Fig. 1. A simple water-tube
boiler, with part of the brickwork removed to show
the construction. ENGINEERING 17

Babcock & Wilcox, Ltd.

Plate 36   *Volume III*

the steam generated. There are many different types of boilers, developed for different conditions of operation, but these three parts are always present, although occupying very different degrees of prominence in the different types.

In order that a boiler may operate at maximum efficiency, there are two important requirements to be fulfilled. These are (1) the maximum possible amount of heat must be generated from the fuel, and (2) the maximum possible amount of this heat must be transferred to the water. The first is a furnace problem and requires the complete combustion of the fuel, while the second is a heating surface problem and requires that the temperature of the products of combustion, that is, the waste gases, should be reduced as low as possible before being discharged to the atmosphere.

The combustible part of the fuel consists mainly of carbon and hydrogen, and heat is generated during combustion, i.e. the combination of these elements with the oxygen of the air. If the proportions of carbon and hydrogen in the fuel be known, the quantity of air required for the complete combustion of the fuel may be determined. In practice, however, more air than this quantity must be provided, because otherwise it would not be possible to mix the fuel and air so thoroughly that all the oxygen would find carbon or hydrogen with which to combine. Thus for complete combustion there must be a certain amount of excess air supplied, that is, in excess of that theoretically required. This excess of air must, however, be reduced to the minimum, because the air not usefully employed carries away useful heat, due to its temperature leaving the boiler.

Boiler Operation. The heat is generated at a much higher temperature than the water; heat flows through the heating surface, and the temperature of the products of combustion falls during the passage of the hot gases from the furnace to the boiler exit. By increasing the boiler heating surface, more heat may be taken from the gases, but a limit is fixed by the saturation temperature corresponding to the particular pressure employed. This is the temperature inside the steam and water space, and no more heat can flow through the heating surface when the products of combustion have been reduced to this temperature. With the high pressures used in modern boilers, the quantity of heat contained in the flue gas at the saturation temperature is quite large; this heat may be usefully employed in heating the feed water before it enters the boiler, and in some cases for heating the air used for the combustion of the fuel. The feed water is heated by passing it through an economizer, a series of tubes around which flows the flue gas leaving the boiler.

The size of a boiler depends upon the quantity of steam required, the passage of the necessary heat from gases to water determining the area of heating surface. The quantity of fuel also depends upon the steam generated, and, for a given rate of combustion in the furnace, this fixes the size of grate required. The rate of combustion may be increased by supplying the air at a high temperature, and by increasing the rate at which the air is supplied. Three methods are adopted to ensure the flow of air to the fuel on the grate, viz. natural draught, forced draught, and induced draught.

Natural draught is the draught produced by a chimney The column of hot gas is less dense than the surrounding atmosphere, and therefore tends to rise and draw in a fresh supply at the front of the boiler. The draught depends upon the height of the chimney and upon the temperature of the flue gas ; while sufficient for small plants, the rate of combustion with this method is not high enough when large quantities are dealt with. With forced draught the air for combustion is forced into the furnace by a fan, so that the rate at which it is supplied may be varied at will. Induced draught is similar to forced draught in that a fan is used to provide the draught, but the fan is placed in the flue above the surface, so that the air is drawn, not forced, through the boiler. With both these methods the height of the chimney is determined only by the necessity of discharging the products of combustion into the atmosphere at a suitable height.

The type of boiler shown diagrammatically in Fig. 1 is commonly used for small installations, and for low pressures. It consists of a cylindrical steel shell, A, with two internal cylindrical flues, B, extending the whole length. If solid fuel is used it is burnt on the grate C ; the products of combustion pass right along the flue to the rear of the boiler, and then along brickwork passages in contact with the outside of the shell, and are finally discharged into the chimney. The water level in the boiler is maintained above the tops of the internal flues, otherwise the intense heat would burn the material.

STEAM GENERATION

The type of boiler just described, called the Lancashire boiler, has certain distinctive features. The volume of water and steam is large, so that sudden variations in the demand for steam may be readily met. On the other hand, it takes a long time to heat up this large volume of water when " getting up steam "; also it is not suitable for very high pressures, as the thickness of the shell plate becomes excessive.

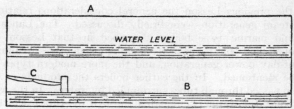

STEAM GENERATION. **Fig. 1.** Diagram showing the Lancashire type of boiler used for small installations.

A sectional view of a boiler used for marine purposes is shown in Fig. 2 (plate 36). On account of questions of space on board ship, the boiler is made larger in diameter and shorter in length than the Lancashire boiler. There are two furnaces arranged for burning oil fuel in the boiler shown; usually there are three furnaces, and sometimes four. The products of combustion pass from the furnace into the chamber at the back, and thence through the tubes leading to the front of the boiler. The ends of these tubes open into a smoke-box fitted to the front of the boiler, and leading to the funnel. The furnaces, combustion chambers, and tubes are all covered with water, so that heat is being transferred from the hot gases to the water during the whole of the passage through the boiler.

The marine boiler is similar to the Lancashire boiler in general characteristics as regards storage volume and unsuitability for high pressures. Other types of boilers, very different in these respects as well as the methods of firing and burning different classes of fuels, will be discussed in the next Lesson.

LESSON 17

Steam Boilers: Their Construction and Operation

(See plates 36—38)

IN the previous Lesson the general considerations relating to steam generation were briefly discussed. The Lancashire and marine type boilers described in that Lesson were developed for conditions less exacting than those ruling in present-day power generation, and the more modern types may now be mentioned. In the earlier boilers the products of combustion passed through tubes surrounded by water. In the water-tube boiler the water is circulated through the tubes, which are disposed so as to absorb as much as possible of the heat in the gases. A boiler of this type is shown in Fig. 1 (plate 36), with part of the brickwork removed to show the construction. The boiler is arranged to burn coal, fired by hand. The fire-door is shown open at the front of the boiler, at the left of the illustration. The grate is just below the front half of the nest of sloping tubes ; the flames and hot gases pass upward across these tubes, then down and up again across the same tubes, directed by brick baffles built in between the tubes, and, finally, away to the chimney. The sloping tubes are connected at front and rear to the steam and water drum on top. The steam stop valve, through which the steam is withdrawn from the boiler, is on the top of the steam drum. A safety valve is also fitted to the drum, arranged to allow the steam to blow off when the pressure exceeds a certain predetermined value. A pressure gauge and a water-level gauge are fitted on the front of the drum.

In the water-tube boiler the quantity of water in the system is comparatively small, so that the process of getting up steam takes much less time than in the case of the shell type boilers discussed earlier. Further, as the diameters of the drums are small, the boilers may be built to withstand very high working pressures. On the other hand, owing to the small steam storage capacity, a sudden demand for more steam will result in a drop in pressure, unless the rate of combustion is correspondingly increased at the same time.

In modern engines the steam is invariably superheated—i.e. heated above the saturation temperature corresponding to the particular boiler pressure. The steam is taken from the steam drum and passed through a series of tubes in the path of the hot gases, and then goes to the engine. Steam does not conduct heat away from the metal of the tubes as readily as does water, so that the tubes of the superheater tend to become much hotter than those of the boiler. For this reason the superheater is usually placed just after the first pass of the products of combustion across the boiler tubes. It is thus shielded from the highest temperature of the furnace, and yet the gases are sufficiently hot to raise the temperature of the steam as high as required.

Modern water-tube boiler construction is illustrated by Fig. 2 (plate 37). Coal is spread to the proper depth on the travelling-grate mechanical stoker, which is an endless chain driven by gearing at the front of the boiler. The depth of the coal on the grate and the rate at which the coal is carried towards the back of the furnace are arranged so that enough heat is generated to evaporate the required quantity of steam, and so that combustion is complete when the coal reaches the back of the grate. The fire-brick furnace arch projecting from the front of the boiler over the grate assists in the rapid and efficient combustion of the coal ; the arch becomes white hot from the heat of the furnace, and, by radiating intense heat on the entering coal, promotes rapid combustion. The brickwork baffles directing the flow of the products of combustion are shown. The gases first flow over the upper end of the sloping tubes, and then over the superheater placed above these tubes. There are two more passes over the boiler tubes before the gases pass up to the economizer, over which there are three passes. The feed water is pumped first into the economizer, where it takes heat from the flue gases and rises in temperature, before entering the steam and water drum arranged along the front of the boiler. The water flows to the lower ends of the boiler tubes and rises up these inclined tubes as it becomes heated and is converted to steam, the steam being discharged back into the main drum. The pipe leading from the top of the drum conveys the steam to the superheater, through which it flows while its temperature is further raised. The steam is then ready for use in the engine.

Combustion of Pulverized Coal. In comparatively recent years the use of pulverized coal has been extensively adopted for large power stations. In this method the coal is ground to a powder before being blown into the furnace, where it is quickly mixed with the air for combustion, and is burnt in a very short time. A typical installation is shown in Fig. 3 (plate 38). The coal is delivered to the raw coal bunker from a belt conveyer. From the bottom of the bunker the coal passes through a drier before it enters the pulverizer, where it is ground to the required degree of fineness. A fan draws a stream of air through the pulverizer, and the fine coal is carried in suspension and delivered into the cyclone separator, where the coal falls into the ready-for-use bin, while the air returns to the pulverizer for a fresh consignment of coal. A feeder at the bottom of the pulverized coal bin is supplied with enough air to carry the coal dust into the boiler. Combustion takes place very rapidly, and the flue gases pass over the boiler tubes, then over the economizer tubes, before entering the induced draught fan and being discharged to the chimney.

On account of the high rates of combustion attained, the furnace temperature is very high, and, in the boiler shown, water tubes are arranged around the furnace walls to prevent melting of the fire-brick lining ; these tubes also add to the evaporative power of a boiler of given size. The chief advantages of pulverized coal as compared with the mechanical stoker are : (a) Inferior quality coal may be successfully burnt, being supplied to the furnace in a finely divided state and mixed with air ready for combustion. (b) The rate of combustion may be controlled very readily, by varying the speeds of the motors driving the fans and the pulverizer. Any variation in the quantity of coal supplied to the furnace has an immediate effect on account of the rapidity of combustion. (c) The high rates of combustion increase the output available from a given size of boiler, or, alternatively, the size of boiler for a given output is correspondingly reduced.

On the other hand, the additional plant required for the preparation of the coal before it enters the boiler tends to increase the first cost of the pulverized coal boiler. A more important difficulty is met with in the suspension of ash and grit in the flue gas. In order that combustion may take place in the short time available, the coal must be finely ground, and the ash remaining after combustion is so light that it is carried away by the draught of the boiler, suspended in the products of combustion. Various methods are used to remove this ash from the gas before it leaves the chimney, else it would be distributed over the neighbourhood.

Oil as a Fuel. The combustion of oil in a boiler is very similar to that of pulverized coal. The oil is pre-heated to assist the rapidity of combustion, and is forced into the furnace through a burner which pulverizes the oil into a fine spray. This oil spray becomes intimately mixed with the air supplied through suitable ducts, and combustion takes place rapidly. The same furnace may readily be arranged to burn either pulverized coal or oil. The advantages of oil over coal are, briefly : oil does not deteriorate in storage ; oil has a higher heating value than the same bulk of coal ; oil is more easily handled and stored ; absence of dust and ashes ; ease of control over the combustion, small quantity of excess air, therefore high efficiency. Disadvantages are danger of fire and high cost (in this country) compared with coal.

LESSON 18

Principles of the Internal Combustion Engine

IT has beeen pointed out in Lesson 13 (volume 2, page 222) that the different types of engines in use are necessary on account of the different qualities of the various fuels available, and also on account of the different purposes for which the engines are used. For stationary engines the weight of the plant is of importance only in so far as it affects the first cost, and the size of the buildings required ; for transport purposes, on the other hand, where the engine forms part of the total load which can be carried, the smaller the weight of the engine the greater is the useful carrying capacity. The efficiency of the engine is also a very important factor from the point of view of carrying capacity, apart from the question of actual cost of operation. For a given voyage by a ship, for instance, or for a given flight by an aeroplane, the efficiency of the engine determines the total weight of the fuel and the space occupied by it. With a more efficient engine the weight and space occupied by the fuel are correspondingly decreased, and the available carrying capacity increased. With aircraft, in particular, in which the power required for a given total weight is much greater than in any other type of transport, the aim is to reduce the weight of the engine, and to increase its efficiency.

The steam engine is an external combustion engine, the fuel being burnt in the furnace of the boiler; the heat generated is conveyed to the engine cylinder by the steam. On account of the losses of heat unavoidable with a boiler, the size and cost

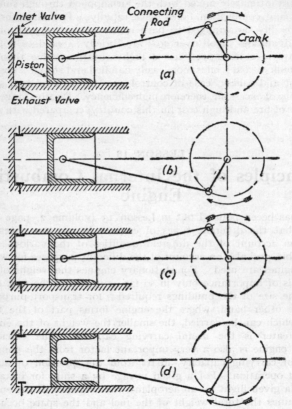

CYCLE OF OPERATIONS. Fig. 1. Simple diagrams illustrating the four-stroke cycle in an internal combustion engine.

of the boiler as compared with the engine, and the additional attention required, repeated efforts have been made to eliminate the boiler and to generate the heat directly inside the engine cylinder.

In the internal combustion engine the working fluid is air and gaseous fuel. Heat is generated by the combustion of the fuel with the oxygen in the air ; the temperature of the air is thereby raised, and it expands, doing work on the piston as the temperature falls. The greater the temperature range the greater the amount of heat converted to work, and, hence, the more efficient the engine. After expansion down to a low pressure and temperature, the products of combustion are discharged to the atmosphere, and a fresh charge of air is drawn into the cylinder and the cycle is repeated.

Four-Stroke Cycle. In engines working on this cycle the operations are in the sequence indicated in Fig. 1, and are as follows :

(a) *Suction.* The piston moves outwards, the inlet valve being open, and a fresh charge is drawn into the cylinder. The pressure during this stroke is approximately atmospheric, and is shown by line (1) in the indicator diagram of Fig. 2.

(b) *Compression.* The crank returns and forces the piston inwards, all valves being closed. The mixture in the cylinder is compressed into the clearance space, and the pressure rises as shown by line (2) in Fig. 2. At the end of the compression stroke combustion takes place, and the heat thus suddenly generated raises the pressure, as shown by the vertical line in the indicator diagram. The time at which combustion begins and the rate of combustion are arranged so that the pressure may reach its maximum value before the piston has moved an appreciable distance outwards on

(c) *Expansion.* In this stroke the high-pressure products of combustion force the piston outwards, doing work on the crankshaft, while the pressure falls as shown by the curve 3 in Fig. 2.

(d) *Exhaust.* At the end of the expansion stroke the crank returns, forcing the piston inwards, and the waste products of combustion are discharged to the atmosphere. The pressure which is attained in the course of this stroke is just slightly above the pressure of the atmosphere, as shown by line 4 in Fig. 2.

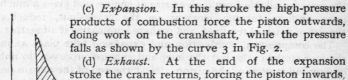

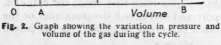

Fig. 2. Graph showing the variation in pressure and volume of the gas during the cycle.

(297)

The complete cycle of operations occupies two revolutions of the crankshaft, and during this period there is only one stroke, the expansion stroke, during which useful work is done on the crankshaft. During the other three strokes the energy required to drive the piston backwards and forwards must be supplied from the engine flywheel. The fluctuation of energy during a cycle is, therefore, much greater than with a steam engine, which, having a working stroke in each direction, gives four working strokes in two revolutions, as compared with one working stroke from the internal combustion engine. In order to avoid large fluctuations in speed between successive working strokes, a large flywheel must be provided for single-cylinder engines. The size of the flywheel may be reduced by using a number of cylinders and suitably arranging the cranks. In a four-cylinder engine, for example, the four working strokes are equally distributed over two revolutions, that is, the cranks are set 180 degrees apart.

The inlet and exhaust valves, by which the charge enters and leaves the cylinder, are operated by cams, through the medium of suitable rods and levers. As each valve opens once in two revolutions, the camshaft makes one revolution while the crankshaft makes two, suitable gearing being used to give this speed reduction.

Two-Stroke Cycle. This is a modification of the four-stroke cycle considered above, giving a working stroke from each cylinder for each revolution of the crankshaft. This increases the power available from a given size of engine, and gives a much more uniform turning moment on the crankshaft, reducing the size of flywheel required, and perhaps eliminating it altogether.

The compression, combustion and expansion take place as in the four-stroke cycle, but the inlet and exhaust processes do not occupy full strokes of the piston. Near the end of the expansion stroke the piston uncovers a port in the wall of the cylinder, as shown in Fig. 3, and some of the waste gases flow out through this exhaust port while the pressure falls to that of the atmosphere. Just after the exhaust port has been uncovered, the further outward movement of the piston opens the inlet or scavenging port. The charge for the next cycle, already compressed to a pressure slightly higher than that inside the cylinder, enters by the scavenger port and drives out the remainder of the products of combustion from the previous cycle. As the piston moves inwards again, first the inlet port is covered and then the exhaust port, and during the remainder of the stroke the charge is compressed ready for combustion.

The important advantages of the two-stroke cycle are : (1) a more uniform turning moment due to having a working stroke in each revolution from each cylinder ; (2) the elimination of the mechanical complication attending the operation of the

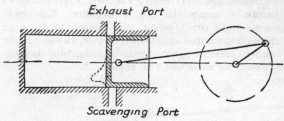

Fig. 3. Diagram of a cylinder for an engine working on the two-stroke cycle.

inlet and exhaust valves of the four-stroke cycle. On the other hand, the scavenging process presents certain practical difficulties. The time available for the process is very short. The entering charge must flow in such a direction that it forces all the waste products into the exhaust port. The returning piston should cover the exhaust port when all the waste gases have been expelled, but before any of the fresh charge is lost in the same way. Finally, the supply of scavenging air necessitates the provision of some form of compressor or blower. Specially shaped inlet and exhaust passages, and projections on the face of the piston, such as shown dotted in Fig. 3, are used to direct the incoming charge in the proper direction for scavenging.

Ratio of Expansion. In the indicator diagram shown in Fig. 2, the shaded area inside the diagram represents the work done during the cycle. It will be seen that the work done depends upon the length of the diagram, i.e. it may be increased by an increase in the volume of the cylinder, as shown by the dotted extension of the diagrams. The efficiency of the engine depends, therefore, upon the ratio of expansion, that is, the ratio of the volume after expansion to that before expansion, or $\dfrac{OB}{OA}$. This is the same as the ratio of compression for the type of diagram considered, and the term " ratio of compression " is more commonly used. It will be seen, however, that the increase in efficiency with increase in compression ratio is due really to the greater expansion of the products of combustion.

The cycle of operations through which the working fluid passes differs in different types of engines, depending largely on the methods employed in the preparation of the combustible mixture. The two main types, which are considered in subsequent Lessons, are : (1) Engines in which the mixture is prepared before it enters the engine cylinder. Gas and petrol engines come under this heading. (2) Engines in which air alone passes through the initial stages of the cycle, the fuel being introduced under pressure just before combustion begins. This method is used for all modern oil engines.

LESSON 19

Petrol Engines and Gas Engines

(See plate 39)

I**N** both petrol and gas engines the combustible charge is prepared outside the engine cylinder. Apart from the methods used for the preparation of the charge, the modes of operation are similar for these two types of internal combustion engines. In fact, the petrol engine was a development of the gas engine, modified to use liquid instead of gaseous fuel. In the gas engine, the gas is supplied either from the gas main or from a special gas-producing plant. The gas is kept separate from the air until it is just about to enter the cylinder, and a non-return valve is incorporated to prevent the results of an accidental back-fire causing any ill effects in the gas main. The mixing of the air and gas is generally performed by a special mixing valve, so arranged that the gases are mixed in the correct proportions. The charge, therefore, flows into the cylinder in a mixed stream, and this mixing goes on automatically during the suction and compression strokes, so that the charge may be regarded as ready for combustion before ignition takes place.

In the case of a liquid fuel such as petrol, which vaporizes readily at ordinary temperatures, the liquid is allowed to evaporate and mix with the air stream as it is drawn towards the engine by the suction of the piston. In order to facilitate the vaporization of the petrol and its admixture with the air, it is sprayed through a fine jet into the air induction pipe, and is broken up into a fine mist and carried along with the air stream. The apparatus used for metering and atomizing the fuel, and mixing it with the air, is called a carburetter.

In the type of carburetter generally used on petrol engines, the petrol is supplied from a small chamber in which the height of the liquid is kept constant on a level with the opening of the jet. There is, therefore, no tendency for the petrol to flow out of the jet while the engine is at rest. When the crankshaft is revolved air is drawn through the induction pipe by the suction of the pistons ; the air flow is arranged so that there is a reduction of pressure at the jet, and the pressure difference thus set up forces the petrol through the jet in a fine spray. When the engine is turning over slowly, as at starting and when idling, the speed of the air in the induction pipe is correspondingly reduced, and special arrangements are necessary for the production of a satisfactory spray. The petrol vaporizes as the mixture passes through the induction passages and into the cylinder. The vaporization should be complete as early as possible, and in some engines the induction pipe is placed close to the exhaust pipe, so that the heat of the exhaust assists in fuel evaporation.

Ignition. Near the end of the compression stroke, when the charge has been raised to a high pressure and temperature, a spark is produced electrically in the mixture, and combustion follows. The rate at which combustion proceeds depends upon the extent to which the charge has been compressed, and upon the proportions of air and fuel in the charge. The mixture may be too weak (too much air) or too strong (too much fuel) ; in either case the rate of combustion is reduced, and the time during which burning takes place increased. Even with the correct mixture, a certain period of time elapses between the passage of the spark and the attainment of maximum pressure due to the combustion ; ignition is, therefore, arranged to take place shortly before the end of the compression stroke, so that the maximum pressure may be reached before the piston has moved an appreciable distance on the expansion stroke.

The spark is produced by an electrical discharge across an air-gap in the cylinder. The high voltage required to break down the resistance of the air-gap is obtained by the use of an induction coil, the action of which will be explained later.

Compression Ratio. It was shown in the preceding Lesson that the efficiency of an engine increases with the compression ratio. There is, however, a limit to the extent to which the compression ratio of a gas engine or petrol engine may be raised. The compression of the combustible charge raises its temperature as well as its pressure, and, if raised too high, the charge will ignite spontaneously, before the passage of the spark. This is called pre-ignition, and it tends to slow the engine down, the too-early combustion of the fuel producing a high pressure resisting the motion of the piston during the compression stroke. The compression ratio must, therefore, be kept below that at which pre-ignition would occur.

A second phenomenon which fixes a limit to the compression ratio is the occurrence of detonation, or pinking. This is a sharp metallic knock caused by a wave of very high pressure striking the walls of the cylinder, the pressure wave being the result of very rapid combustion of the fuel. The occurrence of detonation depends upon the temperature and pressure of the charge, and the strength of the mixture, before ignition, and also upon the design of the cylinder, as regards the shape of the combustion chamber, and upon the nature of the fuel. For a given cylinder and a given fuel there is a maximum compression ratio beyond which detonation may be expected. Much has been done in the way of improved cylinder design as well as improvements in fuels, with the object of raising the compression ratio at which engines will operate, and thus increasing their efficiency. Special dopes, such as tetra-ethyl lead, may be used to retard the rate of combustion, thus allowing the use of higher compression ratios.

Cylinder Cooling. The intense heat of combustion would raise the metal of the piston and cylinder to a very high temperature unless some method of cooling were provided. In practice, two alternative cooling agents are available, namely, air and water. Air cooling is used only for small sizes and for purposes where there is a plentiful supply of cold air, e.g. motor-cycles and aeroplanes. Metal fins on the surface of the cylinder increase the area in contact with the cooling air, and assist in dispersing heat.

With water cooling, a jacket is fitted around the cylinder providing a space through which the water flows, carrying away heat from the cylinder walls. The temperature of the water rises in its passage through the engine, and if the same cooling water is to be used continuously it must be cooled to its original temperature before it again enters the cylinder jacket. Hence the use of the radiator on the motor-car, or cooling tanks for stationary engines.

Petrol Engine Construction. A section through a modern four cylinder petrol engine, used for buses and lorries, is shown in Fig. 1 (plate 39). The illustration is arranged to display as much as possible in one view, the overhead camshaft being broken to show the valves for two of the cylinders. In the other two cylinders the pistons and connecting rods are seen in section The crankshaft A is supported in five bearings, supplied with oil under pressure from the oil pump B. Each piston has four rings, fitting in grooves in the piston and pressing against the cylinder thus preventing loss of pressure by leakage. In contrast with the steam engine, the petrol engine is single acting, that is, work is done on the upper side of the piston only. This removes the necessity for a piston rod and cross-head, and the connecting rod, C, is connected directly to the piston by a gudgeon pin, D.

The overhead camshaft, E, is driven from the crankshaft through chains and gears at the front of the engine, the radiator fan, F, being mounted on one of the intermediate shafts of this drive. The valves, two for each cylinder, are operated by cams through rocking levers, G, better seen in the sectional end view of Fig. 2. The mixture of petrol and air is delivered from the carburetter, H, Fig. 2, into the induction manifold, J, from which a passage leads to each inlet valve, K. The exhaust valve and passage, not shown in Fig. 2, discharge the waste products to the exhaust manifold, L, and thence to the atmosphere. The sparking plug, M, is shown in Fig. 2, while the cooling water spaces are shown at N in both illustrations.

LESSON 20

Principles of Heavy Oil Engines

(See plate 40)

THE preceding Lesson was concerned with internal combustion engines of the explosion type, that is, engines in which a combustible mixture is compressed to a comparatively high pressure and temperature, and is then ignited by a spark. The rate of combustion is dependent upon the extent to which the mixture has been compressed, the instant at which the spark occurs, and the strength of the mixture. It was shown that the compression ratio used in engines of this type is limited by the occurrence of pre-ignition and detonation, and, since the efficiency increases with increased compression ratio, there is, for the same reason, a limit to the efficiency obtainable with explosion engines.

Ignition of the Fuel. The essential difference between oil engines and engines of the explosion type is that in the oil engine air alone, and not a mixture of air and fuel, is compressed in the cylinder. There is, therefore, no possibility of pre-ignition during compression, and, consequently, no limit, under this heading, to the extent to which the compression ratio may be raised. The fuel is injected in a fine spray into the compressed air at the end of the compression stroke, and the temperature of the air is so high that the oil ignites spontaneously and combustion proceeds as the oil is being sprayed into the cylinder. The instant at which the fuel begins to enter the cylinder, and the rate at which injection proceeds, determine the maximum pressure reached during combustion. Although the combustion should be complete as early as possible in the expansion stroke, care must be taken to prevent the pressure rising at an excessive rate, as this leads to noisy running.

In order to ensure the ignition of the spray, the air must be compressed to a higher pressure and temperature than is the case with the petrol engine. In most oil engines the compression ratio is of the order of 12 or 14, as compared with 5 or 7 for the petrol engine. On account of the higher compression ratio the oil engine is more efficient than the petrol engine. Apart from the fact that, at present at any rate, oil is much cheaper than petrol, a smaller quantity of fuel is required for the oil engine. This is of special importance for engines used for transport purposes, where the weight of the fuel reduces the useful load that may be carried. A petrol engine consumes about 50 per cent more fuel than an oil engine of the same power, so that, for a given journey, the vehicle fitted with the petrol engine suffers a corresponding loss in carrying capacity. This point is bound to ensure attention for the oil engine in connexion with long-distance aeroplane flights, where the range of the plane is limited by the weight of fuel with which it can rise from the ground. The main objection to the oil engine at present for this purpose is that it is heavier than the petrol engine, but it is probable that the weight will be considerably reduced when more experience has been gained with this comparatively new type of engine. Another factor which is greatly in the favour of the oil engine for aircraft purposes is the comparative absence of risk of fire ; the reason why so many air accidents are fatal at present is not that the plane crashes, but that an outbreak of fire so often follows the crash before the occupants have time to get clear.

The most important point in the operation of the oil engine is the injection of the fuel into the air compressed in the cylinder. The fuel must be broken up into a fine spray and intimately mixed with the air in the combustion chamber, in order that combustion may be completed in the short time available. In the earlier oil engines the fuel was forced into the cylinder by a blast of high-pressure air, and was thus well atomized and distributed over the combustion space. The supply of compressed air for this purpose necessitated the use of a special air compressor, thus adding considerably to the weight and cost of the engine. In modern engines, especially for purposes where weight is of paramount importance, the air compressor has been eliminated, and *airless* injection of the fuel is employed. In this method the oil is forced through a fine orifice under a very high pressure, any required type of spray being obtained by variations in the pressure behind the nozzle, or by variations in the size of the orifice itself. The oil is supplied by the fuel pump, a separate plunger being provided for each cylinder. The pump is driven from the engine by suitable gearing, so that injection takes place at the correct time and at the desired rate to ensure satisfactory operation of the engine.

Types of Oil Engine. The constructional details of the oil engine are very similar to those of engines previously considered. For high-speed engines, for example, the construction follows the lines of the petrol engine. Fig. 1 (plate 40) shows a six-cylinder engine fitted in buses and lorries. The distinctive feature is the fuel pump, mounted on the side of the engine, with the six delivery pipes leading to the fuel injectors, one for each cylinder. Fig. 2 is a section through one cylinder of the engine, and shows the piston at the upper limit of its stroke. The connecting rod is not shown in this illustration. The combustion chamber is of spherical shape, and is connected to the cylinder by the tangential passage shown. During the compression stroke the air is forced into the spherical chamber, the shape of the connecting passage ensuring a definite swirl. Thus the air is forced to flow past the injection nozzle with a high velocity, so that, when injection begins and combustion takes place, the products of combustion are swept away from the neighbourhood of the nozzle, and a continuous supply of fresh air is available for the combustion of the fuel as it enters.

LESSON 21

Compressed Air as a Source of Power

WHEN air is compressed, work is done on it, and energy is thus stored in the air. This energy is rendered available for useful work by the subsequent expansion of the compressed air. This forms a very convenient method for conveying energy from place to place, and is used to an increasing extent in all branches of engineering. One of the most general applications, and the one best known to the general public, is the road-breaking equipment which seems to have become a more or less permanent feature of the life of our large cities. The air is compressed in an air compressor, usually driven by a petrol engine, the whole plant being built so that it may easily be moved from one place to another. The compressed air is distributed through flexible hoses to the pneumatic tools ; these tools operate by the expansive action of the compressed air, on the same principles as those considered when dealing with engines.

Compressed air is also used largely in all forms of constructional engineering, for riveting, caulking, drilling, etc. The type of compressing plant depends upon the particular conditions involved. In a shipyard, for example, it is most economical to compress the air in a central power station, and to distribute the air under pressure through pipes to the required points. It is then possible to use the most convenient form of engine to drive the air compressor, without having to consider the portability of the plant. In practice, large air compressors are driven by either steam engines, oil engines, or electric motors.

Air Compressors. The operation of an air compressor is similar to that of a reciprocating steam engine, but the action is reversed. In a steam engine, steam at a high pressure is admitted to the cylinder for a portion of the stroke; the pressure then falls as the piston continues to be forced out to the end of the stroke. The exhaust valve then opens, and the low-pressure steam is expelled from the cylinder during the return stroke of the piston. In the air compressor, the suction valve remains open as the piston moves out, and air at a low pressure is drawn into the cylinder. At the end of the outstroke the suction valve closes, and the air is compressed during the early part of the return stroke of the piston. When the air in the cylinder has been compressed to the pressure on the delivery side, the delivery valve opens, and the compressed air is discharged into the receiver in which the air is stored, or from which it is distributed to required points.

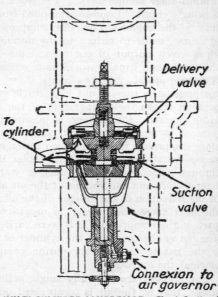

The suction and delivery valves of an air compressor are generally automatic in their action, each valve consisting of a plate pressed on to its seat by a light spring. The arrangement of a pair of valves is shown in Fig. 1. It will be seen that the suction valve will open only when the pressure in the cylinder is reduced, by the outward movement

MULTI-CYLINDER COMPRESSOR. Fig. 1. Sectional diagram showing arrangement of a pair of valves. The arrows show the direction of flow of the air.
Courtesy of Messrs. Broom & Wade, Ltd.

of the piston, below that of the surrounding atmosphere, by the slight amount necessary to move the spring; also, the valve will close as soon as the pressure inside the cylinder rises, at the end of the outstroke of the piston, above the pressure at which the valve opened. Similarly, the delivery valve is kept closed by the pressure on the discharge side until, on the compression stroke, the pressure inside the cylinder rises sufficiently to cause the valve to open.

Fig. 1 also shows one method used to control the quantity of air delivered by the compressor. As will be seen, the compressor has a hand-wheel at the bottom, and when this is revolved, the fork-shaped piece rises and the suction valve is held in the " open " position. The air is then only drawn in and pumped out again through the suction valve, and consequently no compression takes place.

Multi-Stage Compressors. The work done on the air while it is being compressed must be supplied from some external source, that is, the engine driving the compressor, and every effort is, of course, made to reduce to the minimum the power required for a given output of compressed air. For high-pressure air, the compressor usually works more efficiently if the compression is divided up into two, or perhaps three, stages than if the whole compression is carried out in a single stage. During the compression stroke the temperature of the air is raised, and, for a given pressure, the volume is greater than it would be if no increase in temperature took place. Consequently, in a multi-stage compressor the air is passed through an inter-cooler between successive stages. In the inter-cooler the air flows over tubes through which passes the cooling water ; thereby both the temperature and the volume of the air are reduced. As a result of the reduction in the volume of the air, less work is required in the next stage than would be necessary for the corresponding part of the compression if it were carried out in a single stage. The better the cooling of the cylinder of the compressor, the less is the rise in temperature during compression, and the more efficient the operation.

Compressors are generally single acting, except in the larger sizes ; that is, the air is compressed on one side of the piston only. It is preferable to use a number of small cylinders rather than one large cylinder giving the same volume, as the cooling surface is increased with multiple cylinders. Fig. 2 shows a part-section through one cylinder of a vertical, single-stage compressor, suitable for pressures up to 120 lb. per sq. inch. In this case the delivery valve is of the plate type described above, but the inlet valve is of the poppet type, being operated by the motion of the connecting rod, acting through the system of links shown in the illustration.

COMPRESSED AIR AS SOURCE OF POWER

The governor is usually arranged to limit the pressure on the delivery side to some pre-determined figure. The compressor is driven at constant speed, and if there is a reduction in the quantity of compressed air required the pressure on the delivery side will increase. This increase of pressure is made to operate the plunger of the governor, lifting the inlet valve from its seat, as shown in

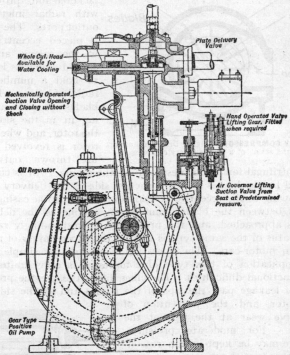

Whole Cyl. Head Available for Water Cooling

Plate Delivery Valve

Mechanically Operated Suction Valve Opening and Closing without Shock

Hand Operated Valve Lifting Gear. Fitted when required

Oil Regulator

Air Governor Lifting Suction Valve from Seat at Predetermined Pressure.

Gear Type Positive Oil Pump

TWIN CYLINDER COMPRESSOR. **Fig. 2.** Part-section through one cylinder of a vertical, single-stage compressor

Fig. 2, or as shown in Fig. 1 for an automatic valve, so that the air in the cylinder is forced back to the suction side and is not compressed. As soon as the delivery pressure falls to the correct value, the governor piston moves back to its original position and the inlet valve proceeds to operate again in the normal manner.

Rotary Compressors. For dealing with large quantities of air at comparatively low pressures—say, up to 40 lb. per sq. inch—the rotary type of compressor is more suitable than the reciprocating type. The principle underlying the action of this type of compressor may be explained with reference to Fig. 3. The

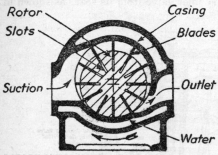

ROTARY COMPRESSOR. **Fig. 3.** Diagram illustrating the action of a simple rotary compressor.

main casing is water-jacketed and is provided with radial inlet and outlet ports. The rotor is placed eccentrically in the casing, and is slotted along its length to hold a number of radial blades. These blades are made a sliding fit in the slots in the rotor, and when the rotor is revolved they are thrown outwards by centrifugal force and press against the casing. Air is carried around by the blades from the suction side to the delivery side, and, owing to the eccentric position of the rotor in the casing, the spaces between the blades diminish in volume as the delivery side is approached, and the pressure is correspondingly raised Apparatus of the same type is used in the supercharger of many modern motor-cars. The operation is remarkably simple, and the application of this type of compressor is only limited by constructional difficulties. The chief difficulties are the prevention of leakage past the tips of the blades and at the sides of the rotor, and the prevention of excessive wear at the tips of the blades. For moderate pressures, leakage may be kept within reasonable bounds without excessive pressure between the guides and the casing, and, therefore, without excessive wear. Fig. 4 shows a complete rotor for one of these compressors, with the blades in position.

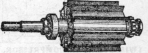

Fig. 4. A complete rotor showing the blades in position.

Our Course in Engineering is continued in Volume 4.

LESSON 13

The Two Principal Auxiliary Verbs

IN English, verbs, like nouns, have two numbers, singular and plural. The latter is without inflexion in all verbs save " to be." Verbs are inflected, however, for person. There are three persons, first, second and third—the person(s) speaking, the person(s) spoken to, and the person(s) spoken of.

CONJUGATION OF VERB " TO BE."

INFINITIVE MOOD.

Present.	*Past.*
to be	to have been

PARTICIPLES.

being	been, having been

GERUNDS.

Simple.	*Compound.*
being	having been

INDICATIVE MOOD.

Past.	*Present.*	*Future.*
	Indefinite.	
I was	I am	I shall be
	Complete.	
I had been	I have been	I shall have been

SUBJUNCTIVE MOOD.

Past.	*Present*
	Indefinite.
I were, or might be	I be, or may be
	Complete.
I had been, or might have been	I have been, or may have been

NOTE.—A third form of the subjunctive past tense is formed with *should* instead of *might* : I should be ; I should have been.

IMPERATIVE MOOD.

Singular.	*Plural.*
Be (thou)	Be (ye)

The full conjugation of the Present Indefinite Indicative is : I am, thou art, he is, we are, you are, they are ; and of the

(311)

Past : I was, thou wast, or wert, he was, we were, you were, they were.

In the compound tenses there is no inflexion, except of the auxiliary verbs " have," " shall," etc., to be given later.

All the tenses of *to be* can be used as auxiliaries to form the compound tenses of other verbs (e.g. " I shall have been writing ").

CONJUGATION OF VERB " TO HAVE."

INFINITIVE MOOD.

Present.	*Past.*
to have	to have had

PARTICIPLES.

having	had, having had

GERUNDS.

Simple.	*Compound.*
having	having had

INDICATIVE MOOD.

Past.	*Present.*	*Future.*
	Indefinite.	
I had	I have	I shall have
	Incomplete.	
I was having	I am having	I shall be having
	Complete.	
I had had	I have had	I shall have had
	Perfect Continuous.	
I had been having	I have been having	I shall have been having

SUBJUNCTIVE MOOD.

Past.	*Present.*
Indefinite.	
I had	I have
I might have	I may have
I should have	
Incomplete.	
I were having	I be having
I might be having	I may be having
I should be having	
Complete.	
I had had	I have had
I might have had	I may have had
I should have had	

(312)

Perfect Continuous

I had been having	I have been having
I might (or should) have been having	I may have been having

IMPERATIVE MOOD

Singular	*Plural*
Have (thou)	Have (ye)

The full conjugation of the Present Indefinite Indicative is : I have, thou hast, he has, we have, you have, they have ; and of the Past : I had, thou hadst, he had, we had, you had, they had.

Only the Indefinite tenses of *to have* can be used as auxiliaries for the purpose of forming compound tenses of other verbs.

KEY TO EXERCISE IN LESSON 12.

1. I had wanted to see him. 2. Trusting you are well, I remain, yours truly. (In the faulty sentence the participle *trusting* agrees with *you*, which is the suppressed subject to *believe ;* it therefore means : " Do you, trusting you are well, believe me," which is nonsense.) 3. The sentence should run either " In *reading* the Psalms " (gerund), or " In the *reading* of the Psalms " (abstract noun). 4. If he were to go, he would regret it (subjunctive mood). 5. If he had gone (*or*, had he gone), he would have regretted it.

LESSON 14

Conjugation of an Ordinary Verb

WE begin this Lesson by giving in tabular form the conjugation of an ordinary verb (other than an auxiliary) in its various voices, moods, and tenses. The alternative forms for the indicative indefinite (*did see, do see*, etc.) are used only in negative interrogative and emphatic sentences.

COMPLETE CONJUGATION OF THE VERB " TO SEE."

(A) *Active Voice.* INFINITIVE MOOD.

Present Indefinite : (To) see
Present Incomplete : (To) be seeing
Perfect : (To) have seen
Continuous Perfect : (To) have been seeing

PARTICIPLES.

Present : Seeing. *Perfect :* Having seen
Continuous Perfect : Having been seeing

INDICATIVE MOOD.

Past.	Present.	Future.

Indefinite.

I **saw** (*or,* did see)	I see (*or,* do see)	I shall see

Incomplete.

I **was** seeing	I am seeing	I shall be seeing

Perfect.

I **had** seen	I have seen	I shall have seen

Continuous Perfect.

I **had** been seeing	I have been seeing	I shall have been seeing

IMPERATIVE MOOD.

Singular : See (thou)   *Plural :* See (ye).

SUBJUNCTIVE MOOD.

Past.	Present.

Indefinite.

I saw	I see
I might see	I may see
I should see	

Incomplete.

I were seeing	*I be seeing
I might be seeing	I may be seeing
I should be seeing	

Perfect.

I had seen	I have seen
I might have seen	I may have seen
I should have seen	

Continuous Perfect.

I had been seeing	I have been seeing
I might have been seeing	I may have been seeing
I should have been seeing	

(B) *Passive Voice.*   INFINITIVE MOOD.

Indefinite.	*Perfect.*
To be seen	To have been seen

CONJUGATION OF AN ORDINARY VERB

PARTICIPLES.

Indefinite : Being seen.
Perfect : Seen, *or* having been seen.

INDICATIVE MOOD.

Past.	Present.	Future.
	Indefinite.	
I was seen	I am seen	I shall be seen
	Incomplete.	
I was being seen	I am being seen	*I shall be being seen
	Perfect.	
I had been seen	I have been seen	I shall have been seen

(No Continuous Perfect in the Passive.)

IMPERATIVE MOOD.

Singular : Be (thou) seen.
Plural : Be (ye) seen

SUBJUNCTIVE MOOD.

Past	Present.
	Indefinite.
I were seen	*I be seen
I might be seen	I may be seen
I should be seen	
	Incomplete.
*I were being seen	*I be being seen
*I might be being seen	*I may be being seen
*I should be being seen	
	Perfect.
I had been seen	I have been seen
I might have been seen	I may have been seen
I should have been seen	

Note. The forms marked with an asterisk are seldom, if ever, used in modern speech. It will be seen that many forms in the Subjunctive of the Active Voice are the same as in the Indicative.

The four simple tenses of the Active Voice are now given in full :

INDICATIVE MOOD.

Past Indefinite.		*Present Indefinite.*	
I saw	we saw	I see	we see
thou sawest	you saw	thou seest	you see
he saw	they saw	he sees	they see

SUBJUNCTIVE MOOD.

Past Indefinite.	*Present Indefinite.*	
(Same as Indicative.)	I see	We see
	thou see	you see
	he see	they see

Impersonal Verbs. In such expressions as " it thunders," " it hails," " it seems," the subject is general and undefined. These verbs are, therefore, called impersonal, there being no person expressed or understood as subject. They are always in the third person singular, though, of course, they can be of different tenses—e.g. it thundered, it will hail. While *it* is usually employed as the grammatical subject of such verbs, occasionally there is no subject expressed at all : as methinks (=it seems to me), meseems, maybe ; also, if you please (=if it please you).

Auxiliary and Principal Verbs. If we compare the sentences " I have lost sixpence " and " I have sixpence," we see a great difference in the two uses of *have*. In the first sentence it simply " helps " to form the present perfect tense of " lose." In the second sentence it has a meaning of its own, namely, " I possess." In the first case it is an auxiliary (helping) verb, in the second a principal verb. The same applies to *shall, will, may, do, be*— e.g. " I shall go tomorrow " (*auxiliary*), and " You *shall* (i.e. must) do it " (*principal*). " I will see you before long " (*auxiliary*), and " I *will* have my own way " (*principal*). " It may be wet tomorrow " (*auxiliary*), and " You *may* (i.e. are permitted to) go " (*principal*). " Do you think so ? " (*auxiliary*), and " What will you *do?*" (*principal*). " I am coming " (*auxiliary*), and " I *am* a man " (*principal*).

All the above-mentioned verbs (except *have* and *be*), when used as auxiliaries, are " deficient " in certain tenses. They have no infinitive and no participles and, therefore, have no compound tenses. Of course, when used as principal verbs, they are not necessarily defective. Thus, " to will " (meaning " to resolve ") has all the compound tenses. " I have willed," etc.

LESSON 15

Analysing the Sentence

I N this Lesson we turn aside from our study of words as independent units (the study of *Accidence*), and deal with them in their relationship to other words grouped with them to form a sentence. The unit of speech is the sentence, and it is quite as important to be able to break a sentence up into its component parts as it is to be able to compare an adjective or conjugate a verb. We cannot properly parse a word—that is, say to what part of speech it belongs—until we see it in a sentence ; and before we can parse it then as it should be parsed, we must make a mental analysis of the sentence. Analysis, then, logically comes before parsing.

Analysis of a Simple Sentence. A simple sentence has only one subject and one predicate. The subject is that about which something is asserted ; the predicate is what is asserted concerning the subject. In every sentence there must be a subject and a predicate ; this is the irreducible minimum, as " Fire burns." In addition, there may be a word or words limiting or qualifying either the subject or the predicate, or both, as : " *This* fire burns *well*." Finally, if the predicate contains a transitive verb, this will take an object, and this object, too, may have a word or words limiting it, as : " Fire burns your finger " (*finger* being the object and *your* the limitation of the object).

ANALYSIS OF SENTENCES, SHOWING THEIR STRUCTURE.

" The freshening breeze of eve unfurled that banner's massy fold."

Subject.	Limitation of Subject.	Predicate.	Object.	Limitation of Object.
breeze	1. The freshening 2. of eve	unfurled	fold	that banner's massy

---

" Here rests his head upon the lap of earth   A youth to fortune and to fame unknown."

Subject.	Limitation of Subject.	Predicate.	Limitation of Pred.	Object.	Limitation of Object.
youth	1. A 2. to fortune and to fame unknown	rests	1. Here 2. upon the lap of earth	head	his

---

ANALYSIS OF SENTENCES, SHOWING THEIR STRUCTURE (continued).

" Cromwell's enemies have often called him a bloodthirsty monster."

Predicate.

Subject.	Limitation of Subject.	Verb.	Complement.	Limitation of Complement.	Limitation of Predicate.	Object.
enemies	Cromwell's	have called	monster	a bloodthirsty	often	him

Parts of a Simple Sentence. As a rule, a simple sentence does not consist of more than the following parts : subject ; limitation of subject ; predicate ; limitation of predicate ; object ; limitation of object.

For example : " The freshening breeze of eve unfurled that banner's massy fold " consists of five parts, which may be isolated as in the table given in the preceding page.

Sometimes the predicate consists of a verb and a complement, especially after verbs of *making, calling,* and so on. For example : " Cromwell's enemies have often called him a bloodthirsty monster." An analysis of this sentence appears in tabular form at the top of this page.

Analysis lays bare the structure of the sentence. From a grammatical point of view, a sentence is not grasped until it has been mentally analysed and all its component parts set forth in their utter nakedness.

LESSON 16

Some Defective Verbs

IN this Lesson, and in Lesson 17, we note the defective verbs and their uses. Some of their parts were already missing in the Old English period. At this time also they were employed chiefly as auxiliaries, though their uses did not correspond exactly with those of Modern English. In English, helping or auxiliary verbs are numerous, and most auxiliaries can be also employed as independent verbs : e.g *have* meaning *possess,* and *do* meaning *perform.* We now give the conjugation of the auxiliary verbs *do, will, shall* and *may.* The two principal auxiliary verbs, *to be* and *to have,* have been considered in Lesson 13.

DEFECTIVE VERBS

CONJUGATION OF VERB " DO."

INFINITIVE MOOD.

Present.	*Incomplete.*	*Past.*
(To) do	(to) be doing	(to) have done

PARTICIPLES.

doing done

INDICATIVE MOOD.

Past.		*Present.*	
I did	we did	I do	.we do
thou didst	you did	thou doest	you do
		or dost	
he did	they did	he doeth	they do
		or doth	
		or does	

NOTES. When used as a notional verb, *do* is conjugated **in** full (Future : *I shall do*, etc. ; Incomplete : *I was doing*, etc.) ; but when as an auxiliary, only the present and past indefinite are used (*do* and *did*). *Doest* and *doeth* are only used in the notional sense, e.g. " *Doest* thou well to be angry ? " and, of course, **are** now archaic.

CONJUGATION OF VERB " WILL."

INDICATIVE MOOD.

Past.	*Present.*
I would	I will
thou wouldest	thou wilt, or willest
he would, etc.	he will, or wills, etc.

NOTES. The past of the subjunctive is the same as the **past** indicative (*I would*, etc.) ; there is no present tense in the subjunctive. The forms *willest* and *wills* (Pres. Indic.) are not used when the verb is an auxiliary. When *will* means " to exercise the will," or " to bequeath by will," it has a full conjugation. The past indicative *would* is used as an auxiliary only in reported (or indirect) speech, to take the place of *will* in direct speech, e.g. " he *will* come soon " (*direct*) ; " he said that he *would* come soon " (*indirect*).

Will is also used to express a customary or frequently repeated action, as : " He *will* play for hours " ; " when he was young, he *would* spend whole days in the fields and hedgerows."

Won't comes from *wol* (not), an old form of *will*.
When *will* is an auxiliary verb, it has no compound tenses.

CONJUGATION OF VERB "SHALL."
INDICATIVE MOOD.

Past.	*Present.*
I should	I shall
thou shouldst	thou shalt
he should, etc.	he shall, etc.

NOTES. The past of the subjunctive is the same as the past indicative ; there is no present subjunctive, nor any infinitive, imperative or participles, whether *shall* is used as auxiliary or notional verb. The past indicative *should* is used as an auxiliary only in reported speech, representing *shall* in direct speech.

Shall comes from *sculan*=to owe, and hence arose the meaning of obligation, e.g.=" he *shall* do it," " you *should* answer when your mother speaks." When *shall* retains this idea of " obligation " it is a notional verb ; used as an auxiliary it loses this force.

CONJUGATION OF VERB "MAY."
INDICATIVE MOOD.

Past.	*Present.*
I might	I may
thou mightest	thou mayest
he might, etc.	he may, etc.

NOTES. The subjunctive mood is the same as the indicative. *May* has no infinitive, imperative, or participles ; and in its indicative mood it is never auxiliary, but always notional, e.g. " you *may* go " (i.e. " you are permitted to go ") ; " the fish *might* be seen rising at any hour almost " (i.e. it was possible to see them). In the subjunctive mood, of course, it can be an auxiliary, e.g. " we eat in order that we *may* live " ; " may it be so " ; " I came early so that I *might* see you."

We have now discussed all the auxiliary verbs, namely, *be, have, do, will, shall,* and *may*. Three verbs, *can, must,* and *ought,* are sometimes called auxiliaries ; but they do not help to form any tense, mood, or voice of any verb. These are fully treated in the next Lesson.

Our Course in English Language is continued in Volume 4.

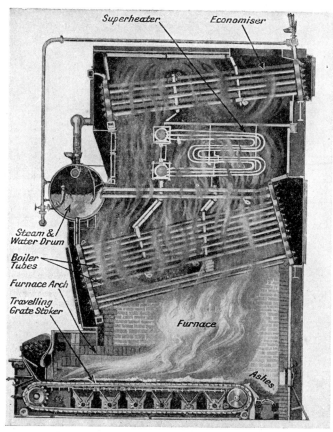

Superheater   Economiser

Steam &
Water Drum

Boiler
Tubes

Furnace Arch

Travelling
Grate Stoker

Furnace

Ashes

STEAM BOILERS. Fig. 2. Modern water-tube boiler, fitted with a travelling-grate mechanical stoker. ENGINEERING 17

Babcock & Wilcox, Ltd.

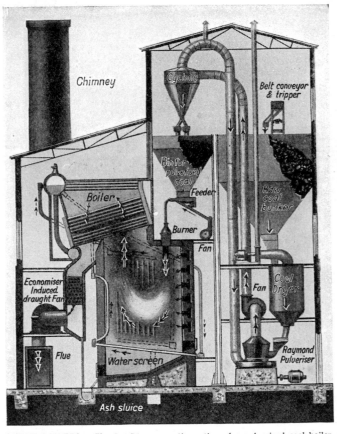

Chimney

Cyclone

Belt conveyor & tripper

Bin for pulverised coal

Feeder

Boiler

Raw coal bunker

Burner

Fan

Economiser Induced draught Fan

Coal Dryer

Flue

Fan

Water screen

Raymond Pulveriser

Ash sluice

STEAM BOILERS. **Fig. 3.** Diagrammatic section of a pulverized coal boiler.
ENGINEERING 17
Internal Combustion, Ltd.

Plate 38　　　　　　　　　　　　　　　　　　　　　　　　*Volume III*

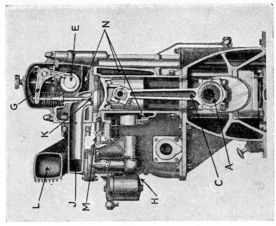

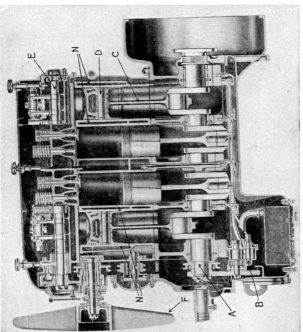

FOUR-CYLINDER PETROL ENGINE. Fig. 1 (left). Cross-section of a modern four-cylinder engine as used in buses and lorries, showing the arrangement of pistons, crankshaft and other parts. **Fig. 2** (right). Sectional end view of the same engine. Reference should be made to the text where the lettering in these photographs is explained ENGINEERING 19

Courtesy of Associated Equipment Co., Ltd.

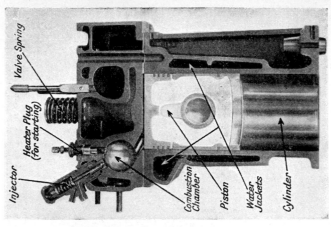

Valve Spring

Heater Plug
(for starting)

Injector

Combustion
Chamber

Piston

Water
Jackets

Cylinder

HIGH SPEED OIL ENGINE. Fig. 1 (above). This six-cylinder heavy oil, or oil injection, engine is fitted with the A.E.C.-Ricardo head (seen in section in Fig. 2) and produces 130 h.p. on the brake. It works at more than double the compression of a comparable petrol engine, the fuel being injected in spray form at the point of highest compression of the air in the cylinder. Note the fuel pump with separate pipes for each of the six injectors at the cylinder heads. **Fig. 2** (right). In this section are seen the compression space above the piston, the fuel injector with a special spherical combustion chamber and cooling water spaces.

ENGINEERING 20

Courtesy of A. E. C., Ltd.

Plate 40

Volume III

LESSON 21

The Poetry of Cowper, Crabbe and Burns

(See Plate 41)

WILLIAM COWPER (1731–1800) wrote : " It is a great thing to be indeed a poet, and does not happen to more than one man in a century." It happened to him. Although his poetry has passed through periods of comparative neglect in the century and more that has gone since his death, it has never been quite under eclipse. It was the religious nature of his poetry that earned its first great vogue. At the close of the eighteenth century and in the early years of the nineteenth century the whole middle-class community of England was " brought up on Cowper." Yet it was a piece of joyous ballad poetry, " John Gilpin," that first won the popular favour and will longest retain it. He was fifty-four when he published " The Task," which made him famous and established him in the front rank of contemporary poets.

Begun in the winter of 1783, it was written at the suggestion of a friend, Lady Austen, and its success was complete, for here Cowper showed himself in his natural spirit. " The Task " has been said to be a poem about Cowper himself, and, although it contains hardly a hint of the tragedy of his life, in it his ailings, his walks, his friends, his abhorrence of slavery, and his religious views are delightfully portrayed. A modern appreciation of Cowper is to be found in Lord David Cecil's " The Stricken Deer."

Among Cowper's contemporaries were James Macpherson (1736–96), the reputed author of Ossian ; Charles Churchill (1731–64), author of the satirical " Prophecy of Famine " ; Michael Bruce (1746–67), who probably wrote that exquisite lyric, " Ode to the Cuckoo," which has also been claimed for John Logan (1748–88) ; and Thomas Chatterton (1752–70), who wrote the Rowley Forgeries at the age of sixteen, and the exquisite " Balade of Charitie " at eighteen.

The marvellous boy,
The sleepless soul that perished in his pride !

Chatterton came to London full of hope and confidence in his precocious powers. He died of starvation and poison in a wretched garret, and was buried in the paupers' pit of Shoe Lane Workhouse.

Burns. When Cowper talks about only one poet arising in a century he is somewhat wide of the mark. His own century produced Pope, Crabbe, and Burns in addition to himself. To Robert Burns (1759–96) fame came early, and a sorry business he made of it.

> He left his land her sweetest song
> And earth her saddest story.

But the universal renown and affection which have grown for the works and character of Burns since his death are unprecedented in the history of literature. There are good reasons for this. The lyric gift of Burns more nearly touched perfection than that of any English poet before or since. The epithet " English " is used with a full sense of responsibility, because Burns is something more than an Ayrshire bard, and there are objections to the word " British " as applied to matters of taste. There is a further reason for emphasizing his English quality, despite what Cowper, who was admired by Burns, called his " uncouth dialect," and it is this.

Burns is a writer of the purest, smooth-flowing English. In all his serious poetry there is hardly one Scottish word. He reserves the Scottish tongue for his lighter moods. his satirical vein, and it is to be observed in such a poem as " The Cottar's Saturday Night," that as the thought changes in character or deepens in seriousness the language changes also. Burns himself tells us in the famous dedication to the noblemen and gentlemen of the Caledonian Hunt that the poetic genius of his country bade him sing the loves, the joys, the rural scenes and rural pleasures of his wild, natal soil in his native tongue, and he tuned his " artless " notes as she inspired. There has been a tendency to accept him a little too much at his own valuation in that matter of art and artlessness. Actually he is one of the most finished of English poets and his prose is obviously that of one who is an artist in words. Let it be declared here that he was a conscious artist and no untutored genius of the plough.

It has to be remembered that Burns was no infant phenomenon of the muse. The bulk of the poetry on which his fame is based was written round about the age of 25—by no means an early age for a poet of genius—when his inspiration was at its freshest and his education had been carried far beyond the average of his class, both in reading and in writing. He was already an artist when he made his bid for fame. That is an aspect of the poet which students should consider. Burns was a ploughman, but in the Scotland of his day and perhaps in the Scotland of today, the ploughman may be a man of culture as well as agriculture. Burns was no counterpart of the English Hodge, plus inspiration. He was a well-educated, bookish young Scotsman of poor but decent parentage, a description that would be true of fifty per cent of his countrymen.

Robert Burns is the peculiar glory of Scotland. There never was a poet at once so local and so universal in his appeal. He brought the quality of pity into poetry and stirred it in the hearts of men at a time when the blighting shadows of Calvinism-cum-Knoxism still lay upon Scotland and made its religion bleak and forbidding. For every lowly thing, for all downtrodden, unhappy folk, Burns was full of pity. And that pity has immortal expression in many of his poems, while there is also a wistfulness about much that he wrote that goes straight to our hearts and brings the poet there also.

Crabbe. Although in his birth George Crabbe (1754–1832) pre-dates Burns, his principal achievement falls within the nineteenth century, and Burns had died four years before that opened. " Nature's sternest painter and her best," says Byron : a description that is not free from poetic enlargement, though the first half of the line might safely be accepted. For Crabbe's chief work was to restore a sense of the realities ; to smash up the pretty-pretty, meretricious, porcelain stuff that had come to pass as pastoral poetry. This he did lustily, and in fine, vigorous verse that pleased the ear while it sustained interest in the pity or the horror of his story. Humour is not Crabbe's strong point, and yet we grow to like the poet by reason of his evident sympathy with the unfortunate subjects of his verse. He is a satirist moved by a passionate attachment to the truth and a warm heart for human suffering, so that where others were seeing nothing but idyllic scenes in a rural England that never was—Goldsmith among them—and it was the fashion to pretend that the country life was arcadian in its unalloyed delights, Crabbe in his poem " The Village," could remind us of the sordid realities of " the parish house " in this fashion :

Theirs is yon House that holds the parish poor,
Whose walls of mud scarce bear the broken door ;
There where the putrid vapours, flagging, play,
And the dull wheel hums doleful through the day,
There children dwell who know no parents' care ;
Parents who know no children's love dwell there ;
Heart-broken matrons on their joyless bed,
Forsaken wives, and mothers never wed,
Dejected widows with unheeded tears,
And crippled age with more than childhood fears ;
The lame, the blind, and, far the happiest they !
The moping idiot and the madman gay.

Influenced by Goldsmith, Gray and Pope, Crabbe may be considered as the chief founder of the rural school and as the forerunner of Wordsworth. We read Crabbe for what he says more than because of his style which, notwithstanding its vigour, is unequal and frequently faulty. His knowledge of humanity is extensive ; and he showed a charming lyric gift when he sought relief from the heroic couplet. " The Parish Register," published in 1807, is, perhaps, most worthy of study.

LESSON 22

From Blake to Wordsworth

(See plate 41)

THE poetry of the nineteenth century struck its roots in the soil of the eighteenth and its branches stretch into the twentieth. In its style, a notable characteristic is a certain reaction against artificiality and mere rhetoric. In its spirit is distinguishable the influence of the Germany of Goethe and Schiller, of the France of Rousseau and Victor Hugo, and of the " problem " writers of Norway and Denmark. The movements towards political freedom in France, Italy and Greece, and the evolution of English democracy, all affected it vitally. Thus, to its understanding must be brought some knowledge of the historic happenings amid which it arose and flourished.

It is possible to take the works of two or more of the greatest poets of the period, and to derive pleasure from the isolated perusal of them. But while there is much to be said for the study of the poetry of any writer for its own sake, the more we know of the main facts in the life and times of a great writer, the better shall we understand and appreciate what he has written.

The great name of William Blake is placed here instead of in Lesson 21, because, though born two years previously to Robert Burns, Blake (1757-1827) is a link between the Elizabethans and Wordsworth. He towers above lesser men of his own day by reason of his imaginative genius, and the authentic accounts of his life prove him, in the light of modern understanding, to have been of better balanced temperament than has sometimes been allowed. He was irritable, even violent in his bitterness against accepted forms of injustice, but enlivening his passionate sincerity was a great gift of humour. His love of children speaks to us in his exquisite " Songs of Innocence "; his feelings of horror at the cruelty of life in his " Songs of Experience." He was a mystic, with a contrast of simplicity and subtlety in his work ; he felt keenly and expressed keenly social wrongs and ecclesiastical tyranny. Like Crabbe, he had to fight poverty, and owed his knowledge to his own self-improving efforts.

In his youth Blake was fascinated by notions of an early mythological Britain. He was also imbued with the ideas of the mystic Swedenborg. These influences are traceable in the " Prophetic Books," in which he evolved a complete symbolism, and in which lovely passages abound amidst their strange and often obscure mysticism. We have space only to quote one of these, from " The Four Zoas " :

What is the price of Experience ? Do men buy it for a song,
Or Wisdom for a dance in the street ? No ! it is bought with the price
Of all that a man hath—his house, his wife, his children.
Wisdom is sold in the desolate market where none come to buy,
And in the wither'd field where the farmer ploughs for bread in vain.

Born in London, where he had lived for sixty-seven of his seventy years, in his day Blake met with little encouragement, though he had his own circle of friends and a devoted wife. Poet, engraver and painter, his illustrations to his poems are superb (see Plate 19). Of him his friend, disciple and patron, John Linnell, wrote : " He feared nothing so much as being rich, lest he should lose his spiritual riches."

Among the lesser poets, Samuel Rogers (1763-1855) wrote a long poem in heroic metre on " The Pleasures of Memory." and caught, in his blank verse poem " Italy," some of the beauties of that southern land. Robert Bloomfield (1766-1823), first a rural " hand " and then a shoemaker, wrote, in a London garret, " The Farmer's Boy," which gives a sympathetic view of the life indicated by its title. He derived his style from Thomson's " Seasons." Another poet of humble life, though on a much higher level, is James Hogg (1770-1835), the " Ettrick Shepherd," who stands next to Burns in the order of Scotland's peasant-poets. He described himself to Scott, to whom he sent contributions for the latter's " Border Minstrelsy," as " King of the Mountain and Fairy School of Poetry," and this piece of self-description is accepted by the critics. "When the Kye Come Hame" and " Kilmeny " are among Hogg's most popular compositions.

Wordsworth One of the greatest poets of the nineteenth century now claims attention in William Wordsworth (1770–1850). In his early days he was greatly influenced by the ideals of French republicanism and the teaching of William Godwin, the author of " Political Justice," a work basing morals on necessity, who also had a marked influence on Coleridge. When France. having first debased them, forsook her humanistic ideals for dreams of world conquest under Napoleon, the effect on Wordsworth would have been disastrous but for the devotion of his sister Dorothy and the fact that a legacy of £900 left to the brother and a sum of £100 bequeathed to the sister enabled them to settle down quietly, first at Racedown, in Dorset—where Wordsworth's one tragedy, " The Borderers," was written —then at Alfoxden, by the Quantock hills—which district inspired his and Coleridge's contributions to the volume of " Lyrical Ballads "—and, finally, at Grasmere. This was the home of the Wordsworths from 1799 till the poet's death. " The Prelude : or, the Growth of a Poet's Mind," an autobiographical poem in blank verse, reflects the influence of ideas acquired during his visits to Germany, Italy, Switzerland and France. That poem and " The Excursion " are parts of a scheme never completed.

Wordsworth has to be considered in three aspects—critic, teacher and poet. His critical opinions may be studied in the preface and appendix to the " Lyrical Ballads," the preface to ' The Excursion," and in numerous letters. In the preface to the " Lyrical Ballads " he writes :

FROM BLAKE TO WORDSWORTH

" It may be safely affirmed that there neither is, nor can be, any essential difference between the language of prose and metrical composition. We are fond of tracing the resemblance between poetry and painting, and accordingly we call them sisters ; but where shall we find bonds of connection sufficiently strict to typify the affinity between metrical and prose composition ? They both speak by and to the same organs ; the bodies in which both of them are clothed may be said to be of the same substance, their affections are kindred and almost identical, not necessarily differing even in degree."

The best proof of the error inherent in this view of poetry is to be found in Wordsworth's own work. Elsewhere, in his intense scorn for the artificial and the meretricious, which were so characteristic of much of the poetry of the eighteenth century, Wordsworth went to the verge of the trivial. But though he raised a storm of criticism, which delayed due recognition of his genius and is not yet exhausted, it is well to remember with Coleridge, one of the greatest of literary critics—especially where Wordsworth is concerned—that, but for the prefaces and appendices, much of what has been said against Wordsworth's poems would be reduced to absurdity. The few pages that gave such an opportunity to the pungent parodists of " Rejected Addresses," to Byron, to Leigh Hunt, to Jeffrey, and to others to pour scorn on Wordsworth, would, but for the fear that they represented an intention to overthrow the accepted canons of art, have been " passed over in silence as so much blank paper, or leaves of a bookseller's catalogue," and " only regarded as so many light and inferior coins in a rouleau of gold." Popularity and honours at length rewarded the poet. In 1839 Oxford gave him the Doctorate, and in 1843 he succeeded Southey as Poet Laureate.

As a teacher Wordsworth took his vocation seriously. " The poet," he averred, " is a teacher. I wish to be considered as a teacher or as nothing." What did he teach ? George Brimley, in one of the most brilliant of his essays, written in 1851 and still applicable, contends, with reason, that the value of Wordsworth's teaching

" lay mainly in the power that was given him of unfolding the glory and the beauty of the natural world and in bringing consciously before the minds of men the high moral function that belonged in the human economy to the imagination, and in thereby redeeming the faculties of sense from the comparatively low and servile office of ministering merely to the animal pleasures. . . . He has shown the possibility of combining a state of vivid enjoyment, even of intense passion, with the activity of thought and the repose of contemplation. He has, moreover, done more than any poet of his age to break down and obliterate the conventional barriers that, in our disordered social state, divide rich and poor into two hostile nations ; and he has done this, not by bitter and passionate declamation on the injustices and vices of the rich, and on the wrongs and virtues of the poor, but by fixing his imagination on the elemental feelings, which are the same in all classes, and drawing out the beauty that lies in all that is truly natural in human life."

Was Wordsworth a poet ?   Indubitably ; as Plato and Dante were poets. None but a great poet could have written such lines as those " Composed a few miles above Tintern Abbey," in 1789 : or his " Lines suggested by a picture of Peele Castle in a Storm." But Wordsworth's claim to rank among the immortals might be based on his sonnets alone. From whatever standpoint it may be looked at, the sonnet " Composed upon Westminster Bridge, September 3rd, 1802," quoted here, is one of the very finest in the language.

> Earth has not anything to show more fair ;
> Dull would he be of soul who could pass by
> A sight so touching in its majesty ;
> This city now doth like a garment wear
> The beauty of the morning ; silent, bare,
> Ships, towers, domes, theatres and temples lie
> Open unto the fields, and to the sky ;
> All bright and glittering in the smokeless air.
> Never did sun more beautifully steep
> In his first splendour valley, rock, or hill :
> Ne'er saw I, never felt, a calm so deep !
> The river glideth at his own sweet will ;
> Dear God ! the very houses seem asleep :
> And all that mighty heart is lying still.

There is nothing in the Elizabethan writers of the sonnet to surpass it in perfection of form.

LESSON 23

Shelley, Byron and Other Early 19th Century Poets

(See plates 42 and 43)

CHIEF of Wordsworth's contemporaries was Samuel Taylor Coleridge (1772–1834). Coleridge was a talker, a preacher, a philosopher, and a mystic. His best work belongs to his early years, when he was inspired by his love of Nature and by the revolutionary idealism of France. His ballad epic of " Christabel," though a fragment, exercised in MS. form, some twenty years before it was published, a wonderful influence on Scott and other English poets.

For an explanation of the dreamland beauty of " Christabel " and the " Rime of the Ancient Mariner " recourse must be had to the German philosophers, particularly to Goethe, Herder, Schelling, and others of their school, to whom Coleridge was much indebted.

Sir Walter Scott (1771–1832) sought and restored to letters the romance of the past. " The Lay of the Last Minstrel," " Marmion," and " The Lady of the Lake," his best poems, are for the million what " Christabel " and " The Ancient Mariner " are for the comparatively few. For pure joy in Nature and love of humanity Scott was not excelled by either Wordsworth or Coleridge, but there is a certain mechanical touch in his verse and a mannerism which prevent its being classed with the greatest English poetry.

Robert Southey (1774–1843), as a poet, is little honoured today, though Professor Saintsbury boldly champions his cause. His choice of subjects and his ponderous treatment are reasons for neglect. Of his longer works, " Roderick, the Last of the Goths," is the best. The others are " Thalaba, the Destroyer," a rhymed epic of Arabia ; " Madoc," a semi-historical poem, descriptive of the adventures of a Welsh prince ; and " The Curse of Kehama," a poem in irregular rhymes, the theme of which is drawn from Hindu mythology. Southey is better known by such spirited ballads as " The Battle of Blenheim," " The Well of St. Keyne," and " The Inchcape Rock."

The place of Walter Savage Landor (1775–1864) is with the prose writers of the nineteenth century, for he wrote poetry for amusement and prose as an occupation. But it was with a poem, "Gebir," that his genius first flashed into enduring flame. He also wrote some beautiful lyrics, notably the exquisite elegy that enshrines the name of his much loved Rose Aylmer, whose early death in India he never ceased to mourn.

Thomas Campbell (1777–1844) is, like Southey, best remembered by his lyrical poems—"Hohenlinden," "Ye Mariners of England," "The Soldier's Dream," "Lord Ullin's Daughter," and the "Song of the Evening Star" are among them. "Pleasures of Hope" is an echo of Thomson and Gray.

Thomas Moore (1779–1852) the Bard of Erin, had in abundance the double gift of vocal and poetic melody. An Irishman by birth, he achieved the more enduring part of his reputation by his "Irish Melodies," lyrics of haunting beauty written to be sung to native airs instinct with an equally tender spirit of music. His social success was also due in part to his witty gift of political satire, exemplified by him in "The Twopenny Post Bag" and "The Fudge Family."

While still at the zenith of his fame, he forsook lyrical for narrative poetry and in 1817 published "Lalla Rookh," a poem which, despite certain obvious faults, of which the chief is an excess of sensuousness, has many passages of rare beauty and some of splendour.

Moore rendered a real service to English verse by introducing a great variety into the use of the lyric metres. Poetry was still fettered by a too rigid insistence upon the iambic and trochaic metres and, possibly for the satisfaction of his own musical instinct, he made a free use of dactylic and anapaestic measures, managing them with astonishing dexterity and contributing greatly to the emancipation of all lyric poets who have followed him. It is Moore's great distinction, his fellow countryman Stephen Gwynn has remarked, that he brought into English verse something of the variety and multiplicity of musical rhythms.

Byron. Since the reaction following the excessive hero-worship to which he was at first subjected, George Gordon, Lord Byron (1788–1824), has enjoyed a greater popularity on the Continent than in England. He is a figure of romance. His poetry is part of his personality. He lived and moved in an atmosphere for ever electrical with presage of storm, joyous intervals of sunniest beauty alternating with others of sombre melancholy. In this he was intensely human ; he was exceptional only in being able to give to all his moods a romantic glamour, which made even his melancholy a thing of tenderness and human pity.

Of all our great poets, he is the most subjective : he found all his emotional material within himself. In everything that he wrote it is himself that clamours for expression : the personages of his poems are but varying aspects of the poet. His poetry may be regarded as really an extraordinarily brilliant and fascinating autobiography.

Thus it is especially true of Byron that without some knowledge of the successive stages of his short but crowded life, his belongings, his surroundings, his friendships and his fortunes, a great deal of his poetry lacks significance. His output was large. It comprises two epics, or quasi-epics, " Childe Harold " and " Don Juan "—which constitute his best work—twelve narrative poems, eight dramas, seven or eight satires and a multitude of occasional poems, lyrics, epigrams and jeux d'esprit. That his verse had many technical faults is true ; as Sir Edmund Gosse points out, " he lacked the power to finish : he offended by a hundred careless impertinences : but his whole being was an altar on which the flame of personal genius flared like a conflagration." Byron, indeed, had the true poetic " glamour " ; he could not be shackled by any laws of rhythm or rhyme. He was, however, shackled and mentally warped by his one personal defect—his lameness, which helped to make him cynical and jaundiced his outlook on life.

His contemporary Trelawny, in " Recollections of Shelley and Byron," writes :

" Byron's spirit was always on the fret and fume to be doing something new and strange ; he exhausted himself in speculating, plotting and planning ; but when it came to the point of execution, the inertness of his body and his halting gait held him fast, so that few men even among the poets did more in imagination and less in reality than he did."

The French author André Maurois has written interesting biographical studies of both Byron and Shelley (" Ariel, ou la vie de Shelley ") which have been translated into English, and which shed much light on the romantic picturesqueness of the former and on the sensitive personality of the latter poet.

Shelley. Percy Bysshe Shelley (1792–1822) was, as Byron was, a herald of revolt ; but he was also, what Byron could hardly be said to be, an idealist. Byron was at times sincere ; Shelley always so. If Shelley erred against the social and religious conventions of his day, it was not out of contempt or in any spirit of reckless libertinism, but because he had constructed for himself a philosophy and adhered to it. Among his principal works are " Queen Mab," " Alastor," " The Revolt of Islam," " Prometheus Unbound," that dark and poignant drama, " The Cenci," " Julian and Maddalo," the " Witch of Atlas," " Epipsychidion," " Adonaïs," and " Hellas." In " Queen Mab " were expressed the mingled idealism and atheism of the Revolution. " Prometheus Unbound " is well described as " the finest example we have of the working out in poetry of the idea of a regenerated universe." " Adonaïs," one of his loveliest poems and most finished pieces of art, was a lament for the death of John Keats. Shelley's was a divided personality ; he lived in the world, but all his thoughts soared into the empyrean. As a poet of the imagination, he was immeasurably superior to Byron. Of his lyrics, the " Ode to the West Wind " is as imperishable as anything in English poetry.

In his introduction to " The Life of Shelley," as comprised in the three principal contemporary " Lives " of the poet by Hogg, Trelawny and Peacock (Dent, 1933), Mr. Humbert Wolfe, with his close knowledge of Shelley's life and work, writes :

" Whatever brainstorms might from time to time have disturbed him, Shelley could and did reason more closely than almost any poet of them all. He held resolutely to the path of his ideal, and in all the relations of life if he was sometimes surprising as a man, it was because his Maker had painted him, in Browning's phrase with only so much body as showed soul."

Keats. To turn from Byron and Shelley to John Keats (1795–1821) is like passing from a storm in which body and soul have been engaged to some sweet resting-place. Keats leaves the problems of passion—whether physical or purely intellectual—alone, and tunes his lyre to hymns of beauty and the praise of Nature. He is one of the first of modern literary poets, drawing his inspiration largely from ancient Greece and Elizabethan England, though the influence of his friendship for Leigh Hunt is distinguishable in his early poems. When the critics attacked "Endymion," the attack was meant to reach, through it, the detested politics of Leigh Hunt. Not only Browning and Tennyson, but Dante Gabriel Rossetti, William Morris, and Algernon Charles Swinburne owe much to Keats. "Hyperion" is a beautiful fragment ; the odes "On a Grecian Urn" and "To a Nightingale," the sonnet, "On first Looking into Chapman's Homer," and the poems, "The Eve of St. Agnes" and "La Belle Dame Sans Merci," stand by themselves in the foremost ranks of their kind. They are the work, be it remembered, of one whose father worked in a livery stable, and who began life as a surgeon's apprentice and was dead at the age of twenty-six.

Other poets calling for brief mention are : Ebenezer Elliott (1781–1849), whose "Corn Law Rhymes" have served to distract attention from his transcripts from Nature; Leigh Hunt (1784–1859), whose reputation, largely due to his prose writings, would not be inconsiderable were it based only on "The Story of Rimini" and his other and shorter poems, of which "Abou Ben Adhem" and "Jenny Kissed Me" are most familiar ; Thomas Love Peacock (1785–1866), who wrote a number of delightful lyrics which are to be found in his novels ; Bryan Waller Procter ("Barry Cornwall") (1787–1874), who, while he is better known for his appreciations of poetry than as a poet himself, wrote at least one good song, "The Sea" ; Sir Aubrey De Vere (1788–1846), who wrote several fine sonnets and two dramas of much poetic strength, "Julian the Apostate" and "Mary Tudor" ; Thomas Hood (1799–1845), whose "I remember, I remember," "The Dream of Eugene Aram," "The Song of the Shirt," and "The Bridge of Sighs" are as truly poetry of the heart as his inimitable humour was original ; Lord Macaulay (1800–59), whose spirited "Lays of Ancient Rome" used to be the popular ideal of the heroic ; William Barnes (1801–86), the pastoral poet of Dorsetshire ; Winthrop Mackworth Praed (1802–39), a writer of bright, witty "society verse" ; and Robert Stephen Hawker (1803–75), the inspired poet-priest of Morwenstow.

Attention must be drawn to the poems of the gifted Brontë sisters, published in 1846 under the pen names of Currer, Ellis, and Acton Bell. Emily Brontë was the greatest genius of the family. Her poems show a sense of vision which those of the other sisters lack ; they have been slow in gaining the appreciation they deserve—though both Matthew Arnold and Swinburne fully recognize her genius—but as a poetess her place is now surely fixed.

Elizabeth Barrett Browning (1806–61), the publication of whose first volume of " Poems " in 1844 was an event of importance in the history of Victorian literature, was gifted with fervour, imagination and sympathy. Among these poems was the often quoted " Cry of the Children." Her most notable work was her " Sonnets from the Portuguese," inspired by Robert Browning's courtship, and this was followed by " Casa Guidi Windows," the metrical romance " Aurora Leigh," and the posthumous " Last Poems," published by her husband. Her work is sometimes marred by slipshod rhythm and the diffuseness which was a fault more of the fashion of her period than innate.

LESSON 24

Greatest Poets of the Victorian Age : Tennyson and Browning

(See Plate 43)

ALFRED, LORD TENNYSON (1809–92), is the " bright particular star " in the crowded galaxy of Victorian poets. One of the most scholarly and exact of poets since Milton and Gray, he was, with the possible exceptions of Burns and Byron, the most popular since Shakespeare. Not even Wordsworth took his vocation more seriously. From a period of idealism he passed to one of something very like pessimism. Always hating the petty conventions of the present, he became in his later years too much of a social critic for his poetry to benefit. From first to last, however, he was a master of word-music, acutely sensitive to every vibration and capable of rendering his impressions with almost miraculous fidelity. He saw no less clearly than he heard.

Although after half a century of extreme popularity among his contemporaries, Tennyson has suffered from the inevitable reaction, his value to the student is twofold. On the one hand, he teaches by example the qualities and possibilities of the English language ; on the other hand, his poems may not inaptly be described as " the voice of the century " in all its modulations between the extremes of buoyant hope and despair. " Locksley Hall," and its sequel, " Locksley Hall Sixty Years After," sum up the difference between liberal aspiration and democratic achievement. In " Maud," his favourite work, he entered an eloquent protest against material views of life.

If it be granted that Tennyson's poetry did not profit by his sensitiveness to the social problems of the time, or by the way in which he criticized the trend of policies and the fickleness of public opinion, it can hardly be gainsaid that he was a great teacher for all who care to give ear to his message. The best of Tennyson is not to be gathered by the pastime of hunting out plagiarisms from his poems. As the stirring events of Elizabeth's reign inspired Shakespeare, so was Tennyson inspired by the Battle of Waterloo and " the fairy tales of science " to the vision of a time when

The war-drum throbb'd no longer, and the battle-flags were furl'd

In the Parliament of man, the Federation of the world.

But he saw the peril, first of an excessive insular patriotism, and then of mere " talk."

From a technical standpoint " Maud " is regarded by competent critics as one of the best and most finished of Tennyson's poems ; it is the one, moreover, of which the poet himself was specially fond. It contains the exquisite lyric " Come into the Garden, Maud." Perhaps the best of Tennyson's work was his earliest. That which penetrates the heart of the many is comprised in the lyrics, such as the song just referred to, together with " Break, Break, Break," " Sweet and Low," and his swan song, " Crossing the Bar." But the " Idylls of the King " are also widely loved. " The Lady of Shalott," " Mariana in the South," " The Miller's Daughter," " Oenone," " The Palace of Art," " The May Queen," " The Lotos Eaters," " A Dream of Fair Women," " The Morte d'Arthur," " Love and Duty," and " Locksley Hall," have been rightly placed among the poems which have " profoundly affected English literature."

Robert Browning. With Robert Browning (1812–89) " form " was but a secondary consideration. Its requirements, in fact, constituted for him almost an obstacle to the flow of thought.

He is as difficult and obscure as, for the most part, Tennyson is clear and easy to the common understanding. With Browning, far more than with Tennyson, it is necessary to consider the life and the poetry as interdependent and inter-explanatory. It has been well said that " much of the apparent obscurity of Browning is due to his habit of climbing up a precipice of thought, and then kicking away the ladder by which he climbed."

There is no gloom in Browning. He is all virility. His dramas and his poems are the appurtenances of an intellectual gymnasium. With Browning, " Life is—to wake, not sleep," " Rise and not rest," he cries ; but " press—

> From earth's level, where blindly creep
> Things, perfected, more or less,
> To the heaven's height, far and steep,
> Where, amid what strifes and storms
> May wait the adventurous guest,
> Power is love."

Few poets have given rise to such a body of criticism and interpretation as Browning. Tennyson has needed no Tennyson Society to expound what he meant. The Browning Society may have done its hero a disservice. But it is not always what is best worth knowing that is clearest of comprehension, and although many people would rather spend an evening with Tennyson for the certain solace of his word-music, the same time spent in mental sparring with Browning might be more stimulating in effect if less agreeable in experience. Professor Dowden, who remains Browning's most competent critic, says :

" Browning as a poet had his origins in the romantic school of English poetry ; but he came at a time when the romance of external action and adventure had exhausted itself, and when it became necessary to carry romance into the inner world, where the adventures are those of the soul. On the ethical and religious side he sprang from English Puritanism. Each of these influences was modified by his own genius and by the circumstances of its development. His keen observation of facts and passionate inquisition of human character drew him in the direction of what is termed realism. . . . His Puritanism received important modifications from his wide-ranging artistic instincts and sympathies,

and again from the liberality of a wide-ranging intellect.
. . . He regarded our life on earth as a state of probation
and of preparation. . . . In his methods Browning would
acknowledge no master ; he would please himself and compel his
readers to accept his method, even if strange or singular. . . .
His optimism was part of the vigorous sanity of his moral nature ;
like a reasonable man, he made the happiness which he did not
find. . . . The emotions which he chiefly cared to inter-
pret were those connected with religion, with art, and with the
relations of the sexes."

It is especially important to remember that Browning's thought
where it is most significant is often more or less enigmatical if
taken by itself ; " its energetic gestures, unless we see what they
are directed against, seem aimless beating in the air." That
portion of his work, therefore, which is primarily polemical bids
fair to fail in interesting posterity. His masterpiece is the living
human epic of " The Ring and the Book." " How They Brought
the Good News from Ghent," " Saul," " The Lost Leader," and
" The Pied Piper of Hamelin " are among his widely popular
poems. A more vitally dramatic poet than Browning never
existed ; though his remarkable series of poetic dramas—
" Strafford," " A Blot on the Scutcheon," " Colombe's Birthday,"
etc., lack the lucidity essential to the theatre—being too nimble
in action and too clever for the audience to follow—his dramatic
lyrics, which he began to write about 1841, and some of which are
included in the series, " Men and Women," published in 1855,
embody his most original, poignant, tragic, grotesque and lively
genius of expression.

LESSON 25

More About the Victorian Poets

(See plates 44 and 45)

SWINBURNE, D. G. Rossetti, Christina Rossetti, William
Morris and Coventry Patmore were the leading poets of
that romantic revival in art and literature, the Pre-
Raphaelite Brotherhood. Both Tennyson and Matthew Arnold,
though apart from the movement, showed in much of their poetry
what may be defined as the ideal of Pre-Raphaelitism, a blend of

(337)

serene clarity and refined luxury. The decadence of this ideal was an effete romanticism expressed by many of the poets of the 'nineties ; its revival can be traced in the work of such diverse modern poets as Edith Sitwell and Walter de la Mare.

Of Algernon Charles Swinburne (1837–1909), Tennyson said : " He is a reed, through which all things blow into music." A younger contemporary of Browning's, Swinburne was, indeed, a poet of a different mould. Browning was a thinker striving to utter his thoughts in poetic form, and never a stringer-together of mellifluous words for the sake of their metrical charm. Form was paramount with Swinburne, and the content of the verse seemed secondary. His verse is as near to actual music as that of any poet who ever lived.

No English poet more definitely felt himself a poet than Swinburne did. From his earliest years he consecrated himself to the tuneful muses, and even when his verse is disfigured by excess of passionate phrase, as it often is in " Poems and Ballads," still it is verse that produces in the reader a sense of exaltation which no prose can create.

Our finest lyrist after Tennyson and an artist even more comprehensive in the mastery of varied metres, it would be wrong to leave the impression that Swinburne's concern was so fixed upon the form of his poetry that he was careless of its content, or, again, that he was obsessed by the sensuous side of life. His poetry abounds in passages where high thought and true emotions are expressed in lines of genuine and enduring beauty, and which prove that his soul was in tune with life's inmost and profound harmonies. It is worth noting also how he competes in " Tristram of Lyonesse " with Tennyson in his treatment of the Arthurian story, that touchstone of romance so beloved of the Pre-Raphaelites.

Next in importance to Swinburne must be reckoned Matthew Arnold (1822–88), whose poems, austere in form, classic in spirit, breathe the indefinable sadness of culture threatened by anarchy. Swinburne uttered no criticism that rings more true than his dictum that Matthew Arnold's " best essays ought to live longer than most ; his poems cannot but live as long as any of their time." Matthew Arnold would have won lasting distinction among the few had he written only " The Strayed Reveller " (that perfect anticipation of modern free verse), " Empedocles on Etna," " The Scholar Gipsy," " Sohrab and Rustum," and his fine

Arthurian poem " Tristram and Iseult," with its exquisite Pre-Raphaelite glamour and naturalism.

The poems of Frederick Tennyson (1807–98) and Charles Tennyson Turner (1808–79) may be studied with those of their illustrious brother. Frederick was joint author of the famous " Poems of Two Brothers," and his poem " The Isles of Greece " is well worth reading. Charles is best represented by his sonnets.

The Pre-Raphaelites Dante Gabriel Rossetti (1828–82) was the fountain-head of Pre-Raphaelitism. As A. C. Benson observes, " he has stimulated the sense of beauty, the desire to extract the very essence of delight from emotion, form and colour ; he has inculcated devotion to art." Rossetti's sister Christina (1830–94) was, in all she wrote and in her attitude to life, an essential poet. A devotional writer of the finest quality, her lyric gift was rare and distinguished, and her poetry will engage the student's interest as conveying the Pre-Raphaelite ideal in its purest form. Mr. R. L. Megroz, in " Modern English Poetry," says that Coventry Patmore (1823–96) " in his ' Unknown Eros ' odes opened a way in a new direction, for he was the least Romantic of the poets who contributed (as he does in the Odes) to Pre-Raphaelite poetry, and the most original after Rossetti." Of that other great leader in the P.R.B., William Morris (1834–96), Mr. Megroz (ibid) observes, " Morris always lacked the artistic mastery of the literary medium which might have made his poetic fame secure, but his genius as a poet of the day-dreaming imagination, like Masefield's indeed, is not to be denied, and will for a long time yet hold youthful readers in thrall."

We have now reached a stage in our survey when not even the pretence of naming the lesser poets of the period can be made. Their name becomes legion, and they must pass in scores un-heralded. The explanation of the phenomenon is that there was now a steady raising of the mean of poetry ; and as the average rises and the number of competent artists swells it would seem that poetic genius becomes diffused ; the sporadic outbursts which produced the giants are fewer or by contrast less astonishing.

Each reader will in his own way discover for himself favourite specimens of the work of other men whose reputation as poets was high among their contemporaries, all with their contribution of pleasure and experience to give, though not perhaps vitally important to English literature. Arthur Hugh Clough (1819–61), as shown by " The Bothie of Tober-na-Vuolich," was not altogether given over to the philosophic doubt usually associated with his name. In the Irish songs of William Allingham (1824–89) is to be traced something of Christina Rossetti and of the glamour of archaic things in which lay the origin of the " Celtic revival."

Poets of the Later Victorian Age. The poetic output of Robert Louis Stevenson (1850–94), limited in quantity, is notable in quality. W. E. Henley (1849–1903) possessed an innate fineness which rings through his verse. George MacDonald (1824–1905) wrote many short lyrics ; his " Diary of an Old Soul " was declared by Ruskin to be one of the three great religious poems of the century. Francis Turner Palgrave (1824–97) was greater as a critic than as a poet ; his " Golden Treasury of Songs and Lyrics " bears witness to his powers of discrimination, though he owed much to the advice of Tennyson. Gerald Massey (1828–1907) wrote some tenderly emotional lyrical poetry, notably the exquisite " Ballad of Babe Christabel." Sir Edwin Arnold (1832–1904), in his " Light of Asia," interpreted Buddhism for Western readers. Sir Lewis Morris (1833–1907), the author of " The Epic of Hades," an attempt to read the Greek myths in the light of Christian sentiment, " The Ode of Life," a review of life's stages, and " A Vision of Saints," was in his day the most popular poet next to Tennyson. James Thomson, " B.V." (1834–82), depicted the dark side of London in " The City of Dreadful Night," and ranks among the unfortunates of genius. The same might almost be said of Francis Thompson (1859–1907), that powerful visionary, the author of " The Hound of Heaven," whose intuition reached the " smouldering core of mystery " ; and of John Davidson (1857–1909), who, like his predecessor, James Thomson, fiercely revolted against the narrow prejudices and oppressions of contemporary life. Notable among his poems are the " Fleet Street Eclogues " and his " Ballads and Songs."

There is the daintiest of art in everything of Austin Dobson's, and if Robert Bridges (1844–1930) is an improvement on his predecessor in the laureateship, Alfred Austin (1835–1913), it is chiefly in the technique of verse, where his cleverness is obvious. For the rest, his work suffers from an absence of true poetic fire, and even his last and most ambitious work, " The Testament of Beauty," can never be expected to make more than the most restricted appeal to critical admiration. Yet other figures of the 'nineties were Wilfrid S. Blunt (1840–1922), a genuine poet, noted for his versions of the " Seven Golden Odes of Pagan Arabia " ;

Alice Meynell (1850-1922), the foremost woman poet of her time, whose work was marred by preciosity, but distinguished by charm; Katherine Tynan, who then made her first serious appeal as a poet with " Ballads and Lyrics," and Sir Henry Newbolt, whose naval ballads possess a true lyrical gift.

Special mention must be made of George Meredith (1828-1909), whose poetry was influenced by the P.R.B. movement, and concerning whom critical opinion is still divided. In the modern mind there is little doubt that he is destined to live as a poet when his long novels will be little read. We find his natural voice in his poetry and a forthright vigour of expression that is not characteristic of his prose.

Special mention is also due to William Watson (1858-1935), who is certainly one of our chief poets of these later times. He started and continued as a Wordsworthian, and has some of the defects as well as many of the merits of his master. His mastery of the sonnet form is complete, and he has written odes of grave beauty and serene simplicity.

Rudyard Kipling (1865-1936) became popular with his racy poems and ballad rhythms. He is at his best in his "Barrack Room Ballads."

LESSON 26

British Poetry of the Twentieth Century

(See plate 45)

ALTHOUGH he was born so long ago as 1840 and ranks as the last Victorian master of fiction, Thomas Hardy is dealt with here among the poets of the twentieth century, since he stands as a poet on the most notable achievement of his life, the epic drama of " The Dynasts," which appeared in three successive parts in the years 1903, 1906 and 1908. There is no more curious work in modern literature. It is labelled by its author " An Epic-Drama of the War with Napoleon, in three parts, nineteen acts and one hundred and thirty scenes, the time covered by the action being about ten years." It is at times narrative, at others dramatic ; " voices " from the unseen world are heard—" phantom intelligences " discuss the dark, perplexing problems of human destiny ; the author is now withdrawn, like one apart watching the play of men ; at other times as intimately interested in the narrative as a novelist in the children of his fancy ; and, withal, the reading of the vast drama scene by scene, in which movement is effected largely by means of " stage directions " that are really masterly pieces of prose narrative and description, produces in one a sense of the spaciousness of the realms where man's character is evolved.   In its own sphere of an elemental vision, the poetry of Thomas Hardy is unequalled. The reader is continually impressed with the splendid and audacious largeness of the poet's plan, for not even the blank verse which Napoleon has to speak sounds strange or unnatural in this strangely familiar, newly created world of old, historic things.

The rhythm of Hardy's verse is architectural rather than musical, and of the poetry that " makes love to the ear and woos it with music " Hardy is not a master   Five volumes of collected poems stand to his credit, but the average quality of style in the lyrical and elegiac interludes of " The Dynasts " is equal to his best, and it is there that this manifestation of his genius should be studied first.

Another poet and great prose writer, Charles Montague Doughty (1843-1927), only published his verse early in this century and is now increasingly appreciated.   The dominant note of his imaginative poetry is a grand sonority.   In his epics, " Mansoul, or the Riddle of the World," and " The Dawn in Britain," he touches the finest visionary poetic level.

It is a commonplace of journalism to talk about the decadence of the eighteen-nineties, and that much of the poetry of that period reveals a moral and spiritual disorder, due to enervating external influences in operation at the time, is undoubtedly true.   It can be seen in the work of Ernest Dowson, Richard Middleton, Arthur Symons, Edmund John, Stephen Phillips, and others who, nevertheless, produced poetry of high merit when not marred by artificiality and egotism.   That phase passed away with the century, and anti-decadence characterizes the work of Sir Henry Newbolt, G. K. Chesterton, Hilaire Belloc, Alfred Noyes, Walter de la Mare and John Masefield, who, in 1930, succeeded Robert Bridges as Poet Laureate.   Polished, discreet and pleasantly readable poetry emanates from Laurence Binyon, John Drinkwater and Maurice Baring.   With the restrained beauty of the verse of Siegfried Sassoon, and that of Rupert Brooke, we reach the war poetry, so characteristic an element in modern poetry.

In Masefield (b. 1874) strength is not infrequently replaced by violence, a fault that may have had a compensating good effect in startling the large public into interest in and knowledge of new poetry. It is as a narrative poet that most people chiefly think of Masefield ; but many who are attracted first by this aspect of his work, as manifested in " The Everlasting Mercy," " The Widow in the Bye-Street," " The Daffodil Fields," " Dauber," and " Reynard the Fox," will speedily become aware of the large quantity of beautiful description, lovely imagery and fine thoughts with which these poems are charged. Strength also distinguishes the work of Alfred Noyes, as may be seen in his " Tales of the Mermaid Tavern," in his " Drake," and in his scientific epic " The Torch Bearers " ; in addition Noyes has a happy ear for music, which imparts also to his short poems, such as " Seagulls on the Serpentine," a charming grace.

Atmospheric glamour, mystical symbolism and traditional romance are found in the work of W. B. Yeats (1865–1939) and in that of many of those other modern Irish poets whom he has grouped as belonging to the " Celtic Twilight " (1893). Yeats has a wide range and is a master of technique ; he is inclined to the metaphysical and in his mystical verse is linked with that greatest of all mystical poets, Blake. Apart from his lovely shorter poems and his narratives, Yeats has made a notable contribution to the poetry of the theatre. His work stands as the achievement of a great creative artist in splendours of language and metaphor and the true poetry of dreams.

George William Russell (A.E.) (1867–1935) is another Irish poet whose genius is clothed with ancient lore and symbolism. His collected poems, published in 1913, reveal in almost everyday language rare beauties of vision and quiet rapture. James Stephens, Padraic Colum, Bertram Higgins and F. R. Higgins are among the " Celtic " poets, whose work combines clarity with genuine artistry of diction and rhythm.

Only the briefest reference can be made here to the work of those two remarkable poets, Charlotte Mew (1870–1928) and Sir Ronald Ross (1857–1932). R. L. Megroz, in " Modern English Poetry," says of the former :

" Charlotte Mew is one of those simple poets whose work makes that of most seem cheap. . . . The two modest collections of her poems ' The Farmer's Bride ' (1915) and ' The Rambling

(343)

Sailor ' (1929) contain such treasure that praise of her is tempted towards extravagance."

Sir Ronald Ross, whose poetry was unheard of for the half-century that he was doing work in medical science in India and at the Ross Institute at Putney, published in 1930 a volume of poems which included pieces written as far back as the 1870's. There is a certain amount of satire in his poetry, but he reaches us by reason of his passionate sincerity and his expression of deep feeling. His verse possesses the true lyrical quality.

In accuracy of description and in vivid beauty of word-painting the nature poetry of D. H. Lawrence (1895–1930) is supreme, and in his " Collected Poems " the separate sections " Fruits," " Trees," " Birds," " Reptiles," etc., show his wide range, vision and keen perception of the wonders of natural life. He uses all forms, but free verse seems his most forcible means of poetic expression.

Edmund Blunden (b. 1896) in his maturer work also stands in the front rank of nature poets with W. H. Davies (b. 1871), who is truly original and spontaneous in the fine simplicity of his utterance ; with Wilfred W. Gibson (b. 1878), to be appreciated for his dramatic sketches of rural life, and with Lascelles Abercrombie (1881–1938), an eloquent modernist.

It is, however, impossible in the available space of this Lesson to look at the poets of today in any detail. So astoundingly good is the verse written by many whose names are quite unknown to the larger reading public that it would be invidious to attempt even a glimpse at them, as many deserving notice would have to be ignored.

It is an age of short poems. In the prefatory note to " Selections from Modern Poets " made by Sir J. C. Squire—whose own poetry is a valuable contribution to modern verse—the compiler observes :

" The era of Wordsworth, Coleridge, Byron, Shelley and Keats was an age during which a vast amount of great poetry was written by a few great poets : there was very little healthy undergrowth. Should our literary age be remembered by posterity solely as an age during which fifty men had written lyrics of some durability for their truth and beauty, it would not be remembered with contempt."

TWENTIETH CENTURY POETRY

There is, however, a quest for the bizarre as well as a decadence observable in many of the moderns. Such brilliantly intellectual poets as Edith Sitwell and T. S. Eliot (b. 1888) were able to develop a technique which, according to R. L. Megroz, " can only be described as decadent, for expressing their reaction to the spiritual ' waste land ' of contemporary society."

The student of the technique of verse should study the prosodic experiments of that magnificent poet Gerard Manley Hopkins, whose collected poems, edited by Robert Bridges, were only published in 1918, although Hopkins died in 1889. Belonging temperamentally and technically to our own day—or beyond it— he must be included with the modern poets. His great contribution to technique is his successful practice of " sprung rhythm." Strong alliterations and rhyming on unusual words are necessary to sprung rhythm, which Hopkins tells us is found in common speech when rhythm is perceived in it.

Almost equally important in the respect of technical development is Ezra Pound (b. 1885), and the influence of these two men upon the future of the form of English poetry cannot fail to be powerful and long-enduring. It can be seen operating already in the work of such poets as Lascelles Abercrombie, Richard Aldington, Sacheverell Sitwell, Edith Sitwell, T. S. Eliot and others, not excluding more generally known writers such as Walter de la Mare and, in a less degree, John Masefield. Besides his wide range of scholarly wisdom, Ezra Pound possesses a most pungent and versatile wit, which flashes through his poetry.

The 'thirties saw the flowering of a new school of English poetry, which asserted that the romantic idiom of the Georgian poets—the Rupert Brooke generation—had become stylized, and that poetic imagery had become artificial. Thus the factory, the pylon, the railway train, the living background of post-War society, found their place in contemporary poetry. At the same time the amelioration of social conditions was a principal theme, for the poet is concerned with the aspirations of man, his hopes, sufferings and triumphs. Prominent in this School are W. H. Auden (b. 1907), Cecil Day Lewis (b. 1904), Stephen Spender (b. 1909), and Louis MacNeice (b. 1907). In "A Hope for Poetry," by C. Day Lewis, and in Michael Roberts' introduction to "New Signatures," an anthology of the exponents of the new poetry, will be found surveys of the aims of these poets.

Our Course in English Literature is continued in Volume 4.

LESSON 21

More About the Auxiliary Verbs

IN French there are several idiomatic uses of the verb *avoir*.

1. *Y avoir* is used with the meaning of " to be the matter ": *qu'est-ce qu'il y a ?* or simply *qu'y a-t-il ?* What is the matter ? *Avoir* without *y* is used for " what is the matter with (you, him, etc.) ? " *Qu'a-t-elle ?* or *qu'est-ce qu'elle a ?* What is the matter with her ? *Qu'avez-vous ?* or *qu'est-ce que vous avez ?* What is the matter with you ? *Je n'ai rien*, Nothing is the matter with me. 2. Instead of " to be," and the adjective " old," *avoir* and the noun *âge* are used in French in asking or telling the age. The word *ans*, years, must always be used in the answer. *Quel âge avez-vous ?* How old are you ? *J'ai dix-huit ans*, I am eighteen. 3. *Avoir* helps to form the idiomatic expressions *avoir l'air*, to look ; *avoir envie*, to feel inclined ; *avoir lieu*, to take place ; *avoir soin de*, to take care of.

4. With the adjective *beau*, *avoir* forms an idiomatic expression which is placed before a verb in the infinitive to indicate the uselessness of the action expressed by that verb : *Nous aurons beau dire, on ne nous croira pas*, It will be no use our saying anything (we may say what we like), we shall not be believed.

5. *Il y a* not only means " ago," but is also applicable to future time. It is also used with a verb in the present instead of the English perfect, or in the imperfect instead of the English pluperfect, to express an action or state, begun at a past time and still going on : *Je l'ai vu il y a quinze jours*, I saw him a fortnight ago. *Il y avait trois mois que nous étions à Paris*, We had been in Paris three months. *Il y aura demain huit jours que nous sommes ici*. We shall have been here a week tomorrow. *Il y a une heure que je vous attends*, I have been waiting for you for the last hour. *Il y avait une heure que je l'attendais*, I had been waiting for him an hour.

EXERCISE.

1. They were afraid of us, but they will be still (*encore*) more afraid of you. 2. Are they not ashamed of their conduct ? 3. We should be right and you would be wrong. 4. We have been very (*bien*) cold. 5. Was there not anyone in the house ?

6. How old is that child ?   7. He will be twelve next month.
8. He is a little more than two years older than his sister.   9.
Are you very (*bien*) hungry ?   No, thanks (*merci*), but I am very
thirsty.   10. If there were no fire we should be very cold.   11. My
hands have never been colder.   12. Will you not be too warm so
near the fire ?   13. I was sixteen a fortnight (15 days) ago.
14. What was the matter with those children ?   They were afraid
of that big dog.   15. They would have been less afraid of the cat
than of the dog.   16. When did the first performance of the
comedy (*comédie*, f.) take place ?   17. It took place a little more
than six months ago.   18. If you require a dictionary, take
(*prenez*) mine, but take great (*bien*) care of it.   19. We have been
waiting for you for the last ten minutes.   20. It will be no use
your talking ; you will not be believed.

The Verb Etre.   The auxiliary verb *être*, to be, helps to
conjugate the passive voice, which has really no conjugation of
its own, and consists of the tenses of *être* with a past participle
added to them.   *Etre* is conjugated as follows :

INDICATIVE MOOD.
Simple Tenses.
Present.

je suis, I am, etc.	*nous sommes*
tu es	*vous êtes*
il, elle est	*ils, elles sont*

Imperfect.

j'étais, I was, etc.	*nous étions*
tu étais	*vous étiez*
il, elle était	*ils, elles étaient*

Past Definite.

je fus, I was, etc.	*nous fûmes*
tu fus	*vous fûtes*
il, elle fut	*ils, elles furent*

Future.

je serai, I shall be, etc.	*nous serons*
tu seras	*vous serez*
il, elle sera	*ils, elles seront*

Compound Tenses.
Past Indefinite or Perfect.

j'ai été, I have been, etc.	*nous avons été*

Pluperfect.

j'avais été, I had been, etc.	*nous avions été*

Past Anterior.

j'eus été, I had been, etc.

Future Anterior.

j'aurai été, I shall have been, etc.

CONDITIONAL MOOD.

Present.

je serais, I should be, etc.	*nous serions*
tu serais	*vous seriez*
il, elle serait	*ils, elles seraient*

Past.

j'aurais été, I should have been, etc.

IMPERATIVE MOOD.

Present.

sois, be (thou)

qu'il soit, *qu'elle soit*, let him be, let her be, **soyons, let us be**

soyez, be (ye)

qu'ils soient, *qu'elles soient*, let them be

SUBJUNCTIVE MOOD.

Present.

que je sois, that I may be, etc.	*que nous soyons*
que tu sois	*que vous soyez*
qu'il, qu'elle soit	*qu'ils, qu'elles soient*

Imperfect.

que je fusse, that I might be, etc.	*que nous fussions*
que tu fusses	*que vous fussiez*
qu'il, qu'elle fût	*qu'ils, qu'elles fussent*

Perfect.

que j'aie été, that I may have been, etc.

Pluperfect.

que j'eusse été, that I might have been, etc.

INFINITIVE MOOD.

Present.	Past.
être, to be	*avoir été*, to have been

PARTICIPLES.

Present.	Past.
étant, being	*été*, been ; *ayant été*, having been

NOTE.—The past participle *été* is always invariable.

(348)

LESSON 22

Progress in the Study of Verbs

THERE are various idiomatic uses in French of the auxiliary verb *être*, to be, which the student should note carefully as follow : 1. *Etre* is sometimes used impersonally instead of *y avoir* : *Il était un roi d'Yvetot, peu connu dans l'histoire* there was a king of Yvetot, little known in story. 2. *Etre à même de*, followed by an infinitive, means " to be able to," " to be in a position to " : *Il est à même de nous aider*, he is in a position to help us. 3. *Etre à*, followed by the active infinitive, is equivalent to the English construction in which " to be " is followed by a passive infinitive : *Il est à craindre*, he is to be feared. 4. *Y être* is used idiomatically, sometimes with the meaning of " to be at home," sometimes with that of " to be ready," " to understand " : *J'ai besoin de parler à votre frère ; y est-il ? Non, il n'y est pas*, I want to speak to your brother ; is he at home ? No, he is not at home. *Y êtes-vous ? Oui, j'y suis*, are you ready ? Yes, I am ready. 5. The expressions *être bien avec* and *être mal avec* mean " to be on good terms with," " to be on bad terms with " : *Il est bien avec tout le monde*, he is on good terms with everybody.

When referring to the state of health, " to be " is rendered either by the reflexive verb *se porter*, to carry oneself, or by *aller*, to go : How are you ? *Comment vous portez-vous ?* or more usually *Comment allez-vous ?* " To be," is rendered by *valoir* in the expression " to be better (preferable) " : It is better late than never, *il vaut mieux tard que jamais*.

Etre is conjugated negatively with *ne* and *pas* :

INDICATIVE

Present.	Past Indefinite.
je ne suis pas, etc.	*je n'ai pas été.*
Imperfect.	Pluperfect.
je n'étais pas, etc.	*je n'avais pas été.*
Past Definite.	Past Anterior.
je ne fus pas, etc.	*je n'eus pas été, etc.*
Future.	Future Anterior.
je ne serai pas, etc.	*je n'aurai pas été, etc.*

This verb is also conjugated interrogatively.

INDICATIVE.

Present.	Past Indefinite.
suis-je ?	*ai-je été ?*
est-il, est-elle ?	*a-t-il été, a-t-elle été ?*
Imperfect.	Pluperfect.
étais-je ?	*avais-je été ?*
Past Definite.	Past Anterior.
fus-je ?	*eus-je été ?*
Future.	Future Anterior.
serai-je ?	*aurai-je été ?*

Note the position of the pronoun when *être* is conjugated interrogatively and negatively.

INDICATIVE.

Present.	Past Indefinite.
ne suis-je pas ?	*n'ai-je pas été ?*
Imperfect.	Pluperfect.
n'étais-je pas ?	*n'avais-je pas été ?*
Past Definite.	Past Anterior.
ne fus-je pas ?	*n'eus-je pas été ?*
Future.	Future Anterior.
ne serai-je pas ?	*n'aurai-je pas été ?*

In English, a positive statement followed by the negative-interrogative form of " have," " be," or one of the modal auxiliaries " do," " can," " ought," " should," etc., is used to indicate that the answer " Yes " is expected. In French, the one expression *N'est-ce pas ?* is used, whatever be the auxiliary, the tense, or the person : He is a friend of yours, is he not ? *C'est un de vos amis, n'est-ce pas ?* You speak French, do you not ? *Vous parlez français, n'est-ce pas ?* He wrote to you last week, did he not ? *Il vous a écrit la semaine dernière, n'est-ce pas ?* They will be there, will they not ? *Ils y seront, n'est-ce pas ?*

EXERCISE.

TRANSLATE INTO FRENCH : 1. Whose books are those ? They are my brother's. 2. I wanted to speak to your father, but he was not in. 3. The ass is temperate (*sobre*) and patient ; it would be the handsomest of domestic animals if there were no horse. 4. The Gauls (*Gaulois*) were brave and strong (*robuste*). 5. Marshal Lannes had been (a) dyer ; Marshal Ney was a cooper before being (to be) (a) soldier. 6. The father of the philosopher (*philosophe*) Diderot, and that of the historian (*historien*) Rollin were cutlers (*couteliers*). 7. Pardon is better than revenge (*la vengeance*). 8. The Romans (*Romains*) were the masters of the world (*le monde*). 9. There were once two men who were very poor and very wretched (*malheureux*). 10. The first was blind (*aveugle*) from his birth (*de naissance*) ; the second was paralysed. 11. They were both incapable of doing (*faire*) anything. 12. The blind (man), who was strong, carried (*porta*) the paralytic (*paralytique*). 13. The paralytic, who was endowed (*doué*) with (a) good sight (*la vue*), guided (*dirigea*) his companion. 14. Alone they would have (*être*) died (*morts*) of hunger. 15. United (*unis*) they were able to gain their living (*vie*).

Regular Verbs. There are four conjugations of verbs distinguished from each other by the ending of the infinitive. The infinitive of the first conjugation ends in *er*, as *donner*, to give ; of the second in *ir*, as *finir*, to finish ; of the third in *oir*, as *recevoir*, to receive ; of the fourth in *re*, as *vendre*, to sell.

Regular verbs are those of which all the tenses are formed uniformly from the primitive tenses, or principal parts. The primitive tenses, or principal parts, are five : (a) the present of the infinitive, (b) the present participle, (c) the past participle, (d) the present indicative, and (e) the past definite.

The principal parts are : 1st conjugation : *donner, donnant, donné, je donne, je donnai* : 2nd conjugation *finir, finissant, fini, je finis, je finis ;* 3rd conjugation : *recevoir, recevant, reçu, je reçois, je reçus ;* 4th conjugation : *vendre, vendant, vendu, je vends, je vendis.*

From the present of the infinitive are formed (a) the future indicative, and (b) the present conditional by changing *r* of the first and of the second conjugation, *oir* of the third conjugation, and *re* of the fourth conjugation into *rai, ras, ra, rons, rez, ront* for the *future*, and into *rais, rais, rait, rions, riez, raient* for the *conditional* :

DONNE-R.	FINI-R.
	Future.	
je donne-rai	je fini-rai
tu donne-ras	tu fini-ras
il donne-ra	il fini-ra
nous donne-rons	nous fini-rons
vous donne-rez	vous fini-rez
ils donne-ront	ils fini-ront

Conditional.

je donne-*rais*	je fini-*rais*
tu donne-*rais*	tu fini-*rais*
il donne-*rait*	il fini-*rait*
nous donne-*rions*	nous fini-*rions*
vous donne-*riez*	vous fini-*riez*
ils donne-*raient*	ils fini-*raient*

RECEV-*oir*.   VEND-*re*.

Future.

je recev-*rai*	je vend-*rai*
tu recev-*ras*	tu vend-*ras*
il recev-*ra*	il vend-*ra*
nous recev-*rons*	nous vend-*rons*
vous recev-*rez*	vous vend-*rez*
ils recev-*ront*	ils vend-*ront*

Conditional.

je recev-*rais*	je vend-*rais*
tu recev-*rais*	tu vend-*rais*
il recev-*rait*	il vend-*rait*
nous recev-*rions*	nous vend-*rions*
vous recev-*riez*	vous vend-*riez*
ils recev-*raient*	ils vend-*raient*

EXCEPTIONS.

Infinitive.	Future.	Conditional.
aller, to go	*j'irai*	*j'irais*
envoyer, to send	*j'enverrai*	*j'enverrais*
acquérir, to acquire	*j'acquerrai*	*j'acquerrais*
courir, to run	*je courrai*	*je courrais*
cueillir, to gather	*je cueillerai*	*je cueillerais*
mourir, to die	*je mourrai*	*je mourrais*
tenir, to hold	*je tiendrai*	*je tiendrais*
venir, to come	*je viendrai*	*je viendrais*
asseoir, to seat	*j'assiérai*	*j'assiérais*
avoir, to have	*j'aurai*	*j'aurais*
falloir, to be necessary	*il faudra*	*il faudrait*
savoir, to know	*je saurai*	*je saurais*
valoir, to be worth	*je vaudrai*	*je vaudrais*
voir, to see	*je verrai*	*je verrais*
vouloir, to wish	*je voudrai*	*je voudrais*
être, to be	*je serai*	*je serais*
faire, to make	*je ferai*	*je ferais*

WILLIAM COWPER (1731–1800). His life was marked by melancholia and attacks of insanity. His poetic genius was made plain in 1785 with the publication of "The Task." He also translated Homer and was a hymn-writer of considerable note.

ENGLISH LITERATURE 21

Lemuel Abbott

GEORGE CRABBE (1754–1832). Born at Aldeburgh, his poem "The Library" appeared in 1781. "The Village" and "The Newspaper" quickly followed, but Crabbe, who had now taken holy orders, published nothing further until 1807.

ENGLISH LITERATURE 21

ROBERT BURNS (1759–96). Born at Alloway, Ayrshire, of peasant-farmer stock, he "first committed the sin of rhyme" when about 16, and most of his best work was written before he was thirty. This portrait, by Nasmyth, is in the National Portrait Gallery.

ENGLISH LITERATURE 21

WILLIAM WORDSWORTH (1770–1850). Born at Cockermouth, his first poem was published in 1793. "Lyrical Ballads" followed in 1798, and "The Excursion" in 1814. He became Poet Laureate in 1843. This portrait is part of a painting in the National Portrait Gallery.

ENGLISH LITERATURE 22

TWO POETS OF GENIUS. Left, Elizabeth Barrett (1806–61), who, after years of invalidism, married Robert Browning in romantic circumstances, and lived to produce some verse of high quality. Right, Emily Brontë (1818–48), considered nowadays to have been the most gifted of the Brontë family. The poems she contributed to the volume by the three sisters, published at their own expense in 1846, show her unmistakable genius. This picture is a fragment from a portrait group painted by her brother Branwell Brontë. ENGLISH LITERATURE 23

National Portrait Gallery

SUPREME ARTISTS IN VERSE. Left, John Keats (1795–1821). After being apprenticed to a surgeon, he devoted himself to literature. His first volume (1817) was coldly received, and "Endymion," in the next year, was savagely reviewed on political grounds. A third volume followed in 1820, but in the spring of 1821 he died at Rome of consumption. Right, Percy Bysshe Shelley (1792–1822). Son of a wealthy landowner, he early developed a "passion for reforming the world" and was expelled from Oxford for his atheistic views. His "Queen Mab" appeared in 1813, and other imperishable monuments of his genius speedily followed. He was drowned in a storm off the coast of Italy. ENGLISH LITERATURE 23

National Portrait Gallery

CONTRAST IN POETS. Left, Samuel Taylor Coleridge (1772–1834). Born
at Ottery St. Mary, his first poems appeared in 1796 and in the next year
began his long friendship with Wordsworth. His poems reveal his intense
interest in metaphysics and philosophy, whereas Lord Byron (right : 1788–
1824) was essentially a master of the picturesque and romantic. Born in
London, from 1807 onwards Byron poured out a stream of splendid verse.
A voluntary exile from England as the result of his unhappy marriage, he lived
on the Continent and died of fever at Missolonghi, in Greece, where he had
gone to help the Greeks in their fight for independence against the Turks.
ENGLISH LITERATURE 23

National Portrait Gallery; Courtesy of Mr. John Murray

MASTERS OF VICTORIAN VERSE. Left : Alfred, Lord Tennyson
(1809–92). Born at Somersby, Lincs, he published his first poems in
1827. " The Princess " (1847) was his first success, and in 1850 he succeeded Wordsworth as Poet Laureate. Right : Robert Browning
(1812–89), whose " Pauline " (1833) was followed by other publications
at frequent intervals. His poem of passing, " Asolando," published
on the day of his death, appeared with Tennyson's " Crossing the Bar "
on the same theme. Both poets, within an interval of three years,
were buried in Westminster Abbey. ENGLISH LITERATURE 24

PRE-RAPHAELITE POETS. Above, left, William Morris (1834–96), born at Walthamstow; his first published verse was "The Defence of Guenevere" 1858, followed by "Love is Enough" in 1872. Right, Algernon Charles Swinburne (1837–1909), born in London. His first volume, "The Queen Mother" (1860), was dedicated to Rossetti. "Poems and Ballads" appeared in 1866 and "Songs Before Sunrise" in 1871. Below left, Dante Gabriel Rossetti (1828–82), who was the fountain-head of Pre-Raphaelitism and wrote "The Blessed Damozel" about 1847. "Ballads" and "Sonnets" appeared in 1870 and 1880. Right Christina Rossetti (1830–94), from a drawing by D. G. Rossetti. Her most imaginative piece of lyrical writing. "Goblin Market," appeared in 1862 ENGLISH LITERATURE 25

Frederick Hollyer; Elliott & Fry, Ltd.

Plate 44   *Volume III*

1. Ils avaient peur de nous, mais ils auront encore plus peur de vous. 2. N'ont-ils pas honte de leur conduite ? 3. Nous aurions raison, et vous auriez tort. 4. Nous avons eu bien froid. 5. N'y avait-il pas quelqu'un dans la maison ? 6. Quel âge cet enfant a-t-il ? 7. Il aura douze ans le mois prochain. 8. Il a un peu plus de deux ans de plus que sa sœur. 9. Avez-vous bien faim ? Non, merci, mais j'ai bien soif. 10. S'il n'y avait pas de feu, nous aurions bien froid. 11. Je n'ai jamais eu plus froid aux mains. 12. N'aurez-vous pas trop chaud si près du feu ? 13. J'ai eu seize ans il y a quinze jours. 14. Qu'avaient ces enfants ? Ils avaient peur de ce gros chien. 15. Ils auraient eu moins peur du chat que du chien. 16. Quand a eu lieu la première représentation de cette comédie ? 17. Elle a eu lieu il y a un peu plus de six mois. 18. Si vous avez besoin d'un dictionnaire, prenez le mien, mais ayez en bien soin. 19. Il y a dix minutes que nous vous attendons. 20. Vous aurez beau dire ; on ne vous croira pas.

LESSON 23

Concluding Remarks on the Tenses

IN this Lesson we conclude the section on the formation and uses of the tenses. From the present participle are formed (a) the three persons plural of the present indicative, by changing *ant* into *ons, ez, ent ;* the third person plural of the 3rd conjugation changes *e* into *oi* in the penultimate syllable :

DONN-ANT	FINISS-ANT
nous donn-ons	*nous finiss-ons*
vous donn-ez	*vous finiss -ez*
ils donn-ent	*ils finiss-ent*

RECEV-ANT	REND-ANT
nous recev-ons	*nous rend-ons*
vous recev-ez	*vous rend-ez*
ils (reçoiv-ent)	*ils rend-ent*

Exceptions are : *Allant,* going ; *ils vont. Ayant,* having : *nous avons, vous avez, ils ont. Sachant,* knowing ; *nous savons, vous savez, ils savent. Etant,* being ; *nous sommes, vous êtes, ils sont. Disant*, saying ; *vous dites. Faisant*, making ; *vous faites, ils font*.

(b) The Imperfect of the indicative, by changing *ant* into *ais, ais, ait, ions, iez, aient*.

DONN-ANT	FINISS-ANT
je donn-ais	*je finiss-ais*
tu donn-ais	*tu finiss-ais*
il donn-ait	*il finiss-ait*
nous donn-ions	*nous finiss-ions*
vous donn-iez	*vous finiss-iez*
ils donn-aient	*ils finiss-aient*

RECEV-ANT	VEND-ANT
je recev-ais	*je vend-ais*
tu recev-ais	*tu vend-ais*
il recev-ait	*il vend-ait*
nous recev-ions	*nous vend-ions*
vous recev-iez	*vous vend-iez*
ils recev-aient	*ils vend-aient*

Exceptions are : *Ayant*, having ; *j'avais*, etc. *Sachant*, knowing ; *je savais*, etc.

(c) The present subjunctive by changing *ant* into *e, es, e, ions, iez, ent ;* but, in the 3rd conjugation, the three persons singular, and the third person plural require the further change of the *e* of the penultimate syllable into *oi*. The preceding *c* then takes a cedilla.

DONN-ANT	FINISS-ANT
que je donn-e	*que je finiss-e*
que tu donn-es	*que tu finiss-es*
qu'il donn-e	*qu'il finiss-e*
que nous donn-ions	*que nous finiss-ions*
que vous donn-iez	*que vous finiss-iez*
qu'ils donn-ent	*qu'ils finiss-ent*

RECEV-ANT	VEND-ANT
que je (reçoiv-e)	*que je vend-e*
que tu (reçoiv-es)	*que tu vend-es*
qu'il (reçoiv-e)	*qu'il vend-e*
que nous recev-ions	*que nous vend-ions*
que vous recev-iez	*que vous vend-iez*
qu'ils (reçoiv-ent)	*qu'ils vend-ent*

ON THE TENSES

Exceptions are : *Allant*, going ; *que j'aille, que tu ailles, qu'il aille, qu'ils aillent. Acquérant*, acquiring ; *que j'acquière, que tu acquières, qu'il acquière, qu'ils acquièrent. Mourant*, dying ; *que je meure, que tu meures, qu'il meure, qu'ils meurent. Tenant*, holding ; *que je tienne, que tu tiennes, qu'il tienne, qu'ils tiennent. Venant*, coming ; *que je vienne, que tu viennes, qu'il vienne, qu'ils viennent. Fallant* (not used), it being necessary ; *qu'il faille. Mouvant*, moving ; *que je meuve, que tu meuves, qu'il meuve, qu'ils meuvent. Pouvant*, being able ; *que je puisse, que tu puisses, qu'il puisse, que nous puissions, que vous puissiez, qu'ils puissent. Valant*, being worth ; *que je vaille, que tu vailles, qu'il vaille, qu'ils vaillent. Voulant*, wishing ; *que je veuille, que tu veuilles, qu'il veuille, qu'ils veuillent. Etant*, being : *que je sois, que tu sois, qu'il soit, que nous soyons, que vous soyez, qu'ils soient. Buvant*, drinking ; *que je boive, que tu boives, qu'il boive, qu'ils boivent. Faisant*, making ; *que je fasse, que tu fasses, qu'il fasse, que nous fassions, que vous fassiez, qu'ils fassent.*

Only three verbs—*être* (to be), *pouvoir* (to be able), and *faire*, (to make) are irregular throughout the whole of the present subjunctive ; *que je sois ; que je puisse*, etc. ; *que je fasse*, etc.

From the past participle are formed all the compound tenses by adding it to the respective tenses of the auxiliary *avoir* or, in the case of certain active verbs, with the auxiliary *être*, e.g., *j'ai donné ; j'avais fini ; j'aurai reçu ; que j'aie vendu.*

From the present indicative the imperative is formed by omitting the personal pronouns. In the first conjugation the final *s* of the second person singular is dropped. The imperative has no third persons, but borrows those of the subjunctive :

INDICATIVE.	IMPERATIVE.
1. *tu donnes*	*donne*
nous donnons	*donnons*
vous donnez	*donnez*
2. *tu finis*	*finis*
nous finissons	*finissons*
vous finissez	*finissez*
3. *tu reçois*	*reçois*
nous recevons	*recevons*
vous recevez	*recevez*
4 *tu vends*	*vends*
nous vendons	*vendons*
vous vendez	*vendez*

Exceptions are : *Avoir*, imperative, *aie, ayons, ayez*. *Savoir*, indicative, *tu sais* (thou knowest) ; imperative, *sache, sachons, sachez*. *Etre*, imperative, *sois, soyons, soyez*.

From the past definite the imperfect subjunctive is formed, by changing *s* of the second person singular into *sse, sses, t, ssions, ssiez, ssent*. In the third person singular, the vowel immediately preceding the final *t* takes a circumflex accent :

<table>
<tr><td>

tu DONNA-S
que je donna-sse
que tu donna-sses
qu'il donnâ-t
que nous donna-ssions
que vous donna-ssiez
qu'ils donna-ssent

</td><td>

tu FINI-S
que je fini-sse
que tu fini-sses
qu'il finî-t
que nous fini-ssions
que vous fini-ssiez
qu'ils fini-ssent

</td></tr>
<tr><td>

tu REÇU-S
que je reçu-sse
que tu reçu-sses
qu'il reçû-t
que nous reçu-ssions
que vous reçu-ssiez
qu'ils reçu-ssent

</td><td>

tu VENDI-S
que je vendi-sse
que tu vendi-sses
qu'il vendî-t
que nous vendi-ssions
que vous vendi-ssiez
qu'ils vendi-ssent

</td></tr>
</table>

KEY TO EXERCISE IN LESSON 22.

1. A qui sont ces livres ? Ils sont à mon frère. 2. J'avais besoin de parler à votre père, mais il n'y était pas. 3. L'âne est sobre et patient ; il serait le plus beau des animaux domestiques s'il n'y avait point de cheval. 4. Les Gaulois étaient braves et robustes. 5. Le Maréchal Lannes avait été teinturier ; le Maréchal Ney fut tonnelier avant d'être soldat. 6. Le père du philosophe Diderot et celui de l'historien Rollin étaient couteliers. 7. Le pardon vaut mieux que la vengeance. 8. Les Romains ont été les maîtres du monde. 9. Il y avait une fois deux hommes qui étaient bien pauvres et bien malheureux. 10. Le premier était aveugle de naissance ; le second était paralysé. 11. Ils étaient l'un et l'autre (tous deux) incapables de rien faire. 12. L'aveugle, qui était robuste, porta le paralytique. 13. Le paralytique qui était doué d'une bonne vue dirigea son compagnon. 14. Seuls ils seraient morts de faim. 15. Unis ils furent à même de gagner leur vie.

LESSON 24

Important Points in Syntax

THE student, by noting carefully the remarks below, will have no difficulty in translating into French the exercise which follows. All prepositions but one require the verb which follows them to be in the infinitive. The single exception is *en* (in) which takes the present participle after it : *il joue au lieu de travailler*, he plays instead of working ; *il me regarda sans rien dire*, he looked at me without saying anything ; *après avoir lu la lettre il me la donna*, after having read the letter he gave it to me ; *les ouvriers travaillaient en chantant*, the workmen sang as they worked.

In English, " one," " ones," frequently take the place of a noun after an adjective. In French, there is no such construction, and the adjective alone must be used : there are two books on the table, a large one and a small one, *il y a deux livres sur la table, un petit et un grand ;* take the good ones and leave the bad ones, *prenez les bons et laissez les mauvais*.

An adverb must never be placed between subject and verb. Its usual place is after the verb in a simple tense, and between the auxiliary and the verb in a compound tense : I never see him, *je ne le vois jamais ;* he has never spoken to me, *il ne m'a jamais parlé*.

An " if " clause must have its verb in either the present or the imperfect indicative. With an " if " clause in the present, the " result " clause must be either in the present or the future indicative, or in the present imperative. With an " if " clause in the imperfect, the " result " clause must be in the conditional : *s'il est ici, il doit nous voir*, if he is here, he must see us ; *s'il est ici, il nous verra*, if he is here, he will see us ; *s'il vient demain, nous le verrons*, if he comes tomorrow, we shall see him ; *s'il est ici, qu'il vienne nous parler*, if he is here, let him come and speak to us ; *s'il était ici, il viendrait nous parler*, if he were here, he would come and speak to us.

Assez, enough, always precedes the adjectives which it modifies : *le plus petit ennemi est toujours assez grand pour être dangereux*, the smallest enemy is always big enough to be dangerous.

Vocabulary.

le bout, end, tip
la cause, cause
le charançon, weevil
le chef-d'œuvre, masterpiece
la chenille, caterpillar
la chose, thing
le commencement, beginning
la contrariété, vexation
le crime, crime
le défaut, defect
la dent, tooth
envie (f.), envy
éléphant (m.), elephant
enfant (m. and f.), child
ennemi (m.), enemy
ennui (m.), annoyance
la famille, family
la fluxion de poitrine, inflammation of the lungs
la haine, hatred
importance (f.), importance
insecte (m.), insect
la jalousie, jealousy
le laboureur, husbandman

le mal, ailment
la maladie, illness
le mensonge, falsehood
la moisson, harvest
la mouche, fly
le nez, nose
le panier, basket
la perte, loss
le point, spot, speck
la postérité, posterity
la progéniture, progeny
le rhume, cold
la ruine, ruin
la sauterelle, grasshopper, locust
la ténuité, tenuity, minuteness
le tour, turn
la treille, vine-stalk
la vanité, vanity
la verrue, wart
le vice, vice
le voisinage, neighbourhood
le voisin, the neighbour
le voleur, thief

continuel, continual
dangereux, dangerous
durable, lasting
imperceptible, imperceptible
implacable, implacable
indifférent, indifferent, of no consequence
indulgent, indulgent

innocent, innocent
insupportable, unbearable
mortel, deadly
permanent, permanent
petit, little, slight
pourri, rotten, bad (of fruit)
seul, alone, only
vilain, ugly, nasty

arriver, to arrive, come
causer, to cause
coûter, to cost
craindre, to fear
dépouiller, to despoil, plunder

gâter, to spoil, decay (of teeth)
mépriser, to despise
négliger, to neglect
réformer, to reform, cure

(358)

à cause de, because of
assez, enough
aujourd'hui, today
bien, very
bien de (des), many
bientôt, soon
contre, against
d'ailleurs, moreover
demain, tomorrow
en herbe, in the blade
en outre, in addition

ensuite, afterwards, then
malheureusement, unfortunately
presque, almost
parmi, amongst
quand, when
quelquefois, sometimes
sans, without, but for
seulement, only
sur nos gardes, on our guard
toujours, always

EXERCISE.

TRANSLATE INTO FRENCH : Those who despise small defects
are very wrong. The smallest enemy is always big enough to be
dangerous. It is not elephants that cause the loss of harvests
and the ruin of husbandmen ; it is locusts and little caterpillars,
when the corn is in the blade ; weevils and other imperceptible
insects, when it is ripe. It is not big robbers only that despoil
the vine-stalk and the orchard of their fruit ; it is little ones
also, sparrows and even flies. Without being deadly, little
ailments are sometimes enemies as unbearable as the big illnesses
of which we are afraid. It is almost always through little
neglected ailments that the serious (great) ones come. Tomorrow the little cold of today will perhaps be inflammation of
the lungs. But for little defects there would not be any vices.
Moreover, a little defect is not a slight thing, and where there is
one, there will never be any masterpiece. A wart is not very
big, but if you have it on the tip of your nose, it will be for you
a continual cause of annoyance and of vexation. A small defect
is never of slight importance if it is permanent. What is lasting
is never slight. Moreover, a little defect is always the beginning
of a big one ; vices themselves are the children of little defects.
The little defect will soon be great ; where there was one there
will soon be several. A little defect is never alone. It always
has a family. If it is not for itself, it is for its posterity that
it is to be feared. You have a tooth that has a little black spot.
It is nothing ; but, if you neglect it, it will soon be the whole
tooth that will be decayed. After that one it will be the neighbour (f.), and then the neighbour's neighbour, and the little
black speck that you have neglected will have cost you several

teeth. If there is a bad plum in a basket of plums, all the plums will soon be bad. The neighbourhood of a little defect is never of no consequence. Vanity seems to be a slight defect; but it is a slight defect that has a very nasty progeny. It has for (its) son, falsehood, which, unfortunately, is not its only child. It has, in addition, two daughters, who are jealousy and envy. Amongst their posterity they will have hatred, which will, in (à) its turn, be the mother of many crimes. It is because of their very minuteness that little defects are so dangerous. If they did not look so innocent we should be afraid of them, we should be on our guard against them. Be indulgent towards (à) the little defects of your friends.

LESSON 25

Correct Use of the Tenses

THE correct use of the tenses is of great importance and the subject, therefore, is fully explained. The present tense of the indicative mood is used to express : (a) an action which is taking place at the moment of speaking : *je vois qu'il pleut*, I see that it is raining ; (b) an action that habitually takes place : *je le vois tous les jours*, I see him every day. In French there is no " periphrastic," or " progressive " form of the present. " I am writing," " we are reading," etc., must be rendered by the simple present, *j'écris, nous lisons*.

After *si* (if) the present indicative is used both of present and of future action : *s'il pleut nous ne pouvons pas sortir*, if it is raining we cannot go out ; *s'il part demain je vous le ferai savoir*, if he starts tomorrow I shall let you know.

A special use of the French present, instead of the English perfect, is to express an action begun at a past time, and continuing up to the present. In this construction it requires either *depuis* or *il y a . . . que* : *nous sommes ici depuis trois semaines*, we have been here for (the last) three weeks ; *je vous attends depuis dix minutes*, I have been waiting for you for (the last) ten minutes ; *il y a trois semaines que nous sommes ici*, we have been here for three weeks ; *il y a dix minutes que je vous attends*, I have been waiting for you for ten minutes.

CORRECT USE OF THE TENSES

With " point of time since when " *depuis* only can be used , *nous sommes ici depuis le premier août*, we have been here since the 1st of August. When the expression of " time since when " is identical with an expression indicating the time of day, *il y a* must be used to avoid ambiguity ; *je vous attends depuis une heure* means : " I have been waiting for you for the last hour " ; but it also means, " I have been waiting for you since one o'clock." When the former meaning is intended, it is therefore better to say, *il y a une heure que je vous attends*.

The imperfect indicative is used to express what was taking place when something else took place : *je lisais quand vous êtes entrés*, I was reading when you came in. It is also used to express what used to take place : *l'année dernière je le voyais tous les jours*, last year I used to see him every day.

It is the descriptive past tense, and, in a narrative, is used to express attendant circumstances, natural phenomena, manners, customs, etc. : *les rayons de la lanterne éveillaient les insectes et attiraient les phalènes qui venaient en battre la corne de leurs ailes poussiéreuses. Le temps était noir. Un coin de la lune se devinait à peine à travers les crevasses d'un nuage couleur d'encre*, the rays of the lantern awoke the insects and attracted the moths, which came and beat its horn with their dusty wings. The weather was black (lowering). A corner of the moon could barely be traced (lit., guessed) through the chinks of an ink-coloured cloud.

The imperfect indicative is used after *si* in hypothetical sentences : *s'il était ici, nous le verrions*, if he were here, we should see him.

The imperfect indicative is used in French instead of the English pluperfect to express an action, which, having been begun at a past time, was still going on at a time now also past. In this construction *depuis* or *il y a . . . que* must be used just as they are used in the analogous construction with the present tense : *il y avait deux ans que durait le siège—le siège durait depuis deux ans*, the siege had lasted two years.

The past definite is used to present an action as completely past, and in such a way that the beginning and the end of that action are brought before the mind : *en mil six cent huit, le Français Samuel de Champlain fonda la colonie du Canada*, in 1608, the Frenchman, Samuel de Champlain, founded the colony of Canada.

The duration of an action is expressed by means of the past definite provided it be considered as a single definite point in past time. When this is the case, the verb is usually modified by an adverb or adverbial phrase of time : *Louis XIV régna soixante-douze ans,* Louis XIV reigned seventy-two years.

The past definite is the tense of historical narrative, and is used to express a succession of actions of which each is complete in itself : *Pythéas de Marseille, vers le milieu du quatrième siècle avant Jésus-Christ, fit un voyage dans le nord de l'Europe, longea les côtes de la Gaule, entra dans la Manche, visita les côtes méridionales et orientales de l'île de Bretagne, détermina la latitude de l'extrémité nord de cette île, et après six jours de navigation parvint à Thulé.* Pytheas of Marseilles, about the middle of the fourth century B.C., made a voyage in the north of Europe, skirted the coasts of Gaul, entered the Channel, visited the southern and eastern coasts of the island of Britain, ascertained the northern latitude of that island, and after six days' sailing, reached Thule.

In the following passage, the change from past to imperfect illustrates the difference between the narrative and the descriptive tense, between that which expresses transition from one state to another, and is used for successive actions, and that which expresses state or condition at a certain moment, and is used for simultaneous actions : *la lune se leva derrière la redoute de Cheverino. . . . Elle était large et rouge comme cela est ordinaire à son lever. Mais ce soir-là elle me parut d'une grandeur extraordinaire. Pendant un instant la redoute se détacha en noir sur le disque éclatant de la lune. Elle ressemblait au cône d'un volcan au moment de l'éruption. Un vieux soldat, auprès duquel je me trouvais, remarqua la couleur de la lune. " Elle est bien rouge," dit-il.* The moon rose behind the Cheverino redoubt. It was broad and red, as is usual at its rising. But that evening it seemed to me of extraordinary size. For a moment the redoubt stood out in black on the bright disk of the moon. It resembled the cone of a volcano at the time of an eruption. An old soldier near whom I happened to be, noticed the colour of the moon. " It is very red," he said.

The pluperfect indicative and the past anterior of the indicative are both rendered by the same English form—viz. : had + past participle : *j'avais donné* and *j'eus donné* both mean I had given. But the pluperfect merely indicates that, at a point of time now past, an action had already taken place, whilst the past anterior presents one action as immediately preceding another. They are usually preceded by " when," " after," " as soon as," " hardly," " no sooner "—*quand* or *lorsque* ; *après que* ; *dès que, aussitôt que* ; *à peine* ; *ne . . . pas plus tôt . . . que* ; *j'avais terminé mes affaires quand vous partîtes*, I had finished my business when you went away ; *quand j'eus fini je sortis*, when I had finished I went out.

The future tense expresses that something will take place. To express the " promissive future," in which " shall " and " will " are " notional verbs "—I will speak, you shall go—independent words must be used : *je veux parler, il faut que vous alliez*.

The future must never be used after *si*, if, except when introducing an indirect question : *il nous écrira s'il a besoin de nous*, he will write to us if he has need of us. In English the present frequently occurs instead of the future, after " when," " as soon as," and similar expressions. In French the future must always be used : I shall speak to him when I see him, *je lui parlerai quand je le verrai*.

EXERCISE.

TRANSLATE INTO FRENCH : 1. Bears (*ours*) climb up (*grimper sur*) trees. 2. The sun shines (*briller*) for everybody (*tout le monde*). 3. The earth refuses (*refuser*) nothing to those who cultivate (*cultiver*) it. 4. Railways have contributed (*contribuer*) to the progress (*le progrès*) of commerce. 5. If he lends you his book do not forget (*oublier*) to thank (*remercier*) him for (of) it. 6. We have been working for more than an hour. 7. He who has not tilled shall not reap (*récolter*). 8. You will regret (*regretter*) not having (to have) spoken to him. 9. They prevented me from entering (*entrer*). 10. Your parents desire that you should work assiduously (*assidûment*). 11. I had been waiting two hours for him when his letter was brought me. 12. The siege (*siège*) of Troy (*Troie*) lasted (*dura*) ten years. 13. If I dared (it) I would ask him to lend me twenty francs. 14. He told me (that) he would explain (*expliquer*) that rule to me. 15. When we had finished (*achever*) our work, we went (*allâmes*) and played. 16. I told him yesterday that I should come (*viendrais*) and speak to him today. 17. He never meets (*rencontrer*) us without borrowing (*emprunter*) money from us. 18. I would not have given him anything if he had not looked so wretched.

Key to Exercise in Lesson 24.

Ceux qui méprisent les petits défauts ont bien tort. Le plus petit ennemi est toujours assez grand pour être dangereux. Ce ne sont pas les éléphants qui causent la perte des moissons et la ruine des laboureurs ; ce sont les sauterelles et les petites chenilles quand le blé est en herbe ; les charançons et autres insectes imperceptibles quand il est mûr. Ce ne sont pas les gros voleurs seulement qui dépouillent la treille et le verger de leur fruit, ce sont les petits aussi, les moineaux et même les mouches. Sans être mortels, les petits maux sont quelquefois des ennemis aussi insupportables que les grosses maladies dont nous avons peur. C'est presque toujours par de petits maux négligés que les grands arrivent. Demain le petit rhume d'aujourd'hui sera peut-être une fluxion de poitrine. Sans les petits défauts il n'y aurait pas de vices. D'ailleurs un petit défaut n'est pas une petite chose, et où il y en a un il n'y aura jamais de chef-d'œuvre. Une verrue n'est pas bien grosse, mais si vous l'avez sur le bout du nez, ce sera pour vous une cause continuelle d'ennui et de contrariété. Un petit défaut n'est jamais de petite importance s'il est permanent. Ce qui est durable n'est jamais petit. D'ailleurs un petit défaut est toujours le commencement d'un grand ; les vices eux-mêmes sont les enfants des petits défauts. Le petit défaut sera bientôt grand ; où il y en avait un il y en aura bientôt plusieurs. Un petit défaut n'est jamais seul. Il a toujours une famille. Si ce n'est point pour lui, c'est pour sa postérité qu'il est à craindre. Vous avez une dent qui a un petit point noir. Ce n'est rien ; mais si vous le négligez, ce sera bientôt toute la dent qui sera gâtée. Après celle-là, ce sera la voisine, puis la voisine de la voisine, et le petit point noir que vous avez négligé vous aura coûté plusieurs dents. S'il y a une prune pourrie dans un panier de prunes, toutes les prunes seront bientôt pourries. Le voisinage d'un petit défaut n'est jamais indifférent. La vanité semble être un petit défaut ; mais c'est un petit défaut qui a une bien vilaine progéniture. Elle a pour fils le mensonge, qui, malheureusement, n'est pas son seul enfant. Elle a en outre deux filles, qui sont la jalousie et l'envie. Parmi leur postérité ils auront la haine, qui sera à son tour la mère de bien des crimes. C'est à cause de leur ténuité même que les petits défauts sont si dangereux. S'ils n'avaient pas l'air si innocent, nous en aurions peur, nous serions sur nos gardes contre eux. Soyez indulgents aux petits défauts de vos amis.

LESSON 26

Three Moods of the Verb

THE conditional mood expresses state or action as depending on some condition, and is connected with an " if " clause in past time : *Les soldats feraient bien leur devoir s'ils étaient bien commandés,* the soldiers would do their duty properly if they were properly commanded. It is also used as a future in past time : *Il m'a dit hier qu'il viendrait aujourd'hui,* he told me yesterday that he would come today.

The conditional must never be used after *si,* if, except in the case of indirect speech : I would write to you if I should have need of you, *je vous écrirais si j'avais besoin de vous.* In English the past is frequently used instead of the conditional after " when," " as soon as," etc. ; in French the conditional must always be used : I told him I should speak to you about it as soon as I saw you, *je lui ai dit que je vous en parlerais dès que je vous verrais.*

If " would " and " should " are " notional verbs " in English, the conditional does not suffice to express them. An independent verb, usually *devoir,* must then be used ; if you have not yet done it, you should do it without further delay, *si vous ne l'avez pas encore fait, vous devriez le faire sans plus tarder.*

Subjunctive Mood. The subjunctive is used in subordinate sentences, as its name implies. It usually follows main clauses expressive of a wish, desire or command, prohibition, pleasure, regret or necessity, or containing a negative or an interrogative verb : *je souhaite que vous réussissiez,* I wish you may succeed ; *je désire qu'il vienne,* I desire him to come ; *j'ordonne que vous lui obéissiez,* I order you to obey him ; *nous sommes ravis que vous ayez réussi,* we are delighted that you have succeeded ; *je ne savais pas que vous fussiez amis,* I did not know you were friends ; *croyez-vous qu'il vienne ?* Do you think he will come ?

The subjunctive is also required after certain conjunctions, such as *afin que,* in order that ; *quoique,* although : *de crainte que,* for fear lest ; *pourvu que,* provided that : *ce livre est toujours sur le bureau, afin qu'on puisse le consulter,* that book is always on the desk, so that it may be consulted ; *quoiqu'il soit pauvre, il est heureux*, although he is poor, he is happy.

The present subjunctive follows a present or future in the main clause. The imperfect follows any of the past tenses and also the conditional.

Infinitive Mood. The infinitive is used without any intervening preposition after certain verbs, of which the most common are : *aimer mieux*, and *préférer*, to prefer ; *croire*, to believe ; *désirer* and *vouloir*, to wish ; *devoir*, to have to (ought, must) ; *falloir*, to be necessary ; *faire*, to make, to cause to ; *laisser*, to let ; *oser*, to dare ; *pouvoir*, to be able ; *regarder* and *voir*, to look at, to see ; *savoir*, to know how to ; *entendre* and *écouter*, to hear, to listen to ; *j'aime mieux ne rien dire*, I prefer to say nothing ; *il croit bien faire*, he thinks he is doing right ; *il veut parler*, he wishes to speak ; *il a laissé tomber sa canne*, he has let his walking-stick fall ; *je le vois venir*, I see him coming ; *il sait lire et écrire*, he can read and write.

In English verbs of motion are frequently connected by " and " to another verb in the same tense. In French the second verb is put in the infinitive : I shall go and see him, *j'irai le voir*. Of the verbs that require *à* before an infinitive, the following are of frequent occurrence : *aimer*, to like to ; *apprendre*, to learn, to teach ; *commencer*, to begin ; *consentir*, to consent ; *enseigner*, to teach ; *renoncer*, to give up ; *réussir*, to succeed ; *il aime à jouer*, he likes to play ; *elle apprend à tricoter*, she is learning to knit.

Of the verbs that require *de* before an infinitive, the following are the most common ; *achever*, to complete, finish ; *finir*, to finish ; *cesser*, to cease ; *commander*, to command ; *conseiller*, to advise ; *craindre*, to fear ; *défendre*, to forbid ; *empêcher*, to prevent ; *prier*, to beg ; *refuser*, to refuse ; *regretter*, to regret ; *il cessa de parler*, he ceased speaking ; *il commanda aux soldats de faire feu*, he commanded the soldiers to fire ; *je vous conseille de ne pas y aller*, I advise you not to go there.

Impersonal expressions made up of *être* and an adjective require *de* before the infinitive : *il est impossible de l'arrêter*, it is impossible to stop him. When not occurring in impersonal expressions, adjectives are usually followed by *à* : *il est difficile à contenter*, he is difficult to please. An infinitive is usually preceded by *de* when it is used as the complement of a noun : *le désir de plaire*, the wish to please ; *il est l'heure de dîner*, it is the dinner hour.

KEY TO EXERCISE IN LESSON 25.

1. Les ours grimpent sur les arbres. 2. Le soleil brille pour tout le monde. 3. La terre ne refuse rien à ceux qui la cultivent. 4. Les chemins de fer ont contribué au progrès du commerce. 5. S'il vous prête son livre n'oubliez pas de l'en remercier. 6. Il y a plus d'une heure que nous travaillons. 7. Celui qui n'a pas cultivé ne récoltera pas. 8. Vous regretterez de ne pas lui avoir parlé. 9. On m'a empêché d'entrer. 10. Vos parents désirent que vous travailliez assidûment. 11. Il y avait deux heures que je l'attendais quand on m'a apporté sa lettre. 12. Le siège de Troie dura dix ans. 13. Si je l'osais je lui demanderais de me prêter vingt francs. 14. Il m'a dit qu'il m'expliquerait cette règle. 15. Quand nous eûmes achevé notre travail, nous allâmes jouer. 16. Je lui ai dit hier que je viendrais lui parler aujourd'hui. 17. Il ne nous rencontre jamais sans nous emprunter de l'argent. 18. Je ne lui aurais rien donné s'il n' avait pas eu l'air si malheureux.

LESSON 27

Participles and the First Conjugation

THE present participle always ends in *ant*, and is invariable. It expresses an action, and differs in this from the verbal adjective, which also ends in *ant*, but expresses a quality and agrees in gender and number with its noun : *Voyez-vous la rosée dégouttant des feuilles ?* Do you see the dew dropping from the leaves ? *Voyez-vous ces feuilles dégouttantes de rosée ?* Do you see those leaves dripping with dew ?

The past participle of regular verbs ends in *é* in the first conjugation, *donné* ; in *i* in the second, *fini* ; and in *u* in the third and fourth, *reçu, vendu*.

The past participle, when not accompanied by *être* or *avoir*, plays the part of an adjective, and agrees in gender and number with its noun ; *les méchants ont bien de la peine à demeurer unis*, the wicked have great difficulty in remaining united.

When the past participle is accompanied by *être* it agrees with the subject of the verb : *la vertu obscure est souvent méprisée*, obscure virtue is often despised.

When a past participle is accompanied by *avoir* it agrees with the direct object, provided that object precedes the verb : *les meilleures harangues sont celles que le cœur a dictées*, the best harangues are those which the heart has dictated.

First Conjugation. The infinitive of verbs of the first conjugation ends in *er* ; example : *donner*, to give. The principal parts are : *donner, donnant, donné, je donne, je donnai*.

SIMPLE TENSES.	COMPOUND TENSES.

INDICATIVE MOOD.

Present.	Past Indefinite.
I give, am giving, etc.	I have given, etc.
je donne	*j'ai donné*
tu donnes	*tu as donné*
il, elle donne	*il, elle a donné*
nous donnons	*nous avons donné*
vous donnez	*vous avez donné*
ils, elles donnent	*ils, elles ont donné*

Imperfect.	Pluperfect.
I was giving, used to give, etc.	I had given, etc.
je donnais	*j'avais donné*
tu donnais	*tu avais donné*
il, elle donnait	*il, elle avait donné*
nous donnions	*nous avions donné*
vous donniez	*vouz aviez donné*
ils, elles donnaient	*ils, elles avaient donné*

Past Definite.	Past Anterior.
I gave, etc.	I had given, etc.
je donnai	*j'eus donné*
tu donnas	*tu eus donné*
il, elle donna	*il, elle eut donné*
nous donnâmes	*nous eûmes donné*
vous donnâtes	*vous eûtes donné*
ils, elles donnèrent	*ils, elles eurent donné*

Future.	Future Anterior.
I shall give, etc.	I shall have given, etc.
je donnerai	*j'aurai donné*
tu donneras	*tu auras donné*
il, elle donnera	*il, elle aura donné*

nous donnerons   *nous aurons donné*
vous donnerez   *vous aurez donné*
ils, elles donneront   *ils, elles auront donné*

CONDITIONAL.

Present.	Past.
I would give, etc.	I would have given, etc.
je donnerais	*j'aurais donné*
tu donnerais	*tu aurais donné*
il, elle donnerait	*il, elle aurait donné*
nous donnerions	*nous aurions donné*
vous donneriez	*vous auriez donné*
ils, elles donneraient	*ils, elles auraient donné*

IMPERATIVE.
Present.

donne, give (thou)
qu'il donne, let him give
qu'elle donne, let her give
donnons, let us give
donnez, give (ye)
qu'ils donnent, let them (*m.*) give
qu'elles donnent, let them (*f.*) give

SUBJUNCTIVE.

Present	Past.
that I may give, etc.	that I may have given, etc.
que je donne	*que j'aie donné*
que tu donnes	*que tu aies donné*
qu'il, qu'elle donne	*qu'il, qu'elle ait donné*
que nous donnions	*que nous ayons donné*
que vous donniez	*que vous ayez donné*
qu'il, qu'elles donnent	*qu'ils, qu'elles aient donné*

Imperfect.	Pluperfect.
that I might give, etc.	that I might have given, etc.
que je donnasse	*que j'eusse donné*
que tu donnasses	*que tu eusses donné*
qu'il, qu'elle donnât	*qu'il, qu'elle eût donné*
que nous donnassions	*que nous eussions donné*
que vous donnassiez	*que vous eussiez donné*
qu'ils, qu'elles donnassent	*qu'ils, qu'elles eussent donné*

INFINITIVE.

Present. | Past.
donner, to give | *avoir donné*, to have given

PARTICIPLE.

Present. | Past.
donnant, giving | *donné, e*, given
| *ayant donné*, having given

The verb *donner* is conjugated negatively thus:

INDICATIVE MOOD.

Present. | Past Indefinite.
I do not give, etc. | I have not given, etc.
je ne donne pas, etc. | *je n'ai pas donné*, etc.

Imperfect. | Pluperfect.
I was not giving, etc. | I had not given, etc.
je ne donnais pas, etc. | *je n'avais pas donné*

Past Definite. | Past Anterior.
I did not give, etc. | I had not given, etc.
je ne donnai pas, etc. | *je n'eus pas donné*, etc.

Future. | Future Anterior.
I shall not give, etc. | I shall not have given, etc.
je ne donnerai pas, etc. | *je n'aurai pas donné*, etc.

CONDITIONAL.

Present. | Past.
I would not give, etc. | I would not have given, etc.
je ne donnerais pas, etc. | *je n'aurais pas donné*, etc.

IMPERATIVE.
Present.
ne donne pas, do not give, etc.

SUBJUNCTIVE.

Present. | Past.
that I may not give, etc. | that I may not have given, etc.
que je ne donne pas | *que je n'aie pas donné*

Imperfect. | Pluperfect.
that I might not give, etc. | that I might not have given, etc.
que je ne donnasse pas | *que je n'eusse pas donné*

FIRST CONJUGATION

INFINITIVE.

Present.	Past.
not to give	not to have given
ne pas donner	*ne pas avoir donné*

PARTICIPLE.

Present.	Past.
not giving	not having given
ne donnant pas	*n'ayant pas donné*

Interrogative Conjugation. When a verb is used interrogatively, the pronoun subject is placed after it in the simple tenses, and between the auxiliary and the past participle in the compound tenses : *Que penseront-ils de nous ?* What will they think of us ? *Nous avez-vous envoyé du raisin ?* Have you sent us any grapes ?

When the verb ends in mute *e* in the first person singular, it takes an acute accent, to prevent two mute syllables from following each other. This occurs in the first person singular of the present indicative of the first conjugation : *donné-je ?* do I give ?

When the third person singular of the verb or of its auxiliary ends with a vowel, the subject is joined to it by the letter *t* between two hyphens : *donne-t-il ?* does he give ? *a-t-il donné ?* has he given ? *A-t-elle fait venir le médecin ?* has she sent for the doctor ?

If the verb has a noun for its subject, that noun does not come after the verb. It takes its place as in an ordinary affirmative or negative sentence, and a personal pronoun agreeing with it is placed after the verb, or the auxiliary : does that lady sing ? *cette dame chante-t-elle ?* has your brother lent you his book ? *votre frère vous a-t-il prêté son livre ? Son père va-t-il en France cette année ?* is her father going to France this year ?

If the noun be accompanied by the interrogative adjective *quel*, the verb does not require to be followed by a personal pronoun : *quelle raison peut triompher du préjugé ?* what reason can overcome prejudice ?

Interrogative sentences are very frequently formed without inversion, by the use of *est-ce que*. Its place is immediately before the verb : *est-ce que vous le connaissez ?* do you know him ? *est-ce que vous lui avez écrit ?* have you written to him ? This form is used to avoid the awkward inversion of *je* in the first person singular of the present indicative, thus : *est-ce que je chante faux ?* rather than *chanté-je faux ?*

LESSON 28

More About the Regular Verbs

W E begin this Lesson with certain peculiarities of the first conjugation. Verbs ending in *-cer*, such as *avancer*, to advance ; *prononcer*, to pronounce, take a cedilla under the *c* before *a* and *o*, as an indication that the soft sound of the *c* is to be retained : *nous prononçâmes, nous avançons.* Verbs ending in *-ger*, such as *manger*, to eat ; *partager*, to share, retain *e* after *g* before *a* and *o*, so that the *g* may have the same soft sound as in the infinitive : *nous mangeâmes, nous mangeons.*

Verbs ending in *-eler* and *-eter* double the *l* and *t* before a mute *e*, so that two mute syllables may not follow each other. The tenses and persons affected by this rule are those ending in *-e*, *-es*, *-ent* and the whole of the future and the conditional. Examples : *j'appelle, j'appellerai ; je jette, je jetterai.*

A few verbs in *-eler* and *-eter*, instead of doubling the *l* and the *t*, take a grave accent on the *e* that precedes those consonants before the mute endings *-e*, *-es*, *-ent* and in the future and conditional. Examples : *j'achète, j'achèterai.* Among the verbs that follow this rule are :

bourreler, to torment	*acheter*, to buy
celer, to conceal	*becqueter*, to peck
ciseler, to carve	*breveter*, to patent
geler, to freeze	*crocheter*, to pick (a lock)
démanteler, to dismantle	*décolleter*, to uncover the neck
denteler, to indent	*déchiqueter*, to cut up
écarteler, to quarter	*épousseter*, to dust
harceler, to harass	*étiqueter*, to label
peler, to peel	*haleter*, to pant

Other verbs that have a mute *e* in the last syllable but one of the infinitive follow the same rule as the verbs just given. Examples : *je mène, je mènerai ; je lève, je lèverai.*

Verbs that have *-é-* in the last syllable but one of the infinitive, like *espérer*, to hope, *céder*, to yield, change the acute accent into a grave accent before a mute syllable, but they keep the *-é-* in the future and the conditional : *céder, je cède,* but *je céderai.*

MORE ABOUT REGULAR VERBS

Verbs ending in *-yer* change *-y-* into *-i-* before a mute syllable : *ployer*, to bend, *je ploie*, I bend ; *essuyer*, to wipe, *j'essuierai*. The tenses and persons affected by this rule are the same as those that double the *l* and the *t* in verbs in *-eler* and *-eter*.

If the ending *-yer* is preceded by *-a-*, as in *payer*, to pay, the *-y-* may be, and usually is, retained before a mute syllable : *payer*, *je paye*, *je payerai*.

EXERCISE.

TRANSLATE INTO FRENCH : 1. The more he advanced in age, the more he advanced in wisdom (*la sagesse*). 2. The manner (*la manière*) in which (*dont*) the Romans pronounced Latin was very different from that in which we pronounce it nowadays (today). 3. He divided his fortune between (*entre*) his three children. 4. According to (*selon*) a French proverb (*le proverbe*), appetite comes from (*en*) eating. 5. He invokes (calls) upon his benefactor (*bienfaiteur*) the blessings (*bénédictions*) of heaven. 6. It is said of a man who squanders (*dissiper*) his fortune, that he throws his money out of (*par*) the window. 7. That letter brings us (*annoncer*) good news. 8. The lesson begins at page seventy. 9. Send that watch to the clockmaker (*horloger*) so that he may put it right (*arranger*). 10. I would willingly (*volontiers*) wager (*gager*) a hundred francs that it is not he who will carry off the prize. 11. In 1660, Charles II was recalled (*rappeler*) to the throne (*le trône*). 12. That fish is too small : throw it back (*rejeter*) into the water. 13. When the fishermen are out at sea (*en pleine mer*) they will cast their net (*le filet*). 14. Those who employ (*employer*) their time badly are the first to complain (*se plaindre*) of its shortness (*brièveté*). 15. Light takes (employs) from seven to eight minutes to come to us from the sun. 16. We often pardon (*pardonner à*) those who bore (*ennuyer*) us ; but we rarely pardon those whom we bore. 17. We have bought the victory at the price of our best soldiers. 18. What is bought retail (*en détail*) is dearer (*cher*) than what is bought wholesale (*en gros*). 19. It has frozen all night ; if it still freezes tomorrow, we shall perhaps be able (*pourrons*) to skate (*patiner*) on Saturday. 20. Every road leads to Rome, says the proverb.

Second Conjugation. The infinitive of the verbs of the second conjugation ends in *-ir*. Taking *finir*, to finish, as an example, the principal parts are : *finir*, *finissant*, *fini*, *je finis*, *je finis*.

Indicative Mood.

Simple Tenses.	Compound Tenses.

Present.

I finish, am finishing, etc.

je finis
tu finis
il, elle finit
nous finissons
vous finissez
ils, elles finissent

Past Indefinite.

I have finished, etc.

j'ai fini
tu as fini
il, elle a fini
nous avons fini
vous avez fini
ils, elles ont fini

Imperfect.

I was finishing, etc.

je finissais
tu finissais
il, elle finissait
nous finissions
vous finissiez
ils, elles finissaient

Pluperfect.

I had finished, etc.

j'avais fini
tu avais fini
il, elle avait fini
nous avions fini
vous aviez fini
ils, elles avaient fini

Past Definite.

I finished, etc.

je finis
tu finis
il, elle finit
nous finîmes
vous finîtes
ils, elles finirent

Past Anterior.

I had finished, etc.

j'eus fini
tu eus fini
il, elle eut fini
nous eûmes fini
vous eûtes fini
ils, elles eurent fini

Future.

I shall finish, etc.

je finirai
tu finiras
il, elle finira
nous finirons
vous finirez
ils, elles finiront

Future Anterior.

I shall have finished, etc.

j'aurai fini
tu auras fini
il, elle aura fini
nous aurons fini
vous aurez fini
ils, elles auront fini

Conditional.

Present.

I would finish, etc.

je finirais
tu finirais

Past.

I would have finished, etc.

j'aurais fini
tu aurais fini

il, elle finirait	*il, elle aurait fini*
nous finirions	*nous aurions fini*
vous finiriez	*vous auriez fini*
ils, elles finiraient	*ils, elles auraient fini*

IMPERATIVE.
Present.

finis, finish (thou)
qu'il finisse, let him finish
qu'elle finisse, let her finish
finissons, let us finish
finissez, finish (ye)
qu'ils finissent, let them (m.) finish
qu'elles finissent, let them (f.) finish

SUBJUNCTIVE.

Present.	Past.
That I may finish, etc.	That I may have finished, etc.
que je finisse	*que j'aie fini*
que tu finisses	*que tu aies fini*
qu'il, qu'elle finisse	*qu'il, qu'elle ait fini*
que nous finissions	*que nous ayons fini*
que vous finissiez	*que vous ayez fini*
qu'ils, qu'elles finissent	*qu'ils, qu'elles aient fini*

Imperfect.	Pluperfect.
That I might finish, etc.	That I might have finished, etc.
que je finisse	*que j'eusse fini*
que tu finisses	*que tu eusses fini*
qu'il, qu'elle finît	*qu'il, qu'elle eût fini*
que nous finissions	*que nous eussions fini*
que vous finissiez	*que vous eussiez fini*
qu'ils, qu'elles finissent	*qu'ils, qu'elles eussent fini*

INFINITIVE.

Present.	Past.
finir, to finish	*avoir fini*, to have finished

PARTICIPLES.

Present.	Past.
finissant, finishing	*fini, -e*, finished
	ayant fini, having finished

Our Course in French is continued in Volume 4.

LESSON 16

The Iberian Peninsula

A MASS of old primeval rock, an elevated plateau, forms the core of the Iberian Peninsula, which is divided between the republics of Portugal and Spain. Against the bastion of this rock rose up the western end of the world's greatest wrinkle, the Alps-Carpathian-Caucasus-Himalayan uplift. Between the bastion known as the *meseta*, and the wrinkle's end, known as the Sierra Nevada, is the trough of the Guadalquivir and Andalusia ; between the bastion and the Pyrenees is the basin of the Ebro and Catalonia. East of the bastion lies the Mediterranean ; west, the Atlantic Ocean ; south is the desert land of North Africa, and north is France. The bastion is a knot, a convergence. From the south came the mountains as a continuation of the Atlas Mts. ; also from the south came the Moors and Islamic culture, and the Mediterranean climate with its wonderful winter weather and its summer heat and dryness.

Europe is a peninsula of Asia ; Iberia is the peninsular extremity of Europe. Across the isthmus lie the well-nigh impassable Pyrenees, which have been claimed as the frontier of Europe. Be that as it may, the Pyrenees separate Iberia from Western Europe. North of them lie the cloudy lands, the lands of humid or semi-humid airs, where the harsh dankness of the climate is an incentive to exertion ; south of them the skies are clear—for a third of the year cloudless—and there the solar intensity is a nuisance, because Man has not yet harnessed the sunshine. From the north-east creep along the margin of the middle sea European influences, with profound results at Barcelona and in the valley of the Ebro.

The western side of the bastion is oceanic. Hence Portugal is separated from Spain and has an oceanic marginal climate, and an outlook westward, which led to the explorations of the captains sent forth in the 15th century by Prince Henry the Navigator and the former possession by Portugal of Brazil. Eastwards Spain has contact with the Latin lands, with Rome and all that Rome stands for in the world of yesterday and today. In the extreme south, Cadiz and Huelva lie on the ocean, and thus Spain, like Portugal, took advantage of the southerly latitude, for here the trade winds blow in the summer months from the peninsula south-westwards and these winds blew Columbus to the West Indies. But for these winds gold from the Americas would not have created the power of Spain, which provoked English resistance and resulted in a British empire.

Physically, the land is elevated, arid, rocky, dusty, rising here into saw-toothed ridges, the Sierras, falling there into gorge-

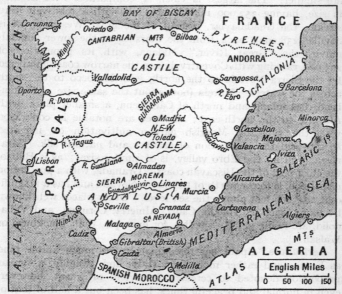

SKETCH MAP OF SPAIN AND PORTUGAL

deep river trenches, such as that of " the gash " of the Tagus. Near the coast are smallish lowlands, especially near Lisbon and Seville, and, in more constricted ways, near Cartagena and Valencia. The total area of the peninsula is slightly larger than that of France ; Portugal is ‘15 per cent of the area. The total population equals that of Poland, Portugal having 20 per cent.

Centres of Population. Portugal contains but two and Spain (the figures refer to conditions before the civil war of 1936–9) only ten places with a population in excess of 100,000. Lisbon, the Portuguese capital, with 594,000 inhabitants, ranks between Sheffield and Turin, and is the third city of Iberia, while Oporto, at the mouth of the Douro, has a population of 232,000, about equal to that of Seville or Kiel. Madrid, with a population of 1,048,000, is in the heart of the *meseta*, south of the Sierra de Guadarrama, and approaches the size of Glasgow. Barcelona, on the north-east coast, ranks with Hamburg, having 1,148,000 people, and is the largest city of the peninsula. Other places are smaller. The largest is Valencia, comparable with Bremen in size, having 352,000 inhabitants, but with a relatively tiny stream, the Guadalaviar, instead of the great Weser ; next is Seville (238,000), back from the marshes of the lower Guadalquivir, the "Great River." Malaga, with its population of 203,000, ranking with Coventry, lies on the narrow côast hampered by the Sierra Nevada to the north, with Morocco to the south across the waters. Murcia (now about the same size as Birkenhead) lies inland and north of Cartagena, a smaller place, with Alicante to the north-east ; all three are notable in connexion with the typically Moorish garden cultivation on irrigated *huertas* and the production of oranges and natural silk. Saragossa, well up the Ebro valley, is of similar size ; as is Bilbao, the chief port of the Biscayan coast. Granada, with a population of 124,000, is to the north of the Sierra Nevada and has a magnificent site 200 feet above the sea level. Other places well known by name, such as Toledo, Cadiz, Almeria, Corunna, and Valladolid, are really small—smaller, for example, than Blackburn or Walsall.

Agriculture. Spain has three-quarters as much arable land as France and rather more than Italy, and, roughly, a similar proportion devoted to cereals ; her yield of wheat, however, even in normal and peaceful times, has been but a half of that of these countries. Barley is more important, the crop being double that of France or Britain ; the yield of maize is relatively small. The potato crop equals that of Holland or Belgium. With an area of vineyards almost equal to that of France, Spain produces less than half as much wine ; the Portuguese wines total about a quarter of the Spanish production.

Most of the Spanish wheat is grown on the *meseta*, in Castile, yet New Castile grows insufficient for local needs, and wheat has to be imported for the coastal areas of the north-west and north-east and south-east. Oranges and citrous fruits are grown mainly on the east coast strip near Murcia, Valencia and Castellon. Spain has as many cattle as Ireland—a third of them in the north-west, where marine conditions affect the climate and wheat is scarce. Its sheep are almost as numerous as those of Britain ; they are widely scattered, yet most are collected in Estremadura, in the south-west of the *meseta*, this district being the chief producer of wool.

Spain's Mineral Wealth. Spain mines half as much coal as Belgium, chiefly on the Oviedo coal-field. The iron mines, especially in the north-west, and the copper mines in the south-west (Huelva) are important ; Spanish iron ore vies with Swedish iron ore as a British import. Spain mines as much ore as Luxemburg, yet sells it in the raw. As much lead is mined, mainly near Linares, as in Canada, so that Spain comes next after the U.S.A. and Australia in regard to the production of lead ore. Spain competes with Italy as the largest producer of mercury in the world ; the mines are at Almaden. The trade of Spain is mainly with the U.S.A., France and Britain ; the exports are chiefly minerals and wines. Catalonia, chiefly in and around Barcelona, is the chief industrial district, its cotton factories ranking with those of Poland.

Portugal is, on the whole, more densely peopled than Spain, of which it is, except for minerals, a western extension. The narrow Spanish valleys give place to wider valleys and coastal plains ; the sparse population of the *meseta* to the denser concentration of people round Oporto, the port wine country. Among the minerals found are sulphur, copper, lead, coal, tin, silver and iron ; salt is obtained from lagoons and salt marshes. There are large forests of cork and oak trees and plants of semi-tropical nature flourish.

Gibraltar lies just inside the strait, opposite Ceuta across the strait and Algeciras across the bay. The Rock exceeds 1,000 feet in height, the signal station is 1,225 feet up, with steep faces ; and use has been made of the limestone caves. Water for domestic purposes is stored underground, and the safe and commodious harbour is a coaling station and naval head-quarters.

The Balearic Islands, Majorca, Minorca, etc., in the western basin of the Mediterranean, are Spanish. Peopled by folk akin to the Catalans of the neighbouring coast, these islands are expected to achieve some renown as insular winter resorts.

LESSON 17

Present-day Asia

THE dominant note of the continent of Asia is extensive uselessness. Between the latitudes of 40° and 60° N., the important temperate latitudes, Asia covers a third of the width of the world—mainly to no useful purpose beyond the mere filling of space.

North of 60° N. the land slopes down to the Arctic Ocean by the great Siberian plain, merely that part of the Arctic basin accidentally not sea-submerged. There, in mid-winter, the actual temperatures experienced by the inhabitants are below zero Fahrenheit—at least 32 degrees of frost. There life is a futile struggle ; along the northern shores is the widest strip of tundra in the world. South of 40° N., in places as far south as 30° N., lies the major portion of the great east-west run of folded mountains, part of which has been picturesquely labelled the " roof of the world "—an area redeemed from complete uselessness by the Chinese coastal lowlands and river valleys.

Still farther south, reaching almost to the equator at Singapore, Asia is still comparatively useless, even in the favoured monsoon lands. Unhappy Arabia, a useless hot desert in the west, is paralleled by the north-south ridges which terminate in Malaya, useless heights which separate the true monsoon area of India from the semi-monsoon area bordering the South China Sea. Attached are the islands of the East Indies, which, with Formosa and Japan, are mountainous festoons separated from the mainland by deep seas.

In the southern area there is a great massing of people ; roughly 1,000 millions of folk overcrowd the areas which can support life. Were these folk other than a useless agglomeration of mouths to be fed and bodies to be somehow clad ; were they but one-tenth as capable as the people of western Europe and the U.S.A.—the south of Asia would be the equal of the rest of the world. As it is, they provide a market to be exploited, developed, and controlled. The west has invested its capital, in the guise of exports of machinery and manufactures, in the east. The returns on the investment are tea, silks, tin, rice, rubber, etc.

Stagnation point has been reached. The markets are saturated with western goods; and cruder and cheaper eastern manufactures, somewhat feeble imitations of western produce, are in demand—for the east seems unable to face the steadily increasing rates of interest due to be paid in return for the capital accumulations which have been sunk in the eastern lands. The rate of progress has not kept pace with the rate of investment and the east is disturbed, for the returns from its labours tend to be swallowed in payments for past benefits, which were of high value in the past but are of comparatively insignificant value now. The limit of the uselessness of southern Asia as a land in which to invest capital seems to have been reached. The returns from land come on a simple interest scale, the returns for invested capital are demanded on a compound interest scale ; and the time comes inevitably when the scalar differences are of supreme importance. The English farmer knows the difficulty ; the Asiatic is faced with its beginnings ; neither is happy.

Physical Features. Physically, Asia is a continent of contrasts. The Himalayas and the seven hundred miles wide plateau of Tibet are contrasted with the Siberian plain. The coldest spot in the world, in the Lena valley, opposes the heat in the East Indies. The wettest place in the world, in Assam, is in the same latitude as the driest stretches of the Arabian desert. The monsoons—very wet in the hottest months and very dry in the coolest months—characterize India, and are an extreme example of seasonal rainfall variation ; they are opposed to the steady drought of the Thar desert in India and the steady downpours of Malaya.

There are forests in Asia. The vegetation map asserts that the coniferous and deciduous forest extends over the greater portion of the northern plain, and that the tropical forest clothes the slopes of the south. In relation to their mapped extent these forests are commercially useless ; those of the north lie beyond the limit of exploitation at present prices for timber, and those of the south are of relatively useless timber types. There are grasslands, the steppes—at present comparatively useless in competition with the prairies. There are wide-spreading riverine lowlands. Those of the Ganges, for example, are extensive tracts of stoneless, treeless alluvium of remarkable fertility ; yet they are comparatively useless, since the density of population condemns them to service by spade cultivation — the most wasteful and extravagant form of tillage—so that they yield little surplus, and are at best marginal lands.

Standards of Living. In Asia primitive life in its crudest form is opposed to civilizations of ancient lineage but doubtful modern value. In Afghanistan, Iran and China banditry persists; it has not entirely been stamped out in Malaya and the Philippines. In India and China—so-called lands of increment, where bountiful Nature is alleged to make life easy for Mankind—men gorge and starve alternately, just as do the Eskimo or the Bantu. Human labour and human porterage cost as little as among the African blacks; the plantation coolie, the rickshaw man, many Japanese toiling along a rope to drag a primitive boat against the fierce current of their streams as a human canal horse, the Chinaman limited to porterage since his tracks are too narrow for vehicles with axles, the miner working slowly for a day or so a week getting coal in primitive fashion, the cotton spinner doing a tithe of the work done in a western factory—all spell futility, only acceptable because it is forced by the agglomeration of people. In the mass, the Taj Mahal and all the other monuments, temples, and other signs of wealth count for little against the low standard of living of the people as a whole.

Western Influence in Asia. Politically, Asia consists in the main of India and other portions of the British Empire, a complex of British provinces and native states under British tutelage; China, an inchoate amorphous mass; Japan, the Britain of the east; and the Siberian section of the Soviet territories. France is interested in French Indo-China, Holland in the Dutch East Indies, the United States in the Philippines. The Turkish area lies in Asia Minor, which is in reality a portion of Asia attached to Europe. Japan and Thailand (Siam), both independent, represent the two extremes of Asiatic development. Japan has copied Western ideas, and appears to be engaged with China in a replica of the Hundred Years' War, in which England settled how little of Continental Europe was to be English. Japan, faced with the pressing modern need of catering for a population which tends to outgrow the material resources of its limited insular capacity, appears to be trying to copy Western methods in the exploitation of the Chinese market; but while centuries ago the Western traders acquired interests and sank their capital in India almost just as they pleased, Japan meets competition in an attempt to acquire interests in a satiated continent.

Finally, Asia is intensely sectional. An infinity of races, a superabundance of creeds, tend to keep men separate and to preserve local pride and local animosities. Separatism prevails, so that it is rare to find a consciousness either of large issues concerning the state as a whole or a realization that combined efforts minimize labour ; most of the worth-while work done

SKETCH MAP OF ASIA

in Asia is done in obedience to commands issued by foreigners. It is claimed for the Dutch that their administration of Java is the supreme example of efficient colonial activity in tropical lands from a commercial standpoint ; it is claimed for Britain that the political administration of British Asia is an example of efficient interference in tropical lands for the ultimate benefit of the majority of the inhabitants. The peculiar development of Japan is associated with an insular environment, which has led to the copying of Western methods without the Western overlordship.

In summary, Asia has reached a climax—the old order has achieved its purposes. Commerce in the hands of one or two nations has to give way to commerce on a world basis ; English prices are no longer insular, but are world prices ; English wages and earnings in England are now related closely not to the spending power of India's millions, but to the earning ability of the increasing numbers of Indian workers.

LESSON 18

Asia Minor

SUPERFICIALLY, Asia Minor is like Scandinavia ; both are elevated areas set amid the seas. Scandinavia is on the edge of Europe outlooking on America, with expansive tendencies towards the New World ; Asia Minor is on the edge of Asia outlooking on Europe, with expansive tendencies towards what was a New World to the Asiatics of olden time. The Atlantic and the Mediterranean are oceanic highways ; the Baltic and the Black Seas are marine frontiers.

Historically, Asia Minor is unique. Whether we think of Troy or Tyre, of Armenia or Palestine, of Smyrna or Damascus, matters little, for we are thinking of the dead past, the museum of things that were. In this sense, Asia Minor claims our thought as a source of human effort, a birthplace of disturbing movements ; but today the tide ebbs and the outpourings of Turk or Semite revert whence they came. There is tragedy embalmed in this land, whence came peace and war to mould western Europe.

Here is an area comparable in mere acreage with Scandinavia ; here live as many folk as inhabit the deltaic lands of the Rhine. This relatively useless area includes a boiled-down Turkey, Syria, Palestine, and the states south of the Caucasus ; it fringes Arabia, Iraq (Mesopotamia), and Iran (Persia)—lands of fabled romance. Were financial Europe ready to cut her losses, these lands might well be isolated financially to settle their own differences. Here are Izmir (Smyrna), Ankara (Angora), Baku, Damascus, Jerusalem—historic cities.

MATTHEW ARNOLD (1822–88). Born at Laleham, Middlesex, he won the Newdigate Prize in 1840. "The Strayed Reveller" appeared in 1849, "Empedocles on Etna" in 1852, and "Poems" in 1853. ENGLISH LITERATURE 25

National Portrait Gallery

FRANCIS THOMPSON (1859–1907). Born at Preston, he unsuccessfully studied medicine and then suffered privation in London until his "Poems" (which included "The Hound of Heaven") appeared in 1893. ENGLISH LITERATURE 25

Courtesy of Burns, Oates & Washbourne

WILLIAM BUTLER YEATS (1865–1939), leader of the Irish Literary Revival, who helped to found the Abbey Theatre, Dublin. Among his many publications are "The Countess Kathleen," 1892, "The Celtic Twilight," 1893, and "Cathleen ni' Hoolihan," 1902. He received the Nobel Prize for literature in 1923. ENGLISH LITERATURE 26

JOHN MASEFIELD (b. 1874), who succeeded Robert Bridges as Poet Laureate in 1930. His "Salt-water Ballads" were published in 1902. In 1911 came the first of his long narrative poems "The Everlasting Mercy." It was followed by "The Widow in the Bye-Street," "The Daffodil Fields," and similar works. ENGLISH LITERATURE 26

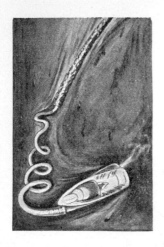

LIFE IN THE CAMBRIAN PERIOD. In Cambrian mudbanks there lived innumerable shellfish like the brachiopods shown above—top, a two-valved creature known as Lingula pyramidata, and below, a crustacean. Most characteristic of the Cambrian fauna were the trilobites—crustaceans (now extinct) related to crabs. Fossils of three varieties are shown in the left-hand photograph, where in the bottom right-hand corner is a reconstruction of the form on the left. GEOLOGY 8

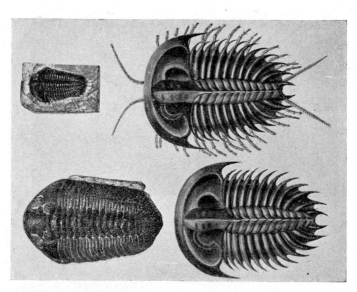

Plate 46

Volume III

ORDOVICIAN SCENERY   This photograph of the Cumbrian mountains as seen from the east side of Gavel Fell, Loweswater, is typical of Skiddaw slate (Ordovician) scenery.   All the hills shown are made of hard mudstones.   GEOLOGY 9
Courtesy of the Geological Survey

ORDOVICIAN ROCKS IN CUMBERLAND.   A great part of Cumberland is composed of rocks dating from the Ordovician period.   This photograph shows the steeply-dipping Loweswater Flags (Skiddaw Slates) at Darling Fell, Loweswater.   GEOLOGY 9
Courtesy of the Geological Survey

LIVING GARDENS OF SILURIAN SEAS. During the Silurian period sea lilies—not plants, but a species of starfish—grew in dense groves which, in the course of ages, have been compressed in to beds of limestone. The upper photograph shows a fossil sea-lily, while below is a reconstruction after Mr. Charles R. Knight.

GEOLOGY 10

British Museum

Plate 48

Volume III

Physically, the peninsula is a roof, flat-topped after the local pattern, without large rivers or large lakes, steep-sloped to its gutters in the surrounding seas, with a single ridge in the Caucasus mountains, an Alpine chain, and a unique trough in the Jordan rift. The Dead Sea and the Jordan occupy the bottom of a typical rift valley, where the surface has sunk through tectonic disturbance. The coastal flats of Georgia and Azerbaijan, on the south of the Caucasus uplift, recall in miniature the flats of the Ganges and the Indus ; the heights of Armenia and Ararat may recall the Deccan, a plateau of ancient land.

Rainfall and Temperature. North are the grass-lands, the steppes ; south lie the deserts, Arabia and the Sahara ; lying

SKETCH MAP OF ASIA MINOR

between them is the plateau, a transition zone. Skies are clear— a cloud the size of a man's hand may be a notable portent ; rain should be a winter phenomenon in Mediterranean latitudes, but winter is the rainiest season only along the margins where the Lycian, Taurus, and Pontic mountains are responsible for a reasonable precipitation of, roughly, 40 inches annually ; summer rainfall, mainly of thunderstorm type, reaches the interior from the Black Sea and the steppes ; but another type of summer rainfall occurs in the southern interior as an extension from the sub-tropical region to the south-east. The plains surrounding Ankara are arid and, hence, saline. On the extreme heights precipitation tends to be heavy and snow is extensive. Apart from variations due to differences in elevation, the summer is a season of high temperatures. The winter temperatures are low in the north and increase rapidly southward ; the January freezing point isotherm crosses the Black Sea, while the Mediterranean area experiences temperatures 20 degrees higher. This is a steep temperature gradient from north to south for an area almost sea-surrounded, and should be compared with the gradient in Great Britain, which does not exceed 5 degrees over a longer distance.

Vegetation should, naturally, be mixed woodland and grassland, yet both timber and grass are meagre in quantity. The heights tend to be wooded, the plateau lacks true forest, but large patches of woodland suggest that once true forest was more extensive ; the timber has been cut and destroyed. It is suggested by observant travellers that the semi-arid steppe is naturally capable of more prolific yields than are obtained. All this implies that Man has destroyed more than he has maintained: and arable usage of the land has not been acquired.

Country of Nomads. Pastoral nomadism is the keynote of human existence, and it is suggested that this nomadism is a racial characteristic and that Man in Asia Minor has failed to respond to the possibilities of his environment. In this respect the Magyar on the Hungarian plain implies similar failure. The interior is described as the ancient home of nomadism. The seasonal and climatic variations near the coast arouse two types of nomadism : dwellers on the upland valley flats make use, in summer, of more elevated pastures at some distance, as in Transylvania ; coastal folk pasture sheep on the mountains during the summer, as in Rumania. Summer huts may stand in the midst of small belts of temporary tillage. These nomads are true wanderers, since they are not required by climatic exigencies to erect protections for their flocks, as are the nomads of more northern areas.

Statistical details of the region are scanty. Syria, for example, is stated to till 5 per cent of its area, mainly for cereals. Turkey is credited with a production of tobacco roughly equal to that of

Italy or Greece. Cyprus appears as a minor producer of grapes, wine and cotton. Turkey mines as much coal as Rhodesia, and mines ores of lead and mercury in small quantities. Turkey produces raw silk. The Baku district is, of course, a notable source of petroleum, and this is responsible for the importance of Batumi on the Black Sea, whither oil is conveyed by pipe-line.

Railway development has been dictated by outside considerations, mainly in order to connect Istanbul and Bagdad ; the total mileage is but half that of Belgium, and, in proportion to the population to be served, less than that of Portugal or Greece. The chief ports are Samsun, which ranks statistically with Brindisi ; Izmir and Batumi, which roughly rank with Bolton. As producers and as consumers compared with the inhabitants of the Low Countries, the folk of this zone simply do not count.

LESSON 19

Arabia and the Middle East

IN the historical museum of antiquities evidence accumulates that the cradle of many of the earliest groupings of humans was the area that lies between the high mountains which run east-west through Eurasia and the sea-passages which lie between the eastern oceans and the old middle seas. In the study of origins this area stands pre-eminent, but in the geographical story of life today it is the supreme example of the extensive uselessness which is characteristic of the world's largest continent.

Between the Caucasus and the Caspian Sea on the west and the Roof of the World on the east stretches a high mass of connecting folded mountains. This mass bounds the area for a thousand miles ; the high ground widens southwards as Iran and Afghanistan. Here is a plateau, where it is said that the only shade from a tropical outdoor sun is the occasional telegraph pole. Here are the plateau folk interested in themselves, marauders by instinct in the neighbouring fertile areas. Their land has no value to the world except for its minerals ; in this case, oil is exploited and accounts for the world's interests in Iran.

The plateau abuts on the Persian Gulf in a useless coastline, and the pipe-line and the oil tanker represent the outside world.

The Gulf itself terminates, as does the Adriatic Sea, in an accidental coastline, where the débris of the Tigris-Euphrates floods and the deeper seas compete for settlement ; north-west, up the valleys of these streams, lies Iraq, formerly known as Mesopotamia, museum of the glory that once was Babylon. Here is a flood plain which challenges comparison with Lombardy and with the Indo-Gangetic plain farther east. Iraq is the least useful of the three—largely, no doubt, because of its isolation, yet also because of its folk, who matter little except to themselves, for they neither supply nor consume, have neither granaries nor markets.

Beyond the gulf and the flood plain is Arabia, a peninsula, but called by the Arabs " the island of the Arabians." This great hot desert area is nominally in Asia, but separated from the Sahara merely by the accidental rift of the Red Sea. In the past here arose the great culture of Islam, with its missionary zeal; in the present a hot desert is useless. Arabia occupies the middle of the passage way between Istanbul and Bombay. This broad corridor, a thousand miles in width, is at least nine-tenths valueless from a commercial point of view.

The western edge of the passage way is the more frequented channel, for the Red Sea has seen continuously argosy or dhow or liner connect the east and the west, and the Suez Canal is but evidence that human purposes demanded that Man should complete the rift and give the vessels loaded with eastern wealth access to a western world ready to admire and use the produce of the east. This area, then, holds east and west apart. Intrinsically, it has little to offer the world as recompense for the huge expenditure of effort entailed by its mere existence as a lengthy passage to be traversed.

In an area the whole of which is some twenty times as large as Rumania, there are as many people as in that country. Only three centres of population, Bagdad, Teheran, and Tabriz, are of any size : they rank in population with Sofia, the capital of Bulgaria.

Political Importance. Commercially and physically unimportant, this section of the Middle East has an exaggerated value politically, else Europe would not continue its old policy of sinking capital uselessly here. Because Mecca, the birthplace of Mahomet, lies in Arabia, Britain, with millions of Moslems in India, is interested ; and the construction of the Hejaz railway to Medina—the other holy city of the Moslem world, where Mahomet was buried—demands British attention.

Because the short way by or over land to the east passes Bagdad, railways and air routes to the east also require British attention to the control of these ways. Political interference follows and exploitation is advocated. Because irrigation schemes are likely to be profitable and are desirable in the interests of the crowded populations of the Indo-Gangetic plain, and are equally likely to be of advantage in the case of the Sudan and Egypt in

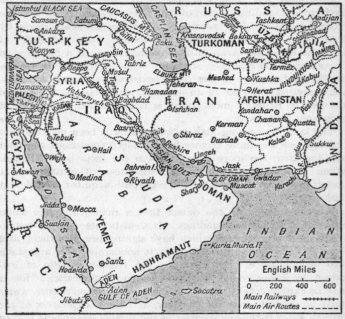

SKETCH MAP OF ARABIA AND THE MIDDLE EAST

the Nile valley, it is suggested that irrigation schemes should be set up in Iraq and that the floods of the Tigris-Euphrates should be harnessed to revive the pristine glories of the alluvial plain, which once meant wealth and power to ancient Nebuchadrezzars.

Aden, at the extreme south of the area, exemplifies the necessity that the traffic routes should be effectively policed. This coaling station and calling-place is roughly half-way ; very approximately, it is 1,500 miles in each direction between Suez and Bombay ; modern developments will accelerate its decline. The curious find much of interest in this area of futility. The customs and the practices of the picturesque Bedouin, the ancient monuments and their contents of the flood plain, the bizarre produce of Iran, the ways of the hill tribes—be they Kurds or Afghans—the isolation of Mecca as a forbidden city, the semi-sanctity of this cradle land, combine to arouse western minds.

Geography has been specified as the study of Man in his environment, and this aspect of the subject has led to the accumulation of masses of detail regarding the adjustments made by Man to his habitat throughout the world. From this point of view the life of the Arab in his oasis has acquired a picturesque importance, and has been studied ; while the life of the slum-dweller in Glasgow, or the potter existing in a state of semi-starvation for the sake of an industry which is probably one of the last of Britain's monopolies, is not regarded as worthy of geographical study.

The facts concerning Man in an area have been collated and charted, and the more remote from modern conditions the man and the area, the more valuable have the facts been labelled. When, however, we begin to ask : what use is the man ? what importance has his habitat ? geography acquires a different outlook.

We can assume at the outset that a man will make some adjustment to his surroundings. It then becomes important to study those adjustments which have significance for others, and from this view-point the simple facts concerning this area fade into insignificance. For example, the Iranian system of irrigation by underground channels has no significance ; for it is to be expected that, where excessive evaporation occurs, water must be made to flow under cover, and the cheap cover of the Iranian karez is the counterpart of the British water-pipe in lead or earthenware. Again, it may be assumed that men will use for transport the animals suited to their climate, and that the camel of Arabia " controls " the habits of its owner ; but the facts concerning camel breeding and culture count for little, since few of the important peoples in the world resort to these animals. From this point of view this passage way has little intrinsic value : it just does not matter.

LESSON 20

India, the Land of Contrasts

CEYLON is an island pendant to India ; India is practically an island pendant to Asia. The mountain wall of the Himalayas, which severs the land from the rest of Asia, is sufficiently high (5½ miles at its maximum) throughout its thousand miles of length not only to hinder and almost prevent the movement of peoples and animals and plants across it, but also to cut off from the north and east and west those lower levels of the atmosphere which are the prime control both of climate and weather. Most of us are familiar with the blanket of mist visible in the lower levels near valley floors ; some of us have experienced delays due to a fog blanket completely filling the lower levels of the Rhine gorge. In the case of India this circumstance exists on a stupendous scale ; the blanket of moist air, either visible as fog or cloud or rain, or invisible yet always present, prevents India from being an Arabia.

This blanket is subject to periodic disturbances, which result in the monsoon downpours. The blanket itself is not continuously of the same character, for in the north-west, over the desert of Thar and Rajputana, the water-content of the air is exiguous, and in the north-east, in the lower valley of the Brahmaputra, the moisture in the atmosphere is at a maximum for the world. Looked at from above and from without, the air over India is but an eddy swirling within a cul-de-sac, limited on three sides by the high land, and open at sea level to the ocean, the equator, and conditions from the southern seas. It is believed that, from a view-point which gives historical perspective, India has always had an eddying swirl of folks from without and mainly from the sea.

India is thus a residuum, a dump, apparently condemned by circumstances to the continuous interplay of accretions of outworn things. There is scarcely a single scale along which human activities are rated—from agriculture and the crafts to the arts of letters and the intricacies of philosophy, from the most primitive to the most cultured of people—which does not apply when we attempt to estimate that which is India, and on each of these scales India supplies examples at the lowest levels and, usually, examples of the best ; but the lower levels predominate, for India is a residual legatee. Asia is a continent of extensive uselessness ; India is an example, not for mere acreage, although this is equal to half of Europe—to all Europe outside the Soviet areas—but for its agglomeration of men and women, for India includes one sixth of the inhabitants of the globe—as many people as there are in civilized Europe.

To appreciate the commercial uselessness of India, make mental comparisons between its best territory, Bengal or the Punjab, and either France or Germany or Britain ; between the deltaic lands of the Ganges and of the Rhine ; and go steadily down the scale, to finish with a comparison between the hill-folk of Balkania and the hill-men of the Deccan or Ceylon. Compare the factory hand of Bombay with the operative of Burnley, the coal miner of Bihar with the hewer of South Wales, the iron worker of Singhbhum with his compeer of the Black Country, the Tamil on the plantations with any yokel in Europe at work growing grain or sugar beets for market. These folk in India do not pull their weight in the world's struggle for the amenities of existence.

Physical Divisions. Physically, India is a trinity. The Deccan, the southern peninsula, is a tableland of old rock, scarp-fringed to the seas, an area with a surplus coastline where the folk have not become seafarers, as is usual in Europe, where the Norwegians or the Greeks are characteristic maritime peninsular people. The mountains and the mountain forelands are an abrupt wall of up-folded younger rocks, which are a massive barrier. Between these two distinct areas lies the plain, the Indo-Gangetic Plain, a débris-filled trough—stoneless, treeless, sun-parched in the west, sodden in the east, where rivers wind almost at will, leaving towns and villages stranded along the edge of a deserted meander ; annually visited by the monsoon rain-clouds, which deposit their water-burden promiscuously, leaving famine and pestilence in the populated tracts, which they temporarily miss.

The plain is relatively useless, for there are so many people that labour has little or no value, the work to be done being so subdivided that there is a little for everyone and not enough for anyone ; there are no surpluses to be saved, no excesses of income over expenditure, no increases of capital ; labour-saving machinery is not worth while. Here is an area where the stranger, the foreigner, the outsider, for his own purposes and mainly in his own interests, imposes other standards on an untrained, illiterate, and unskilled folk; his efforts imply the sinking of his capital, the creation of new conditions, the persistence of his interference The outsider steadily spreading his activities tends to an over-capitalization. As the west outstrips the east, because the rate of development in the west is faster, this tendency to over-capitalization of eastern exploitations must strengthen.

Tendencies of Indian Commerce. India's story is a story of desuetude. Spices from India were desired in the west, but the west learnt how to make its foods palatable and wholesome, even

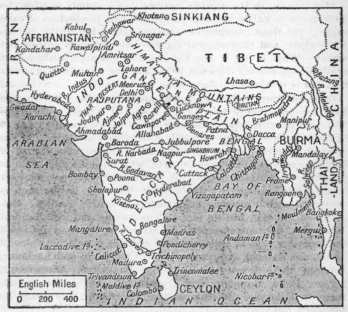

SKETCH MAP OF INDIA, CEYLON AND BURMA

in the depths of winter, and the spices ceased to be needed; Indian gold and jewels were important from their rarity, but the Rockies and the Rand and the Australian desert, Kimberley and Brazil, all provided excesses of these precious commodities, which discounted the value of Indian supplies and stores; Indian opium has ceased to be important; Indian rice and wheat have relatively declined in face of the competition from Canada and the greater skill of the farmer in the west ; Indian cotton and silk, as the bases of western textile manufactures, have never dominated the world situation, and in the face of the scientific production of artificial fibres the production of raw cotton and silk must follow the production of indigo, for the synthetic threads, like the synthetic dyes, will oust them from the markets Indian teak and hardwoods are less valuable since metals can be fashioned to serve the purposes of these timbers ; Indian jute matters less since sailing ships are vanishing from the seas.

Statistically, in the world's records, India stands out for the numbers of its cattle and the quantities of its production of cane sugar ; yet these commodities matter not to the world, but to India alone, and they suggest the fate which awaits cotton and wheat. What is left ? For the moment tea stands alone, yet synthetic tea essence does not lie outside the bounds of imagination, nor is synthetic rubber a sheer impossibility.

Cities and Ports. Despite its size and the numbers of its people India has few cities or towns ; it is a land of villages. There are fewer places with a population in excess of 100,000 than are to be found in Britain. Space forbids more than a catalogue. At the level of Sheffield or Leeds, with half a million inhabitants, is Madras ; only Bombay and Calcutta, which are roughly twice as populous, exceed this size. All three are traditional seaports brought into existence by the outsider. Bombay, on the west, is associated with a growing manufacture of coarse textiles ; Calcutta, on the east, has its jute and its mining and metallurgical industries ; both are commercial centres. At the level of Cardiff and Leicester, and at approximately half the population value of Leeds, are Karachi, Amritsar, Poona, Cawnpore, and Lucknow. Between these levels are Colombo, Bangalore, Ahmadabad, Lahore, Delhi, Rangoon, and Hyderabad. Delhi, the capital, Rangoon, Colombo, and Karachi, the minor ports, accentuate the outsider's activities.

Of lesser importance from this intermediate level are Indore, Agra, Benares, Allahabad, Mandalay, Nagpur, Srinagar, Madura, Bareilly, Meerut, Trichinopoly, Sholapur, Jaipur, Patna, Dacca, Multan, Ajmer, Jubbulpore, Peshawar, and Rawalpindi. These rank with the smaller towns of industrial England in size, but are not industrial, being mainly centres of administration, British or native.

INDIA

This is an external view of India, for it is not possible to do more than hint at the multiplicity of creeds, from animism to higher forms of religious culture ; of political conditions, from the tiny to the great native states such as Rajputana ; of rivers, from the Cauvery to the sacred Ganges, all of which serve some useful local purposes ; of scenery, from the downlike beauties of parts of the Deccan to the grandeur of the Pamirs ; of wealth, from the debt-loaded peasant to the spectacular opulence of princes and merchants ; of vegetation, from the deserts round the lower Indus to the forests which clothe the sides of the rivers of Burma, which was separated from India in 1937. Ceylon is a colony.

The geography of India from other points of view is to be found in many volumes by many authors of note. Everywhere there are signs within this vast land that it is on the eve of reconstruction. From the westerner's point of view India is disconcerting, obscure in the profundity of its problems. Light is shed on its geography by study of those chapters referring to it in " The Travel Diary of a Philosopher," by Keyserling, a book, obtainable in most libraries, which enlarges the reader's outlook on the whole East. Another interesting viewpoint is that of Hendrik van Loon, who observes at the end of the chapter on India, in his " Home of Mankind " :

" Two thousand years before the learned councils of holy men in Nicea and Constantinople tried to formulate the creed which afterwards was to conquer the western world, the ancestors of these people about whom I am writing in so familiar a fashion had already settled obscure points of doctrine and faith which to this very day disturb the minds of my own neighbours, and will probably continue to disturb them for another dozen centuries or so. It is easy, far too easy, to condemn things that are strange to us. Most of what I know about India is strange to me and gives me a feeling of discomfort, a bewildered sense of uneasy irritation. But then I remember that I used to feel the same way towards my grandfather and grandmother. And now at last I am beginning to realize that they were right. Or at least that, if they were not always entirely right, neither were they always as absolutely wrong as I used to think them to be."

LESSON 21

South-East Asia and its Products

THE south-east of Asia stretches in general trend towards the southern hemisphere and the eastern side of Australia. From the eastern end of the great east-west fold of world mountains, the Alps-Himalayas, roughly parallel ridges stretch southwards ; between them are the valleys of the Salween and the Mekong. Here is a section of the world which has only been partially explored. Immediately south of the tropic of Cancer the Shan States of Burma and the western confines of Chinese Yunnan meet ; communication across these homelands of very primitive peoples between Burma and China has been vastly improved by a new road completed in 1938.

South from this spot extends the mountainous backbone of the Malay peninsula. This is on the west, and on the east a similar ridge through Annam forms a smaller backbone for French Indo-China. This ridge terminates at 10° N., on the South China Sea ; the other ends at Singapore, almost on the equator. Between the ridges lies Thailand, formerly Siam, comprised of alluvial flats, across which meander the Menam and the Mekong ; Thailand is one of the few kingdoms of Asia. Beyond the peninsula, as a continuation, are the East Indies, in a double line—first, Sumatra, Java and Timor ; second, Borneo, Celebes, and New Guinea ; and, lying off Borneo to the north, the Philippines. Most of the land surface is elevated. Java is entirely upland ; Sumatra has an eastern coastal plain ; the shapes of Celebes and the Philippines are an index of the lack of lowland. Most of the sea surface covers deep waters.

Distances are important ; they are mainly sea-distances, for traffic is by boat. Singapore, the Lion City, is more than 1,100 miles from Rangoon, 800 miles from Bangkok, 640 miles from Saigon, 1,340 miles from Manila, 1,550 miles from Colombo. Batavia is more than 2,000 miles from Thursday Island.

Exploitation by Europeans. Here is the historic area in which Europeans have continuously exploited Asiatics since Europeans first trod these lands. The story begins before the times of the first circumnavigations of the globe, with Batavia and the Dutch traders at work in Java. Landmarks in the story are the development of Singapore—which was jungle at the beginning of the 19th century—the Straits Settlements, Penang, etc., the British colonies of Labuan and North Borneo, and that curiosity of a British dynasty in Sarawak; then came the work of the United States in the Philippines as a correlated movement. Finally, almost in our own time, is the development of the Federated and

SKETCH MAP OF SOUTH-EAST ASIA

Unfederated States of Malaya. On the mainland is the chief French colony in Asia, Indo-China.

The story is in the main one of pacification. Much of human nature may still be met in the raw, but the Filipinos of the island interiors, the Dyak head-hunters of Borneo, the Malays running amok, give less frequent evidence of primitive passions. Over the whole has tended to spread an influx of peaceable toilers, indentured labourers, from India and China, for the white man has not found sufficient labour strength in the natives.

The whole area is one of great heat and copious rains, either as a semi-monsoon seasonal downpour or as constant tropical outpourings ; the vegetation is naturally hot, wet forest, and the native crops may be inferred from the fact that the Dutch East Indies, French Indo-China, Thailand, and the Philippines all produce considerable quantities of rice, which jointly amount to roughly half the total of India.   Here are more than 100,000,000 people, of whom two-fifths are in Java, an island with a larger population than that of England and Wales concentrated in 80 per cent of the home area.   Java is four times the size and has five times the population of Holland.   Singapore has, roughly, half a million people, and is about the size of Rotterdam ; Bangkok has an even larger population than Singapore.   Batavia has rather more folk than Singapore ; and Surabaya, the second place in Java, and Manila, the chief town of the Philippines, run to 350,000 ; Saigon has about 110,000 inhabitants ; Semarang and Surakarta, both in Java, are larger than Saigon.

Spices, Tobacco and Sugar.   Exploitation began in relation to spices and condiments ; today Singapore is an entrepôt for pepper, tapioca and coffee, collected within this area and distributed to western Europe, the U.S.A., and Australia.   Tobacco is a product of Java, Sumatra, Indo-China, Thailand and the Philippines, with a total yield for the area—nearly half from the Philippines— equal to about a sixth of that of the U.S.A.   Java produces about half as much tea as Ceylon.   The Dutch East Indies, mainly Java, produce about half the coffee grown in the Old World, yet the total is relatively insignificant in comparison with the huge yields of Brazil.

The exploitation of Cuba, Jamaica and other islands in the West Indies, and of Mauritius in the Indian Ocean, to provide western Europe with cane sugar—an exploitation which lost its force in some measure when the semi-synthetic beet sugar process was perfected—may be paralleled by the Dutch exploitation of Java, which now produces about half as much cane sugar as Cuba, and the American exploitation of the Philippines, which now produce nearly four times the cane sugar provided by Mauritius.

Sources of the World's Tin.   Between Sumatra and Borneo are two smallish islands, Bangka and Belitong, where the Dutch have long exploited mines of tin.   So successful is the exploitation that the Dutch East Indies are responsible for a fifth of the world's production of tin ore.   More recently similar exploitation of tin ores has been extended to the Malay peninsula, where the quantity of ore mined has been almost doubled in a decade, so that Malaya is responsible for nearly half the tin ore which is mined. The only other tin area of importance is Bolivia, which produces slightly more than the Dutch East Indies. This winning of a metallic ore by the toil of natives or indentured labourers, brought from similarly situated lands of primitive folk, is largely in the interests of Britons, for Britain dominates the world's work in the reduction of the ores to the metal itself ; in Britain the quantity of ore treated thus has been almost trebled in a recent decade.

Rubber. The story of rubber production presents the latest features in the exploitation of south-east Asia. Plantation rubber has ousted wild rubber from the world's markets since the Great War, during which time the total world production of rubber, now almost entirely plantation rubber, has been, roughly, trebled. With the single exception of Ceylon, which is responsible for a tenth of the supplies, the whole of this change has occurred within Malaya and the Dutch East Indies. Throughout the period of development the Dutch East Indies have produced roughly a quarter, Sumatra yielding rather more than Java. Production in the Straits Settlements has been small and constant. In the Federated Malay States production, which is roughly a quarter of the world total, has been doubled ; and the Unfederated Malay States, which now produce as much as Sumatra, have increased their yield of plantation rubber fivefold.

Exploitation has proceeded apace, and has reached the stage of over-production and defeated its own ends. Most of this production has been for the U.S.A. market, which has increased its purchases of rubber threefold during the period of expansion of production ; Britain takes but a fifth of the supplies consumed in the U.S.A. The influx of white planters and exotic labourers, the expenditure—apparently, the over-expenditure—of the white man's capital has necessitated the policing of the indigenous population, which has tended to become semi-civilized. Yet the process is slow, and as a background to the relatively feverish anxiety of the white man to amass wealth, at the expense of the native lands and the native labourers, are the more primitive time-worn habits, religions, and occupations of the East. These form the subject matter of descriptive geography, and for them the student is referred to books of travel and exploration.

Our Course in Geography is continued in Volume 4.

Rocks and Fossils of the Cambrian Period

(See plate 46)

W E now come to the Palaeozoic Era, which, being the first to reveal precise evidence of species in the form of definite fossils, is also known as the Primary. The Palaeozoic or Ancient Life Era is divided into six Periods : Cambrian, Ordovician, Silurian, Devonian, Carboniferous, and Permian. It must be remembered that these eras and the periods into which they are divided are more or less artificial divisions of a continuous but changing record ; and though the existing strata which are the visible evidence of the periods are not always continuous, they follow a regular sequence.

The various beds of rock composing the strata of the Cambrian Period (so called because the beds were first recognized to be fully developed in Wales—Cambria) follow those of the Archaeozoic Era. They are divided into the *Lower Cambrian, Middle Cambrian,* and *Upper Cambrian.* In Wales the *Lower Cambrian* is represented by the Caerfai beds of the St. David's area, among the oldest fossiliferous rocks in Britain, and by the Lower Harlech beds in North Wales. The *Middle Cambrian* is represented by the Solva or Menevian group and the Upper Harlech beds. The *Upper Cambrian* comprises 6,000 feet of Lingula Flags, including bluish and black slates and sandstones, together with 1,200 feet of the Tremadoc group of dark-grey slates. These strata have been estimated to attain a thickness of 20,000 feet.

In England the Cambrian strata come to the surface only in small areas near Nuneaton, the Wrekin area of Shropshire, the Malvern hills, the Lickey hills in north Worcestershire, and the Lake District, where the beds are present as dark-coloured slates round Skiddaw and the Derwent and Crummock Waters. The greater part of the Isle of Man is covered with the famous Manx slates, together with the grits, shales, and flagstones of the Cambrian Period. In the Irish counties of Dublin, Wicklow and Wexford, Cambrian beds similar to those of the Manx slates exist. In Scotland the beds of the Cambrian Period come to the surface only in the extreme north-west, where they overlie the Torridonian sandstone of the Archaeozoic Era. They attain a thickness of about 2,000 feet, and are represented by fossiliferous limestone, Serpulite grit, quartzite and a thin bed of conglomerate. These beds indicate the very varied conditions which prevailed during each epoch of the long Cambrian Period.

On the Continent the Cambrian strata are present in Brittany, in the Ardennes district of Belgium, in Leon, Asturias, Galicia, Seville, and generally over the western districts of Spain and Portugal. In Norway, Sweden, and northern Russia the Cambrian strata are presented as broad, flat deposits apparently but little altered by earth movements since they were laid down between 1,000,000,000 and 500,000,000 years ago. Throughout south-west Canada and in the United States east of the Alleghanies the Cambrian strata are extensively displayed, having a thickness of from 2,000 to 10,000 feet and lying remarkably flat and undisturbed, as in northern Europe, over the vast Archaeozoic beds, there estimated to be at least 50,000 feet thick. The Cambrian rocks crop out from under the Andes in Argentina ; they appear in places as far apart as Korea, India, south-east Australia, Tasmania, and even South Victoria Land in Antarctica. Throughout all these areas the rocks are just as varied as in Britain, consisting of shales, slates, sandstones, greywackes, grits, quartzite, quartz-schist, mica-schist and limestone.

How do geologists know that all these strata, composed of such diverse material, were deposited in the Cambrian Period ? Partly by the position of the beds relative to those above and those below ; chiefly, however, by the type of fossils.

Fossil Remains. We have already seen that in the Archaeozoic Era vast beds of metamorphosed remains of animal and plant life exist in the marbles and graphite veins, limestones and sandstones ; but it is not until we come to the lowest Cambrian beds that we find preserved relics of individual forms of life. Trilobites existed in such profusion that different species of them have been used to designate the Cambrian divisions, e.g. the Lower Cambrian is also known as the Olenellus, for in the beds comprising it the Olenellus trilobite has been found in large numbers. In the period when the beds of the Middle Cambrian were being deposited, the trilobite Paradoxides became paramount, reaching in some species a length of two feet. The Upper Cambrian has the more differentiated trilobite Olenus as a distinguishing fossil. These creatures, of which the nearest living representative is the king crab, attained such a degree of development during the Cambrian Period that it is often called the age of trilobites.

Though plant remains are scarce as individual fossils, the lower forms of animal life were plentiful. Brachiopods in particular, both hingeless forms and the horny Lingulella, were so numerous that the name Lingula Flags has been given to beds which contain them. This genus—the oldest representative of the Lamp-shells or Brachiopods—still lives in modern seas. Brachiopods became more and more numerous as the Middle and Upper Cambrian times progressed. The bivalve shells of the Lamellibranchs included species akin to the modern mussel. The univalve Gasteropods had appeared in the Upper Cambrian and also Cephalopods, Orthoceras, and Nautilus, allied to the cuttlefishes, squids and paper nautilus of the present time.

The Echinodermata were much in evidence, beginning with the primitive Cystidians, from which all the genera and species of Echinoderm appear to have been derived. These flourished from the Lower Cambrian times until the Carboniferous, when they became extinct; but their allied types, the Crinoids or sea-lilies, were plentiful, together with star-fishes. The Medusae or jelly-fishes were present in the Middle Cambrian times; and the Annelids, the soft-bodied sea-worms which flourished in the Archaeozoic Era, must have been equally plentiful in the Cambrian times, judging by the surviving traces of their burrows and trails. Corals built up immense beds of limestone, as found in North America and in lesser degree in north-west Scotland.

Hydrozoa are represented by a variety of Graptolites of the Dendroid form in the Upper Cambrian, while there are many remains of early types of sponges. Radiolarians and other forms of Protozoa are in evidence, including the much-discussed Oldhamia and Serpulites, about which there is some doubt. The length of time that has elapsed since these creatures had the world more or less to themselves may be roughly estimated as at least 500,000,000 years; it may have been much more, for some geologists speak of a thousand million years. Nor do we know how long it endured or when it began, although, judging from the development of the fauna, it is often considered that this would have required a period as long as that which stretches between the Cambrian and the present day.

LESSON 9

Ordovician Rocks in Britain

(See plate 47)

THE rocks of the Ordovician period are named after an ancient British tribe, the Ordovices, who inhabited that part of Wales, now represented approximately by the counties of Merioneth, Montgomery and part of Shropshire, in which the rocks were found by the pioneer geologists to be distinctively developed. It was the English geologist, Charles Lapworth, who coined the name, in 1879, and since then it has been generally adopted for rocks of the particular period.

The Ordovician strata reach a great thickness in some parts—15,000 feet in Galway and Mayo and 12,000 feet in the Lake District. They lie immediately above the Cambrian, of which they were at one time considered to form a part. The Ordovician period, in fact, was a continuation of the Cambrian, in which similar conditions prevailed, but with later and more highly developed forms of life than were present in the Cambrian. It was during the Ordovician period that backboned creatures first made their appearance.

It was a period of great volcanic upheavals and much subsidence and oscillation, during which vast quantities of sediment were deposited at the bottom of enormous seas and oceans. Thus were laid down the beds of strata composing the Ordovician rocks, many of them thousands of feet in thickness, composed usually of either grits, sandstones, conglomerates, quartzites, greywackes, shales or limestones.

The Ordovician rocks are divided into four distinct series : Upper Ordovician or Bala, known as Ashgillian and Caradocian ; Middle Ordovician or Llandeilo, known as Llandeilian ; Llanvirn or Llanvirnian ; and Lower Ordovician or Arenig, known as Arenician. They are so called after the districts in Wales in which the particular series is exceedingly well developed. Since the names were given, however, the rocks in question have been identified in much greater deposits in other parts of the world.

The Ordovician beds come to the surface and cover a large area in Wales, including the greater part of Carnarvonshire, a large district in Montgomery and Merioneth, the whole of Cardigan, most of Carmarthen and the adjoining districts of Radnor and Pembrokeshire.

In England they are not much in evidence at the surface except in south Shropshire, where they constitute a continuation of the Montgomery strata and attain a thickness of 10,000 feet. They are found on the western side of the Longmynd and on the eastern side in the Caradoc area. In Cumberland they compose all the mountainous region north-west of Ambleside and Coniston Water and, extending to Wastwater, combine with volcanic material to compose the grand mountainous masses of Scafell and the surrounding peaks. The Skiddaw slates and the whole area extending north, east and west of Keswick to beyond Crummock Water are Ordovician. In the Lizard district and in south Devon are contorted sedimentary rocks of Ordovician age.

In Scotland the Ordovician rocks exist chiefly in the southern uplands, extending in a belt from northern Wigtownshire to the Lammermuir hills. This belt extends across to Ireland, where it forms a succession of outcrops, attaining a grand development in Mayo and Galway. An obvious extension of the Welsh series spreads over Wexford, Waterford, Wicklow and Kildare. There is little doubt that Ordovician rocks are bedded under the greater part, if not all, of southern Britain and Ireland, and that they extend beneath the Irish Sea and the English Channel to Brittany and Normandy, where they are again much in evidence.

Ordovician Rocks Outside Britain. The north coast of Spain and other areas of the Iberian peninsula present Ordovician rocks of very similar description, attaining to a thickness of about 1,800 feet. In Bohemia it is estimated that they are about 3,000 feet thick. In the Baltic provinces of Germany, in Latvia, Finland, and throughout Scandinavia, they are extensively present, chiefly in the form of limestone only about 300 feet thick.

In North America the Ordovician period is well represented by strata containing fossils of trilobites, identical with those found in the British series ; this suggests that Ireland and Scotland were linked up with a shore line across what is now the Atlantic in Ordovician times. Ordovician rocks occur over large areas of eastern Canada, the United States, and British Columbia. They are present, too, in South America, the south-eastern area of Australia, in Tasmania and New Zealand, in the northern Himalayas, northern China, Siberia and south Greenland.

Fossils of the Period. Throughout these wide areas the identity of each series of Ordovician rocks may be established by means of the fossils present. The most distinctive of these are the graptolites. These have generally been preserved as *impressions*, some resembling quill-pens (hence their name), others fine filaments of seaweed or coral. They belong, however, to an extinct order of Hydrozoa, and were marine creatures, each encased in a small horny cell. The graptolite represents a colony or assemblage of individuals arranged, some species on one side of a single stem, some species on both sides. There were a great many varieties ; some were curved, as the *Didymograptus* of the Llanvirnian series ; others had many-branched forms, as the *Tetragraptus* of the Arenician series ; the *Phyllograptus*, also of the Arenician series, had leaf-like forms, while the *Climacograptus*, of the Llandeilo and Bala series, was straight. Thus many distinct species of graptolites date, as it were, the successive divisions of Ordovician time.

Trilobites were also very plentiful, and, as in the case of the Cambrian period, particular species are identified with the strata of certain epochs. Most noteworthy are the trilobite *Illaenus* of the Bala series ; *Ogygia buchi*, *Asaphus tyrannus* and *Agnostus* of the Llandeilian series ; *Phacops* in the Llanvirnian series ; *Trinucleus*, which had no eyes, in the Caradocian series, and *Ogygia Selwyni* in the Arenician series. These types were all very distinctive and of world-wide distribution.

The brachiopods, *Orthis* and *Strophomena*, were plentiful in the arenaceous deposits, while corals and crinoids were abundant in the limestones ; most plentiful were the now extinct Cystideans, twenty-three species having been found in the Bala series alone. Lamellibranchs were well represented by *Palaearca* and *Redonia* from the Arenician to the Bala series, together with numerous species of gasteropods, and the cephalopod, *Orthoceras*.

The most impressive find among all the fossil fauna of these times has been the discovery in the Ordovician strata of Colorado of numerous fish-like creatures possessing a backbone—the Ostracoderms. They have not been found in Europe, and, so far as is known, they are the ancestors of all vertebrates.

As regards the Ordovician flora, no individual fossils of terrestrial plants have, so far, been found, but a seam of anthracite at Olonets in Finland testifies to the existence of a prolific vegetation in favoured areas.

Relics of Ordovician Volcanoes. In Britain the Ordovician age was one of great volcanic activity ; in Carnarvon, Merioneth, and Montgomery the mountain ranges of the Arenigs, the great masses of Plynlymmon, Cader Idris and, greatest of all, Snowdon, are the denuded remains of this volcanic area. In Cumberland throughout the Borrowdale district, including the peaks of Scafell and Helvellyn, are masses of volcanic ash and lava reaching to a thickness of 10,000 feet.

In Ireland volcanoes were active in the Dublin and Waterford areas, while in Scotland the region of volcanic activity was restricted to the southern uplands, more particularly the Girvan and Ballantrae areas of Ayrshire. Between this district and the Lammermuir hills in the east there was much folding of the strata and outpourings of lava and ash. The lava on reaching the sea produced the singular pillow-lava (*see* plate 41 in volume 2) as a consequence of the sudden chilling. The evidence that these volcanoes belonged to Ordovician times consists in the existence of great sheets of volcanic ash and lava between the various beds of the Ordovician series ; so distinct are these layers that it is possible in many instances to tell whether the volcanoes were active in, say, early Arenician or the very much later Llandeilian or, still later, Ashgillian times.

The Ordovician rocks provide the following commercial products : silver, zinc, lead, barytes, graphite, road-metal, flag-stones, slates, and quartzite for the manufacture of glass. Thus Man finds many uses for the materials that came into existence between, let us say, four and five hundred million years before his advent.

LESSON 10

Strata and Fauna of the Silurian Period

(See plate 48)

THE rocks representing the Silurian period were so named by Sir Roderick Murchison because the large area in central and south Wales where they are particularly prominent was once occupied by the ancient British tribe of the Silures. In addition to Radnor, Montgomery, and Denbighshire in Wales, the Silurian rocks are found at the surface in England in south Shropshire, in the Malvern hills of Worcestershire, in

Herefordshire, in the Usk district of Monmouth, and over a large area of south Cumberland and Westmorland, enclosing both Windermere and Coniston Water.

In Scotland, the Silurian rocks only appear in the extreme south, where they constitute a broad belt some 30 miles wide, extending from the rocky coast of Berwickshire, through Selkirk, Dumfries, Kirkcudbright and southern Wigtownshire, to the Mull of Galloway. Connecting beneath the sea, the Silurian rocks again form an extensive area in the Irish counties of Down, Armagh, Louth, Monaghan and Cavan, reappearing in small outcrops in Mayo, Galway, Tipperary, Limerick, Kerry and Waterford.

The Silurian strata are extensively developed in Scandinavia, particularly in the region of the Island of Gotland ; for this reason the Silurian system is frequently referred to as " Gotlandian " by Continental writers. Throughout Finland and in northern Russia it forms a belt extending to the Urals. In Poland, Bohemia, Germany, northern France, the Pyrenees and Portugal the Silurian rocks are found, though of no great thickness—usually much under 1,000 feet—but in Scandinavia they reach 4,000 feet.

The Silurian rocks cover large areas in India, Burma, and western China ; they also appear extensively in south-east Australia and New Zealand. In America they are present in the Appalachian Mountains, and in Pennsylvania, Michigan, Ohio, Illinois, Indiana, and throughout Ontario and the area north of the Great Lakes, even to Hudson's Bay and Greenland, while in the south they stretch from Brazil to Peru. Throughout all these areas the Silurian rocks are almost entirely composed of either sandstones, limestones or shales, while there is an almost complete absence of volcanic material of the period. From this we infer a cessation from the volcanic upheavals which were so characteristic of the preceding Ordovician times.

Strata of the Silurian Period. The Silurian period is divided into three successive series of strata, each representing an epoch. The uppermost and, therefore, most recent is noted first:

Downtonian or Ludlovian Series
—represented by .. .. ..
(up to 1,800 feet thick) .. ..
{
Ledbury Shales.
Downton Sandstone.
Upper Ludlow Beds.
Aymestry Limestone.
Lower Ludlow Shale.
}

Salopian or Wenlockian Series— ⌠Wenlock Limestone.
  represented by.. .. .. .. ⟨Wenlock Shale.
  (up to 2,600 feet thick)   ⌡Woolhope Limestone.

Valentian or Llandovery Series— ⌠Tarannon Shale.
  represented by .. .. .. ⟨Upper Llandovery.
  (up to 5,000 feet thick)   ⌡Lower Llandovery.

These thicknesses of strata apply solely to the above districts, whence they derive their names. In the Lake District the whole series attains a thickness of about 14,000 feet, and in Scotland 6,800 feet.

Borings indicate that the system lies beneath the superimposed strata of most of England, and extends south-eastward into France beneath the Channel. There these rocks stretch from Brittany to the Ardennes, while westward they lie beneath most of the superimposed beds of Ireland. Apparently dipping beneath the Atlantic, they reappear, in three corresponding series, in North America, where the Ludlovian series are known as the Salina, the Wenlockian as the Niagaran, and the Llandovery series as the Oswegan.

Dominant Fossils. The identification of the beds of each series is assured by the presence of certain forms of fossilized life, as has been pointed out in previous Lessons in this Course. In the Silurian we find that very different species and types have appeared to serve this purpose, while the trilobites and graptolites still remain very similar to those of the preceding Ordovician period. These are still the dominant and most prolific fossils, but the graptolites now show the cells on one side of the stem only and are known as the Monograptidae.

The trilobites show a decided decline both in numbers and development ; though *Phacops, Illaenus* and *Homalonotus* still abound, many Ordovician types have completely disappeared. The cause of this may have been the remarkable development of the much more highly organized crustaceans of the Eurypterid species, which in late Silurian times attained gigantic dimensions. The lobsters, crawfish and scorpions are their nearest modern descendants. The *Pterygotus* was the largest crustacean known ever to exist, reaching a length of six feet, while the *Eurypterus* attained 18 inches, and were so numerous that certain Downton beds are known as the Eurypterus shales. These great creatures crawled about in the shallow and muddy sea beds, where, close to the shore, they probably spread havoc with their powerful claws among the relatively defenceless trilobites. Thus through millions of years had these large crustaceans developed apparently from the humble little shrimp-like phyllopods of Cambrian times.

Fossil Fishes. The earliest vertebrates, the fishes, were, however, soon to become a still more terrible menace to the teeming fauna of those Palaeozoic seas, and even the giant *Pterygotus* was ultimately to give place to them. The first appearance of fossil fishes in the beds of this country is found in the Ludlow series, in what is known as the " Bone Bed," which is full of the remains of fishes and Eurypterids. The fish-like creatures, the Ostracoderms, which had appeared in the Ordovician rocks of Colorado, are plentifully represented in the Silurian of Britain. One of them was the *Cephalaspis*, and another the *Pteraspis*. These, together with the *Scaphaspis*, *Auchenaspis* and *Eukeraspis*, although probably not true fishes, were a link between them and the crustaceans. The Ostracoda were entirely unlike any living fish or crustacean, but they showed structural affinity to the king crabs. The head and forepart of the Ostracoderms were protected by hard bony plates, and, while there were no limbs or paired fins, dorsal and caudal fins had appeared. Most important of all were the beginnings of the vertebral column ; although this was probably not composed of true bone, it served as a support for the muscular tissue of a powerful tail, which would give the creature great mobility, and enable it to become an increasing menace to other forms of marine life, besides permitting unlimited growth when the head-shields were eventually abandoned and their descendants became true fishes.

The Echinoderms attained their maximum development during the Silurian Period, both crinoids and cystideans composing most of the many massive beds of limestone. Corals also were in increasing abundance, and helped to build the thousands of feet of limestone that are now evidence of the enormous length of time which must have elapsed in the process.

Echinoids, or sea-urchins, first appear in the Silurian strata of Britain—*Echinocystis*, *Palechinus* and *Palaeodiscus* being the ancestors of a most prolific family, which has continued to present times. Starfish were also abundant, as were brachiopods of the Ordovician genera and the *Lingula* and *Orthis* of Cambrian times.

Lamellibranchs became much more abundant, and about 60 species of gastropods have been found in the Silurian strata of

Britain alone. while numerous genera belonging to the nautilus family (now represented by only one living specimen, the pearly nautilus) had come into existence in Silurian seas These had curved and coiled shells as distinct from the straight and often enormous cones of the *Orthoceras* species, which had continued from the Cambrian period, but were now declining in numbers.

Insects and Plants. Remains of insects have also been found in Silurian strata, together with numerous scorpions, which are almost identical with the present-day species : thus there must have been insect life for them to devour.

Plants are first found in the Silurian strata as individual fossils and distinct from beds of graphite and anthracite in which the fossil forms have been lost by age, pressure and probably heat. These, we have seen, were found in the oldest sedimentary rocks, but we have now *Nematophycus*, found in the Wenlock beds, as silicified stems, and *Pachtheca*, which are obviously seeds, as the first traces of plant life, which is hardly likely to be well preserved in a marine deposit, or over a period of time probably between 300,000,000 and 400,000,000 years, if not more. Traces of ferns and lycopods have nevertheless been found, while anthracite diffused through black shales bears witness to a considerable marine flora and possibly the periodical flooding of land areas.

Of the commercial products of the Silurian strata, minerals are not plentiful, owing to the scarcity of plutonic rocks, but veins of gold, silver and lead have been found in Britain, together with graphite in Cumberland. The hard limestones are valuable for building and road-metal, also for the production of cement.

LESSON 11

Old Red Sandstone

(See plate 49)

THE world-wide series of marine strata representing the Devonian period was so named by Sedgwick and Murchison in 1839 because of the distinctive fossils discovered in Devon and Cornwall. The same period of geological time is represented by lacustrine strata, known as the Old Red Sandstone. These are of special interest as revealing the former existence of three or, according to Geikie, four great and well-defined lakes that occupied most of the area between what is now the Bristol Channel and the Orkneys, with probable extensions far across the North Sea.

Over this wide area are found the Old Red Sandstone series of deposits with their peculiarly distinctive type of both rocks and fossils ; these have little in common with the marine or Devonian series of deposits, which are world-wide in extent. That these two series existed contemporaneously is proved from the fact that they both overlie the Silurian and both are immediately below the Carboniferous, but neither the Old Red Sandstone nor the Devonian overlies the other to any extent ; the stratigraphical evidence indicates that they were deposited under different conditions during the same period, generally known as the " Devonian System."

The marine or Devonian series consists of shales, limestones, conglomerates, and grits reaching a thickness of about 8,000 feet in this country, where they are found at the surface only in Devon, west Somerset, and Cornwall. There they are disturbed and contorted, with much igneous material intercalated, thus indicating successive outbursts of volcanic activity. This marine series extends over a large area, beneath the superimposed beds, in southern England, having been found by borings under London and elsewhere. The Devonian rocks evidently continue beneath the Channel, for they cover a large area in Northern France, and continue to the Harz mountains.

All this area was a vast sea ; it extended southwards over Spain and Portugal and north Africa, while eastwards it covered the whole of southern Europe to central and north-eastern Russia, to the Urals and the Arctic regions, central Asia, and south China. It extended westward, evidently across what is now the Atlantic to the Great Lake district of Canada and the United States, where the Devonian rocks are extremely well developed and fossiliferous. In Cape Province and Natal, southern and eastern Australia, and the western states of South America, similar strata afford evidence of the existence of a great southern ocean in Devonian times.

In England and America the Devonian strata are divided into Lower, Middle and Upper, which are further subdivided according to the types of different localities. The fossils of the contemporaneous beds in America are generally similar to those in Europe.

Devonian Fauna. The marine fauna of the Devonian period, while generally similar to that of the Silurian, had certain marked differences. The graptolites had entirely died out. The trilobites were also on the decline and apparently much on the defensive, developing a spiny and very protective covering, as *Homalonotus*.

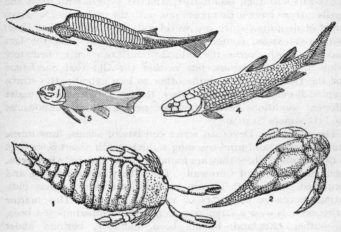

THE AGE OF FISH. Following the Silurian Period true fish became abundant in the Devonian and Old Red Sandstone Periods, predominating over other forms of life. Devonian examples shown here are Pterichthys (**2**) and Cephalaspis (**3**), both armoured. Developments of the Old Red Sandstone are Pterygotus (**1**), a giant lobster or scorpion 6 ft. long; Osteolepis (**4**) and Acanthodes (**5**).

Fishes, which had become very numerous and more varied, acquired still more the protective bone-like plates for the head and forepart of the body. *Cephalaspis, Pterichthys, Homosteus, Coccosteus*, and *Parexus* are notable examples of these protected marine fishes. The singular *Pteraspis*, which had appeared in the Ludlow beds of Silurian times, now became very prolific, but had retreated from that area, with the open sea to the Devonian Ocean farther south; another, the great *Dinichthys*, had a head-case 3 feet in length. It is in the limestones and shales, not the sandstones, that the fossils are prolific. In the European area corals were less prolific than in Silurian times, thus pointing to possibly cooler conditions, or perhaps deeper waters.

The cephalopods had increased both in genera and species; while the great allied group, the *Ammonoidea*, which is now extinct, made its appearance in the new type, the goniatites. The brachiopods reached their greatest development, 1,100 species having been discovered in the Devonian strata.

Plant Life in Fossils. The Devonian flora is chiefly represented by ferns, *Knorria*, lycopods, club-mosses, calamites and *Palaeopteris*. While the conditions were not favourable for the preservation of plant life, it yet appears to have been very abundant in favoured localities, as in New Brunswick, Nova Scotia, and the Gaspé peninsula, where over 100 species of these flowerless plants, including club-mosses and pine trees, have been discovered. Also in the Alleghanies vast quantities of natural gas and oils, obviously due to decomposed organic matter, have been found in the fossiliferous Devonian shales. Insects were also present, wings of the orders *Orthoptera* and *Neuroptera* being found impressed in the rocks.

The best areas for the study of these Devonian rocks and fossils are the coast line from Minehead to Ilfracombe, Combe Martin and, where exposed, on Exmoor ; also Pilton, Chudleigh, Newton Abbot, Torquay ; from Dartmouth to Plymouth and Polperro, Launceston, and the north coast of Cornwall.

The plant and insect life is associated rather with the estuarine deposits of the Old Red Sandstone facies farther north ; these link up the Devonian marine with the purely lacustrine. There is stratigraphical evidence of a ridge of Old Red Sandstone rocks stretching eastwards from what is now the Bristol Channel to Belgium ; this ridge separated the great Devonian Ocean of the south from the mountain and shallow lake area to the north. The sea had since Silurian times retreated southwards and left behind what appears to have been originally one large lake, but in the course of many millions of years there were many changes of level and shore-line, which are revealed by type of deposit. The Old Red Sandstone facies is, therefore, divided into Lower, Upper and Middle series.

There was for long ages a gradual rising of the land above sea level, and great rivers brought down sediment from the mountains, spreading it out fanwise as sand, gravel and conglomerate in an ever-increasing deposition. Winds also added in many localities immense stretches of fine wind-swept sand, the products of disintegration, which covered areas left by the receding sea and drying-up lakes. The Upper Old Red Sandstone beds in Scotland are of a bright red colour and reach 500 feet in thickness.

Formation of Lakes. Four lakes appear to have ultimately formed, the most southerly being the " Welsh Lake " revealed in Monmouth, Shropshire and Herefordshire, where the rocks are 7,000 feet thick. The great " Caledonian Lake," where the strata attained a thickness of 12,500 feet, was the most extensive ; its basin filled the long synclinal folds of strata which stretched across Scotland and north Ireland in a south-west and north-east direction. It can be traced to the Sogne Fiord in Norway, and as far as Finland and Spitsbergen ; while in the west it appears to have reached to Nova Scotia and the Gaspé peninsula, being revealed by the Old Red Sandstone rocks.

The immense amount of material which became deposited in the area of the great " Caledonian Lake " was chiefly provided by the denudation of the crystalline mountain masses, rivalling the Alps in magnitude, which then formed a series of five great chains crossing Britain and Ireland and reaching to an estimated height of at least 12,500 feet. The present mountains are merely the denuded and glacier-worn stumps, which have survived at least 300,000,000 years.

The gradual filling in of the lake bed and rise of the land resulted in subdividing the vast waters, the northern division being known as " Lake Orcadie," while an arm of " Lake Caledonia " to the south became " Lake Cheviot." Other lakes must have existed over the wide northern area, extending even to eastern Canada, to account for the vast fresh-water deposits of the Old Red Sandstone rocks ; for no marine fauna or flora is found therein, no coral, seaweeds, or known denizens of the Devonian sea, except some Eurypterids and fish which, salmon-like, appear to have ascended the estuaries. Fish were very plentiful, most of them scale-covered ; the *Osteolepis* and *Acanthodes* attained their greatest development, while the *Diplopterus*, *Glyptopomus* and *Asterolepis* were other examples.

Periodically, large areas of these shallow lakes appear in later times to have dried up, when the fishes crowded into the circumscribed areas and finally died in masses. Thus they are found as fossils in various places. Most remarkable was the *Dipterus*, which endeavoured to escape these consequences, as does its solitary modern representative, the mud-fish or *Ceratodus* of Australia, which can survive temporary droughts.

The Eurypterids were another remarkable type, which from their powers of migration, like crabs, were able to attain their greatest development in this age. The *Pterygotus*, like a giant lobster or scorpion, to which it was closely allied, continued to flourish from Silurian times under most varied conditions, still attaining six feet in length and being equally at home in marine waters or in those of lakes.

Subsequently, much of this land began to sink and the sea encroached ; the great beds of limestone began to be formed which now comprise the Carboniferous limestone constituting the base of this great age of plants. It is probable that the Devonian period represents an age upwards of 200,000,000 years ago. Many of its products have much economic value. The Old Red Sandstones and limestones furnish good building material ; roofing slates are provided in Devon and Cornwall and the tin-stone in Cornwall ; while lead, copper and iron ores are obtained in central Europe and road-metal from the intrusive granites.

LESSON 12

Deposits of the Carboniferous Sea

(See plate 50)

THE Carboniferous period covers an immensely long era in the earth's history. Although the name is derived from *carbo*, Latin for coal, and was given because of the numerous coal beds laid down during the period, these form but a small proportion of the whole system, which, comprising limestones, shales, sandstones, and bands of ironstone, attains a thickness in many areas of 20,000 feet. The character, or *facies*, of these rocks shows that the Carboniferous period is represented by a marine and a terrestrial series of beds, together with estuarine and freshwater types. There are also intercalated layers of volcanic material which bear witness to successive eruptions in certain areas.

The whole has been divided into Lower Carboniferous and Upper Carboniferous, with further subdivisions into Carboniferous limestones, Yoredale beds, Millstone Grit beds, and the Coal Measures. The lowest beds of the entire series are the lower limestone shales, which also contain layers of sandstone and Carboniferous slate. Above these are the great beds of Carboniferous limestone, which are, of course, marine, and composed largely of corals, crinoids and foraminifera. These beds are overlaid by the upper limestone shales—generally known as the Yoredale beds—which contain bands of radiolarian chert, and are also marine. The next series is the Millstone Grit beds, composed of hard siliceous rocks with bands of shale, sandstones and flagstones. Occasional seams of coal indicate the beginning of the forest era and terrestrial conditions. They form, generally, the foundations of the Coal Measures, and contain remains of terrestrial plants. These beds were apparently deposited in the deltas of rivers, lagoons and shallow waters, constituting the beginnings of the extensive swamps in which flourished the prolific vegetation more particularly associated with the Carboniferous period. The fourth and last series, the Coal Measures, consists of sandstones, shales and clays, with numerous seams of coal in successive layers (some of great thickness), together with bands of ironstone.

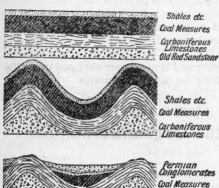

Shales etc.
Coal Measures
Carboniferous Limestones
Old Red Sandstone

Shales etc.
Coal Measures
Carboniferous Limestones

Permian Conglomerates
Coal Measures
Carboniferous Limestones

HOW BRITAIN'S COALFIELDS WERE SAVED. Fig. 1. When at the end of the Carboniferous Period the earth's crust became folded into ridges, most of the coal measures were subsequently lost through denudation and only those preserved that lay in the pockets of the hills. These were covered again later.

The entire Carboniferous system is well developed in Britain, where the beds lie flat, except that the one-time continuous sheet of strata is now divided into synclinal troughs of basins by subsequent foldings. The chief of these folds are the Pennine, extending north and south, together with the Hercynian, extending from the west of Ireland through southern England to Westphalia. Thus great and lesser basins were formed which preserved large areas of coal-bearing strata from denudation in later times (*see* Fig. 1).

Carboniferous Sea. Following the Devonian period came a long era of gradual subsidence over southern Britain and Ireland ; much of the old Red Sandstone area was submerged, and in the clear waters of the warm sea corals, crinoids and

HOW DEVONIAN FISH DIED. In the Devonian Period desert conditions spread, lakes and rivers dried up and fish from large areas were crowded into pools, where they died when the water finally disappeared. The geologist finds them packed close as in this fossil slab from an Old Red Sandstone stratum. In these strata fossils are only present in such scattered pockets together with traces of grasses and fresh water animals thus proving the desiccation theory. GEOLOGY 11

British Museum. Natural History

CARBONIFEROUS FORMATIONS IN BRITAIN. Upper photo, the
cliffs of Cheddar ; lower photo, the South Wales coast looking in the
direction of Mumbles Head—another example of Carboniferous
limestone. GEOLOGY 12

Dixon Scott and W. F. Taylor

Plate 50   *Volume III*

POMPEY THE GREAT (106–48 B.C.). Gnaeus Pompeius, known as Pompey, won glory as a military commander in Africa, Spain and the East. He was, however, defeated by Caesar at Pharsalus, fled into Egypt, and was there assassinated. HISTORY: ANCIENT 18

Ny Carlsberg Museum, Copenhagen

GAIUS JULIUS CAESAR (102–44 B.C.). Born in Rome, of patrician rank, he became consul in 59 B.C. and governor of Gaul. In 55 and 54 B.C. he invaded Britain. By routing Pompey in 48 B.C. he attained supreme power, but he was assassinated in 44 B.C.
HISTORY: ANCIENT 18

Naples Museum

STRIKING A BARGAIN IN THE SLAVE MARKET. In the second century B.C. the conditions of the Roman slave population grew steadily worse, until discontent culminated in the Servile War. The specific traffic in human flesh is illustrated in this bas-relief on a funeral stele from Capua, depicting a naked man standing on a stone pedestal between a Greek slave-dealer and a togaed Roman who is purchasing him. HISTORY: ANCIENT 17

AUGUSTUS (63 B.C.–A.D. 14). Octavian, great-nephew and adopted son of Julius Caesar, assumed the name of Augustus after his defeat of Antony had left him supreme master of the Roman world. He was the first of the emperors.

HISTORY: ANCIENT 19

British Museum

PRAETORIAN GUARDS. A principal mainstay of the imperial power were the Praetorian Guards, some of whom are depicted here in their parade uniform.

HISTORY: ANCIENT 19

The Louvre; photo, Giraudon

Plate 52

Volume III

numerous marine organisms lived and died, their shells, bodies and skeletons combining to build up at the gradually sinking sea-bottom a great bed of grey Carboniferous limestone, which in places reached thousands of feet in thickness. The sea first submerged the south of England and Ireland, extending northward over a ridge which, in the early part of the period, had formed an island where are now the midlands. It extended, finally, to southern Scotland, where the sand and clay washed down from a great northern continent formed layers of sandstone and shale. A large volcanic island then existed over the Galloway region of Scotland and south of the Clyde; Derbyshire was also volcanic about this time, together with the Isle of Man and south-west Ireland.

These convulsions appear to have accompanied a gradual rise in the land; the sea became shallow and filled with sediment destructive to the corals, crinoids and other limestone builders, and shales were deposited instead. The Carboniferous sea, shown approximately in Fig. 2, was thus slowly filled up by the deposit of such sediments, together with sands and, finally, clays. Deltas and swamps formed at the mouths of great

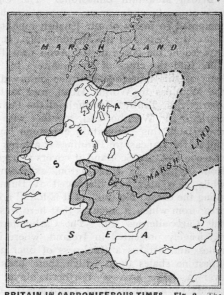

BRITAIN IN CARBONIFEROUS TIMES. Fig. 2. The Carboniferous was a period of marsh-lands wherein swamp-forests rioted. During its later phases the peninsula (obliquely ruled) stretching across England subsided, leaving an island at its extremity. The island in Scotland was volcanic.

After Jukes Brown, "Building of the British Isles"

rivers, one in particular covering northern England and another Devonshire. These formed the deposits known as Millstone Grit, which contain a few marine fossils and a few land plants, but much detritus, angular fragments and much terrestrial material mixed with impure limestone. Bands of shale reveal flood periods or alternate rising and falling, while ripple marks and current-bedding indicate the flow of shallow water in one direction. Then terrestrial vegetation began to get a hold in these great semi-tropical swamps. It decayed while more grew, and so the beginnings of thin seams of coal appeared in this Millstone Grit. Further building up of the land by denudation of the mountainous regions to the north favoured the growth and extension of vast flowerless forests, the great Coal Measures being the result.

British Mountain Limestone. The Carboniferous limestone was originally known as "mountain limestone," because it composed so many of our English mountains, such as the Pennines, the Peak and the Mendip hills. It may also be seen well exposed in the gorge of the Avon near Bristol, in the Cheddar cliffs, and the crags of Derbyshire. In South Wales the thick beds of this limestone may be observed along the cliffs from the Mumbles to Worms Head, and in the St. Gowan's Head district near Tenby. Throughout the Pennine area of Yorkshire, Durham and Westmorland, together with a large part of Northumberland, this "mountain limestone" approaches the surface, and in the Lancashire Pennines it attains the immense thickness of 6,000 feet. In Scotland it covers a large area of the Lowlands from Ayrshire to Haddington, extending over most of Fife, while it is also well displayed at Burntisland and elsewhere along the coast. No trace of it is found north of the St. Andrews area, from which it appears that here was the farthest extent of this Carboniferous sea. The Carboniferous limestone is most extensively presented in Ireland, where it covers 15,000 square miles, and attains a thickness of over 2,000 feet. The lower limestone shales upon which these beds rest are well exposed over a large area of northern Mayo, and in the south of county Cork. In addition, there are the upper limestone shales, also known as the Yoredale beds. These overlie the "mountain limestone," and are well developed at Yoredale, in Yorkshire : they also cover the Pendleside area in Lancashire and merge into the Pennine limestone.

These complete the purely marine series of the Lower Carboniferous. The Millstone Grit series and the Coal Measures, constituting the Upper Carboniferous, are considered in Lesson 13.

The great Carboniferous sea, with its thousands of feet of marine deposits, was not peculiar to Britain. These deposits extend across northern France to Belgium, where in the Meuse area they attain a thickness of 2,500 feet. Thence they continue through south Germany and Bohemia to Russia, whence they stretch across Siberia to northern India, China, Japan and Alaska. In North America they cover an area of about 200,000 square miles. In Australia the Lower Carboniferous attains a thickness of 11,000 feet of shale, sandstones and limestone.

Fossils of the Period. A remarkable circumstance is the similarity of the fossils throughout this vast area—the Australian, for instance, being identical with those found in Britain ; this applies also to the land plants of the Upper Carboniferous. Obviously, it was a very warm period of the earth's existence.

The fossil remains in the Lower Carboniferous series are, of course, marine ; in most genera they resemble the Devonian. The most prolific were the foraminifers, more particularly *Fusulina ;* corals, chiefly rugose types ; while the crinoids were so numerous that their remains produced beds of limestone hundreds of feet thick, known as crinoidal limestone. The genera chiefly represented are *Platycrinus, Actinocrinus, Cyathocrinus* and *Granatocrinus* Brachiopods were plentifully represented by *Spirifer, Productus, Rhynchonella* and *Terebratula.* Polyzoa were very numerous and beautiful. Among the cephalopods, *Orthoceras* and *Actinoceras, Nautilus* and the ammonites (*Goniatites*) were the most numerous.

Trilobites had, however, greatly declined, being represented by the small *Phillipsia, Griffithides, Proetus* and *Brachymetopus.* The whole family of trilobites ceased to exist in the Carboniferous period, while the eurypterids greatly declined. The gasteropods continued to flourish, *Bellerophon* and *Euomphalus* frequently appearing. Fishes became very numerous, judging by the number of teeth and spines which are found, particularly of the ganoid or shark type ; they were of immense size. *Orodus, Psammodus* and *Petalodus* were the most noteworthy. The outstanding event of the long Carboniferous period, which probably goes back to between 100,000,000 and 200,000,000 years, was the first appearance of amphibians. These will be considered with the Upper Carboniferous series.

The chief economic products of this series are limestone for building and the production of lime and sandstones for making glass. Oil is distilled from the shales. Iron ores, lead and zinc occur in veins and pockets in the limestone.

LESSON 13

Coal's Place in the Geological Story

THE Upper Carboniferous series of strata has preserved for us the first extensive record of terrestrial conditions as distinct from marine. Large continental areas of dry land unquestionably existed before the Carboniferous period, but the system of deposition was not favourable to its preservation, as was the marine, since it consisted largely of blown sand and detritus, such as would be easily removed by denudation at a later period.

Circumstances more favourable to the preservation of the terrestrial deposits of the Upper Carboniferous, more particularly the Coal Measures, prevailed at this time. The great thickness of the deposits, together with the hard facies of the coal seams and their frequent situation in synclines between ridges have saved for our use the most valuable of sedimentary rocks.

Below the Coal Measures and constituting the lower series of the Upper Carboniferous facies are the beds collectively known as the Millstone Grit. These consist of hard compact siliceous strata, flags and sandstones together with beds of conglomerate composed of detritus and denuded fragments of granitoid rocks from the great mountain ranges of earlier geological periods, which then extended across Scotland and what is now the North Sea to Scandinavia Occasional thin seams of coal occur, while in places beds of impure limestone alternate with beds of shale and with clear evidence of current bedding indicating that they are largely estuarine or river-formed ; doubtless they were laid down in the huge deltas that had existed from Devonian times, as described in the preceding Lesson.

Millstone Grit is locally known as " Farewell Rock " in South Wales and elsewhere, since it forms the base of the Coal Measures, and it is usually farewell to any further seams as soon as it is reached. It covers a large area of north Devonshire and Cornwall, from Tiverton to Bude, there being no Coal Measures overlying it in this district, or the countryside would wear a very different aspect. The rocks may be observed along the coast from Clovelly to Boscastle, where they are replaced by Devonian. Millstone

Grit also forms the high moorland regions of west Yorkshire, being well exposed in the crags at Ilkley, at Pateley Bridge, also in the Harrogate and Keighley districts and over the Glossop area north of the Peak. These rocks also approach the surface between Lancaster and Settle, and protrude through the Coal Measures farther south. They provide paving stones and silica stone for fire-bricks.

Coal Deposits in England. The Coal Measures exist in numerous basins throughout Britain and Ireland. The beds consist chiefly of shales with lesser beds of sandstone alternating with seams of coal, bands of fireclay and ironstone. The Coal Measures attain their maximum thickness in South Wales, where they are estimated to reach nearly 10,000 feet in some places, though generally they are much less than this ; there are altogether about twenty-five seams of coal. In Lancashire they reach 8,000 feet in thickness and contain about sixty-five seams of workable thickness. In north Staffordshire there are about forty workable seams in beds estimated to total 5,000 feet. In Durham there are about sixty seams of coal in beds 2,000 feet thick. Leicestershire has ten seams of coal in beds about 1,500 feet thick. In Northumberland over a wide area the beds are between 2,000 and 3,000 feet thick and contain fifteen workable seams of coal. In Derbyshire they are about 2,500 feet thick, in south Yorkshire and Nottingham about the same—all being part of one great coalfield, which once linked up with the great coalfield of Durham and Northumberland. In the Whitehaven area of Cumberland the beds are about 1,500 feet thick. In the Forest of Dean are fifteen workable seams in beds about 2,500 feet thick. The Bristol and Somerset Coal beds are about 6,500 feet in thickness.

In Scotland, the Lanarkshire Coal Measures are about 4,000 feet thick and contain fifteen thick workable seams of coal. Others are in Ayrshire, near Edinburgh, in Haddington, Clackmannan and Fifeshire, where they reach nearly 1,000 feet in thickness. Cannel coal and oil shales are present near Glasgow. In Ireland the coalfields are very poor, though they are present over large areas of Kerry, Clare and Limerick, Leix and Kilkenny in the south, with smaller areas in the north.

On the continent of Europe the greatest development of the Upper Carboniferous facies is in Westphalia, where the whole series attains a thickness of about 11,000 feet, the lower 3,000 feet—known as the Flotzeere sandstones—taking the place of the Millstone Grit of this country. The upper 8,000 feet consist of Coal Measures in which as many as ninety seams of coal are present, about sixty of them being seams of good coal. This series reappears in the Mons and Douai areas, thinning out through the Boulonnais region of northern France and extending to Kent, where at a depth of over 1,000 feet not very productive seams are worked. It is considered probable that these continue westward to the coalfields of Somerset and Gloucestershire. A remarkable feature of these Belgian, Boulonnais and south of England beds is the faulted and consequent great displacement; older rocks frequently are superimposed by overthrust faults and so make coal-mining uncertain through the seams vanishing.

The great development of the Westphalian area has resulted in the name Westphalian being given, on the Continent, to the strata represented by the Upper Carboniferous in Britain. There are, in addition, certain uppermost Carboniferous beds absent in Britain, but well developed in northern France, where they are known as the Stephanian, and in eastern Russia as the Uralian.

The Coal Measures in the United States are the most productive and easily worked in the world; this is largely owing to the great thickness of the seams. They are of great extent in Pennsylvania, Ohio and Illinois. Canada has also its coalfields in Nova Scotia. There are deposits in South America awaiting development.

In India and Australia the Coal Measures are proving highly productive. In the New South Wales area, where the Upper Carboniferous merges into the Permian, the strata, intercalated with good coal seams, attain a total thickness of from 11,000 to 13,000 feet, extending over a known area of 25,000 square miles. South Africa has also revealed Coal Measures which are being rapidly developed.

Coalfields of the World. Outside the British Empire, China possesses coalfields rivalling those of the United States, although production there is delayed owing to the lack of up-to-date machinery. Elsewhere, Japan, the Donetz district of U.S.S.R., the Polish coalfields of Silesia—where the coal lies in seams varying from six to 24 feet thick, at no great depth from the surface—and those of Bohemia-Moravia, together with the undeveloped coalfields in the Arctic regions, offer the most promise, in addition to those already referred to. Italy and Spain are poorly situated in this respect.

COAL IN GEOLOGY'S STORY

The table given below shows the annual production of coal in the countries named, and is based on the most recent statistics which are available.

Country				Total production in tons
U.S.A.	..	..	..	440,000,000
Germany (including lignite)		..		360,000,000
U.K.	..	..	..	237,000,000
U.S.S.R.	..	..	..	122,000,000
France	..	..	..	44,000,000
Japan	..	..	..	42,000,000
Poland	..	..	..	35,000,000
Other countries	..	..	..	210,000,000
The World	..	..	..	1,490,000,000

In value this colossal amount of coal is worth more than twice that of all the metallic ores, including iron and gold, together with diamonds and other precious stones, put together.

Immense wealth, therefore, still remains buried in the coal seams, but the supply is not unlimited. For instance, in Great Britain the coal production for the year 1851 was estimated to be 55,000,000 tons ; now it reaches to nearly five times as much, and produces an annual income of between £150,000,000 and £200,000,000, on an average. The Royal Commission of a generation ago, after exhaustive consideration of all the available geological data, gave in their Final Report on Coal Supplies, issued in 1905, an estimated total of 100,740,210,167 tons of coal remaining unworked in proved coalfields of Great Britain and at workable depths of not more than 4,000 feet. Now this amount has only to be divided by the present annual production, and we see that Britain's coal supplies, upon which so much wealth and prosperity depends, will last barely 420 years, assuming that there is no increase in consumption. Although other forms of fuel and power would help to reduce the necessary output, the ascertained facts point to the necessity of economy in the use of this limited source of wealth. If, however, we consider the world's reserves as a whole, it is estimated that there is sufficient coal to last at least 2,500 years, even if fresh coalfields are not found.

Carboniferous Flora and Fauna. The Coal Measures are rich in fossils of terrestrial flora, and even fauna, for the forests provided the food and shelter for numerous land creatures, while the mud of the marshy lagoons and deltas preserved their remains. Scorpions such as *Eoscorpius*—a small terrestrial descendant of the great Eurypterids of earlier geological periods— were in existence, and insect life attained enormous development ; 1,300 specimens of ants, cockroaches, crickets, dragon-flies, may-flies and locusts, together with great plant-eating millipedes, and beetles, have been collected in one locality where, conditions permitting, the preservation of their fossils existed. Wings of insects reaching to seven inches in length have been found ; also evidence of creatures with a wing-span of over a foot. It was the age of insects, for their arch-enemies the birds had not yet made their appearance.

Most impressive of all was the first appearance of four-footed creatures, the amphibians. These belonged to a long extinct type, the labyrinthodonts (named from the labyrinthine folds in their teeth). They were similar in many respects to the existing salamanders, which are doubtless their descendants. Thirteen genera of these amphibians have been discovered of this Carboniferous Period in Britain, the *Anthracosaurus*, *Loxomma*, *Urocordylus* and *Ophiderpeton*, together with the *Archegosaurus*, in Prussia, having attained considerable development even at this early period. They were from three to twelve feet in length, partly protected by hard fish-like scales, and doubtless fed on crustaceans and lowly forms of insect life, which abounded.

The flora was prolific, lycopods or clubmoss types, having trunks reaching to 60 feet high, lepidodendrons and ulodendrons being most in evidence. The *Equiseta*, or horsetails, are represented by *Calamites*, the jointed stems, and *Asterophyllites* and *Annularia*, which are varieties of this plant's foliage. Numerous ferns, *Neuropteris*, *Sphenopteris*, *Pecopteris* and *Odontopteris*, existed, together with a type known as pteridosperms, which was not a true fern. Many of these types were great tree-ferns, which shared these vast forests with immense trees, whose fossil trunks are known as *Sigillaria*, and their root stems as *Stigmaria*. Conifers and araucarias grew in dense abundance. Their fossil remains include seeds and seed pods, thus exhibiting the minutest details after a lapse of at least a hundred million years.

Our Course in Geology is continued in Volume 4.

LESSON 9

Another Lesson on the Verb

FOR the future tenses the auxiliary verb *werden* (to become) is used, and for the conditional tenses the past subjunctive of the same verb. Note that in the past future and the past conditional tenses the construction in German is: "I shall had have" and "I should had have."

PRESENT FUTURE TENSE OF HABEN.

	INDICATIVE MOOD.	SUBJUNCTIVE MOOD.
Sing. 1.	*ich werde haben,*	*ich werde haben*
	I shall have, etc.	
2.	*du wirst haben*	*du werdest haben*
3.	*er wird haben*	*er werde haben*
Plur. 1.	*wir werden haben*	*wir werden haben*
2.	*ihr werdet haben*	*ihr werdet haben*
3.	*sie werden haben*	*sie werden haben*

PAST FUTURE TENSE.

	INDICATIVE.	SUBJUNCTIVE.
Sing. 1.	*ich werde gehabt haben,*	*ich werde gehabt haben*
	I shall have had, etc.	
2.	*du wirst gehabt haben*	*du werdest gehabt haben*
3.	*er wird gehabt haben*	*er werde gehabt haben*
Plur. 1.	*wir werden gehabt haben*	*wir werden gehabt haben*
2.	*ihr werdet gehabt haben*	*ihr werdet gehabt haben*
3.	*sie werden gehabt haben*	*sie werden gehabt haben*

PRESENT CONDITIONAL TENSE.

	INDICATIVE.	SUBJUNCTIVE.
Sing. 1.	*ich würde haben,*	*ich würde haben*
	I should have, etc.	
2.	*du würdest haben*	*du würdest haben*
3.	*er würde haben*	*er würde haben*
Plur 1.	*wir würden haben*	*wir würden haben*
2.	*ihr würdet haben*	*ihr würdet haben*
3.	*sie würden haben*	*sie würden haben*

Past Conditional Tense.

	INDICATIVE.	SUBJUNCTIVE.
Sing. 1.	*ich würde gehabt haben,*	*ich würde gehabt haben*
	I should have had, etc.	
2.	*du würdest gehabt haben*	*du würdest gehabt haben*
3.	*er würde gehabt haben*	*er würde gehabt haben*
Plur. 1.	*wir würden gehabt haben*	*wir würden gehabt haben*
2.	*ihr würdet gehabt haben*	*ihr würdet gehabt haben*
3.	*sie würden gehabt haben*	*sie würden gehabt haben*

The future and conditional tenses of the verb *sein* (to be) are as follow :

Present Future Tense.

	INDICATIVE.	SUBJUNCTIVE.
Sing. 1.	*ich werde sein,*	*ich werde sein*
	I shall be, etc.	
2.	*du wirst sein*	*du werdest sein*
3.	*er wird sein*	*er werde sein*
Plur. 1.	*wir werden sein*	*wir werden sein*
2.	*ihr werdet sein*	*ihr werdet sein*
3.	*sie werden sein*	*sie werden sein*

Past Future Tense.

	INDICATIVE.	SUBJUNCTIVE.
Sing. 1.	*ich werde gewesen sein,*	*ich werde gewesen sein*
	I shall have been, etc.	
2.	*du wirst gewesen sein*	*du werdest gewesen sein*
3.	*er wird gewesen sein*	*er werde gewesen sein*
Plur. 1.	*wir werden gewesen sein*	*wir werden gewesen sein*
2.	*ihr werdet gewesen sein*	*ihr werdet gewesen sein*
3.	*sie werden gewesen sein*	*sie werden gewesen sein*

Present Conditional Tense.

	INDICATIVE.	SUBJUNCTIVE.
Sing. 1.	*ich würde sein,*	*ich würde sein*
	I should be, etc.	
2.	*du würdest sein*	*du würdest sein*
3.	*er würde sein*	*er würde sein*
Plur. 1.	*wir würden sein*	*wir würden sein*
2.	*ihr würdet sein*	*ihr würdet sein*
3.	*sie würden sein*	*sie würden sein*

MORE ON THE VERB

Past Conditional Tense.

		INDICATIVE.	SUBJUNCTIVE.
Sing.	1.	*ich würde gewesen sein,*	*ich würde gewesen sein*
		I should have been, etc.	
	2.	*du würdest gewesen sein*	*du würdest gewesen sein*
	3.	*er würde gewesen sein*	*er würde gewesen sein*
Plur.	1.	*wir würden gewesen sein*	*wir würden gewesen sein*
	2.	*ihr würdet gewesen sein*	*ihr würdet gewesen sein*
	3.	*sie würden gewesen sein*	*sie würden gewesen sein*

Note *gewesen sein* : to have been.   As *werden* is a verb of motion, its future and conditional tenses are constructed in the same way as those of *sein* : *ich werde werden* (I shall become), *ich werde geworden sein* (I shall have become), *ich würde werden* (I should become), *ich würde geworden sein* (I should have become).

Strong and Weak Verbs. The past tense of verbs in English and German is either formed by an alteration in the root-vowel or by an ending. For instance, examples of strong verbs in English are *to swim, swam, swum, to see, saw, seen* ; and of weak verbs, *to part, parted, parted, to say, said, said.* In German— except for those verbs mentioned in Lesson 10 (page 429)—the root-vowel of a weak verb does not change. The ending in the past is *-te,* and in the past participle *ge-* is prefixed to the root, and *-t* added. Thus, *setzen* (to set), root *setz,* past *setzte,* past participle *gesetzt.*

The following example of the conjugation of the verb *suchen* (to seek) will do as a scheme for all weak verbs. The present participle is *suchend* (seeking), and the past participle *gesucht* (sought).

ACTIVE VOICE.
PRESENT TENSE.

		INDICATIVE.	SUBJUNCTIVE.
Sing.	1.	*ich suche*	*ich suche*
	2.	*du suchst*	*du suchest*
	3.	*er sucht*	*er suche*
Plur.	1.	*wir suchen*	*wir suchen*
	2.	*ihr sucht*	*ihr sucht*
	3.	*sie suchen*	*sie suchen*

(427)

Past Tense.

Sing.	1.	*ich suchte*	*ich suchte*
	2.	*du suchtest*	*du suchtest*
	3.	*er suchte*	*er suchte*
Plur.	1.	*wir suchten*	*wir suchten*
	2.	*ihr suchtet*	*ihr suchtet*
	3.	*sie suchten*	*sie suchten*

The perfect tense indicative mood is formed thus : *ich habe gesucht*, etc. ; the pluperfect tense : *ich hatte gesucht*, etc. In the subjunctive mood the same tenses are : *ich habe gesucht*, etc. ; and *ich hätte gesucht*, etc. In the indicative mood the present future tense is : *ich werde suchen*, etc. ; and the past future tense : *ich werde gesucht haben*, etc. ; for the subjunctive mood these tenses are formed in the same way. The present conditional is : *ich würde suchen*, etc. ; and the past conditional is : *ich würde gesucht haben*, etc., for both indicative and subjunctive moods.

The Passive Voice is constructed with *werden* (to become). In German, we do not say " I am sought," but " I become sought." Thus, the present tense in the indicative and subjunctive moods is : *ich werde gesucht*, etc. The past tense indicative is : *ich wurde gesucht*, etc., while the subjunctive form is : *ich würde gesucht*, etc. The perfect indicative is : *ich bin gesucht worden*, etc., and the perfect subjunctive : *ich sei gesucht worden*.

This formation requires some explanation. When *werden* is used for the passive, the auxiliary past participle drops the *ge*- prefix. *Werden*, as a verb of motion, constructs its compound tenses with the help of the verb " to be," so the German does not say " I have been sought," but " I am become sought." Just as in the English expression " I have been sought " we conjugate only the " have," so in the German expression *ich bin gesucht worden* we conjugate only the *bin* ; *gesucht worden*, of course, remains unchanged, as follows :

Sing.	2.	*du bist gesucht worden*	*du seiest gesucht worden*
	3.	*er ist gesucht worden*	*er sei gesucht worden*
Plur.	1.	*wir sind gesucht worden*	*wir seien gesucht worden*
	2.	*ihr seid gesucht worden*	*ihr seiet gesucht worden*
	3.	*sie sind gesucht worden*	*sie seien gesucht worden*

The pluperfect indicative is : *ich war gesucht worden*, etc., and the subjunctive : *ich wäre gesucht worden*, etc. The present future in both indicative and subjunctive moods is : *ich werde gesucht werden*, etc. Here the first *werde* stands for the future, and that is the part which is conjugated; the second *werden* in the expression *gesucht werden* has a passive function.

The past future tense in both indicative and subjunctive moods is: *ich werde gesucht worden sein*, etc.; *worden sein* stands for the English " have been " in the expression " I shall have been sought." Literally, the German says " I shall be become sought."

In both indicative and subjunctive moods the present conditional tense is: *ich würde gesucht werden*, etc. The past conditional in both moods is: *ich würde gesucht worden sein*, etc. These forms should be carefully studied. They will appear a little unfamiliar at first, but it is very important to be fully conversant with them, as one or other of them occurs almost in every sentence.

There are three forms of the imperative mood, the second person singular, second person plural, and the third person plural plus pronoun, used in polite address. The second person singular is: *suche*, seek; second person plural: *sucht*, seek; third person plural (polite form): *suchen Sie*, seek.

The verb *sein* forms its imperative mood from the same stem as the subjunctive (*see* Lesson 8, volume 2, page 416). The second person singular is: *sei*, be; second person plural: *seid*, be; third person plural (polite form): *seien Sie*, be.

The imperatives of *haben* and *werden* follow the pattern of *suchen* A different method of forming the singular imperative will be discussed later in connexion with certain strong verbs.

LESSON 10

A First Lesson on the Strong Verbs

WHEN, in English, the root of a weak verb ends in a dental, we sometimes find that the dental of the root-ending and the dental ending of the past and past participle coalesce. In that manner we form the pasts and past participles *hit, hurt, put* from the verbs *to hit, to hurt, to put*. The usual method, however, in such cases, is to pronounce the -e of the past tense: *to smart, smarted, smarted*. This is the rule which is invariably followed in German. When the root of a German weak verb ends in -*d* or -*t*, the past ending becomes -*ete* instead of -*te*, and the past participle ending -*et* instead of -*t*, as may be noted in the following examples : *Arbeiten* (to work) ; past : *arbeitete* ; past participle : *gearbeitet. Leiten* (to lead) ; past : *leitete* ; past participle : *geleitet. Warten* (to wait) ; past : *wartete* ; past participle : *gewartet. Baden* (to bath or to bathe) ; past : *badete* ; past participle : *gebadet. Melden* (to announce) ; past : *meldete* ; past participle : *gemeldet. Morden* (to murder) ; past : *mordete* ; past participle : *gemordet.*

Irregular Formation. There are six weak verbs which have an *-e* in their root in the infinitive and present stem, but an *-a* in the past and past participle : *Brennen* (to burn) ; past : *brannte* ; past participle : *gebrannt. Kennen* (to be acquainted with) ; past : *kannte* ; past participle ; *gekannt. Nennen* (to name) ; past : *nannte* ; past participle : *genannt. Rennen* (to run) ; past : *rannte* ; past participle : *gerannt. Senden* (to send) ; past : *sandte* or *sendete* ; past participle : *gesandt* or *gesendet. Wenden* (to turn, wend) ; past : *wandte* or *wendete* ; past participle : *gewandt* or *gewendet.* In *senden* and *wenden* the forms with *-a* are to be preferred.

Subjunctives of the past are sometimes found of the first four of these verbs : *brennte, kennte, nennte, rennte.* They are rare. Usually we find that the past subjunctive is the same as the past indicative, as with all other weak verbs.

The verbs *bringen* and *denken* should not prove difficult to English speakers, as we have preserved the same conjugation as the German. *Bringen* (to bring) ; past : *brachte* ; past subjunctive : *brächte* ; past participle : *gebracht. Denken* (to think) ; past : *dachte* ; past subjunctive : *dächte* ; past participle : *gedacht.*

Strong Verbs. Verbs of the type *swim, swam, swum* are not irregular. They follow a perfectly regular system of vowel variation. This system has, on the whole, been preserved better in German than in English. We shall divide them into seven classes. Note that the past participle of a strong verb ends in *-en.*

In the first class of strong verbs (English type : *to bite, bit, bitten*) the root of the infinitive and present tense is *ei*, the past root *ie* or *i*, and that of the past participle *ie* or *i*. The conjugation of the present tense does not differ from that of a weak verb. Example : *schweigen* (to be silent) :

INDICATIVE.	SUBJUNCTIVE.
Sing. 1. *ich schweige*	*ich schweige*
2. *du schweigst*	*du schweigest*
3. *er schweigt*	*er schweige*

Plur. 1. *wir schweigen*   *wir schweigen*
     2. *ihr schweigt*   *ihr schweiget*
     3. *sie schweigen*   *sie schweigen*

STRONG VERBS (CLASS I).

Infinitive.	Present.	Past.	Perfect.
bleiben, to remain	*ich bleibe*	*ich blieb*	*ich bin geblieben*
gedeihen, to flourish	*es gedeiht*	*es gedieh*	*es ist gediehen*
leihen, to lend	*ich leihe*	*ich lieh*	*ich habe geliehen*
meiden, to avoid	*ich meide*	*ich mied*	*ich habe gemieden*
preisen, to praise	*ich preise*	*ich pries*	*ich habe gepriesen*
reiben, to rub	*ich reibe*	*ich rieb*	*ich habe gerieben*
scheinen, to seem	*es scheint*	*es schien*	*es hat geschienen*
schreiben, to write	*ich schreibe*	*ich schrieb*	*ich habe geschrieben*
schreien, to cry out	*ich schreie*	*ich schrie*	*ich habe geschrieen*
schweigen, to be silent	*ich schweige*	*ich schwieg*	*ich habe geschwiegen*
speien, to spew	*ich speie*	*ich spie*	*ich habe gespieen*
greifen, to grip	*ich greife*	*ich griff*	*ich habe gegriffen*
kneifen, to nip, pinch	*ich kneife*	*ich kniff*	*ich habe gekniffen*
pfeifen, to whistle	*ich pfeife*	*ich pfiff*	*ich habe gepfiffen*
schleifen, to grind, raze	*ich schleife*	*ich schliff*	*ich habe geschliffen*
erbleichen, to grow pale	*ich erbleiche*	*ich erblich*	*ich bin erblichen*
gleichen, to be like	*ich gleiche*	*ich glich*	*ich habe geglichen*
schleichen, to slink	*ich schleiche*	*ich schlich*	*ich bin geschlichen*
streichen, to stroke	*ich streiche*	*ich strich*	*ich habe gestrichen*
weichen, to give away	*ich weiche*	*ich wich*	*ich bin gewichen*
beissen, to bite	*ich beisse*	*ich biss*	*ich habe gebissen*
reissen, to tear	*ich reisse*	*ich riss*	*ich habe gerissen*
gleiten, to glide	*ich gleite*	*ich glitt*	*ich bin geglitten*
steigen, to climb	*ich steige*	*ich stieg*	*ich bin gestiegen*
verzeihen, to forgive	*ich verzeihe*	*ich verzieh*	*ich habe verziehen*
weisen, to show, point out	*ich weise*	*ich wies*	*ich habe gewiesen*
reiten, to ride	*ich reite*	*ich ritt*	*ich bin geritten*
schreiten, to stride	*ich schreite*	*ich schritt*	*ich bin geschritten*
streiten, to quarrel	*ich streite*	*ich stritt*	*ich habe gestritten*
leiden, to suffer	*ich leide*	*ich litt*	*ich habe gelitten*
schneiden, to cut	*ich schneide*	*ich schnitt*	*ich habe geschnitten*
heissen, to be called	*ich heisse*	*ich hiess*	*ich bin geheissen*

NOTES.—The irregular formation of the last three verbs, *leiden*, *schneiden* and *heissen*, should be particularly noted. The *h* in such verbs as *gedeihen*, *leihen*, etc., is not pronounced. If the root-vowel is followed by *-f*, *-ch*, *-sz* (*ss*) or *-t*, the vowel in the past and past participle is short and therefore spelt with *-i*; e.g., *greifen*, *kneifen*. The verb *gleiten* is frequently weak in modern German, and then shows: *gleitete, ich bin gegleitet*. With the exception of a few verbs rarely met with, all other verbs that show *-ei* as stem-vowels are weak.

If the verbal root ends in a dental, the second and third persons singular present have -*est* instead of -*st*, and -*et* instead of -*t*; thus *reiten* (to ride) has *du reitest, er reitet*.

In the past tense the conjugation is a little different. There is no -*e* in the first and third person singular, and a separate form for the subjunctive.

INDICATIVE.		SUBJUNCTIVE.
Sing. 1.	*ich schwieg*	*ich schwiege*
2.	*du schwiegst* or *schwiegest*	*du schwiegest*
3.	*er schwieg*	*er schwiege*
Plur. 1.	*wir schwiegen*	*wir schwiegen*
2	*ihr schwiegt*	*ihr schwieget*
3.	*sie schwiegen*	*sie schwiegen*

The compound tenses show the same formation as with weak verbs. Perfect : *ich habe geschwiegen* ; pluperfect : *ich hatte geschwiegen* ; present future : *ich werde schweigen* ; past future : *ich werde geschwiegen haben* ; present conditional : *ich würde schweigen* ; past conditional : *ich würde geschwiegen haben*. Similarly, the passive is constructed in the same way. In the table in page 431 is a list of the most important verbs belonging to this class.

Second Class. The English type of the second class of strong verbs in German is : to freeze ; froze ; frozen. The root in the infinitive is -*ie*, in the past -*o*, in the past participle -*o*. These verbs show modification of the -*o*- to -*ö*- in the past subjunctive.

INDICATIVE.		SUBJUNCTIVE.
Sing. 1.	*ich bog*, I bent, etc.	*ich böge*
2.	*du bogst*	*du bögest*
3.	*er bog*	*er böge*
Plur. 1.	*wir bogen*	*wir bögen*
2.	*ihr bogt*	*ihr böget*
3.	*sie bogen*	*sie bögen*

The most common verbs in this class are shown in the table in page 433.

All other verbs with -*ie*- in the infinitive, except a few that are of rare occurrence, are weak. For instance : *spielen, spielte, gespielt* (to play), *lieben, liebte, geliebt* (to love), *niessen, niesste, geniesst* (to sneeze). Forms are occasionally found with -*eu*- instead of -*ie*- in the second and third persons singular present ; for instance : *du beust, er beut*, from *bieten* ; they are not permissible in the modern Standard language, but are found in poetry.

Strong Verbs (Class II).

Infinitive.	Present.	Past.	Perfect.
biegen, to bend	*ich biege*	*ich bog*	*ich habe gebogen*
bieten, to offer	*ich biete*	*ich bot*	*ich habe geboten*
fliegen, to fly	*ich fliege*	*ich flog*	*ich bin geflogen*
fliehen, to flee	*ich fliehe*	*ich floh*	*ich bin geflohen*
frieren, to freeze	*mich friert*	*mich fror*	*mich hat gefroren*
schieben, to push, shove	*ich schiebe*	*ich schob*	*ich habe geschoben*
verlieren, to lose	*ich verliere*	*ich verlor*	*ich habe verloren*
triefen, to drip	*es trieft*	*es troff*	*es hat getroffen*
kriechen, to creep	*ich krieche*	*ich kroch*	*ich bin gekrochen*
riechen, to smell	*ich rieche*	*ich roch*	*ich habe gerochen*
fliessen, to flow	*es fliesst*	*es floss*	*es ist geflossen*
geniessen, to enjoy	*ich geniesse*	*ich genoss*	*ich habe genossen*
giessen, to pour	*ich giesse*	*ich goss*	*ich habe gegossen*
schiessen, to shoot	*ich schiesse*	*ich schoss*	*ich habe geschossen*
spriessen, to sprout	*es spriesst*	*es spross*	*es ist gesprossen*
sieden, to boil	*es siedet*	*es sott*	*es hat gesotten*
ziehen, to draw, pull	*ich ziehe*	*ich zog*	*ich habe gezogen*
verdriessen, to annoy	*mich verdriesst*	*mich verdross*	*mich hat verdrossen*

NOTES.—The verb *verdriessen* is only used impersonally with accusative. The consonantal irregularity of the verbs *sieden* and *ziehen* should be observed. If the consonant after the root-vowel is *-f*, *-ch* or *-sz* (*ss*), the *-o-* of the past and past participle and the *-ö-* of the past subjunctive are short. In the first class of strong verbs this difference could be expressed by the spelling (*ie* and *i*). In the second class there is no means of making this graphic distinction. Examples of the verbs belonging here are : *triefen* (this verb occurs also in weak formation : *triefte* and *getrieft*); *kriechen*; *riechen*; *fliessen*; *geniessen*. One of the most important verbs in the German language is *ziehen*: it should be carefully remembered. It occurs in many compounds with a great variety of meanings.

LESSON 11

A Further Study of Strong Verbs

IN the preceding Lesson we discussed the first class of strong verbs and part of the second class. Not all verbs of the second class have an infinitive and present tense in *-ie*. We now deal with the other vowels which can occur; these are *-ä-*, *-au-*, *-e-*, *-ö-* and *-ü-*. Most of these verbs are of frequent occurrence, and for this reason their slight irregularities should be carefully noted by the student. The most common of this second class of strong verbs are shown in the table below.

STRONG VERBS (CLASS II).

Infinitive.	Present.	Past.	Perfect.
(ä): erwägen, to consider	ich erwäge	ich erwog	ich habe erwogen
gären, to ferment	es gärt	es gor	es ist gegoren or es hat gegoren
(au): saufen, to drink (of animals)	ich saufe	ich soff	ich habe gesoffen
saugen, to suck	ich sauge	ich sog	ich habe gesogen
(e): fechten, to fight	ich fechte	ich focht	ich habe gefochten
flechten, to plait	ich flechte	ich flocht	ich habe geflochten
heben, to lift, heave	ich hebe	ich hob	ich habe gehoben
weben, to weave	ich webe	ich wob	ich habe gewoben
quellen, to spring, gush	es quillt	es quoll	es ist gequollen
schmelzen, to melt	es schmilzt	es schmolz	es ist geschmolzen
schwellen, to swell	es schwillt	es schwoll	es ist geschwollen
(ö): löschen, to extinguish	ich lösche	ich losch	ich habe geloschen
schwören, to swear	ich schwöre	ich schwor	ich habe geschworen
(ü): lügen, to tell a lie	ich lüge	ich log	ich habe gelogen
trügen, to deceive	ich trüge	ich trog	ich habe getrogen

NOTES. In the verb gären the weak forms gärte, gegärt also occur. Saufen has 2nd and 3rd persons singular present indicative, du säufst, er säuft; saugen has du saugst, er saugt. Fechten has 2nd and 3rd persons singular present indicative, du fichst, er ficht; flechten has du flichst, er flicht. Löschen frequently has weak forms: löschte, gelöscht. The verb trügen occurs more usually in the form betrügen.

Third Class. The English type of the third class of strong verbs in German is: to swim, swam, swum. The root of verbs of this class (with a few exceptions in -im) ends in -in plus a consonant. The vowel changes to -a in the past and to -u in the past participle.

In the verbs glimmen, to glimmer, and klimmen, to climb, scale, the -o- has also invaded the past tense: glomm, geglommen, and klomm, geklommen.

The modern past subjunctives of this class are usually derived from the *-a-* of the past indicative : *ich bände, ich fände* ; but one frequently encounters the older usage : *ich bünde, ich fünde*. There is no fixed rule or usage which would cover every case ;

STRONG VERBS (CLASS III).

Infinitive.	Present.	Past.	Perfect.
binden, to bind	*ich binde*	*ich band*	*ich habe gebunden*
dringen, to press upon	*ich dringe*	*ich drang*	*ich bin gedrungen*
finden, to find	*ich finde*	*ich fand*	*ich habe gefunden*
klingen, to resound	*es klingt*	*es klang*	*es hat geklungen*
gelingen, to succeed	*es gelingt*	*es gelang*	*es ist gelungen*
ringen, to wrestle	*ich ringe*	*ich rang*	*ich habe gerungen*
schwinden, to disappear	*ich verschwinde*	*ich verschwand*	*ich bin verschwunden*
schwingen, to swing	*ich schwinge*	*ich schwang*	*ich habe geschwungen*
singen, to sing	*ich singe*	*ich sang*	*ich habe gesungen*
sinken, to sink	*ich sinke*	*ich sank*	*ich bin gesunken*
springen, to jump	*ich springe*	*ich sprang*	*ich bin gesprungen*
stinken, to stink	*es stinkt*	*es stank*	*es hat gestunken*
trinken, to drink	*ich trinke*	*ich trank*	*ich habe getrunken*
verschlingen, to devour	*ich verschlinge*	*ich verschlang*	*ich habe verschlungen*
winden, to wind	*ich winde*	*ich wand*	*ich habe gewunden*
zwingen, to force	*ich zwinge*	*ich zwang*	*ich habe gezwungen*

If the root ends in *-nn-* the past participle has *-o-* instead of *-u-* :

beginnen, to begin	*ich beginne*	*ich begann*	*ich habe begonnen*
gewinnen, to win	*ich gewinne*	*ich gewann*	*ich habe gewonnen*
rinnen, to flow	*es rinnt*	*es rann*	*es ist geronnen*
schwimmen, to swim	*ich schwimme*	*ich schwamm*	*ich bin geschwommen*
sinnen, to ponder	*ich sinne*	*ich sann*	*ich habe gesonnen*
spinnen, to spin	*ich spinne*	*ich spann*	*ich habe gesponnen*

NOTES.—*Gelingen* is used only impersonally with dative of person. *Schwinden* occurs more usually in the form *verschwinden*.

the forms with *-ă-* are gradually supplanting those with *-ŭ-*. All other verbs with *-ind-* in root are weak.

Fourth Class. Of the fourth class of strong verbs, the English type is : to speak, spake, spoken. In this class the root-vowel is *-e-*, which changes in the past to *-a-*, and in the past participle to *-o-*. The second and third persons singular present indicative change the *-e-* to *-i-* ; also the imperative has *-i-* instead of *-e-* and drops the final *-e*. Example : *sterben*, to die.

INDICATIVE.	SUBJUNCTIVE.
Sing. 1. *ich sterbe*	*ich sterbe*
2. *du stirbst*	*du sterbest*
3. *er stirbt*	*er sterbe*
Plur. 1. *wir sterben*	*wir sterben*
2. *ihr sterbt*	*ihr sterbet*
3. *sie sterben*	*sie sterben*

The imperative singular of *sterben* is *stirb*. To the fourth class belonged originally the verbs *fechten, flechten, quellen, schmelzen, schwellen*, and the auxiliary *werden*, the imperative of which is, however, regular : *werde*.

STRONG VERBS (CLASS IV).

Infinitive.	Present.	Past.	Perfect.
bergen, to hide	*ich berge*	*ich barg*	*ich habe geborgen*
bersten, to burst	*es birst*	*es barst*	*es ist geborsten*
brechen, to break	*ich breche*	*ich brach*	*ich habe gebrochen*
gelten, to be of value to be considered	*ich gelte*	*ich galt*	*ich habe gegolten*
helfen, to help	*ich helfe*	*ich half*	*ich habe geholfen*
nehmen, to take	*ich nehme*	*ich nahm*	*ich habe genommen*
schelten, to scold	*ich schelte*	*ich schalt*	*ich habe gescholten*
schrecken, to terrify	*ich schrecke*	*ich schrak* (rare)	*ich habe ge-schrocken*
sprechen, to speak	*ich spreche*	*ich sprach*	*ich habe gesprochen*
stechen, to pierce	*ich steche*	*ich stach*	*ich habe gestochen*
stehlen, to steal	*ich stehle*	*ich stahl*	*ich habe gestohlen*
sterben, to die	*ich sterbe*	*ich starb*	*ich bin gestorben*
treffen, to meet	*ich treffe*	*ich traf*	*ich habe getroffen*
verderben, to decay	*ich verderbe*	*ich verdarb*	*ich bin verdorben*
werben, to enlist	*ich werbe*	*ich warb*	*ich habe geworben*
werfen, to throw	*ich werfe*	*ich warf*	*ich habe geworfen*

NOTES.—The important verb *nehmen* has preserved both long and short vowels in its conjugation. The long vowel is always followed by the length-sign -*h*-, the short vowel by a double consonant : *mm*. The 2nd and 3rd persons singular of the present indicative are : *du nimmst, er nimmt* ; the imperative singular is *nimm*. In the verbs *schrecken* and *treffen*, the past has respectively -*k*- and -*f*- to show that the vowel is long. As *stehlen* has a long -*e*- the present indicative is declined in the 2nd and 3rd persons singular *du stiehlst, er stiehlt* ; the imperative is *stiehl*.

The following have irregular infinitives and present tenses : *gebären*, to give birth to, *ich gebäre, ich gebar, ich habe geboren* ; *kommen*, to come, *ich komme, ich kam, ich bin gekommen*.

PRESENT INDICATIVE.

Sing. 1.	*ich gebäre*	*ich komme*
2.	*du gebärst* or *gebierst*	*du kommst*
3.	*sie gebärt* or *gebiert*	*er kommt*
Plur. 1.	*wir gebären*	*wir kommen*
2.	*ihr gebärt*	*ihr kommt*
3.	*sie gebären*	*sie kommen*

The imperfect subjunctives of the fourth class can show *-ä-, -ö-* or *-ü-*. With some verbs all three occur. Again, there is no fixed rule. The following are the usual forms :

ich bärge	*ich stäche*
ich bärste or *börste*	*ich stöhle*
ich bräche	*ich stürbe*
ich gölte	*ich träfe*
ich hülfe	*ich verdürbe*
ich nähme	*ich würbe*
ich schölte	*ich würfe*
ich schräke	*ich geböre*
ich spräche	*ich käme*

LESSON 12

Final Classes of Strong Verbs

WE now deal with the three remaining classes of strong verbs and also with the anomalous verbs *stehen* (to stand) and *tun* (to do), which, as in English, show irregular formation. In the fifth class of German strong verbs (English example : to give, gave, given ; for a list of these verbs see the table in the following page) the root-vowel of the infinitive and present tense, indicative mood, is *-e-*, that of the past tense *-a-*, and of the past participle *-e-*. In verbs of this type the *-e-* of the present tense and the past participle can be either long or short. All verbs of short-vowel type have a double consonant. All other verbs of this type are weak : Examples : *leben, lebte, gelebt* (to live) ; *schweben, schwebte, geschwebt* (to hover) ; *kleben, klebte, geklebt* (to stick) ; *reden, redete, geredet* (to speak), and many others.

Sixth Class. The English type of strong verbs of the sixth class is : to take, took, taken. In this class (see table in page 439) the German root-vowel of the infinitive and present tense is -*a*-, of the past, -*u*-, and of the past participle -*a*-.

Apart from a few verbs with -*a*- in the infinitive that belong to Class VII, all other such verbs are weak. Examples : *warten,*

STRONG VERBS (CLASS V).

Infinitive.	Present.	Past.	Perfect.
essen, to eat	*ich esse*	*ich ass*	*ich habe gegessen*
fressen, to devour	*ich fresse*	*ich frass*	*ich habe gefressen*
messen, to measure	*ich messe*	*ich mass*	*ich habe gemessen*
vergessen, to forget	*ich vergesse*	*ich vergass*	*ich habe vergessen*
geben, to give	*ich gebe*	*ich gab*	*ich habe gegeben*
genesen, to recover	*ich genese*	*ich genas*	*ich bin genesen*
geschehen, to happen (impersonal verb)	*es geschieht*	*es geschah*	*es ist geschehen*
lesen, to read	*ich lese*	*ich las*	*ich habe gelesen*
sehen, to see	*ich sehe*	*ich sah*	*ich habe gesehen*
treten, to tread, kick	*ich trete*	*ich trat*	*ich habe getreten*
bitten, to request	*ich bitte*	*ich bat*	*ich habe gebeten*
liegen, to lie down	*ich liege*	*ich lag*	*ich habe gelegen*
sitzen, to sit	*ich sitze*	*ich sass*	*ich habe gesessen*

NOTES.—In the verb *essen,* -*g*- has been placed between the first and second -*e*- in the past participle for the sake of euphony. As in Class IV we find -*i*- in the 2nd and 3rd persons singular present and in the imperative of the verbs *essen, fressen, messen, vergessen,* which have a short -*e*- ; example : *ich esse, du isst, er isst, wir essen, ihr esst, sie essen* ; imperative : *iss.* Long -*e*- occurs in the verbs *geben, genesen, geschehen, lesen, sehen,* and therefore the 2nd and 3rd persons singular present are also long ; example : *ich sehe, du siehst, er sieht, wir sehen, ihr seht, sie sehen.* In the verb *geben* the modern spelling is *du gibst, er gibt* (not *giebst,* etc.), but the -*i*- is long. The formation of the present of *treten* is a little irregular : *ich trete, du trittst, er tritt, wir treten,* etc. The three verbs *bitten, liegen* and *sitzen* have irregular infinitives and presents , example : *ich bitte, du bittest, er bittet, wir bitten, ihr bittet, sie bitten.* Do not confuse *liegen* (to lie down) with *lügen, log, gelogen* (to tell a lie) or *legen, legte, gelegt* (to lay).

wartete, gewartet (to wait) ; *nagen, nagte, genagt* (to gnaw) ; *sagen, sagte, gesagt* (to say), and many others.

Seventh Class. Of the seventh class of strong verbs, the English type is : to fall, fell, fallen. Most of the verbs in this class have -*a*- in infinitive, present tense, and past participle ; in the past tense -*ie*- (or short -*i*-) is the root-vowel combination. It will be noted in the table (in page 439) that a few verbs have -*au*-, -*o*-, -*u*-, -*e*- for root-vowels.

FINAL CLASSES OF STRONG VERBS

STRONG VERBS (CLASS VI).

Infinitive.	Present.	Past.	Perfect.
backen, to bake	*ich backe*	*ich buk*	*ich habe gebacken*
fahren, to ride, go	*ich fahre*	*ich fuhr*	*ich bin gefahren*
graben, to dig	*ich grabe*	*ich grub*	*ich habe gegraben*
laden, to load, to invite	*ich lade*	*ich lud*	*ich habe geladen*
schaffen, to create	*ich schaffe*	*ich schuf*	*ich habe geschaffen*
schlagen, to hit	*ich schlage*	*ich schlug*	*ich habe geschlagen*
tragen, to carry, wear	*ich trage*	*ich trug*	*ich habe getragen*
wachsen, to grow, wax	*ich wachse*	*ich wuchs*	*ich bin gewachsen*
waschen, to wash	*ich wasche*	*ich wusch*	*ich habe gewaschen*

NOTES. In the verb *backen* note the -*k* for -*ck* in the past to show length of vowel. Weak forms *bachte, gebacht* also occur, but are not literary. In modern German there has been some confusion with the verb *laden*, which literally means "to load." Strong and weak forms —*laden, ladete, geladet*—are both equally used for this verb when it means "to invite," but for "to load" the strong forms are usual. In *schaffen* note the single -*f* in the past tense to show length of vowel. The 2nd and 3rd persons singular present of these verbs show -*ä*-; example : *ich backst, du bäckst, er bäckt, wir backen, ihr backt, sie backen.*

STRONG VERBS (CLASS VII).

Infinitive.	Present.	Past.	Perfect.
blasen, to blow	*ich blase*	*ich blies*	*ich habe geblasen*
braten, to fry	*ich brate*	*ich briet*	*ich habe gebraten*
fallen, to fall	*ich falle*	*ich fiel*	*ich bin gefallen*
fangen, to catch	*ich fange*	*ich fing*	*ich habe gefangen*
halten, to hold	*ich halte*	*ich hielt*	*ich habe gehalten*
hangen, to hang	*ich hange*	*ich hing*	*ich habe gehangen*
raten, to advise	*ich rate*	*ich riet*	*ich habe geraten*
schlafen, to sleep	*ich schlafe*	*ich schlief*	*ich habe geschlafen*
hauen, to hit, hew	*ich haue*	*ich hieb*	*ich habe gehauen*
laufen, to run	*ich laufe*	*ich lief*	*ich bin gelaufen*
stossen, to push	*ich stosse*	*ich stiess*	*ich habe gestossen*
rufen, to call, cry out	*ich rufe*	*ich rief*	*ich habe gerufen*
gehen, to go	*ich gehe*	*ich ging*	*ich bin gegangen*

NOTES. The verbs in this class with root-vowel -*a*- take -*ä*- for 2nd person singular present, as in Class VI ; example : *ich blase, du bläst, er bläst, wir blasen, ihr blast, sie blasen* ; imperative : *blase.* The infinitive and present tense of *hangen* are to-day more frequently *hängen, ich hänge.* The verb *hauen*, in place of past *hieb* often has a weak form *haute*: this is not literary. The present tense of *laufen* is declined : *ich laufe, du läufst, er läuft, wir laufen, ihr lauft, sie laufen.* *Stossen* in the present tense is declined : *ich stosse, du stösst, er stösst, wir stossen*, etc. *Rufen* : *ich rufe, du rufst, er ruft, wir rufen*, etc. *Gehen* : *ich gehe, du gehst, er geht, wir gehen*, etc.

The verbs *falten* (to fold), *salzen* (to salt), *spalten* (to split), still have the strong past participles *gefalten, gesalzen, gespalten ;* but their past tenses are now weak : *faltete, salzte, spaltete.*

Anomalous Verbs. The two following verbs are anomalous : *stehen* (to stand) and *tun* (to do). In the present tense *stehen* is conjugated thus :

	INDICATIVE.	SUBJUNCTIVE.
Sing. 1.	*ich stehe*	*ich stehe*
2.	*du stehst*	*du stehest*
3.	*er steht*	*er stehe*
Plur. 1.	*wir stehen*	*wir stehen*
2.	*ihr steht*	*ihr stehet*
3.	*sie stehen*	*sie stehen*

The past indicative is : *ich stand* (conjugated like *ich band*) ; past subjunctive : *ich stände* or *ich stünde* ; past participle : *gestanden.*

The present tense of the verb *tun* (to do) is conjugated :

	INDICATIVE.	SUBJUNCTIVE.
Sing. 1.	*ich tue*	*ich tue*
2.	*du tust*	*du tuest*
3.	*er tut*	*er tue*
Plur. 1.	*wir tun*	*wir tu(e)n*
2.	*ihr tut*	*ihr tu(e)t*
3.	*sie tun*	*sie tu(e)n*

The past indicative is : *ich tat* (conjugated like *ich bat*) ; past subjunctive : *ich täte* ; past participle : *getan.*

LESSON 13

Special Forms of Verbs

THE present tense forms of the modal verbs (except for *wollen*, will, which is a different type of formation) are really past tenses grammatically. Hence there is no -s in the third person singular present in English and no -*t* in the third person singular present in German. (Compare he goes, he runs, he shoots, to *he may, he can, he shall*.) The details of the usages of the modal verbs will be discussed in a later Lesson in this Course. Here we are concerned only with the grammatical forms. The modal verbs are *dürfen* (to be allowed) ; *können* (to be able) ; *mögen* (to like) ; *müssen* (to have to) ; *sollen* (to have to) ; *wollen* (to wish to). *Dürfen* is the same word as the English " dare," which is regular now with the exception of the dialectal " durst."

PRESENT TENSE OF DÜRFEN.

	INDICATIVE.	SUBJUNCTIVE.
Sing. 1.	*ich darf*	*ich dürfe*
2.	*du darfst*	*du dürfest*
3.	*er darf*	*er dürfe*
Plur. 1.	*wir dürfen*	*wir dürfen*
2.	*ihr dürft*	*ihr dürft*
3.	*sie dürfen*	*sie dürfen*

Past tense : *ich durfte* (conjugated like *ich suchte*) ; past subjunctive : *ich dürfte* ; past participle : *gedurft*.

Note particularly that in this verb, as also in all others of this type, except *sollen*, the indicative singular and plural show a different vowel. With this compare English " I was," " we were," the only English verb to preserve this feature.

PRESENT TENSE OF KÖNNEN

	INDICATIVE.	SUBJUNCTIVE.
Sing. 1.	*ich kann*	*ich könne*
2.	*du kannst*	*du könnest*
3.	*er kann*	*er könne*
Plur. 1.	*wir können*	*wir können*
2.	*ihr könnt*	*ihr könnet*
3.	*sie können*	*sie können*

Past indicative : *ich konnte* ; past subjunctive : *ich könnte* ; past participle : *gekonnt*.

PRESENT TENSE OF MÖGEN.

	INDICATIVE.	SUBJUNCTIVE.
Sing. 1.	*ich mag*	*ich möge*
2.	*du magst*	*du mögest*
3.	*er mag*	*er möge*
Plur. 1.	*wir mögen*	*wir mögen*
2.	*ihr mögt*	*ihr möget*
3.	*sie mögen*	*sie mögen*

Past indicative : *ich mochte* ; past subjunctive : *ich möchte* ; past participle : *gemocht*.

Present Tense of Müssen.

Indicative.	Subjunctive.
Sing. 1. *ich muss*	*ich müsse*
2. *du musst*	*du müssest*
3. *er muss*	*er müsse*
Plur. 1. *wir müssen*	*wir müssen*
2. *ihr müsst*	*ihr müsset*
3. *sie müssen*	*sie müssen*

Past indicative : *ich musste* ; past subjunctive : *ich müsste* : **past** participle : *gemusst.*

Present Tense of Sollen.

Indicative.	Subjunctive.
Sing. 1. *ich soll*	*ich solle*
2. *du sollst*	*du sollest*
3. *er soll*	*er solle*
Plur. 1. *wir sollen*	*wir sollen*
2. *ihr sollt*	*ihr sollet*
3. *sie sollen*	*sie sollen*

Past indicative : *ich sollte* ; past subjunctive : *ich sollte* ; **past** participle : *gesollt.* The student should note that the **sub**junctives of this verb do not show mutation.

Present Tense of Wollen.

Indicative.	Subjunctive.
Sing. 1. *ich will*	*ich wolle*
2. *du willst*	*du wollest*
3. *er will*	*er wolle*
Plur. 1. *wir wollen*	*wir wollen*
2. *ihr wollt*	*ihr wollet*
3. *sie wollen*	*sie wollen*

Past indicative : *ich wollte* ; past subjunctive : *ich wollte* ; **past** participle : *gewollt.* The student should note that the **sub**junctives of this verb do not show mutation.

The irregular verb *wissen* (to know) is conjugated **as follows** :

Present Tense.

Indicative.	Subjunctive.
Sing. 1. *ich weiss*	*ich wisse*
2. *du weisst*	*du wissest*
3. *er weiss*	*er wisse*
Plur. 1. *wir wissen*	*wir wissen*
2. *ihr wisst*	*ihr wisset*
3. *sie wissen*	*sie wissen*

Past indicative : *ich wusste* ; past subjunctive : *ich wüsste* ; past participle : *gewusst*. This verb is archaic in English. Compare such forms as *to wit*, and *wot* in the phrase *God wot*.

Separable and Inseparable Verbs. Many verbs in German are formed by means of a prefix. Usually the prefix is a preposition, though it can also be an adjective, an adverb, or a noun. The following prefixes are inseparable from their verb : *be-, emp-, ent-, er-, ge-, miss-, ver-, wider-, hinter-, zer-*. The prefix *be-* (cf. English belong, believe) is used for forming verbs from adjectives, nouns and verbs : *frei*, free, *befreien*, to free ; *Kleid*, garment, *bekleiden*, to clothe ; *schreiben*, to write, *beschreiben*, to describe. No exact meaning of the prefix can be given. The prefix *emp-* occurs only before *-f-*, and is only usual in three words : *empfangen*, to receive ; *empfehlen*, to recommend ; *empfinden*, to feel. The prefix *ent-* usually denotes negation or separation : *entwaffnen*, to disarm ; *entreissen*, to tear from ; *entsagen*, to resign. The prefix *er-* originally denoted the completion of an action : *laufen*, to run, *erlaufen*, to catch up ; *schlagen*, to hit ; *erschlagen*, to kill. But examples can be found where this rule no longer applies. For instance : *erkennen*, to recognize ; *ersehen*, to perceive ; *erlauben*, to permit. No general meaning can be assigned to the prefix *ge-* : *gestehen*, to admit ; *gebrauchen*, to use ; *geleiten*, to accompany. In a number of words where this prefix is followed by *-l-*, the *-e-* has dropped : *glauben*, to believe.

The prefix *miss-* corresponds in form and meaning to the English mis- as in misapply ; *missbrauchen*, to misuse ; *missverstehen*, to understand wrongly ; *missachten*, to despise, pay no attention to. To the prefix *ver-* no general meaning can be given, though frequently *ver-* implies negation : *kommen*, to come, *verkommen*, to decay ; *laufen*, to run, *verlaufen*, to go astray ; *schreiben*, to write, *verschreiben*, to write wrongly. Corresponding to the English with- in such words as withstand, withhold, is the prefix *wider-* : *widerstehen*, to resist, withstand ; *widerlegen*, to refute.

The prefix *hinter-* is used in the sense of behind : *hintergehen*, to deceive, literally to go behind ; *hinterlegen*, to deposit, literally to lay behind ; *hintertreiben*, to prevent, literally to drive behind. The prefix *zer-* means to pieces : *schlagen*, to hit, *zerschlagen*, to smash to pieces ; *reissen*, to tear, *zerreissen*, to tear to bits ; *laufen*, to run, *zerlaufen*, to run in all directions, to melt.

With the exception of *wider-* and *hinter-* these prefixes can no longer be used as independent words. They have thus lost their accent, and therefore the accent of an inseparable verb is always on the root-syllable, never on the prefix : *beséhen, empfínden, entdécken, erstéhen, geráten, missáchten, verbrénnen, etc.*

These inseparable verbs are conjugated in the same manner as an ordinary verb, with the one exception that they do not use the prefix *ge-* in the past participle :

INFINITIVE.	PAST PARTICIPLE.
behalten, to keep	*behalten*
empfehlen, to recommend	*empfohlen*
entdecken, to discover	*entdeckt*
erweitern, to widen	*erweitert*
geloben, to promise	*gelobt*
missdeuten, to misinterpret	*missdeutet*
verlangen, to demand	*verlangt*
widerraten, to advise against	*widerraten*
hintergehen, to deceive	*hintergangen*
zerpflücken, to pick to pieces	*zerpflückt*

In the case of the prefix *miss-*, however, the *ge-* prefix is sometimes employed, and forms such as *gemissdeutet, gemissachtet* do occur. The student should also note at this point that verbs with the foreign (French) suffix *-ieren* are also used without *ge-* in the past participle, presumably because the accent in such words is on the suffix, and the words, therefore, start with an unaccented syllable : *studieren* (to study), past participle : *studiert* ; *marschieren* (to march), *marschiert* ; *probieren* (to try, test), *probiert.*

LESSON 14

Separable Verbs and the Numerals

WE now come to the separable verbs, i.e. verbs whose prefixes, under certain conditions, can become detached from their verbs. For example, in the verb *aufstehen* (to get up, to rise) the prefix is separated thus in the present and past tenses :

INDICATIVE MOOD.

		Present.	Past.
Sing.	1.	*ich stehe auf*	*ich stand auf*
	2.	*du stehst auf*	*du standest auf*
	3.	*er steht auf*	*er stand auf*

(444)

Plur.	1.	*wir stehen auf*	*wir standen auf*
	2.	*ihr steht auf*	*ihr standet auf*
	3.	*sie stehen auf*	*sie standen auf*

In the past participle the prefix *-ge-* goes between the verbal prefix and the main verb : *aufgestanden.* We should, therefore, have to conjugate in the following way :

		Perfect.	Pluperfect.
Sing.	1.	*ich bin aufgestanden*	*ich war aufgestanden*
	2.	*du bist aufgestanden*	*du warst aufgestanden*
	3.	*er ist aufgestanden*	*er war aufgestanden*
Plur.	1.	*wir sind aufgestanden*	*wir waren aufgestanden*
	2.	*ihr seid aufgestanden*	*ihr war(e)t aufgestanden*
	3.	*sie sind aufgestanden*	*sie waren aufgestanden*

Future simple : *ich werde aufstehen.*

Future perfect : *ich werde aufgestanden sein.*

Conditional simple : *ich würde aufstehen.*

Conditional perfect : *ich würde aufgestanden sein.*

If the preposition *zu* (to) occurs before the verb, this preposition goes between the prefix and the main verb : he ordered me to get up, *er befahl mir aufzustehen.*

It should be noted that in separable verbs the accent is always on the prefix. There is hardly any limit to the number of words that can be used as separable prefixes ; almost any noun and verb, if the sense allows, can be coupled together in this manner, but most of such formations are merely made for the occasion. Apart from such formations, there are many fixed compounds which have been made up by using prepositions, and sometimes adverbs, as prefixes. The table in the next page gives the compound verbs of this type which will be found to be most frequently used.

The student will notice that in many cases the meaning of the compound is obvious, but in others the meaning of the compound is not merely an addition of the meanings of prefix and verb.

If a verb has two inseparable prefixes, it is inseparable : *stehen* (to stand), *verstehen* (to understand), *missverstehen* (to misunderstand). If a verb has an inseparable and also a separable prefix, it is inseparable : *tragen* (to carry), *auftragen* (to commission), *beauftragen* (to commission). *Auftragen* is, of course, separable, so we should have to construct : *ich trage auf,* but *ich beauftrage.*

If a verb has a separable and also an inseparable prefix, the first prefix is separable : *sehen* (to see), *ersehen* (to perceive), *ausersehen* (to choose). We should therefore construct *ich ersehe*, but *ich ersehe aus*.

There are a few prefixes which are separable in some cases, but not in others. When they are separable, the accent is on the

Preposition.	Compound Verbs.
ab, off	*ablassen*, to leave off ; *abschreiben*, to copy.
an, on, at	*anziehen*, to attract, to dress ; *ansehen*, to regard, to look at.
auf, up	*aufziehen*, to pull up ; *aufdecken*, to uncover.
aus, out	*ausziehen*, to extract, to undress ; *ausgehen*, to go out.
bei, by	*beistehen*, to assist, to stand by ; *beitreten*, to join.
dar, there	*darbieten*, to offer ; *darstellen*, to represent.
ein, in	*einlaufen*, to run in, to arrive ; *eintreten*, to tread into, to enter.
fort, forth	*fortgehen*, to go away ; *fortlesen*, to continue reading.
her, hither	*herkommen*, to come hither ; *herstellen*, to place hither, to mend.
hin, hence	*hingehen*, to go hence, to go to ; *hintragen*, to carry to.
mit, with	*mitkommen*, to come with ; *mitnehmen*, to take with.
nach, after	*nachschreiben* to copy ; *nachlassen*, to leave off, to desist.
vor, before	*vorkommen*, to occur ; *vortragen*, to carry before, to recite.
weg, away	*wegnehmen*, to take away ; *weglaufen*, to run away.
zu, to	*zusehen*, to watch ; *zunehmen*, to increase.

prefix ; when they are inseparable, it is not. This usage also occurs in English, and always results in a difference of meaning. Compare : to uphold and to hold up, to overlook and to look over.

There are four prepositions which can be treated in this manner : *durch* (through), *über* (over), *um* (round), *unter* (under) :

Separable.	Inseparable.
dúrchreisen (to travel through)	*durchréisen* (to travel over)
ú'bergehen (to pass over)	*übergéhen* (to omit)
úmreissen (to pull down)	*umréissen* (to sketch)
únterhalten (to hold under)	*unterhálten* (to converse)

Cardinal Numbers. *Ein* (one), apart from being used as an indefinite article, can also be used as an adjective, and is then declined like any other adjective : *der eine Mann*, the one man ; *die eine Frau*, the one woman ; *das eine Kind*, the one child. *Zwei* and *drei* have genitives *zweier* and *dreier*, and datives *zweien* and *dreien*. They are rare. Datives of other numbers also occur, especially after the preposition *mit* : *mit Fünfen*, with five. They also are rare. Otherwise, the cardinal numbers are not declined. They are as follows :

1 *eins, ein*	7 *sieben*	12 *zwölf*	17 *siebzehn* or
2 *zwei*	8 *acht*	13 *dreizehn*	*siebenzehn*
3 *drei*	9 *neun*	14 *vierzehn*	18 *achtzehn*
4 *vier*	10 *zehn*	15 *fünfzehn*	19 *neunzehn*
5 *fünf*	11 *elf*	16 *sechzehn*	20 *zwanzig*
6 *sechs*			

Note that in order to avoid confusion with *drei*, an old feminine form, *zwo*, is used instead of *zwei* on the German telephone.

30 *dreissig*	40 *vierzig*
50 *fünfzig*	60 *sechzig*
70 *siebzig*	80 *achtzig*
90 *neunzig*	100 *hundert* or *einhundert* or *ein Hundert*
21 *einundzwanzig*	22 *zweiundzwanzig*
23 *dreiundzwanzig*	24 *vierundzwanzig*
25 *fünfundzwanzig*	26 *sechsundzwanzig*
27 *siebenundzwanzig*	28 *achtundzwanzig*

29 *neunundzwanzig*, etc.

Eins is used when it comes at the end, *ein* when it comes in the middle of a number, hence : 1, *eins* ; 101, *hundertundeins* ; 401, *vierhundertundeins* ; but 51, *einundfünfzig* ; 731, *siebenhundertundeinunddreissig*. 1000, *tausend* or *eintausend* or *ein Tausend* ; 2000, *zweitausend* or *zwei Tausend* ; 7000, *siebentausend* or *sieben Tausend*, etc. 1,000,000, *eine Million* ; 2,000,000 *zwei Millionen*.

There is no strict rule about the division of numbers in writing. It is usual to write them in one word up to 999, *neunhundertundneunundneunzig* ; but when the number is larger than a thousand, it is better to separate the thousands from the hundreds, thus : 7654, *siebentausend sechshundertundvierundfünfzig*.

All cardinal numbers can be treated as plural nouns, but there is no need to decline them when they are used nominally :

Nom.	*die Sieben*	*die Dreizehn*
Acc.	*die Sieben*	*die Dreizehn*
Gen.	*der Sieben*	*der Dreizehn*
Dat.	*den Sieben*	*den Dreizehn*, etc.

Hundert and *Tausend*, used nominally, are neuter, and have the plurals *die Hunderte, die Tausende*. *Million* is feminine ; plural, *Millionen*.

Ordinal Numbers. The only irregular ordinal numbers are *der Erste*, the first, and *der Dritte*, the third. From 2 to 19 we add *-te* to the cardinal number : *der Zweite*, the second ; *der Vierzehnte*, the fourteenth ; *die Sechzehnte*, the sixteenth (being something feminine) ; *das Neunzehnte*, the nineteenth (being something neuter). When these numbers are used nominally, they are declined like adjectives.

All other ordinals are formed by the addition of the suffix *-ste* : *der Dreiundzwanzigste*, the 23rd ; *der Fünfundvierzigste*, the 45th ; *der Achtundneunzigste*, the 98th ; *der Hundertste*, the 100th ; *der Tausendste*, the 1000th. The *-te* is kept for the numbers from 2 to 19 even if they are preceded by other numbers : *der Hundertundzweite*. the 102nd ; *der Vierhundertvierzehnte*, the 414th.

In writing, the ordinary numeral sign may be used and *-te* or *-ste* affixed : *der 3te, der 17te, der 39ste, der 87ste*. Care should, however, be taken not to omit the declension, if necessary. Thus, May 17th should be written : *am 17ten Mai*, as this is a dative.

Fractions. *Halb* (adjective), half ; *die Hälfte* (noun), the half. All other fractions are formed by adding *-tel* (a weakened form of *das Teil*, the part) to the cardinal number. These fractions are all neuter : $\frac{1}{4}$, *das Viertel* ; $\frac{7}{8}$, *sieben Achtel*. Note $\frac{1}{3}$, *ein Drittel*. It should be noted that $1\frac{1}{2}$ is *anderthalb* (literally, half towards the other, the second, i.e. $1\frac{1}{2}$). Forms such as *achtehalb*, $7\frac{1}{2}$, and *neuntehalb*, $8\frac{1}{2}$, also occur occasionally.

For the English -fold, German uses *-fach* : *einfach*, simple, onefold ; *zweifach*, twofold ; *zwanzigfach*, twentyfold, etc.

For the English -time(s), German uses *-mal* : *einmal*, once ; *zweimal*, twice ; *dreimal*, three times, etc.

The suffix *-erlei* (indeclinable) is used in the sense of " of a kind " : *einerlei*, of one kind, all the same ; *zweierlei*, of two kinds, etc. The adverbs first, secondly, thirdly, etc., are expressed in German as follow : *erstens, zweitens, drittens, zwanzigstens, dreiunddreissigstens*, etc.

Our Course in German is continued in Volume 4.

TIBERIUS. The morose Tiberius (42 B.C. – A.D. 37) proved a suspicious tyrant to the upper-class Roman, but he ruled the Empire with a firm and capable hand. On this famous cameo he is depicted with his family: in the heavens appears the deified Augustus. HISTORY: ANCIENT 20

Bibliothèque Nationale, Paris; photo, Giraudon

CLAUDIUS I (10 B.C.–A.D. 54). Brother of Germanicus and uncle of the murdered Caligula, Claudius was forced out of seclusion by the soldiers and hailed as Caesar. Though weak, he proved a better emperor than might have been expected. Throughout his reign the Empire enjoyed general prosperity.
HISTORY: ANCIENT 20

NERO (A.D. 37–68). The adopted son of Claudius, Nero became emperor in A.D. 54. His latter years constituted a reign of terror. HISTORY: ANCIENT 20

MASTERS OF THE IMPERIAL MACHINE. Of obscure family, Vespasian (A.D. 9–79) rose to high military commands in Germany, Britain and Palestine. Proclaimed emperor by his soldiery in 70, he considerably reorganized the imperial system. Hadrian (A.D. 76–138)—a bronze head of whom, found in the Thames, is shown on the right—was also a reforming emperor and a man of wide culture. He reigned 117–138. HISTORY: ANCIENT 21

Ny Carlsberg Museum, Copenhagen; British Museum

Plate 54   *Volume III*

LESSON 17

Republican Rome's Hundred Years of Revolution

(See plate 51)

IN 202 B.C. Carthage ceased to be a power. The triumph of the once insignificant little group of villages on the Tiber had culminated in the vast expansion of the Roman State. The Senate could not allow any other power to develop after the manner of Carthage and thus endanger Rome's conquests along the shores of the Mediterranean. East of Italy there were the three great kingdoms of the heirs of Alexander : Egypt under the Ptolemies ; Syria under the Seleucids, whose reigning monarch was Antiochus III the Great ; and Macedon under the Antigonid, Philip V, dominating the Greek states. Beyond them were the barbarian Parthians. India and China were practically in another world. In the west there was now no power except Rome, the head of Italy, mistress of Sicily and the islands, and virtually ruler of the native states of the north African littoral. The next task of ascendant Rome was to conquer the Hellenistic world of the East.

Here, then, we have reached the point where the two main streams of eastern and western history have their confluence. The western power, hitherto only in casual contact with Pyrrhus and (at the close of the third century) with Macedon, now came into direct conflict first with Macedon and then with Syria, while maintaining friendly or even protective relations with the third of the major powers, Egypt, who, in 168 B.C., acknowledged vassalage to Rome. In the course of the next sixty years Macedon and Greece, under the name of Achaea, became Roman provinces ; Syria as a power was shattered ; Asia Minor was broken up into several kingdoms.

Campaigns against Macedon Philip V and Antiochus, in 202 B.C., were planning a partition of the Egyptian dominions. The Greek states and leagues, in spite of violent dissensions, resented the domination of Macedon. Rome, answering an appeal from them, intervened. After a series of campaigns Philip was defeated at the battle of Cynoscephalae (197 B.C.). He was

(449)　　　　　　　　　　　　　　P3

allowed to retain his kingdom as a vassal ; and amid wild enthusiasm the freedom of all the Greek cities was proclaimed at the Olympic Games. Then came the challenge from Antiochus of Syria, whose domains in Asia included most of Persia. He endeavoured to profit by Philip's defeat by seizing certain of the cities on which freedom had just been conferred. Urged on by the exiled Hannibal and by Greek factions hostile to Rome, he invaded Greece, was defeated by the Romans, retreated to Asia Minor was pursued thither and was overwhelmingly defeated at Magnesia (190 B.C.). He was forced to surrender all claim to territory west of the river Halys, once the boundary between Lydia and Media ; Pergamum and Pontus became the two most powerful of the several kingdoms of Asia Minor.

Although he was defeated, warfare continued in Macedonia and in Greece. Perseus, the new king of Macedon, gave the Romans trouble. In 170 B.C. a new Macedonian war broke out ; two years later it was ended by the battle of Pydna. Macedon was turned into four vassal republics. In 149 B.C. Rome resolved to eliminate Carthage (the third Punic War) ; the excuse was that the Carthaginians had broken the treaty of 202 B.C. and had been goaded into war with Rome's ally, Masinissa of Numidia. In 146 B.C. Carthage was taken by the younger Scipio Africanus in command of the Roman forces, the city levelled to the ground, and its site formally laid under a religious curse. In the same year perished the surviving liberties of Greece, the Achaean League having defied the orders of Rome ; Corinth, which held out to the bitter end, was destroyed ; the Macedonian republics had already been turned into a Roman province, and most of the Greek cities were now placed under its governor, though later formed into the separate province of Achaea. In the course of the next twelve years revolts in Spain and Sardinia were mercilessly crushed and in 133 B.C. the younger Scipio returned from Spain to Rome to find her in the first throes of that breakdown of government which came to a climax in the civil wars from 49 to 31 B.C.

Government in the Provinces. The expansion of Rome had introduced new temptations. An experiment without precedent had to be made in governing foreign dependencies. Consuls and praetors—the magistrate who stood next to them in rank—had their term of office extended on expiry, but their functions were exercised not in Rome but as governors of the provinces. The pro-praetor or pro-consul—these were the titles which they now bore—was, to all intents and purposes, an absolute ruler during the term of his office. The troops were under his command. He and his officials had almost unlimited opportunities for seeking their own advantage at the expense of the provincials ; and for many of them the temptation proved only too strong.

The armies in the East learned new luxurious habits. The Roman farmer soldiers who returned could not settle down to a simple life. Modern experience has shown that it is hard for a man who has been a soldier for years to return to his old pursuits. There was the usual steady drift of men, bored by a rural life, to the capital—" All roads lead to Rome." When we consider the vast network of roads with which the Romans drew Italy together and abolished distance—to some extent as do our modern systems of transport—we are not surprised that the population massed in Rome.

The best of the native Roman population also had been drawn away from the city for a long time past to form military colonies, first in Italy and then in the provinces ; so that the population of Rome itself had degenerated, and yet, for all practical purposes, it was that population alone which had any active voice in political affairs. A growing evil was the increase in the number of slaves. They were needed for agricultural labour in place of the soldiers ; Roman conquests and piracy made them cheap and plentiful.

Slave Revolts. The first risings of slaves were in Sicily, but there was trouble on the mainland during the second century. The evil done to the Roman character by the slave population is difficult to exaggerate. Slavery is always degrading, and this was especially the case in Rome, where the horrors of cruel treatment were at this time unmitigated. The Italians who had stood so loyally by the State in the wars were now bitterly resenting the refusal of Rome to admit them to equal political rights, while the Roman populace was, for its part, fiercely jealous of any movement in that direction.

These factions, the decrease of the population owing to the casualties of the Punic wars, the decay of farming, the deterioration of the armies, which had been largely drawn from the sturdy rural population, the increase of slavery—all were disquieting signs, and the condition of Rome was becoming such that it was badly in need of a reformer. Expansion needed a reconstruction :

Rome under its old constitution could not control a world empire. It was not yet evident that the solution would be found in the concentration of power in the hands of one individual, who should be not a tyrant ruling for his own advantage, but an incarnation of the State, and that the condition of such power was that the armies of the State should be under his direct control.

Reforms of the Gracchi. The inevitable revolution was started by Tiberius Gracchus, a member of a senatorial family, whose motives were those of a philanthropist rather than a statesman. Elected to the tribuneship, he set himself to remedy the agricultural grievance by re-enacting the laws against the absorption of public lands, and restoring those lands to their legitimate use. The wealthy classes found their prescriptive rights seriously endangered. Gracchus met their attack by unconstitutional procedure ; they took the law into their own hands, and he was slain by a mob of senators (132 B.C.). His younger brother, Gaius, ten years afterwards took up the task more as a statesman than as a philanthropist. He had realised the necessity for recognizing the claims of the Italians ; but he allowed himself to appeal to the populace by such methods as promising them a supply of corn at a fixed rate below the market value. He met with the same fate as his brother. The state became divided between the demagogic and the senatorial or oligarchical factions.

A war in Africa gave the popular party the upper hand through the military successes of the humbly born general, Marius, although those achievements were largely due to his aristocratic lieutenant, Sulla. Meanwhile, a new enemy was threatening the Roman world. German tribes, the Cimbri and the Teutones, appeared on the scene for the first time, bursting into the province of Transalpine Gaul, where they overwhelmed the Roman armies. Marius was dispatched against them, and put them utterly to rout in two great battles. These victories enabled him to reorganize the military system on lines which virtually set up a permanent standing army of professional soldiers.

LESSON 18

Caesarism's Triumph in the Roman State

(See plate 51)

THE Gracchi having taught the people to look up to a leader, from their time dates the beginning of one-man authority in Rome. Though, after the murder (121 B.C.) of the younger brother, Gaius Gracchus, there ensued a lull for some years in the conflict between the senatorial and popular parties, this was renewed when the state was involved in wars which brought the need of reform into glaring light. The leader to whom the people now turned was no politician but the military commander, Marius (157–86 B.C.), who, of humble parentage, had risen by sheer merit. A man of integrity and an able soldier, he had rendered distinguished service, leading to ultimate victory, in the Jugurthine war, after Jugurtha, king of Numidia, relying on the corruption of the Romans of the age, had succeeded in bribing their consul and had inflicted a defeat on the Roman army. During this war Marius was himself elected consul by the people. Subsequently he again achieved victory for Rome against the dangerous armies of the Teutons and Gauls. But Marius was no statesman, and, though elected consul in all seven times, he failed to control the leaders of his party in the Roman political struggles against the Senate and his principal rival, the aristocrat, Sulla.

In the meanwhile a storm was developing in the East. The kingdom of Pontus, on the Black Sea, had been developing mightily under its king, Mithradates, who flung down the challenge to the Roman Republic. There was a sharp contest between the two parties in Rome for the appointment of the commander in the East; the victory fell, after much bloodshed, to Sulla, who thereupon departed with his legions, leaving Marius and the popular leaders dominant in Rome. They used their power to proscribe and put to death large numbers of the senatorial party. There was a revolutionary reign of terror. Marius was elected consul for the seventh time, but died shortly after his election.

Dictatorship of Sulla. Sulla, having triumphantly vanquished Mithradates, returned with his legions to Italy, overthrew the

(453)

demagogues after hard fighting, and crushed them by instituting a reign of terror on his own account. Then, as dictator, he set about reorganizing the constitution, placing the whole power in the hands of the oligarchical party. At the height of his power, when he might have made himself permanently tyrant, he chose to resign, and shortly afterwards died.

Sulla instituted many reforms, but his constitution had in it no permanence. It had deprived the Assembly of the people and the tribunes of power, giving the Senate—the body which had so disastrously failed in the government of Rome since the Punic wars—the supreme leadership. On the death of Sulla the two most powerful men in Rome itself were the extremely wealthy Crassus and young Pompeius, " Pompey the Great " (106–48 B.C.), who had distinguished himself as the lieutenant of Sulla in the fight against Marius, and was now sent to suppress a rebellion that had broken out in Spain.

The brilliant orator, Cicero, was rising to eminence among the moderates of the senatorial party, the " Optimates," though his amiable ideals were very far from coinciding with most of theirs, little as he appreciated the fact. A young man of patrician rank, Julius Caesar (102–44 B.C.), who was, however, a nephew of the plebeian, Marius, was pushing his way to the leadership of the popular party.

Pompey the Great. Such was the position when Pompey returned after the subjugation of Spain. But Pompey did not find the senatorial party ready with so full an acknowledgement of his services as he expected. Caesar offered his alliance, and brought Crassus into the combination. The command of the East was bestowed upon Pompey, with virtually unlimited powers. Pompey, having destroyed the swarms of pirates who dominated the whole eastern Mediterranean, proceeded to the subjugation of Asia as far as the Euphrates. He crushed the remnant of the kingdom of the Seleucids and made Syria a Roman province. Entering Jerusalem, he brought it and the Jews under Roman control.

Meanwhile the extremists of the popular party plotted a revolution, headed by Catiline, a noble of evil reputation, but with a following of the dissatisfied and restive. The conspiracy was discovered and crushed, not without the employment of unconstitutional methods, more or less justified in the emergency, by Cicero, who was consul at the time. There were not wanting enemies who declared that both Caesar and Crassus were implicated, and efforts were made to have Caesar proscribed.

Pompey, on his return with his legions and his laurels, might easily have made himself master of the State ; but when it came to defying the constitution he always drew back, though he needed political influence to secure the Senate's approval of his arrangements after his conquests in Asia Minor. In accordance with the law, he disbanded his forces on landing.

Rise of Caesar. Caesar, on the other hand, had grasped the fact that the military supremacy of one man was a necessity. He meant himself to be the one man, but he could only get the military supremacy by becoming the master of legions, and he could only become a master of legions as a provincial governor. As Pompey's ally, he procured for himself the proconsulship of Gaul for five years, afterwards extended to ten. Crassus was killed on an expedition against the Parthians. During those ten years, while at Rome, Pompey, Caesar's ally, showed no capacity for handling the situation, Caesar himself proved his generalship by the subjugation of the whole of Gaul. Incidentally, he paid two visits to the island of Britain, where he made no attempt at a permanent conquest, though, by extracting something in the nature of a tribute, he was able to claim that he had added the island to the Roman dominions.

Caesar's successes now began to alarm Pompey. As proconsul, Caesar's command over the military forces in Gaul, both Cisalpine and Transalpine, was absolute, but if he led his troops outside his own province he would be committing an act of rebellion against the Republic. The boundary of his province was the river Rubicon, in the north of Italy. He resolved upon the great adventure, and " crossed the Rubicon " with his troops.

He was now in open rebellion. But in Italy itself there were no legions but his own ; the armies were in the provinces ; Pompey withdrew to Greece to gather a force which should crush the enemy of the Republic. Caesar made himself master of Rome and of the treasury. Before engaging in the decisive struggle with Pompey, he entered with his legions into Spain in order to crush any possibilities of a serious resistance to him arising from that quarter. Then he turned upon Pompey, whose great army he routed utterly at the battle of Pharsalus (48 B.C.).

Pompey, retreating to the East to raise fresh armies, made his way to Egypt, but was assassinated as he was landing.

Caesar had now to crush the Asiatics who were in arms under Pharnaces, a son of Mithradates ; this accomplished, he returned to Italy, where his combined vigour and leniency restored order. It was still necessary for him to crush, at the battle of Thapsus, the Pompeians who had rallied in Africa. His victory resulted in triumphs over Egypt and Numidia. He came back to Italy, but Spain rose in revolt under Pompey's son, Sextus. Again he had to take the field, and to crush the revolt at the battle of Munda.

Caesar had crossed the Rubicon in 49 B.C. Munda was fought four years later, in 45 B.C. In the intervals of fighting during those four years, Caesar had procured at Rome his own appointment as dictator for ten years ; he had introduced various reforms, including, incidentally, that of the calendar, establishing almost with accuracy the exact solar year of 365 days, with an extra day in every fourth year. He had reorganized the system of provincial government, and had made himself the authority in the appointment of all military commands. He was now planning a war in the Far East against the expanding power of the Parthians beyond the Euphrates. He was absolute master of the whole Roman world. A monarchy was established under the republican title of dictator. He was in fact the first emperor.

Assassination of Caesar. Caesar, however, had to pay the penalty for the leniency shown to political opponents, who were not wise enough, or magnanimous enough, to recognize the greatness of the man. Although he publicly refused the crown, the dominion of one man was traditionally abhorrent to Romans, who little understood at the time that expansion and military dominion over the world had destroyed the Republic. Self-seeking politicians and fanatical republicans, who dreamed an impossible dream of the restoration of an aristocratic republic, combined in a plot against the dictator's life. In spite of warnings, he scorned to take precautions for his own defence, and on the Ides—that is, the 15th—of March, 44 B.C., Caesar fell beneath the daggers of his assassins, among whom the most notable were Cassius, Decimus Brutus (the ablest soldier among them), and Marcus Brutus, Caesar's friend, who fancied himself a patriot overthrowing a tyrant.

LESSON 19

The Augustan Age of Roman History

(See plate 52)

WHEN Caesar fell, Mark Antony (83–30 B.C.), one of Caesar's trusted lieutenants, the boy Octavian, or Octavianus, great-nephew and adopted heir of Julius, and another of Caesar's lieutenants, Lepidus, all had their own ambitions. They united as a triumvirate to establish their own rule, and to avenge the murdered dictator. The legions who had served and loved Caesar were ready to follow them.

Marcus Brutus and Cassius departed to the proconsulates in the East to which they had been nominated by the murdered Julius to raise forces. Decimus Brutus went to north Italy, but was killed. Octavian, Antony, and Lepidus, who now dominated Italy, having agreed upon an arrangement by which they were to be appointed commissioners for the reorganization of the State the Senate could see no way out of the difficulty other than by ratifying this new and startling triumvirate.

Following the precedents of Marius and Sulla, the triumvirs instituted a proscription against all who had opposed the newly self-constituted authorities. When sated with vengeance on their political adversaries and personal enemies, Octavian and Antony passed into Greece on their way to meet the rival army of Brutus and Cassius, and completely defeated it at Philippi, 42 B.C. Cassius and Brutus, seeing all was lost, chose to die on the field. There was no further possibility of resisting the triumvirate who divided the Roman world between them, Antony taking the East and Octavian the West, while the puppet Lepidus, to whom the other two triumvirs paid little regard, was relegated to Africa.

Antony and Cleopatra. Octavian now settled down to consolidate his power in Italy. Antony went off to secure the East, and there met with Cleopatra, queen of Egypt, by whom he became enslaved. But for that frantic enchantment, Antony might have crushed Octavian and made himself master of the world. But when Rome declared war on Egypt and the inevitable struggle between the rivals took place at the great sea-fight of

Actium (31 B.C.), Cleopatra with her galleys took flight, and the
infatuated Antony followed her. The Egyptian fleet was wholly
defeated, and when his cause seemed lost, Antony, deceived by
a false report of Cleopatra's death, committed suicide by falling
on his sword.

Cleopatra tried the effect of her charms on Octavian, but
found him made of less impressionable stuff than Antony ; and,
rather than grace her conqueror's triumphal procession in Rome,
she put herself to death.

Augustus as Dictator. The battle of Actium was a decisive
moment in the world's history. Lepidus having long ceased to
count, Octavian now stood alone at the head of the Roman
world. On his return to Rome, he resigned the exceptional
powers which had been entrusted to him. The Senate, however,
at once decreed to him a new tenure of the dictatorship for ten
years, with the understanding that the term of office should be
renewed as often as might be deemed necessary in the interests
of the country. Octavian accepted these conditions, and received
from the Senate the titles of Augustus (a term of dignity only)
and Princeps, which might be construed as President. He
was officially invested with the Imperium, or absolute control
of all the armies of the State, hitherto enjoyed only by commanders in the field ; though he stressed the civilian title of
Princeps, not the military title of Imperator, by degrees the
latter (Emperor) became the more prominent. But in popular
parlance he was always Caesar.

To him alone belonged the right of making treaties, of declaring
war, and of offering or accepting terms of peace. These powers
were conveyed to him without destroying constitutional forms,
by extending to him—first for a term of years and then for life—
the tribunician powers in Rome and the proconsular powers in
all the further provinces, as proconsular powers had been extended
to Pompey and Julius Caesar. The Senate continued to sit and
to be in theory the governing body ; the republican magistrates
continued to be appointed, but were in effect the nominees of
Augustus. The new arrangement was officially at first a restoration
of the Republic. Unlike Caesar, Octavian felt a great respect for
the republican institutions and did not wish to destroy them,
but the dual government between Princeps and Senate was
unbalanced. The legions being at the orders of the Princeps,
he held too much power not to become an absolute ruler. The

State, therefore, tended towards a military monarchy, and soon the Roman Empire emerged under Augustus.

The Praetorian Guards. He had been endowed with permanent proconsular authority in all the frontier provinces of the empire, wherein all the troops, except the select bodyguard, were stationed. This select bodyguard was composed of picked veterans, known as the Praetorian Guards. Their importance cannot be exaggerated, for they were a symbol of what the new government stood for, and were soon to become the most important element in its continuance. Under the Republic armies raised in Italy were disbanded after each war. This continued until the last century B.C., when the importance of the commanders had required a special corps for their protection. All the higher officers were appointed by and responsible to Caesar personally as his legates ; consequently he held complete control of the whole effective military force of the empire. The " home " provinces remained in theory under the control of the Senate.

In the recent civil wars these guards had increased in numbers under the rival leaders and become an important part of their forces. Augustus now received permission to retain his guards in Italy, though the legions were sent back to the provinces. The retention of the Praetorian cohorts on the soil of the governing country showed that the new government was a military monarchy. The imperial rule was henceforth based on force and all the soldiers took yearly the oath to the emperor—the sacramentum.

Economic Reforms. Augustus was, above all things, a practical reformer. He established a census, alike of individuals and of property. He introduced a new principle of finance and taxation ; he based his taxing system mainly on the land and the personal possessions of the citizens, and he abolished a large number of unequal and capricious imposts which bore heavily on the poor. The financial accounts of the State were kept with strict accuracy, and he introduced the practice of framing what would now be called an annual State budget. He appointed the governors of all the state provinces, and he personally arranged that the taxation of each province was fairly imposed and properly accounted for. He took an interest in the affairs of the different municipalities, and he established a police force to keep good order in the towns. He developed, as far as possible, that system of municipal government which began in the Roman states under the guidance of Julius Caesar.

The Augustans. Augustus was a lover of literature. He was the patron of poets, historians, and scholars, of painters, and of sculptors and architects. The emperor had a large theatre erected —the Theatre of Marcellus—and a fine open square for the Assembly of the people. Other splendid buildings were erected— public baths among them—by Agrippa, an able minister of Augustus. On the Palatine hill Augustus had his residence. From this royal dwelling on the Palatine was derived the word " palace." In his reign Virgil expressed the great Roman ideals in the noble epic the " Aeneid " ; Horace is famous as the author of lyrical and satirical poems unsurpassed in any literature ; Ovid, Tibullus and Propertius were notable poets ; Livy is one of the most picturesque historians of any era. The literary glories of the reign have caused the term " Augustan Age " to be applied to other eras when classicalism has flourished, such as the age of Louis XIV in France and of Queen Anne in England. A whole society of wits and humorists, makers of verses and writers of essays flourished under the influence and patronage of Augustus or of his famous minister Maecenas.

German Defeat of Varus. Augustus wished to preserve the Rhine, the Danube, and the Euphrates as the frontiers of the empire. German tribes were pressing on the Rhine and Danube, and, late in his reign, a great disaster befell the imperial troops when they crossed the Rhine. A Roman force led by a general named Varus was skilfully drawn into an ambush by the enemy and cut to pieces, Varus himself being among the first to meet with death. The effort was abandoned, and the northern boundary of the empire was made west of the Rhine and south of the Danube, extending from the Black Sea to the North Sea.

Some years earlier an event had occurred in a distant province of Rome which had a tremendous and far-reaching effect on the course of human history. That event was the birth of Christ and the founding of the Christian religion. The tragedy which was enacted in Jerusalem towards the end of the reign of the successor of Augustus was enacted, indeed, under the authority of the Imperial Government, but that Imperial Government and the Roman people took little interest in the rise of the Christian movement and in the steps taken by the authorities in Palestine to resist its influence.

Succession of Tiberius. Augustus died at the close of August in A.D. 14, at the age of seventy-six. He had ruled over Rome for more than forty years, and his reign was the happiest and the most prosperous that Rome had known or was to know for many generations. He had married three times, but left no son to succeed him. His first wife left him a daughter, Julia, who, after the death of her first husband, married Marcus Agrippa, who died in A.D. 12. Augustus adopted two of her sons by this marriage, the elder to be his successor to the throne. Both these sons died in their youth, and the obvious heir to the Principate was Tiberius Claudius Nero, the stepson of Augustus, his last wife's son by a former marriage.

LESSON 20

The Caesars from Tiberius to Nero

(See plates 53 and 54)

TIBERIUS was no longer young when he succeeded to the Principate, or Empire, of Rome. He was experienced both as a soldier and as an administrator ; he had rendered invaluable service under his stepfather Augustus. Tiberius was opposed to any expansion of dominion beyond the lines of the three rivers, the Rhine, the Danube, and the Euphrates ; he himself had had personal experience of the difficulties of campaigning in what is now Germany. He held the Empire with a strong hand, and his legates and procurators knew that they would be called to strict account, regardless of wealth or family connexions, if they misconducted themselves seriously. He had a contempt for the Roman populace, and withdrew their rights of voting for the election of magistrates (under Augustus these votes had become a farce) and he also practised the strictest economy with funds devoted to public amusement. Consequently he was intensely unpopular in Rome. His half-nephew, who is known as Germanicus, conducted, somewhat against the wishes of Tiberius, campaigns among the German tribes, which were reputed to have been brilliantly successful, though there was little enough to show for them ; and the prestige of the Roman arms was maintained.

The picture we have of Tiberius as a tyrant, cruel, greedy and revengeful, is by Tacitus, who was concerned rather with the affairs of Rome and Italy than with the Empire at large ; and in Rome and Italy the reign was almost a nightmare—at least.

during its later years. Modern historians tend to see in him a man soured by the harsh treatment he had received from Augustus, and rendered still more bitter by the later misfortunes in his own family.

Germanicus, who was extremely popular, was recalled from Germany and died while on an eastern tour, amid strong popular suspicions of poisoning. The harsh and generally hated emperor himself became the object of plots ; the city was filled with informers, spies who grew rich by denouncing real or imaginary plotters. Prosecutions for treason had been established under the Republic, but in the Empire the grounds for the charge were seriously extended. " Words," as Tacitus says, " now became sufficient evidence of guilt ; overt acts were no longer necessary for conviction." It would seem that no man of prominence felt that his life was safe.

Tiberius withdrew to the island of Capri, where he was reputed to be living a life of hideous debauchery. He left as the master of Rome Sejanus, the prefect of the praetorians—the great body of picked and privileged troops quartered in the neighbourhood of Rome. Sejanus designed to use his position to seize the imperial purple for himself. The plot was discovered, and with appalling suddenness the favourite was struck down from his high estate and was put to an ignominious death, with all his kin. In the twenty-third year of his reign (A.D. 37) Tiberius died.

Caligula the Cruel. As Tiberius had lost his son, his successor, chosen by the praetorians, was Gaius Caesar, the son of Germanicus, better known as Caligula, a nickname for him among the soldiers of his boyhood. Not long after he became emperor, Caligula was seized with a severe illness which unsettled his reason, and his name has become a byword for frantic cruelties and insane imaginings. The grotesque horrors of his rule were ended by his assassination, when the praetorians, more than half in jest, acclaimed as his successor his uncle Claudius, a feeble pedant, not without cleverness, but unversed in public affairs.

Claudius. When he was enthroned Claudius (A.D. 41-54) was fifty. Although by nature weak and timid he was a statesman. He accomplished much for the Empire, and in Rome itself was greatly interested in making architectural and practical improvements. He built the great aqueducts by which the city was plentifully supplied with water from the mountains. Reviving the plans of Julius Caesar, he conducted in A.D. 43 a successful campaign against Britain, and brought the southern half of the island under the Roman dominion. The frontiers of the Empire, too, were efficiently guarded.

At home, however, Claudius had fallen under the absolute influence of his wife, Messalina, who had a short way of getting rid of personal or political enemies. History and literature have consigned the name of Messalina to eternal infamy, and made it the synonym of profligacy and cruelty in woman. At last her iniquities led to her destruction, and then Claudius took for his second wife Agrippina, sister of Caligula, a woman as ambitious and as merciless as Messalina, though not so profligate. Her great object was to secure the succession for Nero, her son by a previous marriage. After a few years she succeeded. Claudius perished, probably as a result of poison, and in A.D. 54 the boy Nero became emperor. He was descended from the ill-fated family of Augustus on his father's as well as his mother's side.

Nero. For a time the government was wisely and successfully carried on by regents, one being the poet and philosopher, Seneca. Afterwards, when intrigues had removed Seneca and banished Agrippina from the court, Nero's evil and decadent nature led him to a career of vice and cruelty. He condemned his old teacher, Seneca, to death ; later he had the son of Claudius and even his own mother, Agrippina, assassinated. There was in his temperament a singular blending of the furious tyrant and the artistic amateur. He loved music ; he had a passion for the stage and for the arena. It was one of his delights to drive chariots and display his skill in the management of horses before the assembled multitudes in the great Roman amphitheatre.

His reign was marked by his terrible persecution of the Christians, a number of whom he executed with cruel tortures, which he endeavoured to justify by accusing them of having caused a disastrous fire in Rome which consumed half the city, while, according to tradition, Nero looked on and played the fiddle. At great expense he rebuilt the city ; and, the palace of Augustus having been practically destroyed by the fire, erected an enormous " Golden House " for himself.

British Revolt under Boadicea. During his reign took place the famous rising in Britain under Boadicea, the " British Warrior Queen." Boadicea was the wife of a British king who ruled over the Iceni, a people occupying that part of England now known as Norfolk and Suffolk. When her husband died, one of the Roman commanders in the island seized the territory, made the queen a prisoner, brutally scourged her, and ill-treated her daughters. Boadicea escaped from her captors and raised a large army to defend the British soil. Her army defeated the Romans at Colchester, and occupied London. Boadicea's victory seems to have been only a sudden surprise which disarranged the preparations of the Roman garrison. The Roman governor of the island was absent in Anglesey when Boadicea's movement broke out, but, returning, advanced against her and inflicted an overwhelming defeat on her army.

Nero's wild excesses and frantic tyranny had their inevitable result. The disgusted legions in the west proclaimed their general, Galba, as the new Caesar—" a man," says Tacitus, " whom all men judged fit to be emperor—had he never been emperor." He marched on Rome from Spain ; even the praetorians deserted Nero, who fled from the capital and shortly afterwards committed suicide. Thus died (A.D. 68) the last ruler of the line of Augustus.

LESSON 21

From Vespasian to Marcus Aurelius

(See plates 54 and 55)

GALBA, after he had been hailed emperor on the death of Nero, did not display much capacity for dealing with a great crisis, and made himself conspicuous only by his extreme parsimony and reckless severity when he met with opposition. There was a rising of the soldiers against him, chiefly inspired by Otho, a former friend of Nero, and an ambitious man. Otho was proclaimed emperor, and Galba was put to death after a reign of only six months.

In the meanwhile a new claimant had arisen. This was Vitellius, the commander of the Roman legions on the Rhine. Vitellius, although he had never displayed great military qualities, had succeeded in making himself popular with his soldiers, and when the rising against Galba took place the legions of the Rhine proclaimed him emperor. His troops marched to Italy, and defeated the troops of Otho in a decisive battle. This defeat so disheartened Otho that he killed himself, and thus momentarily

(464)

left the field to Vitellius. But in the east Vespasian, who held the command in Syria, with his troops decided that he himself should rule. While, in Rome, Vitellius assumed the purple, Vespasian was proclaimed emperor in Egypt and Syria. Vitellius, who was nothing more than an incompetent glutton, was murdered, and a year later Vespasian, having been proclaimed in Rome, arrived in Italy. Though born of humble parentage he had shown great capacity for political and military leadership.

The accession of Flavius Vespasianus was signalized by the destruction of Jerusalem by his son Titus and the dispersion of the Jews, who from this time were a scattered and landless people, though they preserved their nationality as a distinct community. Another special feature of his reign was the completion of the conquest and organization of the province of Britain by Agricola.

No resistance was offered to the new dynasty. As a soldier Vespasian had no living rival and the army was loyal to him. But he was also a very shrewd man of business, who regarded the reorganization of the imperial government as a business proposition. His rule was very much like that of our Henry VII. He was resolved to establish order and economy, and had no objection to being called sordid, but he removed many unfit and corrupt office-holders who had been put into power by Nero and other emperors. He reorganized the financial system, which was in utter confusion ; restored the Capitol, which had been reduced to ruins by a great fire during the war of the Four Emperors ; built the Colosseum, and established a great public library. Wherever and whenever money was wanted for any purposes of value to the State and the public, he always had an open hand. His health broke down in A.D. 79, and he went to recruit his strength to his country home in the Sabine mountains, but the removal came too late to effect any change in his condition, and in the middle of the same year he died.

Destruction of Pompeii. Vespasian's successor was his son Titus. The only notable event of his brief reign was a terrific calamity. At the opening of November, A.D. 79, a tremendous eruption of Vesuvius brought disaster on some of the neighbouring towns, including Pompeii and Herculaneum, which were almost entirely destroyed by a flood of lava. Herculaneum was buried under masses of ashes and lava, and its actual site was only rediscovered in 1720, when the sinking of a well brought

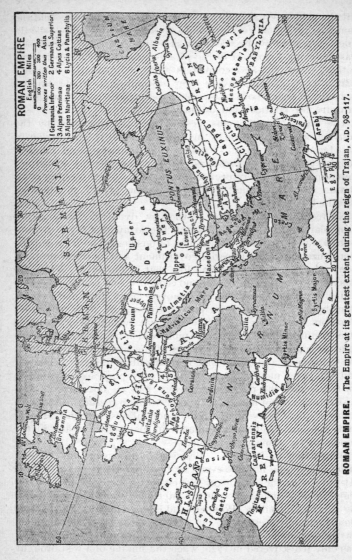

ROMAN EMPIRE. The Empire at its greatest extent, during the reign of Trajan, A.D. 98–117.

the workers to the remains of many of its buildings. Pompeii was more fortunate than Herculaneum, because it stood farther away from the burning mountain, and was covered not so much with the destroying lava as with ashes. The city was, however, completely hidden from sight for many centuries.

Domitian. Titus was succeeded by his brother Domitian. During the earlier part of his rule he pursued a course of moderation and justice, but before long began to reveal the jealousies and passions that afterwards made his reign a calamity. We can read impressive descriptions of some of the worst aspects of his reign in the Life of Agricola, by Tacitus, and his vices, his wanton cruelties, and the ugly conditions prevalent in Rome in his day are pictured in the satires of Juvenal. His death was what might have been expected from his life. There were several conspiracies against him, and one, proving successful, brought him and his reign to an end in A.D. 96.

On Domitian's death the soldiery quietly permitted the Senate to make choice of the elderly civilian Nerva as the new emperor, but Nerva strengthened his position at once by adopting as his junior colleague and heir the extremely capable and successful Trajan, commander of the legions on the Rhine. Nerva was not endowed with much physical energy, and his reign only lasted for two years. The news of Nerva's death and of his own succession reached Trajan at Cologne, where he was engaged in important work for the maintenance of peace along the frontiers and the better discipline of the army. He made no haste to go to Rome, and spent some months over his work in Germany. Then he returned, and, according to his own desire, entered Rome on foot, with his empress, Pompeia Plotina, at his side.

Trajan. Trajan was well qualified for the imperial dignity. He began his reign as a reformer, and in certain paths of reform he remained consistent to the end. He greatly reduced the amount of taxation, and sold for the public benefit many palaces which some of the emperors preceding him had obtained by confiscation. He employed much of the public money for the help of the poor, and especially for their children. He restored to the Senate much of the power which had been taken from it by some of his despotic predecessors. He promoted public works, partly as a means of finding work for the unemployed—the making of roads, the draining of marshes, and the creation of new seaports, some of which were established at his own cost.

He founded a great library, and caused the erection of many splendid public monuments, among them the Trajan Column. Especially noteworthy is his " rescript," or instruction, to the provincial governor Pliny concerning the persecution of Christians. They were not to be hunted down, but people who refused to sacrifice to the " Deity of Rome and the Empire " must suffer the penalty of high treason if they persisted after admonition. The Christians were supposed to practise barbaric and magical rites which could not be tolerated by a civilized government ; while the Jews were the only people privileged to refuse worship of the personified " Spirit of Rome."

Besides being a great ruler, Trajan was a great and ambitious soldier, who extended the empire. His reign saw as many military enterprises and invading expeditions as that of any Roman emperor. Some of these he conducted himself. His conquest and colonization of Dacia created the Rumanian provinces, which still retain on the Danube the traditions of old Rome, and brought many Asiatic regions under the sway of Rome. Historians tell us he declared that if he were a younger man he would undertake the subjugation of the Indies. But his conquests were not, in most cases, of a lasting character. He died while engaged in military operations in the Far East, in August, 117, after a reign of nearly twenty years. Trajan left no son, but had nominated as his successor his kinsman Hadrian.

Hadrian. The new emperor passed a great part of his life travelling through his dominions in order that he might acquire a close personal knowledge of their conditions, and of the improvements that might be made. He strove also to preserve peace with foreign states, and gave no encouragement to the national ambition for conquest. He endeavoured to secure Rome's possessions in Britain against the daring incursions of the Caledonians by constructing the famous wall from the mouth of the Tyne to the Solway Firth, some fragments of which still survive. Many public works of general utility were constructed during his reign, and he left to his country many splendid monumental records of his love for art and architecture. He died in 138, after a reign of twenty-one years.

Hadrian very wisely named as his successor the noble Antoninus Pius, whose reign will ever be remarkable for the fact that he was the first Roman Emperor who definitely discouraged the persecution of the Christians. He took care that the finances of

(468)

the State were administered with economy. His grateful people gave him the title of " Father of the Human Race." His reign was altogether peaceful, containing no record of war more serious than some expeditions for the suppression of disorders here and there on the frontiers. He died in his seventy-fifth year, leaving as his successor Marcus Aurelius, whom he had adopted.

Marcus Aurelius. The new emperor was called " The Philosopher " ; his " Meditations " show a curious but quite unconscious approximation to the Christian ethic, though he was one of the persecutors of that sect, being wholly misinformed as to their tenets. He was tried by many severe troubles during his reign—there were incessant conflicts with Teutonic tribes on the frontier of the empire ; there were devastating earthquakes in many parts of Italy, and a destructive pestilence raged for a long time in Rome. Naturally a student, not a man of action, he shouldered the responsibility of empire and of campaigning in person from a high sense of duty, and devoted himself unswervingly to the welfare of his subjects. While on one of these frontier campaigns, he died (A.D. 180).

LESSON 22

Caesars by Grace of the Legions

WHEN Commodus, the degenerate son of Marcus Aurelius, was assassinated after a twelve-years' reign by the prefect of the Praetorian Guards in A.D. 192, two hundred and twenty-three years had passed since Augustus became master of the Roman world. Caesar had followed Caesar —officially, by choice of the Senate, though in the cases of Caligula, Claudius and Vespasian the choice had been dictated by the soldiery—and since Vespasian each had practically nominated his own successor. Theoretically, each was the first magistrate for life of the Roman Republic, the Princeps, who avoided laying stress on the fact that the basis of his power lay in the Imperium, the supreme command of the military forces of the State. But henceforth the Princeps is merged in the Imperator. Hitherto, with the exception of Trajan, who was a Spaniard, all the emperors had been of Roman or at least Italian descent—though Trajan's family had settled in Spain ; after this a Roman is a rarity, because the Roman army had gradually changed its character with the extension of Roman citizenship, which was the condition of service in the legions, while the legions themselves were supplemented by troops known as auxiliaries, levied from the non-Romans of the Empire. Rude and barbarous mercenary soldiery thus became the most influential authority in the State. The main armies, each with its own commander-in-chief, the lieutenant of Caesar, were those of Syria and Asia (Minor), of the Danube, of the Rhine, Britain and Spain. In Italy, always stationed near the Capitol, there was only the privileged brigade of the Imperial Guards, the Praetorians, whose prefect was always in personal touch with Caesar, ready to bring pressure to bear on the Senate at his command.

Roman Civilization. Hitherto, then, Caesar after Caesar had been able to go his own way, always with a Senate which could only be subservient, unless he made himself personally intolerable, as only Domitian and Commodius had done since Vespasian's accession. Within the bounds of the Empire the Roman peace had been enforced, though fighting on one or another of the frontiers had been almost continuous. In the provinces and in Italy the administrative machinery had worked successfully. By sea there was comparative freedom from the former peril of pirates. Travellers could take ship and reach Spain or Athens in a week from the fine harbour laid out at the mouth of the Tiber by Claudius. The great Government ships, which plied for trade and also carried passengers between Alexandria and Rome, made the journey, in the summer months, in ten days. In winter, traffic was stopped.

Several of the emperors had fostered the well-being of their subjects by means of legislation and public works. During the reign of Vespasian Rome had surpassed Alexandria in the grandeur and number of its public buildings. Two magnificent Forums were erected near the old Forum, in which the business of the capital was transacted. There was thus a group of four new Forums, including those built by Caesar and Augustus ; Trajan added another, and in the court between the two great libraries, also built in his reign, he erected the Trajan Column of Parian marble, on which were carved scenes of his campaigns. At this period Roman builders had mastered the art of building with cast concrete—an art which we are now utilizing again. There was a large educated public in the Rome of Trajan's day and the State libraries were open to all. The last of the great scientists of the ancient world, the famous geographer and astronomer Ptolemy, was working at Alexandria during the reigns of Hadrian and the Antonines ; but in spite of outward signs of culture and prosperity Mediterranean civilization began to wane at this period.

All the world converged to Rome, which thus became cosmopolitan. Unfortunately large numbers of the country agricultural population also moved to the city. The land was neglected, while the financial business of the cities throughout the Empire declined, as the prosperous rural communities were so reduced that city industrial concerns could no longer sell their output. Curtailing their production, many hands were thrown out of work. Business was also affected by the shortage of precious metals for coinage. With the expansion of the Empire love of display had increased among the rich, and vast sums went out of the country to purchase luxuries—pearls, rubies, and other precious stones, silks and choice fruits from the Orient ; while many of the gold and silver mines around the Mediterranean seem to have been worked out. In spite of outward splendour among the apparently wealthy classes, the cities in the provinces, burdened by taxation from Rome, were declining in commerce and in intellectual culture.

Revolution on the Frontier. For more than a century no one except Trajan had attempted aggressive expansion, and Hadrian had been prompt to relinquish most of what Trajan had acquired. But the Parthians in the east were a constant danger ; warlike tribes, Germanic or Scandinavian, were pressing in increasing numbers on the Rhine and upper Danube. The Roman peace of more than two centuries was ended, and we enter now upon a century of revolutions. After the assassination of Commodus there was a struggle among several military usurpers, from which Septimius Severus, the military commander from the Danube, emerged successful ; and the Senate declared him emperor. He was swift of action. He disbanded the Praetorians, organized a new Praetorian Guard, marched against the eastern candidate and slew him, and was back in time to crush the remaining rival advancing from the Rhine, in a desperately fought battle near Lugdunum (Lyons).

The new emperor was a Moor, a soldier who had risen to high command by sheer ability. In the remaining fourteen years of his reign the Empire was troubled by no internal foes, and Severus spent most of his time campaigning against the Parthians in the east, and then in Britain, conpleting the conquest and organization of the province. The domestic administration he left in the efficient hands of the great legist Papinian, who incidentally established the legal doctrine that absolute powers were vested in the emperor. Severus died at York in A.D. 211. Culture had finally declined ; high posts in the government were filled by military leaders of low origin ; and in 212 citizenship was granted to all free men throughout the provinces of the empire.

Period of Chaos. Then came the era of chaos. In the next seventy-three years there were five-and-twenty emperors, of whom only one died in his bed. Battle, murder, and sudden death held sway. Severus was succeeded by his son Bassianus, better known by his nickname Caracalla, who began by murdering his own brother, proved to be a second Caligula with a half-crazed thirst for blood, and was assassinated in the sixth year of his nightmare rule. The troops in the east, where Caracalla was murdered, made his boy cousin Elagabalus emperor — a miserable, dissipated creature whose cruel extravagances became a byword. He is commonly called Heliogabalus by an error. He was assassinated and succeeded by another boy-cousin, Alexander Severus, who showed promise but was killed in a mutiny, the soldiers having by this time got completely out of hand. Emperors rose and fell in rapid succession. We may note among them Philip the Arabian, who is reputed to have been a Christian ; Decius, a member of a once distinguished Roman family, who was killed in fighting a desperate battle with the Goths, now swarming down on the Danube, which ended in a Roman defeat— he is also notorious for a great persecution of the Christians ; Valerian, who marched against the rising power of Persia (the Parthians, who had now passed permanently under the sway of a Persian dynasty), but was taken prisoner and died in captivity; the Illyrian Claudius, who only had time to inflict a heavy defeat on the Goths before dying of the plague (A.D. 270).

Sixty years had passed since the death of Severus. Each of the three emperors last-named had rendered good service to the empire, but the three reigns together covered only eleven years. The successor of Claudius was Aurelian (270–275), who beat back the Germans on the Rhine ; made terms with the Goths, whom he settled in Dacia, and suppressed the independence of Palmyra on the Arabian border, where the queen Zenobia, famous both for her virtues and her beauty, ruled with the philosopher Longinus for her minister. Aurelian defeated her army and took the queen prisoner. In the empire he restored some order and might have accomplished much, but he fell victim to a private conspiracy. He built the great wall round Rome as a protection from raids—that massive wall which stands today. Then, in 284, the death of an emperor while campaigning in the east led the army there to choose from its chiefs the Illyrian Diocletian, who had risen from the ranks by sheer force of ability and character.

The Empire under Diocletian. Diocletian was more than a soldier of genius. Soldier emperors had maintained the frontiers, but none had attempted to depart from precedent and reorganize the imperial system. Diocletian had the political imagination of a great statesman ; he cared nothing for precedent or Roman tradition. He saw that the imperial centre of gravity had shifted from Italy to the east. He deliberately chose a colleague, Maximian, whom he could completely trust, who shared with him the title of Augustus and was in charge of the western half of the empire, while he retained for himself the east.

After a time he carried division or devolution a step farther, and appointed for each Augustus a sub-emperor or Caesar—Galerius in charge of the Danube provinces, and Constantius Chlorus in charge of Britain, Gaul and Spain—but all were ultimately subordinate and responsible to himself as the senior Augustus. The four great divisions of this organization were subdivided into " dioceses "—each with its lieutenant-governor under the Caesar—and the dioceses into provinces. This pyramidal arrangement applied alike to the civil and military administration throughout, though one of its most important features was the total and permanent severance of civil from military functions. In the twenty-first year of his reign, when the system had been well tested and found to work successfully, Diocletian—and Maximian, under pressure from him—abdicated, after appointing the two Caesars as the new Augusti, while Galerius as the senior nominated the new Caesars, choosing his own nephew Maximin as one, but passing over Constantine, the son of Constantius, and Maxentius, the son of Maximian. By fixing his own headquarters at Nicomedia, in Bithynia, he prepared the way for Constantine's transfer of the capital of the empire from Rome to Byzantium. He was responsible for the fiercest of all the persecutions of the Christians.

Our Course in Ancient and Medieval History is continued in Volume 4.

LESSON 11

Some Oddities Among Nouns and Verbs

I**N** Latin grammar many nouns have no plural—e.g. proper names and abstract nouns, and words like *argentum* (silver), *aurum* (gold), *ferrum* (iron), *aēr* (air), *aether* (sky) ; and many nouns have no singular—e.g. certain names of towns, as *Thēbae* (Thebes), *Athēnae* (Athens) ; parts of the body ; names of feasts or days, as *fēriae* (holiday), *nundinae* (market-day) ; and words like *dīvitiae* (riches), *līberī* (children), *mānēs* (ghosts), *penātēs* (household gods), *moenia* (town walls), *tenebrae* (darkness).

Some nouns change their meaning in the plural :

Singular.	*Plural.*
castrum, a fort	*castra*, a camp
aedēs, a temple	*aedēs*, a house
aqua, water	*aquae*, a watering-place
auxilium, assistance	*auxilia*, auxiliary troops
cōpia, plenty	*cōpiae*, supplies, troops
impedīmentum, a hindrance	*impedīmenta*, baggage
littera, a letter (of the alphabet)	*litterae*, an epistle
opem (acc.), help	*opēs*, resources
opera, work	*operae*, workmen
rōstrum, a beak	*rōstra*, the pulpit at Rome
lūdus, play	*lūdī*, public games
carcer, prison	*carcerēs*, the barriers (in horse races)

Many nouns are defective in case. The following, for instance, have no nominative : *dapem* (feast), *frūgem* (fruit), *opem* (help), *precem* (prayer), *vicem* (change). *Vis* (strength) is thus declined :

	Singular.	*Plural.*
N.V.	*vīs*	*vīrēs*
Acc.	*vim*	*vīrēs*
Gen.	(none)	*vīrium*
Dat.	(none)	*vīribus*
Abl.	*vī*	*vīribus*

(474)

ODDITIES IN NOUNS AND VERBS

Other defective nouns are *forte* (by chance [abl.]), *sponte* (by one's own choice [abl.]), *fās* (right), *nefās* (wrong), *nihil* (nothing), *opus* (need), *instar* (likeness), *necesse* (necessity), *māne* (morning). These are practically indeclinable.

The following list of nouns with their genitive singular and nominative plural will be useful. If these two cases of a noun are known, the whole noun can be declined : for if the nominative plural ends in *a*, the noun is neuter, and therefore the accusative will be the same as the nominative, both singular and plural.

Nom. singular.	Gen. singular.	Nom. plural.
pecūs, f. head of cattle	*pecudis*	*pecudēs*
pecus, n. cattle	*pecoris*	*pecora*
grūs, f. crane	*gruis*	*gruēs*
mūs, com. mouse	*mūris*	*mūrēs*
incūs, f. anvil	*incūdis*	*incūdēs*
vulgus, n. common people	*vulgī*	*vulga*
vīrus, n. poison	*vīrī*	*vīra*
tellūs, f. earth	*tellūris*	*tellūrēs*
supellēx, f. furniture	*supellēctilis*	*supellēctilēs*
vās, m. bail	*vadis*	*vadēs*
vās, n. vessel	*vāsis*	*vāsa*
pecten, m. comb	*pectinis*	*pectinēs*
cucumis, m. cucumber	*cucumeris*	*cucumerēs*
pulvis, m. dust	*pulveris*	*pulverēs*
cuspis, f. shield	*cuspidis*	*cuspidēs*
glis, m. dormouse	*glīris*	*glīrēs*
līs, f. lawsuit	*lītis*	*lītēs*
ōbex, com. bolt	*ōbicis*	*ōbicēs*
mās, m. male	*maris*	*marēs*
seges, f. crop	*segetis*	*segetēs*
merges, f. sheaf	*mergitis*	*mergitēs*
mercēs, f. reward	*mercēdis*	*mercēdēs*
hērēs, com. heir	*hērēdis*	*hērēdēs*
compēs, f. fetter	*compedis*	*compedēs*
carō, f. flesh	*carnis*	*carnēs*
margo, com. border	*marginis*	*marginēs*
cupīdo, f. desire	*cupīdinis*	*cupīdinēs*
pugio, m. dagger	*pugiōnis*	*pugiōnēs*
nex, f. death	*necis*	*necēs*
nix, f. snow	*nivis*	*nivēs*

Nom. singular.	Gen. singular.	Nom. plural.
senex, m. old man	senis	senēs
bōs, com. ox	bovis	bovēs
Jūpiter, m. Jupiter	Jovis	
iter, n. journey	itineris	itinera
jecur, n. liver	jecinoris (or jecoris)	jecinora
gigās, m. giant	gigantis	gigantēs
jūs, n. right	jūris	jūra
falx, f. scythe	falcis	falcēs
vātes, com. prophet	vātis	vātēs

NOTE. Bōs has genitive plural boum ; dative and ablative plural bōbus or būbus.

Rēspūblica (commonwealth) and jūsjūrandum (oath), decline both halves : accusative rempūblicam, genitive reīpūblicae, ablative rēpūblica (rēs is fifth declension like diēs). So, accusative jūsjūrandum, genitive jūrisjūrandī.

[The genitive and genders of other nouns can be looked up in the dictionary.]

Deponent Verbs. These are chiefly passive in form, but active in meaning—e.g. vēnor, vēnārī = to hunt ; ūtor, ūtī = to use. They are found in each of the four conjugations. They are conjugated like the passive voice of a verb of the same conjugation : thus, Vēnor (like amor), vēnārī, vēnātus sum. In the infinitive, however, they combine active and passive forms— e.g. Utor :

> Pres. infin. ūtī, to use
> Perf. infin. ūsus esse
> Fut. infin. ūsūrus esse
> Supines. ūsum, usū
> Pres. ptc. ūtens, using
> Perf. ptc. ūsus, having used
> Fut. ptc. ūsūrus
> Gerunds. ūtendum -ī, -ō
> Gerundive. ūtendus

The fact of their having a perfect participle with an active meaning makes them very useful for translating the English " having used," " having hunted," etc. Thus, for " having spoken thus, the queen died," if we use the deponent loquor, loquī, locūtus for " speak," we can say Ita locūta, rēgina mortua est. But if we used dīcō for " speak," we could not use dictus, which means " having been spoken." We should then have to say either (1) *hīs dictīs* (these things having been spoken, abl. abs.) *rēgīna mortua est ;* or (2) *quum ita dīxisset, rēgīna mortua est.*

Semi-deponent Verbs. A few verbs have an active present, and a perfect of passive form ; these are called " semi- or half-deponents " :

Audeō, I dare	Perf. *ausus sum,* I dared
Fīdō, I trust	„ *fīsus sum,* I trusted
Gaudeō, I rejoice	„ *gāvīsus sum,* I rejoiced
Soleō, I am wont	„ *solitus sum,* I was wont

KEY TO EXERCISE IN LESSON 10.

1. Quis primus de mortuo Caesare audivit ? 2. Bello contra Africanos confecto, milites domum in Britanniam rediverunt. 3. Patria nostra a Normannis anno millesimo sexagesimo sexto post Christum natum superata est. 4. Non est dubium quin sol sit major quam lunā (nom.), *or* lunā (ablative, without *quam*). 5. Fortior est quam qui *or* ut mortem timeat. 6. Ante nos sunt duae viae ; altera ad paupertatem et honesta (acc. neut. plu., honourable things), altera ad divitias et dedecus ducit : rogo utram deligatis. 7. Esto fidelis usque ad mortem, et dabo tibi coronam vitae. 8. Ille Brutius, quum araneam in antro observavisset, esse bono animo constituit.

LESSON 12

Further Uses of the Ablative

THE ablative is, more than any other, an adverbial case ; it is the case of circumstances which attend action and limit it adverbially. It answers the questions : Whence ? How ? From what cause ? When ? Where ?

1. The ablative of time answers the questions When ? Within what time ? How long before or after ? (Contrast this with the accusative of time, denoting *duration*—e.g. *decem* annis *post urbem conditam obiit* = he died 10 *years after* the founding of the city ; but *decem* annos *vixit* = he lived *for* 10 *years*.)

2. The ablative of place is used without a preposition, when the question is " By what road ? " or (of a town or small island) " Whence ? "—e.g. *Ibam forte* Via Sacra = I was going by chance

on the Sacred Road ; Corintho *fugit* = he fled *from Corinth ;* (So *domo* = from home ; *rure* = from the country).

Under this heading we may treat the locative case, practically obsolete in classical Latin, and largely replaced by the ablative. The locative answered the question Where ? and ended in *-i*— e.g. *domi*, at home ; *ruri*, in the country ; *humi*, on the ground ; *belli*, at the war. The ablative is always used for the locative in names of towns and small islands of the 3rd declension, and in plural names of towns of the 1st and 2nd declension—e.g. *Athenis*, at Athens ; *Neapoli*, at Naples. But if the town or small island is a singular noun of 1st or 2nd declension, the genitive is used— e.g. *Romae*, at Rome (old locative was *Romai*) *; Corinthi*, at Corinth.

3. The ablative of origin is used after verbs and participles— mostly, though not always, without a preposition—e.g. Jove *natus*, born *of Jupiter.*

4. The ablative of instrument and cause : e.g. *Boni oderunt peccare virtutis* amore = the good hate to sin *from love* of virtue (cause) ; gladio *interfectus est* = he was slain *with the sword* (instrument).

5. The ablative of the agent is used when the " instrument " is a person, not a thing—the preposition *a* or *ab* is necessary—e.g. *Caesar* a Bruto *pugione interfectus est* = Caesar was slain *by Brutus* with (i.e. by means of) a dagger. (But when " with " = together with, the preposition *cum* must be used—e.g. cum fratre meo *veni* = I came *with my brother*.)

6. The ablative of manner, being purely adverbial, is one of the commonest uses of the ablative—e.g. *Injuria fit* duobus modis, *aut* vi *aut* fraude = wrong is done *in two manners*, either *by force* or *by fraud.* Similarly, *hoc modo* = in this manner ; *casu* = by chance ; *consilio* = by design, on purpose ; *jure* = rightly, by right.

7. The ablative of quality and accompaniment is used : (*a*) Quality—e.g. *Senex* eximio ingenio = an old man *of wonderful ability.* (The noun in the ablative must have an adjective with it : we could not say " *senex ingenio*.") (*b*) Accompaniment— e.g. *hoc feci* summa diligentia = I have done this *with the utmost care.* (If we omitted the adjective, we should have to insert *cum* —e.g. *hoc feci* cum *diligentia*.)

8. The ablative of price is used with verbs of buying and selling, usually where some definite figure is given. (Otherwise, and

especially after verbs of valuing and esteeming, the genitive is used.) *Anulum* viginti nummis *vendidit* = he sold the ring for *twenty nummi*.

9. The ablative of measure—e.g. *Sol* multis partibus *major est quam luna* = the sun is *many times* (lit. *by many parts*) larger than the moon ; quo *citius*, eo *melius* = the sooner, the better (lit. *by what* the sooner, *by that* the better).

10. The ablative of comparison—e.g. *Puto mortem* dedecore *leviorem* = I think death easier *than disgrace.*

11. The ablative is used after the following : (*a*) Verbs : Abounding, filling, etc., and their opposites, depriving of, being without. Also the deponent verbs *fruor, fungor, utor, vescor, potior, dignor.* (It is really quite regular to have the ablative after these verbs ; *utor,* for example, means, " I serve myself *with,*" and so comes to mean " I use.") (*b*) Adjectives : *dignus* (worthy), *indignus* (unworthy), *fretus* (relying on), *contentus* (content with), *praeditus* (endowed with)—e.g. *laude dignissimus* = most worthy *of praise.* (*c*) Nouns : *opus* (need) and *usus* (use)—e.g. *opus est mihi* argento = I have need of silver.

The student should read a book of Caesar and a book of Virgil as early as possible. The following passage is from Virgil's " Aeneid," a history of the fall of Troy and the adventures of Aeneas thereafter. There are twelve books, and this passage is from Book II, lines 234–249. It describes the stratagem of the Wooden Horse (containing armed men), by which the Greeks brought about Troy's fall. The Trojans dragged the horse into their city as a prize of war, and in the night the Greeks hidden inside the horse emerged and opened the gates to their comrades outside. Aeneas is relating the events of the night. N.B. " And " is often translated by -*que* joined to the end of a word.

READING EXERCISE.

Dividimus muros, et moenia pandimus urbis.
Accingunt omnes operi, pedibusque rotarum (*a*)
Subjiciunt lapsus (*a*), et stuppea vincula collo
Intendunt.   Scandit fatalis machina muros
Feta armis.   Pueri circum innuptaeque puellae
Sacra canunt, funemque manu contingere gaudent.
Illa (*b*) subit, mediaeque minans inlabitur (*c*) urbi.
O patria, O divom (*d*) domus Ilium et incluta bello
Moenia Dardanidum ! quater ipso in limine portae
Substitit (*e*), atque utero sonitum quater arma dedere (*f*) :

Instamus, tamen, immemores, caecique furore,
Et monstrum infelix sacrata sistimus arce.
Nos delubra deum (g) miseri, quibus ultimus esset
Ille dies, festa velamus fronde per urbem.

NOTES. (a) *Lapsus rotarum* = gliding wheels, or rollers
(literally, glidings of wheels ; *lapsus* is acc. pl., 4th decl., and is
direct object to *subjiciunt ; pedibus* is indirect object, and therefore dative). (b) *Illa* = it, i.e. *machina* : nom. fem. sing. (c)
Inlabitur, though passive in form, is active in meaning : a deponent
verb. (d) *Divom* = *divorum* = *deorum*. (e) Perfect of *subsisto*.
(f) = *dederunt*. (g) *Deum* is often used for *deorum*, gen. pl.

ENGLISH TRANSLATION.

We sunder the walls, and lay open the fortifications of the city.
All gird themselves for the work, and put rolling wheels under its
(i.e. the wooden horse's) feet, and fasten hempen bands on its
neck. The fated engine climbs the walls, big with arms. Around
it boys and unwedded girls sing hymns, and rejoice to touch the
rope with their hand (i.e. to help to pull the horse into the city).
It approaches and glides threatening into the midst of the city.
O native land ! O Ilium (Troy), home of the gods, and fortresses
of the Dardanidae (Trojans) renowned in war ! Four times in the
very gateway did it halt, and four times the arms rattled (literally,
gave a sound) in its womb. Yet we press on, unmindful and blind
with frenzy, and plant the ill-omened monster in our sacred
citadel. We deck the shrines of the gods throughout the city with
festal foliage, wretched people, to whom that day was our last.

LESSON 13

The Dative Case and Anomalous Verbs

IN Latin syntax, the dative is often used after the gerundive
participle in *-dus* (and sometimes after other passive
participles) where we should expect the ablative of the
agent with the prep. *ab* : e.g. *hoc mihi faciendum est* = this is to be
done (must be done) by me. The predicative dative—that which
a thing or person serves as, or occasions—is much used with *sum*,
do, *duco*, and (especially with military terms, *auxilio*, *praesidio*,
subsidio) with verbs of motion : e.g. *quinque cohortes castris*

THE DATIVE AND ANOMALOUS VERBS

praesidio reliquit, he left five cohorts as a guard to the camp ; *quae res saluti nobis fuit*, which thing was for a safety to us, i.e. saved us ; *ipse sibi odio erit*, he will be an object of hatred to himself, lit., he will be for a hatred.

Impedimento esse = to be a hindrance.

Detrimento esse = to be hurtful, etc.

The dative is sometimes used where we should use a possessive pronoun or the genitive, to give greater emphasis to the person mentioned : *tum Pompeio ad pedes se projecerunt* = then they threw themselves at Pompey's feet.

The dative is used after several verbs. With *sum* it denotes possession : *sunt nobis mitia poma* = we have ripe apples. All the compounds of *sum* (except *possum*) take a dative.

Verbs signifying to aid, favour, obey, please, profit, injure, oppose, displease, command, persuade, trust, spare, envy, be angry, etc., take the dative, because they are really intransitive : e.g. *parce pio generi* = spare a pious race, lit., " be sparing to." *Jubeo* (I order), however, takes the accusative.

These verbs that take a dative cannot be used personally in the passive, but only impersonally : e.g. *mihi persuasum est* = I have been persuaded, lit., it has been persuaded to me.

A few impersonal verbs take a dative : *libet* (it pleases), *licet* (it is lawful), *accidit* (it happens), etc. : e.g. *libet mihi* = I am pleased, lit., it is pleasing to me.

Anomalous Verbs. In grammar these are verbs that do not form all their parts according to rule. The following are the most common : *possum* (*pote sum*) = I am able ; *volō* = I wish ; *nōlō* (*ne-volō*) = I am unwilling ; *mālō* (*magis-volō*) = I prefer ; *ferō* = I bear ; *fīō* = I am made, I become (used as the passive of *faciō*, I make) ; *eō* = I go ; *queō* and *nequeō* = I can and I cannot ; *edō* = I eat.

INDICATIVE MOOD.
PRESENT.

Sing.	Plur.	Sing.	Plur.
1. possum	possumus	1. nōlō	nōlumus
2. potes	potestis	2. nōnvīs	nōnvultis
3. potest	possunt	3. nōnvult	nōlunt
1. volŏ	volumus	1. mālō	mālumus
2. vīs	vultis	2. māvīs	māvultis
3. vult	volunt	3. māvult	mālunt

(481)

Sing.	Plur.		Sing.	Plur.		Sing.	Plur.
1. eō	īmus		1. ferō	ferimus		1. fīō	—
2. īs	ītis		2. fers	fertis		2. fis	—
3. it	eunt		3. fert	ferunt		3. fit	fīunt

FUTURE SIMPLE.

Pot-	..erō	eris	erit	erimus	eritis	erunt
Vol-						
Nōl-						
Māl-	am	es	et	ēmus	ētis	ent
Fer-						
Fī-						
I-	..bō	bis	bit	bimus	bitis	bunt

IMPERFECT.

Pot-	..eram	erās	erat	erāmus	erātis	erant
Vole-						
Nōle-						
Māle-	bam	bās	bat	bāmus	bātis	bant
Fere-						
Fīe-						
I-						

PERFECT, FUTURE PERF., AND PLUPERF.

Potu-							
Volu-	1. ī	istī	it	imus	istis	ērunt
Nōlu-							or ērē
Mālu-	2. erō	eris	erit	erimus	eritis	erint
Tul-							
———	3. eram	erās	erat	erāmus	erātis	erant
Iv-							

SUBJUNCTIVE MOOD.
PRESENT.

Poss-						
Vel-						
Nōl-	im	īs	it	īmus	ītis	int
Māl-						
Fer-						
Fī-	am	ās	at	āmus	ātis	ant
E-						

IMPERFECT.

Poss- Vell- Nōll- Māll- Ferr- Fier- Ir-	em	ēs	et	ēmus	ētis	ent

PERFECT AND PLUPERFECT.

Potu- Volu- Nōlu- Mālu- Tul- —— Iv-	1. erim	eris	erit	erimus	eritis	erint	
	2. issem	issēs	isset		issēmus	issētis	
							issent

IMPERATIVE MOOD.

Possum, volō, mālō, have none.

PRESENT.		FUTURE.		
2nd Sing.	2nd Pl.	2nd Sing.	2nd Pl.	3rd Pl.
nōlī	nōlīte	nōlītō	nōlītōte	nōluntō
fer	ferte	fertō	fertōte	feruntō
fī	fīte	—	—	—
ī	īte	ītō	ītōte	euntō

INFINITIVE MOOD.

PRESENT.	PRES. PTC.	SUPINES.
posse	potens (used as adj. = powerful)	—
velle	volens	—
nōlle	nolens	—
mālle		—
ferre	ferens	lātum, lātū
fierī		—
īre	iens (genitive euntis)	itum, itū

PERFECT PARTICIPLE PASSIVE.

Fiō and ferō have perf. ptc. pass. *factus* and *lātus*. *Factus*
is used with *sum*, etc., to form the perfect tenses of *fiō*.

Feror (passive of *ferō*) has pres. indic.: 2. *ferris*. 3. *fertur*.

Queō and *nequeō :* conjugated like *eō*, so far as regards the forms that are found. Cicero uses *non queō* instead of *nequeō* in 1st pers. pres. indic.

Edō (I eat) often changes some of its forms :

IND. PRES.	IND. PRES.
2nd Pers. Sing.	*3rd Pers. Sing.*
edis or *ēs*	*edit* or *ēst*

INFINITIVE.
edere or *esse.*

LESSON 14

The Genitive Case

IN Latin syntax the genitive case denotes : 1. Possession : this is the simplest and most natural use of the genitive : *Caesaris uxor* = Caesar's wife. The gen. sing. of a substantive is often used as a predicate with a copulative verb, to denote such English ideas as nature, token, function, duty, part, mark, etc. : *sapientis est tempori cedere* = it is (the mark) of a wise man to yield to circumstances ; *cujusvis* (gen. of *quivis*) *hominis est errare* = any man may err.

2. The relation of whole to part : partitive genitive : *multi vestrum* = many of you ; *fortissimus Graecorum* = the bravest of the Greeks ; *duo horum* = two of these. Often used after the neut. sing. of adjectives and pronouns expressing quantity or degree, and with *nihil* (nothing), *satis* (enough), *parum* (too little) ; e.g. *parum prudentiae* = too little prudence.

Also used after some adverbs, *quo, eo, tum, ubi,* etc. ; e.g. *ubi gentium* = where in the world ? (*lit.,* where of nations ?) ; *eo ferocitatis* = to such a pitch of savagery.

NOTES. (*a*) The whole of the city = *tota urbs* (not *totum urbis*) ; all of us = *nos omnes*, i.e. we all. For in these circumstances we are not dealing with a part. (*b*) It is equally good Latin to say " *viginti e suis servis misit* " (he sent twenty of his slaves) as to say " *viginti servorum misit.*"

3. Quality or definition. This is very like the ablative of quality, and the substantive in the genitive is always accompanied by an adjective : *homo infimi generis* = a man of the

lowest race ; *vir summae fortitudinis* = a man of the highest courage ; *puer sedecim annorum* = a boy of sixteen years.

4. Price. Used especially with verbs of valuing and esteeming, confined to *pluris, minoris, tanti, quanti* (and their compounds), *magni, maximi, parvi, minimi* (probably through confusion with the old locative, which was the case used in expressions of value) ; e.g. *parvi sunt foris arma, nisi est consilium domi* = of little value are arms abroad, unless there is a policy at home.

5. The genitive is used after verbs and adjectives signifying power and impotence, innocence, condemnation, acquittal, memory and forgetfulness, and compassion ; e.g. *parricidii eum incusat* = he taxes him with parricide ; *alii reminiscentes veteris famae, aetatis miserabantur* = others, remembering their former renown, pitied their age.

Subjective and Objective Genitives. Such a phrase as " the love of children," is capable of two meanings : (1) children's love for us, in which case " of children " is subjective genitive ; (2) our love for children when " children " is objective genitive. Both genitives may be combined in a single phrase : *Helvetiorum injuriae populi Romani* = the wrongs done by the Helvetii (subjective) to the Roman people (objective).

EXERCISE.

Put the following into English, using a dictionary if necessary :

Si linguis hominum loquar et angelorum, caritatem autem non habeam, factus sum aes resonans aut cymbalum tinniens. Et si habeam prophetiam et noverim mysteria omnia, omnemque cognitionem, et si habeam totam fidem, adeo ut montes transferam, caritatem autem non habeam, nihil sum. Et si insumam *alendis egenis* (*a*) omnia quae mihi suppetunt, et si tradam corpus meum ut comburar, caritatem autem non habeam, hoc nihil mihi *prodest* (*b*). Caritas iram cohibet, benigna est caritas, non invidet caritas, non agit perperam, non inflatur : non agit indecore, non quaerit quae sua sunt, non exacerbatur, non cogitat malum. Non gaudet injustitia, gratulatur autem veritati ; omnia tegit, omnia credit, omnia sperat, omnia sustinet : caritas nunquam excidit : sed et prophetiae evanescent, et linguae cessabunt, et cognitio evanescet. Ex parte enim cognoscimus, et ex parte prophetamus. Postquam autem advenerit quod perfectum est, tunc quod est aliquatenus, *ut*(*c*) inutile, tolletur. Quum essem infans, ut infans loquebar, ut infans sapiebam, ut infans ratiocinabar : postquam

autem factus sum vir, ut inutilia *sustuli* (*d*) quae infantis erant.
Cernimus enim nunc per speculum et per aenigma, tunc autem
coram cernemus : nunc novi aliquatenus, tunc vero amplius
cognoscam, prout amplius edoctus fuero. Nunc vero manet fides,
spes, caritas, tria haec : maxima autem harum caritas.

NOTES. (*a*) dative of gerundive = for feeding the needy.
(*b*) from *prosum, prodesse, profui*. (*c*) *Ut* with indic., or used
without a verb, means " as." (*d*) perfect of *tollo* (borrowed from
suffero). [For English of the above passage, see 1 Cor. xiii.]

There are no actual words for yes and no in Latin. An affirmative answer is expressed by *etiam, ita, factum, vero, verum, sane, ita
vero, ita est, sane quidem*, etc., or by the proper pronoun, as *ego
vero* ; or by the verb repeated in the proper person : e.g. *sentio*.
A negative answer is expressed by *non minime, minime vero ;* or
with the pronoun, *minime ego quidem* ; or with the verb, *non
sentio*. When the contrary is asserted by way of reply, we have
immo, immo vero, " No, on the other hand." " Nay rather."

EXERCISE.

Turn the following sentences into Latin, and then correct them
by the translation given below.

1. Do you think (begin the question with *Num*) God to be like
me (genitive, after *similis*), or you ? Certainly you do not think
so. What then ? Am I to call the sun or the moon or the sky
God ? No. assuredly not. 2. Why do you not enjoy what you
have bought (say " the bought things," perf. ptc. pass. of *emo*) ?
Because I have bought them very dear. 3. I was persuaded to
remain ten days at Cicero's house. 4. What is harder than a
rock ? What is softer than a wave ? 5. He had come to such a
pitch of boldness that (*ut*) he was unwilling to obey the general.
6. In a State those who have no wealth (say, those to whom
there are no resources) envy the good (citizens).

TRANSLATION.

1. Num tu mei similem putas esse aut tui deum ? Profecto non
putas. Quid ergo ? Solem dicam aut lunam aut coelum deum ?
Minime vero. 2. Cur non emptis (*abl. after* fruor) frueris ? Quod
(*or* quia) maximi (*or* maximo) emi. 3. Mihi persuasum est ut
decem dies apud Ciceronem manerem. 4. Quid est durius saxo,
quid mollius unda ? 5. Eo audaciae venerat ut imperatori parere
nollet. 6. In civitate, quibus opes nullae sunt, bonis invident.

Our Course in Latin is continued in Volume 4.

LESSON 21

Mathematical Scales and Sequences

PROBABLY one of the chief conceptions which mathematical methods have supplied to Mankind is the notion of scales and sequences along those scales. One of the commonest scales is considered below. By actual division we get the following identities :

(i) $\dfrac{1 - x^2}{1 - x} = 1 + x = \dfrac{x^2 - 1}{x - 1}$

(ii) $\dfrac{1 - x^3}{1 - x} = 1 + x + x^2 = \dfrac{x^3 - 1}{x - 1}$

(iii) $\dfrac{1 - x^4}{1 - x} = 1 + x + x^2 + x^3 = \dfrac{x^4 - 1}{x - 1}$

(iv) (generally) $\dfrac{1 - x^n}{1 - x} = 1 + x + x^2 \ldots\ldots\ldots$

$\ldots\ldots + x^{n-1} = \dfrac{x^n - 1}{x - 1}$

(v) $\dfrac{1 + x^3}{1 + x} = 1 - x + x^2 = \dfrac{x^3 + 1}{x + 1}$

(vi) $\dfrac{1 + x^5}{1 + x} = 1 - x + x^2 - x^3 + x^4 = \dfrac{x^5 + 1}{x + 1}$

(vii) (generally) $\dfrac{1 + x^{2n+1}}{1 + x} = 1 - x + x^2 - x^3 \ldots$

$\ldots\ldots + x^{2n} = \dfrac{x^{2n+1} + 1}{x + 1}$

Obviously, the first four identities indicate that the sum of n terms in the sequence $1 + x + x^2 + x^3$ is either $\dfrac{x^4 - 1}{x - 1}$ or $\dfrac{1 - x^4}{1 - x}$; and obviously, when x is less than 1, i.e. $1 > x$, then each term in the sequence is smaller (actually one-xth part) of the preceding term, so that the final term x^{n-1} is very tiny when n is large.

Hence we say that at the limit of experience $1 - x^n = 1$. Hence

$$\frac{1}{1-x} = 1 + x + x^2 + x^3 + x^4 \ldots\ldots + x^a \ldots\ldots + x^b \ldots\ldots$$

$+ x^{n-1}$ when $1 > x$. x^4 is the fifth term. x^a is the $(a+1)th$ term, x^b is the $(b+1)th$ term, and x^{n-1} is the nth, or limiting term, which equals zero at the limit of experience.

Obviously, similarly, $\dfrac{1 + x^{2n+1}}{1 + x}$ is the sum of a sequence which terminates at x^{2n}, and $\dfrac{1}{1 + x} = 1 - x + x^2 - x^3 \ldots\ldots$ carried to infinity, the limit when $1 > x$.

Actual division shows that :

(viii) $\dfrac{1 + x^2}{1 + x} = 1 - x + 2x^2 - 2x^3 + 2x^4 \ldots\ldots$ which stops only at the limit ;
and, similarly,

(ix) $\dfrac{1 + x^4}{1 + x} = 1 - x + x^2 - x^3 + 2x^4 - 2x^5 + 2x^6 - 2x^7 \ldots$
and, generally,

(x) $\dfrac{1 + x^{2n}}{1 + x} = 1 - x + x^2 - x^3 \ldots\ldots - x^{2n-1} + 2x^{2n} - 2x^{2n+1} \ldots\ldots$

These sequences are of the form :

$(1 - x + x^2 - x^3 \ldots\ldots - x^{2n-1}) + 2x^{2n} (1 - x + x^2 - x^3 \ldots\ldots)$

which equals $\dfrac{1 + x^{2n-2}}{1 + x} + 2x^{2n}\left(\dfrac{1}{1 + x}\right)$

i.e. $\dfrac{1}{1 + x} (1 + x^{2n-2} + 2x^{2n})$

Thus we obtain three sequences :

(a) $\dfrac{1 - x^n}{1 - x} = 1 + x + x^2 \ldots\ldots + x^{n-1}$

(b) $\dfrac{1 + x^{2n+1}}{1 + x} = 1 - x + x_2 - x^3 \ldots\ldots + x^{2n}$

(c) $\dfrac{1 + x^{2n}}{1 + x} = 1 - x + x^2 - x^3 \ldots\ldots - x^{2n-1} + 2x^{2n} - 2x^{2n+1} \ldots\ldots$

The differences between successive terms of sequence (a) are : $(x - 1)$, $x(x - 1)$, $x^2(x - 1)$, $x^3(x - 1)$. If the ath term is x^{a-1} then the $(a + 1)th$ term is x^a, and the difference between them is $x^{a-1}(x - 1)$. From this it follows that we can infer from the differences to the original sequence and conversely: e.g. a difference $x^6(x - 1)$ is the $7th$ term in the sequence of differences, and is the difference between the $7th$ and $8th$ terms in the original sequence ; these are respectively x^6 and x^7.

If x equal a number, say 3, then the sequences are :

       original   1   3 9 27 81........

       differences   2 6 18 54 ....

i.e. the differences sequence is twice the original sequence. $486 = 3^5(3 - 1)$. It is therefore the $6th$ term in the difference sequence ; whence $486 = 3^6 - 3^5$. This is merely a simple illustration of the relation between the two sequences and of the sort of inference which may be drawn ; of these matters more later in the Course.

Approximations. Since when $1 > x$, $\dfrac{1}{1 - x} = 1 + x + x^2......$

it follows when x is very small that $\dfrac{1}{1 - x} = 1 + x$ (approx.) e.g.

$1 \div 0.999 = 1.001$; $3 \div 2.985 = 1 \div 0.995 = 1.005$. Similarly, $1 \div 1.001 = 0.999$; $1 \div 1.006 = 0.994$. More roughly, i.e. with less accuracy, $1 \div 1.01 = 0.99$; and $6497 \div 6503 = 1.08283 \div 1.08338 = 1 \div 1.00055 = 0.99945$.

Cube Roots. The student should refer back to Lessons 12 to 15 (volume 2, pages 470–498).

$(a + b)^3 = a^3 + 3a^2b + 3ab^2 + b^3$.

Hence the difference between $(a + b)^3$ and a^3 is $3a^2b + 3ab^2 + b^3 = (3a^2 + 3ab + b^2)b$. This is the basis of a method of extracting cube roots : e.g. to find the cube root of 400. $7^3 = 343$, $8^3 = 512$.

Hence it is estimated that $\sqrt[3]{400} = 7.4$ approx.

		400	
7		343	
		57	000
trial divisor		46	007
$3 \times 70^2 = 14700$		10	993

14700 into 57000 = 3
whence a = 70, b = 3.

$$3a^2 = 14700$$
$$3ab = 630$$
$$b^2 = 9$$

$$15339$$
$$3$$

$$46017$$

trial divisor

$3 \times 730^2 = 1598700$

	10	993	000
	9	671	256
	1	322	744

1598700 into 10993000 = 6
whence a = 730
       b = 6

$$3a^2 = 1598700$$
$$2ab = 13140$$
$$b^2 = 36$$

$$1611876$$
$$6$$

$$9671256$$

	1	322	744	000
	1	275	368	409
		47	375	591

trial divisor

$3 \times 7360^2 = 141508800$

$$\frac{1322744}{140708} = 9.04$$

and
hence next figure = 9
$3a^2 + 3ab + b^2$ (by division)
$= 141707601$
Hence : $400^{\frac{1}{3}} = 7.36904$

CHECK. $\log 400 = 2.6021$; $\log 400^{\frac{1}{3}} = \frac{1}{3}(2.6021) = 0.8674 = \log 7.369$.

Drill. 1. Simplify, approximately :

(i) $\dfrac{1}{1.007}$; (ii) $\dfrac{1}{0.9991}$; (iii) $\dfrac{4718}{4723}$; (iv) $\dfrac{£6-12-5}{£6-13-1}$.

2. Expand the sequence 4, 12, 36, 108, to the 8*th* term. Find which term in the correlated differences sequence is 648. Hence find an expression for 648 in terms of the original sequence.

3. Find the cube roots of 40 and 4.

Revision. 1. During sale time goods are to be marked down by $17\frac{3}{4}\%$ off the marked prices then ruling, which are 3s. 11d.; 6s. 11d.; 9s. 11d.; and so on, the shillings being successive multiples of 3.

Make a scale of the original and the reduced prices.

2. Given that 1 inch = 2·54 cm., with an error of less than 1 in a million; find the approximate percentage error in the following equivalents: 12 yards = 11 metres; 1 chain = 20 metres; 5 miles = 8 kilometres; 1 acre = 4 decares; 6 sq. yards = 5 sq. metres; 4 cu. yards = 3 cu. metres; $62\frac{1}{2}$ m.p.h. = 100 kilometres per hour.

Expansion. 1. Apply the ideas of approximation given in the Lesson and simplify approximately:

(i) $(1·0025)^2$; $(1·007)^3$; $\dfrac{1}{(1·0031)^4}$

(ii) $\dfrac{9·684}{8·934}$; (iii) $£497 (1·004)^3 - 1)$.

2. In a pack of cards there are four aces, four kings, four queens, four jacks. (a) Find the total number of combinations of four of these court cards, one of each kind, so that each combination is different from every other; (b) How many possible combinations of four court cards would contain two of each value?

Solutions to Problems in Lesson 20.

Exercises. 1. $r = \sqrt{A}\sqrt{\dfrac{1}{\pi}}$; $A = 100$;

$\sqrt{A} = 10$; $\sqrt{\dfrac{1}{\pi}} = 0·5641$; $r = 5·6$

$A = \pi 225$ or $\pi 529$ ratio of areas 225 : 529 or 1 : 2·35 approx. Sequences: e.g. If $r = 1·28$, $A = \pi (1·28)^2 = 5·145$ the sequences are valid within 1%.

2. $r = \sqrt[3]{V}.\sqrt[3]{\dfrac{3}{4\pi}} = \sqrt[3]{1000}\sqrt[3]{\dfrac{3}{4\pi}} = 10 \times 0·62$; i.e. $r = 6·2$

$r = \sqrt[3]{\dfrac{3}{4\pi}}. V$ or $\sqrt[3]{\dfrac{3}{4\pi}.2V}$ i.e. in the ratio of 1 to $\sqrt[3]{2}$ i.e. 1 : 1·26

Sequences : e.g. If $r = 1.47$, $V = \frac{4\pi}{3} (1.47)^3 = 1.33$ the sequences are valid within 1%.

Revision. 1. $2 = (1.05)^n$; whence $n = \frac{0.3010}{0.0212}$ (by logs) = 15 approx.

2. $2500 = P(1.06)^4$ whence log $P = 3.3979 - 4 (0.0253) = 3.2967$; i.e. $P = 1980$.

3. £4 so invested would be worth on the dates named, 1.04 ; 1.0816 ; 1.124864 ; 1.16985856—i.e. $4.41632256 = 4.416$ approx.

Ans. : Present worth $= \frac{400}{£1.104} = £362.3 = £362$.

Expansion. 1. $3^2 + 4^2 + 12^2 = 5^2 + 12^2 = 13^2$.
also $9^2 + 12^2 = 15^2$ and $8^2 + 15^2 = 17^2$.
hence 17 is diagonal to 8 by 9 by 12.

2. Slabs cut vertically from a solid of uniform height are equal in volume if their bases are equal in area.

LESSON 22

More About Solids

ONE of the fundamental capacities is to be able to see solids from flat sketches or diagrams. This Lesson is devoted to one method of using this capacity for purposes of investigation. A regular tetrahedron is a solid with four faces, each an equilateral triangle. Imagine a cube (Fig. 1) with six diagonals AB, BC, CD, DA, DB, CA marked on the faces ; these are the six edges of a tetrahedron.

Imagine that a knife cut along the triangle DCB and the piece were taken away ; it would look like Fig. 2. This piece is a triangular pyramid with its base an equilateral triangle and each of the other three sides half a square. Imagine that the other three pieces were similarly cut away, leaving the tetrahedron. The four pieces like Fig. 2 have corners from the corners of the cube : they can be built up as in Fig. 3.

They will build into a square pyramid with the four " cube " corners touching at O (Fig. 3), with four equilateral faces like BCD. But Fig. 3 is obviously half an octahedron; for a vertex below the square base would give four other equilateral triangles and so the square base would be obscured and only the eight equal faces would be visible.

Conclusion 1. A cube can be split into a tetrahedron and half an octahedron with equal faces, each side of which equals in length a diagonal across the face of the cube.

Now imagine Fig. 4, which is a tetrahedron with each edge twice as long as that of the tetrahedron in Fig. 1 (HG = 2 AB). In each edge find the middle point (M, N, P, etc.). Imagine a

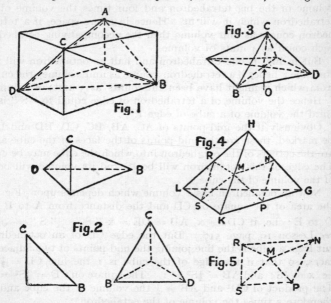

cut is made along MPS and the piece MPKS be taken away : it is a tetrahedron just the size of the tetrahedron of Fig. 1.

Three other tetrahedra—one for each of the other corners—can be similarly cut away. When this has been done the solid which is left is like Fig. 5 to look at. RMS and MNP are quarters of the faces HKL and HKG respectively. RMN and MSP are two cut faces. There are two other faces like RMS, one a quarter of HLG and the other a quarter of LGK ; there are, also, two other cut faces like RMN. That is, there are eight faces each an equilateral triangle, i.e. Fig. 5 is a frontal sketch of an octahedron.

Conclusion 2.   A tetrahedron can be cut into one octahedron and four tetrahedra, each edge of which is half the edge of the original tetrahedron.

Conclusion 3.   Tetrahedra and octahedra with equal faces can be used to fill space just as cubes can.

But in Fig. 4 the volume of the big tetrahedron is eight times the volume of a little tetrahedron ; i.e. the octahedron is half the volume of the big tetrahedron and four times the volume of a tetrahedron which it will fit.   Hence in filling space, if a tetrahedron counts as unit volume then the accompanying octahedra each count as 4 units of volume.

But in Fig. 1, one tetrahedron and half an octahedron will fill the cube ; hence if a tetrahedron counts as unit volume, the cube from which it might have been cut counts as 3 units of volume.

Hence the volume of a tetrahedron of edge equal to " S " is a third the volume of a cube of edge 1.

Obviously if the mid-points of AC, AB, BC, CD, BD and DA be marked, these are the mid-points of the faces of the cube and are the corners of the octahedron into which the cube may be cut. The edge of this octahedron will be $\frac{1}{2}$S and its volume will be $\frac{1}{6}$ of the volume of the cube.

Now an octahedron has a volume which depends upon (Fig. 6) the area of the square on CD and the distance from A to B = D to E ; i.e. if CD = x, AB = DE = x " S." [" S " = $\sqrt{2}$; *see* Lesson 19, page 517.]   But the edge CD of an octahedron cut from a cube is the line joining the mid-points of two adjacent faces, so that if the edge of the cube is 1 the line CD = $\frac{1}{2}$S : i.e. x = $\frac{1}{2}$S ; and AB = $\frac{1}{2}$S² = 1.   The square on CD = $\frac{1}{4}$S² = $\frac{1}{2}$. The product of CD² and AB = $\frac{1}{2}$ the volume of the cube and is therefore 3 times the volume of the octahedron.

Conclusion 4.   The volume of a square pyramid with equilateral triangle faces is one-third the product of the area of the square base and the vertical height of the pyramid.

Skeleton Cubes, etc.   Four wires of equal length appropriately joined and soldered will make a square.   Twelve such wires joined and soldered will make a skeleton cube.

Cut six wires each equal to a diagonal of the square.   These six wires suitably joined and soldered will make a tetrahedron.

Cut twelve wires each equal to half the diagonal of a square.

(494)

These twelve wires can be joined to make an octahedron. The octahedron will fit into the tetrahedron which, in turn, will fit into the cube.

Paper Cubes, etc. Draw two squares one on either side of the line HK; cut out and fold along HK as in Fig. 7. Three folders of this size will make a cube.

Draw HN equal to the diagonal of HMNK. Draw two equilateral triangles one on either side of HN; cut out and fold along HN as in Fig. 8. Two folders of this size will make a

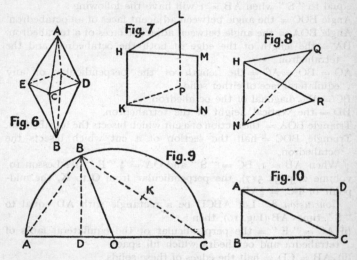

tetrahedron which will fit into the cube. When they do QR = HN.

Draw a smaller folder as in Fig. 8, with the fold half the size of HN. Four such folders will make an octahedron which will fit into the tetrahedron. When they do the line QR = HK, the edge of the cube into which they will fit.

Let us call a folder like Fig. 8 a "butterfly" folder. Then when QR = HN, the four points H, N, Q, R of the butterfly are the corners of a tetrahedron. Then, further, when QR = HN times "S" the four points H, N, Q, R are four of the six corner points of an octahedron.

Conclusion 5. In a butterfly folder when QR = HN, the angle between the butterfly wings is the angle between two adjacent faces of a tetrahedron.

Conclusion 6   In a butterfly folder when QR = HN times " S," the angle between the butterfly wings is the angle between two adjacent faces of an octahedron.

Conclusion 7.   The angle between two adjacent faces of a tetrahedron plus the angle between two adjacent faces of an octahedron equals two right angles.

Hence (Fig. 9) a semicircle ABC with centre O and with BC equal to " S " when AB = 1 will have the following :

Angle BOC = the angle between adjacent faces of an octahedron.

Angle BOA = the angle between adjacent faces of a tetrahedron.

BA = the length of the edge of both the octahedron and the tetrahedron.

AO = BO = AC = the length of the perpendicular of any equilateral face of either solid.

BC = the diagonal of the octahedron.

BD = the vertical height of the tetrahedron.

Triangle BOA = the section of a cut which bisects the tetrahedron.

Triangle BOC = half the section of a cut which bisects the octahedron.

When AB = 1, BC = " S " and OA = $\frac{1}{2}$ " E " (*see* Lesson 19, volume 2, page 517), the perpendicular from O to K, the mid-point of BC, = $\frac{1}{2}$AB.

Conclusion 8.   Let ABCD be a rectangle with AD equal to " S " times AB (Fig. 10), then :

(i) AC = " E " = the perpendicular of the equilateral faces of tetrahedra and octahedra which fill space.

(ii) AB = CD = half the edges of these solids.

(iii) AD = BC = half the diagonal of the octahedron.

(iv) Angle ACD = half the angle between the faces of the octahedron.

(v) Angle ACB = half the angle between the faces of the tetrahedron.

(vi) The rectangle ABCD = half the cut face of a cube which is bisected by being cut by a plane through any two parallel edges each equal to AD, so that AB is half the diagonal of a face of the cube.

Conclusion 9.   The essential sizes of the edge. and angles of cubes, octahedra, tetrahedra, involve the quantities 1 (unity), " S," " E," and do not require measurements upon any scale of lengths, areas, or volumes, or angles. The related measurements are all transcendental quantities.

Revision. 1. Simplify :

(i) $\dfrac{1 - \sqrt{2} + \sqrt{3}}{1 + \sqrt{2} + \sqrt{3}} - \dfrac{1 - \sqrt{2} - \sqrt{3}}{1 + \sqrt{2} - \sqrt{3}}$

(ii) $\left(a - \sqrt{2} + \dfrac{1}{a}\right)\left(a + \sqrt{2} + \dfrac{1}{a}\right)\left(a^2 + 2 + \dfrac{1}{a^2}\right)$

(iii) $\dfrac{4\sqrt{2} - 3\sqrt{3}}{7\sqrt{2} - 4\sqrt{3}} \times \dfrac{4 + \sqrt{6}}{7\sqrt{2} - 2\sqrt{3}}$ (iv) $\dfrac{3 + \sqrt{3}}{3 - \sqrt{3}}$

2. Find factors for :

(i) $20\,m^2 - m - 30$ (ii) $m^4 - 1 - 4\,(m - 1)$

(iii) $d^8 + d^4e^4 + e^8$.

3. Show that :

(i) $\tan \tfrac{1}{2}\,(A + B) = \dfrac{\sin A + \sin B}{\cos A + \cos B}$

(ii) $\dfrac{\sin 3\phi - \sin \phi}{\cos 3\phi + \cos \phi} = \tan \phi$

4. Solve the equations :

(i) $6x + y = 3a + 36$
$y - x = \tfrac{1}{2}x$

(ii) $\dfrac{x - m}{p - m} = \dfrac{y + p}{p + m}$

$\dfrac{x + m}{m - p} = \dfrac{y - p}{p + m}$

Expansion. 1. Given that $(\tfrac{1}{2}\sqrt{5} - \tfrac{1}{2}) = p$, find expressions in terms of " p " and whole numbers for :

(i) $(\tfrac{1}{2}\sqrt{5} - \tfrac{1}{2})$ $(\tfrac{1}{2}\sqrt{5} + \tfrac{1}{2})$; (ii) $(\tfrac{1}{2}\sqrt{5} + \tfrac{1}{2})^2$;

(iii) $\dfrac{1}{\tfrac{1}{2}\sqrt{5} + \tfrac{1}{2}}$; (iv) $\dfrac{1}{(\tfrac{1}{2}\sqrt{5} + \tfrac{1}{2})^2}$; (v) $\sqrt{5}$; (vi) $5 + 2\sqrt{5}$.

2. Given that $(m + n)^2 = m^2 + 2mn + n^2$, and that the sides of any triangle ABC are AB = c, BC = a, CA = b and angle BAC = A, show that $a^2 = b^2 + c^2 \pm 2bc \cos A$, finding the conditions when the + or − sign applies. [*Hint.* Drop a perpendicular, p, from C to the side BA.]

Solutions to Problems in Lesson 21

Drill 1 (i) ·993 ; (ii) 1·0009 ; (iii) ·999   (iv) $\dfrac{1589}{1597} = $ .995·

2, 4, 12, 36, 108, 324, 972, 2916, 8748. (Diff. seq.) 8, 24, 72, 216, etc.

648 = 5th term

648 = 972 — 324. 3. $\sqrt[3]{40}$ = 3·4199. $\sqrt[3]{4}$ = 1·5868

Revision. 1.

100	400	50	450	45	36	110
82·25	329	41·125	370$\frac{1}{8}$	37$\frac{7}{80}$	29·61	90·475

3 shillings down to 29·61 pence.

11 pence down to 9·0475 pence.

3s. 11d.	6s. 11d.	9s. 11d.	12s. 11d.	etc.
3–2$\frac{3}{4}$	5–8$\frac{1}{4}$	8–2	10–7$\frac{1}{2}$	etc.

2. 12 yards = 36 × 2·54 × 12 = 1097·28 cm. = 10·97 m.
= 11 m. % error ·3, about $\frac{1}{3}$.

1 ch. = 22 yards = 20·1168 m. = 20 m. % error ·6, about $\frac{2}{3}$.

5 miles = 8·047 km. = 8 km. % error ·6, about $\frac{3}{5}$.

1 ac. = 4·047 dekares = 4 dekares. % error 1·2.

6 sq. yards = 5·0167 sq. m. = 5 sq. m. % error $\frac{1}{3}$.

4 cu. yards = 3·018 cu. m. = 3 cu. m. % error $\frac{2}{3}$.

62$\frac{1}{2}$ m.p.h. = 100·58 km. per hour = 100 km. per hour. %
error $\frac{2}{3}$.

Expansion.

1. (i) 1·005 ; 1·02 ; ·988.

(ii) $\dfrac{1·076}{·993}$ = 1·083 ; (iii) £497 × 0·12 = £59.

2. (a) With each ace may be joined a king, i.e. 16 sets. With
each set may be joined a queen, i.e. 64 groups. With each group
may be joined a jack, i.e. 256 combinations.

(b) 4 × 3 × 14 × 13 = 2188.

LESSON 23

Mathematics of Land Measurement

LAND is a valuable commodity. Political boundaries are
negatively valuable, since agreement as to their location
saves the expenses of war. The measurement of areas and
their mapping on charts, plans, and diagrams, depend primarily
upon a knowledge of the properties of triangles. The whole

process is summarized under the term " triangulation." Nature does not provide the surveyor with regular triangles ; most of his triangles are scalene. Hence the first step is the extension of " Pythagoras " to scalene triangles. In the diagram both forms of scalene triangle are shown : the first when M, the foot of the perpendicular from A to BC, falls within BC, and the

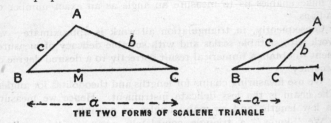

THE TWO FORMS OF SCALENE TRIANGLE

second, when it falls without BC. The code for lengths of sides of a triangle ABC is a, b, c, as shown. The angle opposite a is indicated in code by A, etc.

Let BM = m, then CM = a — m or m — a ; i.e. $CM^2 = a^2 - 2am + m^2$, in both cases. But $c^2 - b^2 = BM^2 - CM^2 = m^2 - a^2 + 2am - m^2 = 2am - a^2$. Whence, the difference between the squares on two sides of a triangle is equal to the difference between the square on the third side and the rectangle contained by the third side and the appropriate segment of this third side, made by the foot of the perpendicular to that side from the opposite angle.

Trigonometrically, $m = c \cdot \cos B$. Whence the formulas :

(i) $c^2 - b^2 = 2ac \cdot \cos B - a^2$.

(ii) $b^2 = c^2 + a^2 \pm 2ac \cdot \cos B$.

Using the + or — as c is obviously greater or smaller than b,

(iii) $\cos B = \dfrac{c^2 + a^2 - b^2}{2ac}$

The confusion which arises because $(m - a)^2 = (a - m)^2$ enforces care in the use of the signs $\pm$ before $2ac \cdot \cos B$.

In actual fact, every line is transcendental. It is not possible to express its length as 5 or 7 or 11 units of length ; if it should occur that, by the millionth chance, a line happens to be exactly 5 or 7 or 11 inches, this is due to the fluke that the line in question is compared with inches—the line in question would not be an exact number of centimetres.

Similarly, every angle is transcendental. Commonly, we measure angles in degrees, and we are satisfied by various mechanical devices that we can obtain an angle of exactly 90° ; but there is another scale of angular measurement based upon π, upon the formula π " angular units " = 180°. These angular units are termed " radians." Thus 90° = $\frac{1}{2}$ π radians, and nothing but a fluke enables us to measure an angle as an exact number of radians.

Consequently, in triangulation all work is approximate ; we work with suitable scales and with suitable delicacy of measurement to obtain a numerical result correctly to a desired degree of accuracy.

We use measuring chains for lengths and theodolites for angles. The chain is the less delicate instrument. Hence we measure as few lengths and as many angles as possible.

We " know " a triangle completely when we " know " :

(A) two sides and the angle between them ;

(B) one side and the two angles adjacent to that side. Hence, practically, we get more accurate results by using (B) than (A), for on a theodolite angles may be measured to the nearest second, i.e. to $\frac{1}{3600}$ of a degree.

For these purposes the code is extended : a new symbolism is used :

$$2s = a + b + c$$
whence :
$$2(s - a) = (b + c - a)$$
$$2(s - b) = (c + a - b)$$
$$2(s - c) = (a + b - c).$$

The formula $\cos B = \dfrac{c^2 + a^2 - b^2}{2ac}$ is termed the cosine rule.

In the diagram AM = c . sin B = b. sin C

whence $\dfrac{\sin A}{a} = \dfrac{\sin B}{a} = \dfrac{\sin C}{c}$

which is termed the sine rule.

$$180 = A + B + C.$$

Whence, if two angles are known, the third is known.

Hence : If three sides of a triangle are known, the cosine rule determines two angles.

Hence : If two sides and their included angle are known, the cosine rule determines the third side, and the sine rule the angles.

To save labour, the elaborate calculations involved in surveying are made logarithmically. Hence the formulas have been adapted to this type of work.

$$2 \sin^2 \frac{B}{2} = 1 - \cos B = 1 - \frac{c^2 + a^2 - b^2}{2ac}$$

$$= \frac{2ac - c^2 - a^2 + b^2}{2ac} = \frac{(b - c + a)(b + c - a)}{2ac}$$

$$= \frac{4(s - c)(s - a)}{2ac}$$

i.e. $\sin \dfrac{B}{2} = \sqrt{\dfrac{(s - c)(s - a)}{ac}}$

$$2 \cos^2 \frac{B}{2} = 1 + \cos B;$$

whence $\cos \dfrac{B}{2} = \sqrt{\dfrac{s(s - b)}{ac}}$

whence $\tan \dfrac{B}{2} = \sqrt{\dfrac{(s - c(s - a)}{s(s - b)}}$

In the diagram, the area of ABC $= \frac{1}{2}a \cdot AM = \frac{1}{2} ac \cdot \sin B = \frac{1}{2} ab \cdot \sin C$.

But $\sin B = 2 \sin \dfrac{B}{2} \cos \dfrac{B}{2}$

$$= \frac{2}{ac} \sqrt{s(s - a)(s - b)(s - c)}$$

Hence $\frac{1}{2} ac \cdot \sin B = \sqrt{s(s - a)(s - b)(s - c)} = $ area of ABC. " s " = the semi-perimeter of the triangle and the formula area $= \sqrt{s(s - a)(s - b)(s - c)}$ is termed the semi-perimeter rule.

Drill. 1. Find the angles of a triangle of which the sides are 3, 7, 8 respectively.

2. Find the length of the perpendicular AD of the triangle ABC from A to BC when AB $= 2$, and AC $= \sqrt{3}$, and BC $= \sqrt{5 + 2\sqrt{5}}$. Completely solve this triangle.

3. Solve the triangle MNP when MN $= 100$, MNP $= 45°$ and NMP $= 60°$.

4. Find the sum of $\dfrac{1}{1 + x}$, $\dfrac{1}{(1 + x)^2}$, $\dfrac{1}{(1 + x)^3}$, $\dfrac{1}{(1 + x)^4}$, when $x = 0\cdot1$, $0\cdot01$, $0\cdot125$ respectively.

5. Evaluate, using logs,

$$\tan \tfrac{1}{2}(C - A) = \frac{c - a}{c + a} \cdot \tan(90 - \tfrac{1}{2}B)$$

when $B = 40°$, $a = 15$, $c = 20$.

Expansion. 1. A solid or trihedral angle is formed when 3 planes meet at a corner, e.g. the corners of an octahedron. Attempt to find a proof that any two trihedral angles are greater than the third.

2. Consider the question of the extreme limit of vision over the sea from the top of a tower 400 ft. above sea-level. Find this distance in miles, given that the earth's radius = 4,000 miles. Generalize the result for a height of F feet.

Solutions to Exercises in Lesson 22.

Revision. 1. (i) $\dfrac{1}{(1 + \sqrt 2)^2 - 3}\Big(1 - (\sqrt 2 - \sqrt 3)^2 - 1 + (\sqrt 2 + \sqrt 3)^2\Big)$

$= \dfrac{1}{2\sqrt 2}(-5 + 2\sqrt 6 + 5 + 2\sqrt 6) = \dfrac{4\sqrt 6}{2\sqrt 2} = 2\sqrt 3.$

(ii) Let $(a + \dfrac{1}{a}) = m$, then $(m - \sqrt 2)(m + \sqrt 2) = m^2 - 2$;

$m^2 - 2 = (a + \dfrac{1}{a})^2 - 2 = a^2 + \dfrac{1}{a^2}$ $(a^2 + \dfrac{1}{a^2})\Big((a^2 + \dfrac{1}{a^2}) + 2\Big) = a^4 +$

$2a^2 + 2 + \dfrac{2}{a^2} + \dfrac{1}{a^4}$

(iii) $\dfrac{4\sqrt 2 - 3\sqrt 3}{7\sqrt 2 - 4\sqrt 3} = \dfrac{(4\sqrt 2 - 3\sqrt 3)(7\sqrt 2 + 4\sqrt 3)}{(7\sqrt 2 - 4\sqrt 3)(7\sqrt 2 + 4\sqrt 3)} = \dfrac{20 - 5\sqrt 6}{50};$

$\dfrac{4 + \sqrt 6}{7\sqrt 2 - 2\sqrt 3} = \dfrac{34\sqrt 2 + 22\sqrt 3}{86}$

Product $= \dfrac{4 - \sqrt 6}{10} \times \dfrac{17\sqrt 2 + 11\sqrt 3}{43} = \dfrac{7\sqrt 2 - 2\sqrt 3}{86}$

(iv) $\dfrac{(3 + \sqrt 3)^2}{9 - 3} = 2 + \sqrt 3$

2. (i) $(5m + 6)(4m - 5)$; (ii) $(m - 1)(m^3 + m^2 + m - 3)$; (iii) $(d^4 - d^2e^2 + e^4)(d^2 + de + e^2)(d^2 - de + e^2)$.

3. (i) $\tan \tfrac{1}{2}(A + B) = \dfrac{\sin \tfrac{1}{2}(A + B)}{\cos \tfrac{1}{2}(A + B)} \times \dfrac{\cos \tfrac{1}{2}(A - B)}{\cos \tfrac{1}{2}(A - B)} =$

$\dfrac{\sin A + \sin B}{\cos A + \cos B}$

(ii) $\dfrac{\sin 3\phi - \sin \phi}{\cos 3\phi + \cos \phi} = \dfrac{2 \sin \phi - 4 \sin^3 \phi}{4 \cos^3 \phi + 2 \cos \phi} = \dfrac{\sin \phi}{\cos \phi} \times \dfrac{1 - 2 \sin^2 \phi}{2 \cos^2 \phi - 1}$

$= \tan \phi$.

4. (i) $x = 8$, $y = 12$; (ii) Multiply throughout by $(p^2 - m^2)$
Then :

$px + mx - pm - m^2 = py + p^2 - my - mp$; and
$- px - mx - pm - m^2 = py - p^2 - my + mp$, whence, by
addition, $- 2m^2 - 2 pm = 2 py - 2 my$; i.e. $y (p - m) =$
$- m (p + m)$;

$y = \dfrac{(p + m)}{(m - p)}m$; and $x = \dfrac{(p - m)}{(p + m)}p$; i.e., $xy = pm$.

Expansion. 1. (i) $1 = P (P + 1)$; (ii) $(1 + P)^2 = 2 + P$:

(iii) $\dfrac{1}{1 + P} = P$; (iv) $\dfrac{1}{(1 + P)^2} = \dfrac{1}{2 + P} = P^2$; (v) $\sqrt 5 = 1 + 2$

$(\frac{1}{2} \sqrt 5 - \frac{1}{2}) = 1 + 2P$; (vi) $\sqrt 5 + 2 \sqrt 5 = 7 + 4P$.

2. Demonstration above, see the diagram.

LESSON 24

Solution of Triangles in Three Dimensions

IN continuation of the last Lesson we may now proceed to the
extension of the formulas therein obtained. The " semi-
perimeter " rule is adapted to the use of logs, and when
s, (s-a), (s-b), etc., are known numerically, the calculation of the
angles by logs is a simple exercise. If one angle of a triangle be
known, say B, then $(180 - B) = C + A$; and $(C - A)$ may be
calculated by another formula, which is deduced thus :

$\dfrac{\sin C}{\sin A} = \dfrac{c}{a}$; $\dfrac{c - a}{c + a} = \dfrac{\sin C - \sin A}{\sin C + \sin A}$

$= \dfrac{2 \sin \frac{1}{2} (C - A) \cos \frac{1}{2} (C + A)}{2 \cos \frac{1}{2} (C - A) \sin \frac{1}{2} (C + A)}$

$= \dfrac{\tan \frac{1}{2} (C - A)}{\tan \frac{1}{2} (C + A)}$

$= \dfrac{\tan \frac{1}{2} (C - A)}{\tan (90 - \frac{1}{2}B)}$

whence $\tan \frac{1}{2} (C - A) = \dfrac{c - a}{c + a}$. $\tan (90 - \frac{1}{2}B)$.

(503)

It one angle of a triangle is known, and it is not the included angle between two known sides, then the sine rule may be used to determine the included angle : there may be two possible triangles as in Fig. 1.

There A, c, and a are known. Obviously, b may be AC or AD, if BD = BC = a.

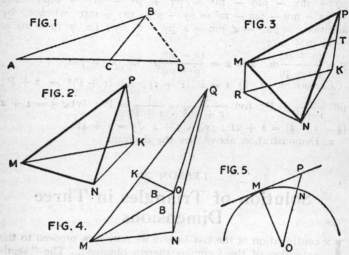

FIG. 1

FIG. 2

FIG. 3

FIG. 4.

FIG. 5.

The condition of this ambiguity is that sin C = sin (180 − C) = sin BCD = sin BDC.

In practice, triangulation proceeds by the fixation of a third point, P, in relation to two points M and N, a known distance apart.

The simplest case occurs when PMN is a plane triangle. This is obviously the case of the triangles in Fig. 1, Lesson 23. To fix A in relation to BC, the triangle ABC must be solved. If the observer may not reach A, but can see A, he can measure the angles ACB and ABC. He " knows " a, B, and C. He calculates A. By the sine rule he calculates b and c.

A more complex case occurs when the third point P is elevated as in Fig. 2, where MNK is the plan of the triangle MNP which is to be solved.

He measures angles MNK and NMK, and thus " obtains " triangle MNK. He measures angle KNP and " obtains " triangle

NPK. He measures angle KMP and " obtains " triangle MPK to check his work, for he " obtains " separately two values for PK which should agree. PK being vertical angles PKN and PKM are each 90°.

A still more complex case occurs when both M and P are elevated as in Fig. 3, where RKN is the plan of MNP, which is to be solved. Angle MNR is measured and RN obtained from MN. Angles RNK and NRK are measured, triangle RKN is solved. Angle KNP allows PN to be obtained. In the same way, angle TMP allows PM to be obtained.

The reverse cases are interesting. Suppose the observer is at P and knows MN ; what must he do to solve MNP ? He can directly measure angle MPN. If he can obtain angles NMP and MNP, he can solve MPN. If he knows MPN, he can measure angles of depression from P down to N, i.e. angle PNK and from P down to M, i.e. PMT (Fig. 3). He can then obtain PK.

To obtain angles NRK and RNK he needs : (a) a map and a compass ; (b) in default of a map, compass direction information telephoned or wirelessed from N and M ; (c) an altimeter record by which he knows PK and can obtain KN and KR ; (d) time signals from M and N by which he can obtain the ratio between MP and PN, thence the ratio between RK and KN ; and map information by which he can obtain RN : thence he solves RKN.

It is assumed throughout that MN, NP, and MP are straight lines. When they are parts of the earth's curved surface the solutions are complicated, since the curved lines must be " reduced " to their corresponding straight lines as chords of a circle of the size of the earth. This " reduction " or " correction " may not be important if MN, etc., are short lines, or if the degree of accuracy required is outside the limits of accuracy which the " reduction " would introduce.

Drill. 1. Solve the triangle DEF wherein DE = 15 miles, DEF = 44°, EDF = 46°.

2. Solve the equations :—

(a) $\dfrac{1}{x} + \dfrac{1}{y} = \dfrac{x+y}{15} = \dfrac{8}{x+y+7}$

(b) $x^2 + y^2 = 11$
$2x + 3y = 12$

(c) $x + y + z = 15$
$2x - y + z = 8$
$x - 2y + z = 0$

3. π radians $= 180°$; find the value of a radian in degrees, minutes and seconds.

4. Find the 6th term in the series: $2\sqrt{2} - 2\sqrt{3} + 3\sqrt{2}\ldots\ldots$ Find the sum of the 6 terms.

Expansion. Consider the problem of piling equal-sized spheres into triangular pyramids. Find the sequences connecting the numbers of spheres used in the pyramid and the number of spheres in each edge of the triangle.

Solutions to Exercises in Lesson 23.

Drill. 1. Use the cosine formula: $a = 3$, $b = 7$, $c = 8$.

$$\cos B = \frac{64 + 9 - 49}{48} = \frac{24}{48} = \tfrac{1}{2}; \quad B = 60°.$$

similarly $A = 22° : B = 180 - 82 = 98°$.

2. Let $BD = m$ and $DC = n$. Then $(m + n)^2 = 5 + 2\sqrt{5}$;

$m^2 - n^2 = 4 - 3 = 1$; whence $\dfrac{(m+n)}{(m-n)} = 5 + 2\sqrt{5}$

whence $\dfrac{m+n}{m-n} + 1 = \dfrac{2m}{m-n} = 6 + 2\sqrt{5}$

and $\dfrac{m+n}{m-n} - 1 = \dfrac{2n}{m-n} = 4 + 2\sqrt{5}$

whence $\dfrac{m}{n} = \dfrac{3 + \sqrt{5}}{2 + \sqrt{5}}$

whence $\dfrac{m}{n} + 1 = \dfrac{m+n}{n} = \dfrac{5 + 2\sqrt{5}}{2 + \sqrt{5}}$

whence $n = \dfrac{2 + \sqrt{5}}{\sqrt{5 + 2\sqrt{5}}} = \sqrt{\dfrac{5 + 2\sqrt{5}}{5}}$

and $m = \dfrac{3 + \sqrt{5}}{\sqrt{5 + 2\sqrt{5}}} = \sqrt{\dfrac{10 + 2\sqrt{5}}{5}}$

Thus $AD^2 = 4 - \dfrac{10 + 2\sqrt{5}}{5} = \dfrac{10 - 2\sqrt{5}}{5}$

and $\sin^2 B = \dfrac{AD^2}{AB^2} = \dfrac{10 - 2\sqrt{5}}{20} = \cdot2764 :$

i.e. $B = 31\tfrac{1}{2}°$, and $\sin^2 C = \dfrac{AD^2}{AC^2} = \dfrac{10 - 2\sqrt{5}}{15} = \cdot3685 :$

i.e. $C = 37\tfrac{1}{2}°$.

Check. $\tan^2 B = \dfrac{AD^2}{m^2} = \dfrac{10 - 2\sqrt{5}}{10 + 2\sqrt{5}} = \tfrac{1}{4}(\sqrt{5} - 1)^2 :$

i.e. B = $31\frac{1}{2}°$.

3. p = 100   N = 45°   M = 60°   P = 75°.

$$\frac{\sin 75}{100} = ·009659 = \frac{\sin 45}{n} = \frac{·7071}{n} : \text{i.e. } n = \frac{·7071}{·009659} = 73$$

$$m = \frac{·866}{·009659} = 90.$$

This can be checked since MNP consists of half a square with diagonal = m added to half an equilateral triangle of side = n.

4. Let $A = \frac{1}{1+x}$ then the sum = S = $A + A^2 + A^3 + A^4 =$

$$A\left(\frac{1-A^4}{1-A}\right) = \frac{1}{1+x}\left(\frac{1-\dfrac{1}{(1+x)^4}}{1-\dfrac{1}{1+x}}\right) = \frac{1}{x}\left(1 - \frac{1}{(1+x)^4}\right) =$$

$$\frac{(1+x)^4 - 1}{x(1+x)^4} = \text{(i) } \frac{1·4641 - 1}{0·1(1·4641)} = \frac{·4641}{·14641} = 3·17$$

(ii) $\dfrac{1·04060401 - 1}{0·01(1·04060401)} = \dfrac{·04060401}{·0104060401} = 3·9$

(iii) $\dfrac{\left(\frac{9}{8}\right)^4 - 1}{\frac{1}{8}\left(\frac{9}{8}\right)^4} = 8\dfrac{9^4 - 8^4}{9^4} = 8\dfrac{6561 - 4096}{6561} = 8\dfrac{2465}{6561} = 3·01$

5. log tan $\frac{1}{2}$ (C − A) = log 5 − log 35 + log tan 70
$$= ·6990 - \bar{1}·5441 + ·4389$$
$$= \bar{1}·5938$$
$$= \log ·7737$$
$$= \log \tan 37\frac{1}{2} \text{ approx.}$$

i.e. C − A = $37\frac{1}{2}$

   C + A = 140

C = $88\frac{3}{4}$ A = $51\frac{1}{4}$

Check. $\dfrac{\sin C}{c} = ·05$; $\dfrac{\sin A}{15} = ·05$

Expansion. 1. If the 3 angles are equal, the theorem follows. If A>B. In Fig. 4 let MOQ = A, MON = MOK = B, and NOQ = C. Let O be the vertex of a pyramid with base MQN such that OK = ON. MN = MK ; and MN + NQ>MQ ; whence QN>QK ; whence C>(A − B) ; whence (C + B)>A.

2. Fig. 5. O = centre of earth ; OM = ON = 4,000 miles.

Let PM = x : PN = $\dfrac{400}{5280}$ miles.

$$\left(4000 + \left(\frac{400}{5280}\right)\right)^2 = (4000)^2 + x^2.$$

$$\frac{8000 \times 400}{5280} = x^2 \text{ (neglecting } \left(\frac{400}{5280}\right)^2 \text{ which is small).}$$

$$x^2 = 400 \times \frac{100}{66} = 400 \times 1\tfrac{1}{2} \text{ approx.}$$

$$x = 20 \times 1 \cdot 225 = 24\tfrac{1}{2} \text{ miles approx.}$$

Generally, $x = \sqrt{F} \times 1 \cdot 225$ miles, where F is the height in feet.

LESSON 25

Arithmetic of Bills of Exchange

ARITHMETICALLY, one of the principal differences between a bank note or a currency note or a cheque and a bill of exchange lies in the fact that a bill of exchange cannot be presented for payment now, but at some future date. The machinery for immediate realization consists in the practice of discounting bills. £100 lent for 73 days at 5% interest will be worth £101 at the end of the period ; i.e. £100 and £101 are equivalent values with reference to the interval of time and the agreed 5% accretion which separates them.

In code we say (A) that £100 was the principal lent, £1 was the interest gained, £101 was the amount; (B) under different circumstances with different code labels, that £101 was the amount due at some future date, £1 was the discount off that amount, £100 was the present worth of the money due. The £1 discount is the cost of the convenience in having cash now instead of in 73 days' time. In practice, money is often due at 30 or 60 days from a given date or on a date specified. The documentary evidence is a bill of exchange. Any bill of exchange due for future payment is worth now something less than its face value : e.g. a B/E (bill of exchange) for £500, due on June 30th, may be cashed on May 1st for £495 at a discount of £5. In code this B/E discount is called banker's discount ; banker's discount is calculated as the equivalent of the simple interest on the value of the B/E ; in the above example £5 is equal to the simple interest on £500 for the period from May 1st onwards at some rate per cent not specified.

In practice the face value of a B/E is not due until 3 days (" 3 days of grace ") after the nominal date and, unless specifically excluded, these 3 days are included in the calculation and discount is calculated to the legal date and not to the nominal date. Example :

What is the cash value on July 1st of a B/E for £940 due on September 6th, interest being reckoned at 4% ?

S.I. on £940 @ 4% for 70 days = £7·211 = £7-4-3. Present worth or cash value on July 1st, £932-15-9.

A distinction is drawn between the practical banker's discount and a theoretical true discount. Suppose that during a given period and at a given rate per cent £100 grows to £103, this being a sample of the relation existing between present worth and future ; then :

Banker's discount = 3/100 = 3% of the amount of the B/E.

True discount = 3/103 = less than 3% of the amount of the B/E.

If the amount of the B/E be £10,300, B.D. (banker's discount) = £103 × 3, T.D. (true discount) = £100 × 3 ; the difference £9 is labelled the banker's gain (B.G.) and is obviously 3% of the T.D.

Since $\dfrac{A}{B} - \dfrac{A}{B-A} = \dfrac{A \times A}{B(B-A)}$

the values for the rate of B.D., T.D., and B.G. are related and any one may be inferred from the others. Example :

Suppose it is known that the rate of B.G. = $\frac{1}{12}$, then it is inferred that B.D. = $\frac{1}{8}$ and T.D. = $\frac{1}{8}$; e.g. given that B.D. = £10 and T.D. = £9-15-0, then it may be inferred that : (i) B.G. = 5s., i.e. $\frac{1}{36}$ of T.D., whence (ii) the amount of the B/E = £390.

Find the B.D., T.D., and B.G. on March 3rd on a B/E for £437 due on May 12th at 6%.

S.I. $= \dfrac{6}{100} \times \dfrac{73}{365} = \dfrac{6}{500}$ of £437   B.D. $= £\dfrac{6 \times 437}{500} = £5·244 = £5-4-10$

T.D. $= £\dfrac{6 \times 437}{506} = £\dfrac{5·244}{1·012} = £5·1818 = £5-3-8$

B.G. $= £\dfrac{6 \times 6 \times 437}{500 \times 506} = £\dfrac{6 \times 5·1318}{500} = £0·0622$
$= $ 1s. 2d.

Pentagons. A regular pentagon has five equal sides, 5 equal angles, and can be split into 5 equal isosceles triangles.

In Fig. 1 ABCDE is a pentagon with centre O. AB=BC=CD, etc.; angles AOB, BOC, COD, etc.=72°; angles ABC, BCD, CDE, etc.=108°; angles BAC, BCA, CBD, CDB, etc.=36°; angles ADB, BEC, CAD, etc.=36°; angles BAD, BCE, ABD, CBE, etc.=72°; angles BAO, ABO, CBO, BCO, etc.=54°.

It is desirable to investigate the proportions between the various sides of the pentagon as they are determined by these

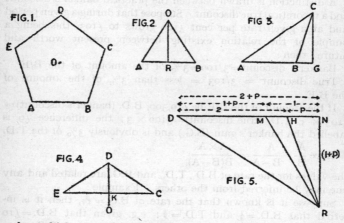

angles, which are, of course, invariable, as they determine the shape but not the size of the figure.

Fig. 2 repeats AOB from Fig. 1; in addition, AR=RB.

AO=OB=the radius of the circumscribed circle to the pentagon, OR=the radius of the inscribed circle to the pentagon.

Let AB=2 units of length, then AR=1, OR=tan 54 and OAcos54=1.

whence $OR = \frac{1}{5} \sqrt{5} (\sqrt{5+2\sqrt{5}})$ and $AO = \frac{\sqrt{5}-1}{\sqrt{5}} (\sqrt{5+2\sqrt{5}})$

whence $AO+OR = \overline{(\sqrt{5+2\sqrt{5}})}$ and $AO=OR (\sqrt{5}-1)$

Fig. 3 shows ABC repeated from Fig. 1 and, in addition, CG perpendicular to AB produced:

then $AC=AD=1/\sin 18=4/(\sqrt{5}-1)=\sqrt{5}+1$. B.G.$=2 \cos 72 = \frac{1}{2}\sqrt{5} - \frac{1}{2}$.

$CG = 2 \sin 72 = \sqrt{\frac{1}{2}(5 + \sqrt{5})}$

Fig. 4 introduces K where DO bisects EC at right angles : $EK = KC = 2 \cos 36 = \frac{1}{2}\sqrt{5} + \frac{1}{2} = \frac{1}{2}\sqrt{AC}$

$KD = 2 \sin 36 = \sqrt{\sqrt{5}(\frac{1}{2}\sqrt{5} - \frac{1}{2})}$

whence $KR = CG = \sqrt{\frac{1}{2}(5 + \sqrt{5})}$

whence $KD = KR \, (\frac{1}{2}\sqrt{5} - \frac{1}{2})$.

These results suggest that $\sqrt{5}$ and $(\frac{1}{2}\sqrt{5} - \frac{1}{2})$ are transcendental lengths fundamental to the pentagon.

Let $\frac{1}{2}\sqrt{5} - \frac{1}{2}$ be represented by P; then :

$1 + P \qquad = \frac{1}{2}\sqrt{5} + \frac{1}{2}$

$P(1 + P) \qquad = 1$

$2 + P \qquad = (1 + P)^2 \qquad = 1\frac{1}{2} + \frac{1}{2}\sqrt{5}$

$3 + 2P \qquad = (1 + P)^3 \qquad = 2 + \sqrt{5}$

$5 + 3P \qquad = (1 + P)^4 \qquad = (2 + P)^2 \qquad = 3\frac{1}{2} + 1\frac{1}{2}\sqrt{5}$

$8 + 5P \qquad = (1 + P)^5 \qquad = 5\frac{1}{2} + 2\frac{1}{2}\sqrt{5}$

whence $\qquad (1 + P)^3 \qquad = (1 + P)^2 + (1 + P)$

whence $\qquad (1 + P)^{n+2} = (1 + P)^{n+1} + (1 + P)^2$

$P^2 \qquad = 1\frac{1}{2} - \frac{1}{2}\sqrt{5}$

$1 + 2P = \sqrt{5} = \text{`` F ''}$

$P^2 + (1 + P)^2 = 3$, i.e. `` E^2 ''

$3 + P = 1 + (1 + P)^2 = 2\frac{1}{2} + \frac{1}{2}\sqrt{5}$

$4 + 3P = (3 + P) \, (1 + P) = 2\frac{1}{2} + 1\frac{1}{2}\sqrt{5}$

$7 + 4P = (4 + 3P) \, (1 + P) = 5 + 2\sqrt{5}$

$1/P = (1 + P) = (2 + P)/(1 + P)$

$1 - P = P^2 = 1/(2 + P) = 1\frac{1}{2} - \frac{1}{2}\sqrt{5}$

$(1 - P)^2 = 2 - 3P = 2P^2 - P = P \, (2P - 1) = 3\frac{1}{2} - 1\frac{1}{2}\sqrt{5}$

$(1 - P)^3 = 5 - 8P = 9 - 4\sqrt{5}$

$(7 + 4P) \, (3 - 4P) = 5 = \text{`` F.''}$

Using the `` P '' Notation :

$AO/OR = \text{circum-radius/in-radius} = 2P \quad KD/KR = P$

$AO = \sqrt{\frac{1}{5}(12 + 4P)} \quad RO = \sqrt{\frac{1}{5}(4P + 7)}$

$KD = \sqrt{P^2 + 1} \quad CG = KR = \sqrt{3 + P}$

$AD = EC = 2 \, (1 + P)$

$EK = KC = (1 + P)$

$BG = P$

$DR = AO + OR = \sqrt{7 + 4P}$

These results are grouped geometrically in Fig. 5 :

$DR = \sqrt{7 + 4P}$; $DNR = 90°$; $DN = (2 + P)$; $NR = (1 + P)$

$HN = P$; $MN = 1$

Then $HR^2 = HN^2 + RN^2 = P^2 + (1+P)^2 = 3 = E^2$, i.e. $HR =$ the perpendicular of an equilateral triangle of edge 2; MNR and RND are similar triangles in the ratio of $1 : (1+P) = P$.

Since $DR =$ the height of a pentagon of edge 2, then $RM =$ the height of a pentagon of edge $2P$; and DR and HR are respectively the perpendiculars of a pentagon and an equilateral triangle of edge 2.

Drill. Tabulate the B.D., T.D., and B.G. for B/E of £100, £200, £700 respectively for 30, 60, and 90, allowing days of grace at 4%, 5%, 7%.

Revision. Draw a square ABCD. Draw AE and AF each at an angle α to AC. E and F fall on the perimeter of the square. Investigate the lengths of AE, EF, and FA in terms of the angle α, taking the side of the square as the unit of length Determine whether A, and E and F can be corners of (i) an equilateral triangle, (ii) corners of a regular pentagon.

Expansion. Determine the vertical height of a pentagonal pyramid in terms of the P notation.

Solutions to Problems in Lesson 24

Drill. 1. $DFE = 90°$; $DF = 15.$ $\sin 44 = 10.4$; $FE = 15.$ $\sin 46 = 10.8$.

2. (i) $(x+y)/xy = (x+y)/15$, i.e. $xy = 15$; $(x+y)^2 + 7 (x+y) = 120$; $(x+y+3\frac{1}{2})^2 = (11\frac{1}{2})^2$; $x+y = 8$ or -15; $(x+y)^2 = 64$ or 225; $(x-y)^2 = 4$ or 165; $x = 5$ or 3 or $\frac{1}{2} (-15 \pm 165)$; $y = 3$ or 5 or $\frac{1}{2} (-15 \mp 165)$).

(ii) $y = 4 - \frac{2}{3}x$; $x^2 - \frac{2}{3}x + 4 = 11$; $x - \frac{1}{3} = \pm \frac{8}{3}$; $x = 3$ or $-2\frac{1}{3}$; $y = 2$ or $5\frac{5}{9}$.

(iii) $2y - x = z$; $3y = 15$; $y = 5$; $x+y = 8$; $x = 3$; $z = 7$.

3. $57° - 11' - 45''$.

4. $-4\frac{1}{2}\sqrt{3}$; sum $(\sqrt{2} - \sqrt{3})$ $9\frac{1}{2} = -1.43$.

Expansion. The base is an equilateral triangle with 3, 6, 10, etc. spheres. The whole has centres of spheres at the corners of tetrahedra. If the edge has n spheres, the sides of the tetrahedron $= d (n - 1)$, where $d =$ the diameter of a sphere.

The number of spheres used is:

Along the
    edge— 1 2 3 4 5 6 7, etc. n
In bottom
layer— 1 3 6 10 15 21 28, etc. $\frac{1}{2}$ n (n+1)
    Total— 1 4 10 20 35 56 84, etc. $\frac{1}{6}$ n (n+1) (n+2).

ROMAN EMPERORS IN THE FIELD. The above scene from Trajan's Column in Rome shows the emperor, during his first campaign against the Dacians, standing at the head of his division just outside his camp on the far side of the Danube. On the right is a relief showing Marcus Aurelius (121–180) receiving the submission of some defeated barbarian chieftains. Succeeding in 161, Marcus Aurelius was the "philosopher king" of the Roman world. HISTORY: ANCIENT 21

Palazzo dei Conservatori, Rome

DESTROYER OF THE TURKS. John Sobieski, king of
Poland, a brilliant soldier and statesman, drove the
Turks out of Poland in 1676 and Hungary in 1683 and
routed the immense Turkish army that besieged Vienna.
MODERN HISTORY 13

RIVAL RULERS OF THE NORTH. Left, Peter the Great (1672–
1725), who made Russia a European power, and, right, Charles XII
of Sweden (1682–1718), who roundly defeated Peter's attack on
Scandinavia at the battle of Narva in 1700, but was himself beaten
at Pultowa in the Ukraine in 1709. MODERN HISTORY 13

Plate 56   *Volume III*

LESSON 26

Pentagonal Pyramids and Their Relations

IN the preceding Lesson the facts concerning the regular pentagon were tabulated, in part, as an example of the analysis of one of the regular polygons, and, in part, as a preliminary to the analysis of the pentagonal pyramid, with which we now deal. Fig. 1 is a sketch of a regular pentagonal pyramid of edge 2, showing DR and HR in relative position. Fig. 2 is a section of this pyramid. Using the " P " notation :

$$DR = \sqrt{7+4P}; \quad HR = \sqrt{3} = \text{"E"}; \quad DO = \sqrt{\tfrac{1}{5}(12+4P)};$$
$$OR = \sqrt{\tfrac{1}{5}(7+4P)}$$
$$HR = 2; \quad \text{whence}:$$

$HO^2 = HD^2 - DO^2$	or $= HR^2 - RO^2$
$= 4 - \tfrac{1}{5}(12+4P)$	$= 3 - \tfrac{1}{5}(7+4P)$
$= \tfrac{4}{5}(2-P)$	$= \tfrac{4}{5}(2-P)$

Fig. 3 goes back to half the pentagon. *See* Fig. 1 of Lesson 25.
OT = OD, whence DAT = 90°
$DA = \sqrt{8+4P}$, whence $DW = \sqrt{2+P} = (1+P)$ $EW^2 = DE^2$
$-DW^2 = 4-2-P = 2-P$, whence $HO^2 = \tfrac{4}{5}EW^2$
$WO/WD = AR/DR$, whence $WO = WD/DR = (1+P)/\sqrt{7+4P}$
$= \sqrt{\tfrac{1}{5}(2-P)}$, whence $WE = \sqrt{5}$ WO and $2WO = HO$,
$AT = 2WO$; whence $AT = HO$,
$RT/AR = AR/DR$; whence $RT = 1/\sqrt{7+4P} = \sqrt{\tfrac{1}{5}(3-4P)}$.

All this argument brings us to the connexion between the cube, the icosahedron and the dodecahedron, and their intimate connexion with the regular pentagon.

By the method of Fig. 4 find $XY = \sqrt{5} = \text{" F,"}$ when $YZ = 1$.

Find $XW = F-1$, and bisect XW at T; $XT = \tfrac{1}{2}\sqrt{5} - \tfrac{1}{2} = P$.

Construct a square so that $EB = (1+P)$ Fig. 5. Divide DC so that $DA = 1$ and $AC = P$.

Then ACB repeats HNR (Fig. 5, Lesson 25), and AB = the perpendicular of an equilateral triangle of edge 2. ADE repeats MNR (Fig. 5, Lesson 25), and AE = the perpendicular of a regular pentagon of edge 2P.

(513)

R3

Fig. 5 gives the essential measurements for a dodecahedron and for an icosahedron. Make three sets of soldered wires after the pattern shown in the sketch, Fig. 6, so that the wires 12, 78, 9, 10 and their parallels are in three dimensions. Note that figures are specially used for marking the ends of the wires.

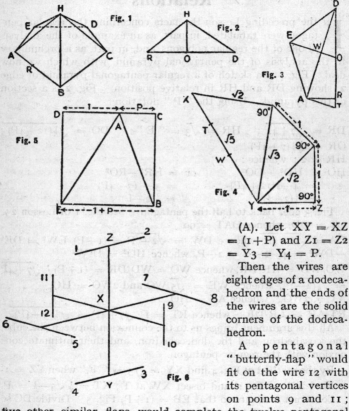

Fig. 1

Fig. 2

Fig. 3

Fig. 4

Fig. 5

Fig. 6

(A). Let $XY = XZ = (1+P)$ and $Z1 = Z2 = Y3 = Y4 = P$.

Then the wires are eight edges of a dodecahedron and the ends of the wires are the solid corners of the dodecahedron.

A pentagonal "butterfly-flap" would fit on the wire 12 with its pentagonal vertices on points 9 and 11; five other similar flaps would complete the twelve pentagonal faces of the dodecahedron.

(B). $XY = XZ = (1+P)$ as in (A), but $Z1 = Z2 = Y3 = Y4 = 1$.

In this case the twelve wires are edges of an icosahedron, of which their ends are the solid corners. Six equilateral triangle butterfly-flaps would fit and supply twelve of the twenty faces of the solid ; the eight other faces connect each of the eight sets of three corners.

From Fig. 5, Lesson 25, it is obvious that in this case (B) a pentagonal butterfly-flap made to fit the wire 12 would reach with the other corners of the flaps 8, 10, and 5 on one wing, and 7, 12, and 6 on the other wing.

Hence a butterfly-flap with pentagonal wings and a pentagonal pyramid on each wing, resting on the wire 12 would attain the points 9 and 11 respectively with the vertices of the pyramids.

In Fig. 5 the angle CAB = half the angle between the wings of a butterfly-flap that fits an icosahedron. Hence 6 equilateral triangle butterfly-flaps with wings set apart at twice the angle CAB would form an icosahedron, leaving 8 faces of the solid indicated only by their edges.

(A). Similarly, the angle EAD in Fig. 5 = half the angle between the butterfly-flaps that fit a dodecahedron. Hence 6 pentagonal butterfly-flaps with wings set apart at twice the angle EAD would form a dodecahedron.

(B). Similarly, 2 butterfly-flaps with pentagonal pyramid wings set apart at twice the angle DEA will connect with equilateral faces 10 of the 12 corners of an icosahedron and will supply 10 of the 20 faces of the solid.

The pentagonal bases of flaps working one on the wire 12 and the other on the wire 34 would intersect, and the lines of intersection would be parallel to the wires, and the angle between these pentagonal bases at their intersection would be twice the angle DEA ; hence these four bases of the two flaps would coincide with four faces of an interior dodecahedron within the icosahedron.

Hence pentagonal pyramids placed on the faces of a dodecahedron would make half an icosahedron.

The edges of this interior dodecahedron would equal $P/(1 + P) = P^2$, when the edge of the icosahedron = 2.

The angles between adjacent faces of a dodecahedron and of an icosahedron are transcendental ; these solids will not fit to fill space.

Both these solids can be constructed without the use of either rulers to measure lengths or protractors to measure angles ; for any line of any length can be given the value P, and therefrom a square like Fig. 5 may be drawn. These solids are transcendental to our codes of (i) enumeration beyond 5 ; (ii) measurements of lengths, areas and volumes ; and (iii) measurement of angles. The other four regular solids can all be cut from a cube, by slicing at specific angles to the faces of the cube and through specific points on the faces of the cube, for the mid points of the wires in Fig. 6 are the places where the diagonals of the faces of a cube intersect.

The student who is good at metal work may make the sets of wires and see how they fit ; he who is good at woodwork may begin with the cubes and carve them down to finish with the solids. The worker in plaster can proceed on similar lines.

Revision. 1. M and N move steadily back and forth between A and B. M moves twice as quickly as N. M starts from A and N starts from B. Taking as a unit of time the time from the start until they coincide, find the relative situations of M and N at the end of 3, 5 and $7\frac{1}{2}$ units of time.

2. ABCD is any quadrilateral. BD is joined and, through C, CN is drawn parallel to BD, so that BN is parallel to CD. Prove that the area of the triangle ACN is equal to the area of ABCD. Hence find an expression for the area of a quadrilateral in terms of its diagonals and the angle between them.

Expansion. Draw graphs of $y = 3x^2 + 7$; $x = 5y^2 - 3y$; $m = 16t^2$; and $a = \pi r^2$, when $\pi = 3\frac{1}{7}$.

Copy the curve in the graph $y = 3x^2 + 7$ and alter the scales on the axes of reference so that the curve represents $x = 5y^2 - 3y$.

Solutions to Exercises in Lesson 25

Drill. B.D. $1/36500 = 0.00002739$; $33/36500 = 0.0009039$; $63/36500 = 0.0017256$; $93/36500 = 0.0025473$.

		£100	£200	£700
" 30 days "	4%	0.36156	0.72312	2.53092
	5%	0.45195	0.90390	2.16365
	7%	0.63273	1.26546	4.42911
" 60 days "	4%	0.69024	1.38048	4.83168
	5%	0.86280	1.72560	6.03960
	7%	1.20792	2.41584	8.45544
" 90 days "	4%	1.01829	2.03658	7.12843
	5%	1.27365	2.54730	8.81555
	7%	1.78311	3.56622	12.48177

$£0.36156 = £100 \times 132/36500 = 7s.\ 3d.$

The B.G. would be :

£100 × 132/36500 × 132/36632, i.e. approx. £100 (0·0036)^2
and so on.

" 30 days "	4%	0·0013	0·0026	0·0091
	5%	0·0020	0·0040	0·0140
	7%	0·0040	0·0080	0·0280
" 60 days "	4%	0·0048	0·0096	0·0336
	5%	0·0074	0·0148	0·0518
	7%	0·0144	0·0288	0·1008
" 90 days "	4%	0·0104	0·0208	0·0728
	5%	0·0162	0·0324	0·1134
	7%	0·0298	0·0596	0·2086

T.D. is obtained by substraction.

Revision. Let the side of the square = a, and let E fall in BC, and let EF cut AC at P.

$$EP = PC = \tfrac{1}{2}\sqrt{2}\ EC. \quad = AE \sin \alpha.$$
$$EC = AE\sqrt{2} \sin \alpha \qquad BE = AE \sin (45 - \alpha)$$

i.e. EC + BE = a = AE ($\sqrt{2}$ sin + sin (45 − α))   whence
AE = a$\sqrt{2}$/(sin α) + cos α) ; EP = a $\sqrt{2}$ sin α/(sin α + cos α)
and EF/AE = 2 sinα.

Whence E and F make with A an equilateral triangle when EC and FC are each 2 sin α /(sin α + cos α) of CB or CD, and α = 30°. When α = 18°, E and F and A are three corners of a pentagon, but the intermediate corners between A and E and between A and F lie outside the square.

Expansion. See above.

LESSON 27

Standard Curves: And Present Worth at Compound Interest

IT has been shown that a straight line or a circle can represent different equations provided the scales on which the lines are drawn are suitably arranged. Shape and size are independent. A straight line may represent different linear equations, i.e. different simple proportional relations, not because it has many shapes, but because it may occupy many positions. A circle is a unique shape and may represent many equations of the general form $x^2 + y^2 = r^2$. The varieties of these equations are represented by differences in position of the circle.

The straight line and the circle are standard curves, and represent standard relations between quantities. Another standard relation is of the pattern $x = y^2$. This relation requires another standard curve, and different expressions of this relation, i.e. different equations of this pattern, will be represented by the new curve in different positions. Fig. 1 is one presentation of this curve, which is labelled a parabola. The curve is not closed

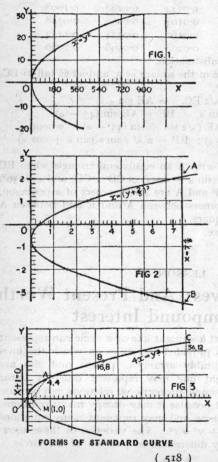

like the circle but open, for there is only one turning point ; the axis of symmetry is OX, and the curve crosses this axis but once. An image of the curve with reference to OY would have the equation $- x = y^2$. If the curve were transferred so that OY were its axis and O still its turning point then the equations would be either $x^2 = y$ or $x^2 = -y$.

So far change of position has been indicated by a change of sign or a change of index. Reverting to Fig. 1, if the scale along OX be divided by 6 to read 30, 60, 90, etc., the equation would become $6x = y^2$. If the scale along OY be multiplied throughout by 5, the equation would become $25x = y^2$. If the curve be moved so that the turning point became 180, O, i.e. if the curve

FORMS OF STANDARD CURVE

were slid along OX, the equation would then become $(x - 180) = y^2$.

Here is a quadratic equation :

$$3y^2 + 4y - 21 = 0.$$

It can be written in the forms :

    (i) $y^2 + \frac{4}{3}y + \frac{4}{9} = 7\frac{4}{9}$.

    (ii) $(y + \frac{2}{3})^2 = 7\frac{4}{9}$.

Let $x = (y + \frac{2}{3})^2$, then x and y may have an infinite number of pairs of associated values numerically, e.g. :

y	0	1	−1	2	−2	−3	−4
$(y + \frac{2}{3})^2 = x$	$\frac{4}{9}$	$\frac{25}{9}$	$\frac{1}{9}$	$\frac{64}{9}$	$\frac{16}{9}$	$\frac{49}{9}$	$\frac{100}{9}$

From these values the curve Fig. 2 has been plotted. From the drawing we read the turning point at O, $-\frac{2}{3}$, and promptly relate this reading to the equation $(y + \frac{2}{3})^2 = x$, and check our reading by the thought that the change from y to $(y + \frac{2}{3})$ in the equation causes a positional change measured by the value $7\frac{4}{9}$ in the equation.

On the drawing we set up the line $x = 7\frac{4}{9}$. We now have $x = 7\frac{4}{9} = (y + \frac{2}{3})^2$, whence we infer the solution of the quadratic equation $3y^2 + 4y - 21 = 0$ at the points where the line cuts the parabola, i.e. at A and B, Fig. 2 ; i.e. when $y = 2\cdot1$ and $-3\cdot5$ (approx.). From this it follows that the expression $(y - 2\cdot1)(y + 3\cdot5) = 0$, is, roughly, the same equation as $3y^2 + 4y - 21 = 0$. Multiplied out $(y - 2\cdot1)(y + 3\cdot5) = 0$ is $y^2 + 1\cdot4y - 7\cdot35 = 0$, i.e. $3y^2 + 4\cdot2y - 22\cdot05 = 0$.

The equation $(y - 2\cdot1)(y + 3\cdot4) = y^2 + 1\cdot3y - 7\cdot14 = 0$,

    i.e. $3y^2 + 3\cdot9y - 21\cdot42 = 0$.

Hence we infer that the value $y = 2\cdot1$ is slightly too large. Fig. 2 shows that the solution of the quadratic equation $3y^2 + 4y - 21 = 0$ is $y = 2\cdot1$ or $-3\cdot4$ (approx.).

The parabola has, therefore, three considerations : (1) the equation of its axis ; (2) the values of the turning point ; (3) the relative values of the scales.

When the equation of the curve is written thus :

$$(y + a)^2 = x + k$$

(1) the equation of the axis is $y - a = 0$.

(2) the values of the turning point are $k, -a$.

(3) the relative values of the scales are what we like to make them ; e.g. the curve of $x = 5y^2 - 9y + 46$, i.e. $\frac{1}{5}x - 8\frac{39}{100} = (y - \frac{9}{10})^2$ turns at the point $41\cdot95$, $0\cdot9$ on the axis $y - \frac{9}{10} = 0$. The curve $y = 7x^2 + 15x + 13$, has an axis $x = -\frac{15}{14}$.

Consider the equation $4x=y^2$.

Pairs of values are :

y	O	1	2	3	4
x	O	$\frac{1}{4}$	1	$2\frac{1}{4}$	4

The curve is plotted as in Fig. 3, and continued from A (4, 4) through B (16, 8) and C (36, 12).

These pairs of values 4, 4 ; 16, 8 ; 36, 12 ; suggest Pythagoras sets for $4^2=(4+1)^2 - (4 - 1)^2$; $8^2=(16+1)^2 - (16 - 1)^2$; $12^2=(36+1)^2 - (36 - 1)^2$; i.e. the Pythagoras sets 3, 4, 5 ; 8, 15, 17 ; 12, 35, 37.

The curve $4x=y^2$ represents these successive Pythagoras sets when the difference between the two larger numbers of the set is 2 ; for when $A - B=2$, $A^2 - B^2=(A+B) (A - B)=2(A+B)$ and $A - 1=B+1=a$ perfect square, i.e. the mean of A and B is a perfect square ; and the smallest number in the set must be twice this perfect square. $(N+1)$, $(N - 1)$, $2\sqrt{N}$ form a Pythagoras set when N is an integer.

Graphically, this relation is shown in Fig. 3. M is the point (1, O) whence $BM= \sqrt{8^2+15^2}=17$, $CM= \sqrt{12^2+35^2}^3=37$.

AM, BM, CM are each as far horizontally (i.e. parallel to the axis of the parabola) from the line $x+1=O$ as they are from M. Hence any point on the curve $4x=y$ is equidistant from the point (1, O) and the line $x+1=O$.

If the curve be slid so that the turning point becomes 1, O the line $x+1=O$ becomes $x=O$, i.e. OY ; M becomes (2, O), A (5, 4), B (17, 8), C (37, 12), and the equation of the curve becomes $4(x - 1)=y^2$. In this position there is a point on the curve (2, 2).

Obviously, if the scale along OX is a, 2a, 3a, etc., and M is (2a, O), then the turning point is at (a, O), and the point A is at (5a, 4a) and the equation is $4a(x - a)=y^2$; whence $4ax=y^2$ is a standard description of a parabola, where the a is a number which depends on the relative scales along OX and OY.

A parabola is a curve in which each point is equidistant from a point, called the focus, which lies on the axis of symmetry and from a line called the directrix, which is perpendicular to the axis of symmetry, such that the turn is midway between the focus and the junction of the directrix and the axis of symmetry. The width of the curve at the focus is four times the distance from the focus to the turning point.

The student should plot each of the seven curves indicated

in page 522 and check the remainder of the tabular summary.

The last equation $3x = 5y^2 - 7y - 11$ is a difficult sample, where the prime numbers are used to betray a method of determining a curve from its equation without plotting it. The process is thus :

(i) $(5y - 7y)$ yields the equation $y - \frac{7}{10} = 0$, and thus the $y -$ value of the turning point and of the focus :

(ii) by substitution in the equation it is found that when $y = \frac{7}{10}$, $x = - 4\frac{29}{60}$, i.e. the $x -$ value of the turning point ;

(iii) $(3x = 5y^2)$ gives the width at the focus, $\frac{3}{8}$; whence the equation of the directrix is $x + 4\frac{19}{30} = 0$.

Present Worth at Compound Interest. The present worth of £1 due in n years at p per cent compound interest is

$$£ \frac{1}{(1 + \frac{p}{100})^n}$$

i.e. the present worth is the reciprocal of the amount at compound interest. Obviously, the values in the compound interest table in Lesson 13 (volume 2, page 477) can be used to construct a table of present worths.

PRESENT WORTH TABLE

Period	Rate %	Present worth of £1 at end of period	
1	4	1/1·04	= 0·9615385
2	4	1/1·0816	= 0·9245562
3	4	1/1·124864	= 0·8889964
4	4	1/1·16985856	= 0·8548042
4	5	1/1·21550625	= 0·8227025
4	6	1/1·26247696	= 0·7920936

From this incomplete table it is possible to find such a present worth as the purchase price of an annuity of £1,000 to be paid at anniversaries of the date of purchase four times at 4 per cent p.a., C.I. The first four present values in the table are added ; they come to 3·6298953, and the total is multiplied by £1,000 and the purchase price is £3,629·8953, i.e. £3,630 (approx.). Other present worths should be calculated and tabulated in order to be able to find the purchase price of annuities and similar values.

The student is advised to keep a mathematical card index in order to preserve in a handy accessible form for ready reference the results of calculations ; for example, he should continuously add to tables of compound interests and present worths. The alternative is to consult a set of tables at the local reference library. At first it is better to perform the calculations and then tabulate the results.

Drill. 1. Solve the simultaneous equations : (a) $x+2y=7$; $x^2 - 4x=7y - 17$; (b) $7x - 3y=25$; $x=4(7 - 6y)^2$.

2. Form the quadratic equation of which the roots are 5 and $- 3$; and show where they occur on the graph of $y^2 - 2y=x$.

3. Find the present worth of an annuity of £100 to be paid on each of the next five anniversaries of the day of purchase at 5 per cent p.a., C.I.

Revision. 1. In any triangle ABC bisect the angles at A and C. Label the meeting points of these bisectors internally O, and externally M, N, and P, so that COP are collinear and AON are collinear. Let M be the common point of MAP and MCN. Prove (i) that MO produced bisects the angle ABC ; (ii) that PN is perpendicular to MB at B ; (iii) AOCM is a cyclic quadrilateral ; (iv) angles MPN, AOM, BON, are equal.

PARABOLA.

Equation of Curve	Turning Point	Axis of Symmetry	Focus	Directrix	Width at focus
$x=y^2$	O, O	$y=0$	$\frac{1}{4}$, O	$x+\frac{1}{4}=0$	1
$4x=y^2$	O, O	$y=0$	1, O	$x+1=0$	4
$4ax=y^2$	O, O	$y=0$	a, O	$x+a=0$	4a
$4ax=(y-b)^2$	O, b	$y=b$	a, b	$x+a=0$	4a
$12x=(y-5)^2$	O, 5	$y=5$	3, 5	$x+3=0$	12
$4a(x-c)=$ $(y-b)^2$	c, b	$y=b$	$(a+c)$,b	$x+(a-c),$ $=0$	4a
$3x=5y^2-7y$ -11	$-4\frac{29}{80}$, $\frac{7}{10}$	$y=\frac{7}{10}$	$-4\frac{1}{8}$, $\frac{7}{10}$	$x+4\frac{19}{30}=0$	$\frac{3}{5}$

2. Draw any triangle MNP. Bisect the sides and build a tetrahedron. Mark on the tetrahedron the six corners of the enclosed octahedron. Unfold the tetrahedron to become again the plane angle MNP. Where are the corners of the octahedron in relation to the sides of MNP ?

Expansion. Let AB be a straight line. (i) Express geometrically the position of a point P between A and B such that AP=PB. (ii) Express geometrically the condition which ensures the position of P when the area of the rectangle $AP.PB=K^2$, a constant smaller than $\frac{1}{4}AB^2$. (iii) When AP becomes next door to nothing, what happens to K ? (iv) When AP is next door to being equal to $\frac{1}{2}AB$, what happens to K ?

Solutions to Problems in Lesson 26

Revision. 1. 3 time units, both at A ; 6 time units, both as at beginning ; $7\frac{1}{2}$ time units, M is at B and N is halfway between A and B.

2 Let AK be perpendicular to CN cutting BD at P. Quadrilateral $ABCD=ABD+DBC=\frac{1}{2}DB.AP+\frac{1}{2}DB.PK=\frac{1}{2}DB.AK=\frac{1}{2}CN.AK-ACN.$ $AK=AC.$ sinACN. Generally, area of a quadrilateral equals the product of the diagonals times the sine of the angle between them.

Expansion : *Summary*.

Equations	Turning point	Axis of symmetry	
$y=3x^2+7$	O, 7	$x=O$	
$x=5y^2-3y$	O, O	$10y=3$	Graph through origin
$m=16t^2$	O, O	$t=O$	
$a=\pi r^2$	O, O	$r=O$	

To change the labelling of the axes of reference work from (i) turning point and (ii) half-width of curve at the focus.

LESSON 28

Progressions in Mathematics

WHEN we reach the edge of experience we have achieved either the infinitely small or the infinitely large. $A+d$, A, and $A-d$ are three values, which differ successively by d. When d is very tiny, so tiny that it is just worthy of consideration, we have reached the limit of experience in differentiating between these three values. At the edge of experience the next reduction in the dimension of d makes $A-d=A=A+d$. At this stage

(i) $d=d^2=d^3=d^n$;

(ii) $(A-d)^2=A^2-2Ad$, $(A+d)^2=A^2+2Ad$, $(A-d)^n=A^n-nA^{n-1}d$, $(A+d)^n=A^n-nA^{n-1}d$;

(iii) $A^2-(A-d)^2=2Ad=(A+d)^2-A^2$, $A^n-(A-d)^n=nA^{n-1}d=(A+d)^n-A^n$.

When $d=$ the unit of measurement $=1$, then

(iv) $A^n-(A-d)^n=nA^{n-1}=(A+d)^n-A^n$.

On this hypothesis we attain pairs of related sequences which may be numerically related thus :

$$A^2 \quad 4 \quad 9 \quad 16 \quad 25 \quad 36$$
$$2A \quad 4 \quad 6 \quad 8 \quad 10 \quad 12$$

or thus :

$$A^n=A^4 \quad 1 \quad 16 \quad 81 \quad 256$$
$$nA^{n-1}=4A^3 \quad 4 \quad 32 \quad 108 \quad 256$$

We may step down from the sequence indicated by A^n to the related sequence nA^{n-1}, or step up from the sequence nA^{n-1} to the related sequence A^n.

Since we are considering scales we may start counting where we will on the scale. We may start at k instead of zero and the general expression becomes A^n+k ; obviously, the related nA^{n-1} is independent of k, hence when we step down the constant k disappears ; but when we step up a constant k must appear, and we must decide whether the particular case we are considering is that which happens when $k=0$, that is to say, we must decide where we start counting on the scale to which we have stepped up,

Our scale units may be changed at will. They may be multiplied by k or divided by k as we wish ; this scalar division must pervade the argument and must refer to both the related sequences.

The code shorthand for the expression that the two sequences are related under the terms of the hypothesis is

$$D(A^n)=nA^{n-1}$$

the expression nA^{n-1} is called the derivative, so that the relation may be described in these terms : " the derivative of a power with respect to its base is found by multiplying by the index and then diminishing the index by 1."

Hence $D(A^n+k)=nA^{n-1}$

$$D(kA^n) \quad =nkA^{n-1}$$

$$D\left(\frac{A^n}{k}\right) \quad =\frac{n}{k}A^{n-1}$$

and $\quad D(kA) \quad =k$

Whence the derivatives with regard to base x of

$$x^4 ; \quad \sqrt{x} = x^{\frac{1}{2}} ; \quad \sqrt[3]{x^2} = x^{\frac{2}{3}} ; \quad 7x^3 \text{ are}$$

$$4x^3 ; \quad \tfrac{1}{2}x^{-\frac{1}{2}} = \frac{1}{2\sqrt{x}} ; \quad \tfrac{2}{3}x^{-\frac{1}{3}} = \frac{2}{3\sqrt[3]{x}} ; \quad 21x^2$$

Since scales are additive the derivatives with regard to base x of $x^4 + 7x^3$ and $7x^3 + 11x^2 + 13x + 15$ are $4x^3 + 21x^2$ and $21x^2 + 22x + 13$.

The derivative with regard to base r of πr^2 is $2\pi r$, which is another method of expressing the relation between the area and the circumference of a circle. The derivative of $\frac{1}{2} g t^2$ with regard to t is gt ; but $\frac{1}{2} gt^2$ is the distance travelled by a falling body from rest in t seconds and $g t$ is the speed acquired by a body falling from rest by the end of the period of t seconds.

Reverting a little, we find that $(A+c)(B+d) = AB+dA+cB+cd$, whence $(A+c)(B+d) - AD = dA+cB$, since the product cd lies beyond the limit of experience. When A and B are both functions of x, then, with regard to base x, $D(AB) = d. D(A) + c. D(B)$, e.g. let $A = 3x^2 + 7$ and $B = 11x^3 + 13$, then $D((3x^2+7)(11x^3+13)) = (11x^3+13) 6x + (3x^2+7) 33x^2 = 66x^4 + 78x + 99x^4 + 231x^2 = 165x^4 + 231x^2 + 78x$.

Check : $AB = 33x^5 + 39x^2 + 77x^3 + 91$, whence $D(AB) = 165x^4 + 231x^2 + 78x$.

With regard to base t : the derivatives of

$$t ; \frac{1}{t^2} ; (t^2 - 3) ; \frac{1}{(t^2 - 3)} ; \text{ are } 2t ; -2t^{-3} = \frac{-2t}{t^4} ; 2t ; \frac{-2t}{(t^2-3)^2}$$

and of $\frac{t^5}{t^3}$, regarding $\frac{t^5}{t_3}$ as the product of t^5 and $\frac{1}{t^3}$, t^5

$\left(-\frac{3t^2}{t^6}\right) + \frac{1}{t^3}(5t^4) = -3t + 5t = 2t$; and of $\frac{t^2 - 3}{t^2 + 3}$, considered

as the product of $t^2 - 3$ and $\frac{1}{t^2 + 3}$ $2t\left(\frac{1}{t^2 + 3}\right) + (t^2 - 3)$

$\left(\frac{-2t}{(t^2 + 3)^2}\right) = \frac{2t(t^2 + 3) - 2t(t^2 - 3)}{(t^2 + 3)^2} = \frac{12t}{(t^2 + 3)^2}$

Stepping down : The code symbol for the complete expression of the relation between the sequences we are considering is D . . . dx, i.e. " the derivative of . . . . with regard to the base x." The results so far obtained are :

$D x^n dx = nx^{n-1}$ $D (x^n + x^{n-1} + x^{n-2} + k) dx = nx^{n-1} + (n-1) x^{n-2} + (n-2) x^{n-3}$; $D (x^2 + 3) (x^3 + 5) dx = 3x^2 (x^2 + 3) + 2x (x^3 + 5)$

$$D \left(\frac{x^2 + 3}{x^3 + 5}\right) dx = \frac{3x^2 (x^2 + 3) - 2x (x^3 + 5)}{(x^3 + 5)^2}$$

Stepping up : The code symbol for the reciprocal process of stepping up is $\int \ldots dx$, which is " the integral of . . . . . with regard to the base x."

The results so far obtained may be summarized in this code, remembering that stepping up always implies the use of a constant, k.

$\int (nx^{n-1}) dx = x^n + k$; $\int (nx^{n-1} + (n-1) x^{n-2} + (n-2) x^{n-3}) dx = x^n + xn^{-1} + x^{n-2} + k$; $\int (3x^2 (x^2 + 3) + 2x (x^3 + 5)) dx = (x^2 + 3) (x^3 + 5)$; $\int \left(\frac{1}{(x^3 + 5)^2} (3x^2 (x^2 + 3) - 2x (x^3 + 5))\right)$

$$= \frac{x^2 + 3}{x^3 + 5}$$

Arithmetical Progressions. When a sequence proceeds by the addition of a constant term, e.g. 3, 7, 11, 15, it progresses arithmetically ; its code symbol is A.P. Generally : n (n + a), (n + 2a), (n + 3a) are an A.P. Successive odd numbers are an A.P.

Any term in an A.P. is the Arithmetical Mean, sometimes called the average of the two terms between which it lies ; e.g. (n + a) is the arithmetical mean between n and (n + 2a).

Geometrical Progressions. When a sequence proceeds by multiplication by a constant multiplier, e.g. 3, 12, 48, 192, it progresses geometrically and its code symbol is G.P. Generally : n, na, na^2, na^3 are a G.P. Any term in a G.P. is the Geometric Mean between the two terms between which it lies : e.g. na^2 = $\sqrt{na, na^3}$.

The Pedal Triangle. The internal and external bisectors of an angle are perpendicular to each other. The bisectors of the internal angles of a triangle are concurrent. The bisectors of the external angles of a triangle are concurrent at three points external to the triangle. Let us call the triangle made by joining these three points the " bisector " triangle. The lines from each corner of the bisector triangle, which are the internal bisectors of the angles of the original triangle, are the perpendiculars from the corners to the opposite sides. The feet of these perpendiculars are the corners of the original triangle ; hence the original triangle is the " pedal " triangle of the " bisector " triangle.

It follows from the argument that the properties of any pedal triangle may be demonstrated not in relation to the pedal triangle itself, but in relation to the bisector triangle, since the concurrent perpendiculars of the bisector triangle are also the concurrent bisectors of the pedal triangle ; the properties of these lines may, therefore, be referred to either triangle. Hence the corners of the bisector triangle are the centres of the three circles which can be escribed to the pedal triangle. The point of concurrency of the perpendiculars is labelled the orthocentre ; hence the orthocentre of any triangle is the in-centre of its pedal triangle.

Drill. 1. Differentiate with regard to x :

(i) $(5x - 2) (3x + 7)$; (ii) $(x + 1) (x - 2) (x + 3) (x - 4)$; and check your results.

2. Differentiate with regard to m :

$$\text{(i)} \quad \frac{(m - 1)^2}{(m^2 - 1)} \text{ ; (ii) } C/(B - Am)$$

Revison. 1. M. can do a job in 15 days of 7 hours each, and N can do the same job in a day less if he works an hour more each day. In how many 10-hr. days can they do the job together ?

2. A man earns A times as much per hour as a boy ; he also does B times as much work per hour as the boy. Find an expression for the composition of the most economical team of men and boys.

Expansion. Find expressions for the areas of the inscribed and circumscribed hexagons to a circle of unit radius. Find the geometric mean of these areas. Find also the geometric mean in the case of similar octagons. Find the ratio between these means and the area of a circle of unit radius. Generalize the result for an n — gon, using radians as angular units.

Solutions to Problems in Lesson 27

Drill. 1. (i) $x = 7 - 2y$; $(7 - 2y) (3 - 2y) = 7y - 17$; i.e. $(19 - 4y) (2 - y) = 0$; i.e. $y = 2$ or $4\frac{3}{4}$, $x = 3$ or $-2\frac{1}{2}$ (ii) $1347 - 2355y + 1008y^2 = 0$, i.e. $(y - 1) (1008y - 1347) = 0$; $y = 1$ or $1\frac{113}{336}$; $x = 4$ or $4\frac{111}{784}$

2. $(y-5)(y+3)=0$, i.e. $y^2-2y=15$. The roots occur at the points 15,5 and 15, -3.

3. If your tables are incomplete, proceed thus : let $x=1\cdot05$.

then $\dfrac{1}{x}+\dfrac{1}{x^2}+\dfrac{1}{x^3}+\dfrac{1}{x^4}+\dfrac{1}{x^5}=\dfrac{1}{x}\cdot\dfrac{1-\dfrac{1}{x^5}}{1-\dfrac{1}{x}}=\dfrac{(x^5-1)}{x^5(x-1)}$ but $x=$

$1\cdot2762815625$; P. W. $=$ £$100\times20\times\dfrac{0\cdot27628}{1\cdot27628}=433.$

Revision. 1 (i) By symmetry PB and NB are collinear as the bisectors of the exterior angles at B ; also M lies on the bisector BO of the angle ABC ; (ii) hence MB is perpendicular to PN ; (iii) OAM and OCM are right angles, hence AOCM is cyclic ; (iv) angles MPN, AOM, BON, each equal half the sum of the angles

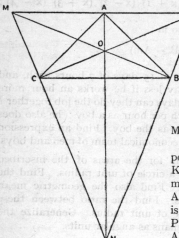

ABC and BAC.

2. Bisect MP, PN, MN at C, B, and A. Bisect MC at F, CP at G, PB at H, BN at K, NA at L, AM at W, AC at X, CB at Y, BA at Z. Then F, G, H, K, L, W, X, Y, Z are the corners, and only four small triangles each a sixteenth of MNP appear in the octahedron.

Expansion. (i) P is the mid-point of AB. (ii) AP is to K as K is to PB, i.e. K is the geometric mean between AP and PB. On AB describe a semicircle, then P is such a point that the line from P to the curve perpendicular to AB is equal to K. (iii) When AP is minute then K is minute, but less minute than AP. (iv) When AP is nearly half AB then AP $=$ K approx.

At the limit of experience of the very small AP and K vanish together or AP and K become equal in size.

Our Course in Mathematics is continued in **Volume 4**

Sweden's Last Bid for Empire

(See plate 56)

BEFORE continuing our history after the death of Louis XIV, we must turn to the other states which were rising or receding during the period of his reign. Though the first half of the seventeenth century had been a time of inertia for the Ottoman power, in the second half its activities were revived, and Turkish aggression threatened to be as dangerous as it had been at its zenith in the sixteenth century. In 1656, four years before Louis' accession, the Grand Vizier of the Ottoman empire had been bent on reviving the conquering glories of Islam. In 1663 the Turks were pouring into Austrian territory and threatening Vienna. They were routed at the battle of St. Gothard, where Leopold had the help of a French contingent. But Leopold only wanted peace, and it was scarcely as a victor that he accepted the ensuing treaty. The Turks retained possession of half Hungary. From Venice they wrested the island of Crete. Then, in 1671, they attacked Poland.

John Sobieski. Poland was theoretically a kingdom ; that is, it owned a nominal king whose crown was bestowed on him by election, while he exercised no real power. In fact, the Polish nobles ruled the country so far as it was ruled at all. Feudalism there had completely triumphed over all attempts at centralization. Nevertheless, Poland was saved by the genius of John Sobieski (1624–96), a shrewd and disinterested statesman as well as a brilliant military commander. He, in accordance with current western ideas, considered it his duty, apart from the menace to his country, to vanquish and slay the enemies of Christendom. In spite of the frightful difficulties with which they had to contend, his forces held the Turks at bay, and routed them in one battle after another, until in 1676, having defied the Turkish efforts to storm the Polish camps entrenched near the Dniester, Sobieski (who in 1674 had been elected king of Poland) made a truce for five years and the Turks retreated from Poland.

Hungary, however, was restive under the rule of the emperor. The disaffected leaders allied themselves with the Turks, and in

1682 a great Turkish army crossed the Danube. The king of France, who, just then, was not at war with Austria, exerted himself only to draw off any possible allies. Poland promised the emperor aid. In 1683 the Turks, under the grand vizier, Kara Mustafa, invested Vienna. The besieged held out until the arrival of Sobieski and his army, reinforced with a large contingent of Germans, when the Turks were utterly put to rout.

End of Turkish Empire. From that time the Turks were gradually driven back, though not without occasional successes. They were cleared out of Hungary and out of a greater part of Greece. Athens had been in Turkish possession since 1458. In 1687 the Venetians laid siege to the city, and one of their shells, falling upon the glorious Parthenon, the most perfect specimen of Greek architecture, used by the Turks as a powder magazine, shattered the middle temple and destroyed the side columns. Subsequently, in 1697, Eugene, in command of the imperial armies, inflicted a great defeat upon the sultan himself at Zenta. At the same moment the Russian tsar, Peter the Great, was attacking the Turkish territories on the Black Sea. In 1699 the Turks accepted the Peace of Karlowitz, which, in effect, made the Danube their boundary. The last struggle took place when the War of the Spanish Succession had just terminated, and in 1718 the Treaty of Passarowitz ended the Turkish war.

The military power of Sweden was in abeyance after the death of Charles X, in 1660, and the possessions acquired through the Thirty Years' War were regarded greedily by the Danish monarchy and the " Great Elector " of Brandenburg. That astute prince, by dint of skilful and unscrupulous diplomacy, succeeded in consolidating his scattered dominions which, under his son Frederick I, were converted into the kingdom of Prussia in 1701. But more notable even than this was the creation of Russia.

By the beginning of the sixteenth century Russia was free of the Mongol supremacy, and was becoming united under a dynasty of whom the most famous member was Ivan the Terrible. Russia was, however, a barbarian power, virtually cut off from communication with the civilization of the west, blocked from the Baltic Sea by territories over which ruled either Sweden or Poland. Until the reign of Peter the Great, who became tsar in 1682, Russia was of no account in the affairs of Europe.

Peter the Great. Peter was possessed of an indomitable will, which shrank from no dangers and no difficulties. He meant to bring Russia into its place among the nations of the west. Within his own dominions he crushed all opposition with a merciless hand. His genius realized that, to advance, Russia must reach the sea—the Black Sea and the Baltic—and must possess a fleet. If Russia was to become civilized, the thing must be done by someone who knew the ways of civilized countries.

He travelled through Europe to learn what European civilization meant ; he laboured in the dockyards of Holland and England to learn what shipbuilding meant. He went back to Russia, and set about training a disciplined army chiefly under the direction of Scottish military adventurers. He abolished time-honoured customs which he condemned as uncivilized. He captured Azof from the Turks, and began his navy building on the Black Sea. He conceived that the accession of a boy of sixteen Charles XII, in Sweden, gave him his chance of acquiring Baltic territory, and he allied himself with Poland and Denmark with a view to the partition of Pomerania. By this time John Sobieski was dead, and the Poles had chosen Augustus of Saxony for their king. The Great Elector was also dead, and his son Frederick, had not inherited his political or military talents ; Brandenburg was left out of court.

Charles XII of Sweden In 1700 Poland had begun, and Denmark was on the point of beginning, an attack on Sweden, when the young Charles, who was now eighteen, seized the control of Sweden by a coup d'état, hurled himself upon Denmark, compelled it to retire from the coalition, and then sprang upon Augustus of Poland, who had attacked Riga, first putting utterly to rout with his small body of troops a great Russian horde which was gathered at Narva. Charles was a fighter, not a statesman. He thought of Saxony, not Russia, as the enemy. He turned on the Poles, who, at his dictation, were quite ready to depose their Saxon king, when Charles set the Polish nobility against him by selecting one of them, Stanislaus Lecszinski, for the crown.

Augustus had to retire and to withdraw from the Russian alliance. But Peter was not disheartened by the rout of Narva : on the contrary, his troops were again overrunning the Baltic provinces, since Charles had no army large enough to leave in occupation. He thought, like Napoleon after him, that he could conquer Russia by striking at Moscow. The Russians treated Charles as their descendants treated Napoleon. They avoided pitched battles, but when the Swedish forces had advanced far enough, fell upon their line of communication. Then as Charles was laying siege to Pultowa, his isolated army was overwhelmed. Charles barely escaped with his life across the Turkish frontier.

Charles remained for a long time in Turkey, endeavouring to bring on a war between Turkey and Russia. He succeeded, but though the Turks got Peter in a trap they contented themselves with a treaty which deprived him of Azof. Meanwhile, all Pomerania was being absorbed by Charles's enemies. Suddenly he hurried back from Turkey, but he was already too late to save his possessions. In 1718 his career was cut short by a stray shot before Frederikshald, in Norway, and, as Dr. Johnson wrote, he

> " Left a name at which the world grew pale,
> To point a moral or adorn a tale."

From the moment of his death Sweden fell permanently out of the group of first-class powers. Peter's activities for the rest of his reign were directed to the east, not the west.

LESSON 14

Britain Becomes a First-class Power

(See plate 57)

AFTER the treaty of Utrecht (1713) and the death of Louis XIV (1715), although France was still the most powerful state in Europe, there was no further menace of a French dictatorship until the turn of the 18th century. The treaty, in fact, marked the defeat of the Grand Monarch's ambitious schemes, and the practical result was a rearrangement of alliances. The French Government, under the Regent Orleans, nephew of the dead king, required the friendship of Britain to secure it against the possible claims to succession of Philip V of Spain, the uncle of the sickly young king ; while in Britain the House of Hanover and the Whigs required the friendship of the French Government, which otherwise would give its support to the exiled House of Stuart. The two countries then usually acted together, with one important consequence—that France, relying on British fleets, neglected her own.

This association, however, was bound to disappear with the disappearance of the chance that the Spanish Bourbon might lay claim to the French throne if Louis XV died without leaving an heir of his body. A rapprochement between the two Bourbon dynasties would then be almost inevitable.

On the other hand, the immediately disturbing factor in European politics was to be found in the jealousies of Austria and Spain under her new dynasty, and the ambitions of Philip's queen-consort, the Italian Elizabeth Farnese, his second wife, for the advancement of her own children, whose succession to the Spanish throne was blocked by her step-children, the offspring of Philip's first marriage.

Schemes of Cardinal Alberoni. Philip V and Charles VI of Austria, who became emperor in 1711, each considered that the treaty of Utrecht had robbed him for the benefit of the other. The Spanish king found a very able minister in Cardinal Alberoni (1664–1752), whose primary desire was the renovation of the Spanish maritime power, as well as the recovery for Spain of possessions which the recent treaties had conferred upon Austria or Savoy. Austria wished Savoy to exchange Sicily for Sardinia ; Alberoni wanted the same exchange to be made, as far as Savoy was concerned, but he wanted Sicily for Spain, not for Austria. An attempt to capture Sardinia was foiled by the intervention of France and Great Britain, each of whom was interested primarily, as we have noted, in maintaining the terms of the Utrecht treaty. Then, while Austria was engaged in her final struggle with the Turk, Alberoni suddenly attacked Sicily itself, but his plans were frustrated by the appearance of a British fleet, which, under Admiral Byng, found an excuse for annihilating the new-born Spanish fleet off Cape Passaro. The capture of Belgrade released masses of Austrian troops, the Spanish attempt to recover power failed completely, and the other Powers united in compelling Philip to dismiss his minister.

Within the next few years Sir Robert Walpole (1676–1745) was firmly established at the helm in Great Britain ; the Regent Orleans died, and young king Louis XV placed Cardinal Fleury (1653–1743) in control of affairs in France. Also, Louis' marriage to the daughter of Stanislaus Lecszinski (who had again been turned out of his Polish kingdom by Augustus of Saxony) made it improbable that the opportunity would ever occur for Philip of Spain to lay claim to the French throne. From this time it was Fleury's object to establish that intimate association between France and Spain at which Louis XIV had aimed in the War of the Spanish Succession. By 1733 this policy had issued in the secret family compact of the two Bourbon Powers, which was directed, in the first place, against Austria, and, in the second place, against Great Britain.

Pacifist Aims of Walpole and Fleury. Both Walpole and Fleury wanted to achieve their ends not by fighting, but by diplomacy. Walpole wanted to secure a material prosperity which would keep the British contented with the Hanoverian dynasty, while material wealth acquired through commerce would also in the long run carry with it fighting power. Fleury wished France to recuperate after the financial exhaustion consequent upon the wars of Louis XIV. For the time, therefore, Fleury and Walpole could act in concert, though Fleury's secret policy was an ultimate menace to Great Britain, and Walpole was perfectly aware of the fact. It is, however, singular that neither statesman made preparations for such a struggle. Fleury, relying on diplomacy to keep Austria and Great Britain apart until Austria should be too much weakened and too resentful towards her old ally to join forces with her, made no attempt to resuscitate the Franco-Spanish navies for a contest with the British navy, while Walpole paid no attention to naval or military organization.

Until 1739 Walpole kept his country at peace, while the nation amassed the great wealth which enabled it to carry through the struggle when it came. By this year the social conditions of the country had fallen to a low level—thanks largely to Walpole's system of political corruption—and the people seemed sunk in moral lethargy. In 1739, however, the Wesleys and Whitefield opened their evangelizing mission, which had the far-reaching effect of directing the energies of the British masses into religious channels while France was in the throes of revolution.

War of the Polish Succession. Europe plunged into the War of the Polish Succession in 1733. Russia wanted the second Augustus of Saxony to succeed his father on the Polish throne ; France wanted the succession for Stanislaus Lecszinski—a " shuttlecock king," who played an undignified part in the vicissitudes of Poland—who was the French king's father-in-law. The quarrel might have been patched up without a European war but for the Emperor Charles VI, who wanted the Austrian succession to go after him to his own daughter, Maria Teresa, although, if a female succession was legitimate at all, his elder brother's daughter, who had been set aside in his favour, had the better claim, which was sure to be asserted by her husband, the Elector of Bavaria. Charles, therefore, wanted the support of the Elector of Saxony for the instrument called the " Pragmatic Sanction," in which he declared that his daughter was his heiress, and for which he had procured the guarantee of most of the Powers. Therefore, he supported the Elector's claim to the Polish succession in opposition to France, and thereupon France and Spain turned the struggle into one in which Italian territories were of more importance than the actual Polish succession. Thus Walpole looked on while half the European Powers were draining their treasuries and exhausting their armies.

The outcome of the war of the Polish succession was that, while Augustus of Saxony got Poland, Naples (the Two Sicilies) was made into a kingdom for a third (Spanish) Bourbon prince, and France strengthened her own position by acquiring Lorraine, whose duke, the husband of Maria Teresa, was compensated by receiving Tuscany instead. Austria, though it lost the Two Sicilies, acquired, in effect, the greater part of north Italy. The exchange of the island of Sicily for Sardinia by the duke of Savoy, who was now king of Sardinia, had been accomplished some time before.

War of Jenkins' Ear. The Bourbons, then, had gained a good deal, though it was at the price of an exhausting war. But Austria was not yet materially weakened. Naturally, the opportunity for carrying out the objects of the family compact would have come with the death of the Emperor Charles VI, which took place in 1740, and the inevitable struggle for the Austrian succession which followed. But, in the first place, the programme was spoilt, not by the statesmen, but by a violent outburst of popular feeling in England and in Spain, which forced the hands of the politicians, and plunged those two countries into a war on their own account, known as the War of Jenkins' Ear, because one of its contributory causes was the cutting off of Captain Jenkins' ear by a Spanish naval officer in 1731. In the next place, when Charles died, all previous calculations were upset by the unexpected action of Frederick II of Prussia.

Conditions in Russia. Before proceeding, however, to the War of the Pragmatic Sanction or Austrian Succession, we must glance at the new Power in the east and north. Peter the Great had compelled Russia to adopt or imitate western customs, which were never naturalized and were resented by Russian conservatism. He had achieved access both to the Black and the Baltic Sea. He had carried his arms eastward against Persia as well as against Turkey in the south ; but Russia was still outside the political system of western Europe He had died in 1725 ; and Russian conditions deteriorated grievously. The bureaucracy which he had " created to be the servant of the country, made the country its servant ; the army . . . he created to be at the disposal of the throne, had the throne at its disposal."

Five years later the crown had been secured by Peter's niece, Anne of Courland, who for ten years maintained her absolute authority ; but, apart from the intrigues of the Court and palace plots, she had been chiefly engaged in indecisive conflict with the Turks. She died in 1740, and in 1741 the succession was secured by Peter's daughter Elizabeth, the ruler of Russia for twenty years to come. Before her accession an indolent woman of abandoned tastes, as empress she ruled with energetic ability and strengthened Russian influence in the councils of Europe. The masses of her people, her peasant people, remained degraded by unjust state law, landlord theory and appalling economic circumstances. Yet they refused to accept hopeless servitude, and maintained against their landlords, in the words of a famous proverb, " We are yours, but the land is ours." In spite of cramping misgovernment, their vitality, the vitality of Russia, is astounding throughout their history.

LESSON 15

War of the Austrian Succession

(See plate 57)

AFTER the death of the great Elector of Brandenburg his son Frederick had done little enough to extend the power of the Electorate. But he had been permitted to assume the royal title as king Frederick I of Prussia. Frederick's son, Frederick William, had devoted himself entirely to the organization of his kingdom as an army. He had built up a highly perfected military machine. His son, Frederick II, who succeeded him at the beginning of 1740, was determined to use that military machine for the consolidation of his kingdom by the acquisition of sundry territories which were strategically necessary to its

political development. Prussia was still separated from Brandenburg by a wedge of Polish territory stretching up to the shores of
the Baltic. Geographically, Silesia, which lay within the Austrian
dominion, was necessary to the completion of the kingdom which
Frederick contemplated, and he had some sort of technical claim
to it, though, indeed, a very inadequate one. At the end of the
same year Maria Teresa (1717–80) claimed the succession to her
father, Charles VI, in Austria in accordance with the decree of the
Pragmatic Sanction.

In 1740, as we saw in the preceding Lesson, the British and
Spaniards were already fighting each other on the high seas over
the latest development of their ancient quarrel about the American
trade. British merchantmen, in spite of the trade privileges
acquired by the Treaty of Utrecht, persisted in evading the
restrictive regulations on that trade, and the Spaniards persisted
in enforcing those regulations in an extremely high-handed and
often illegal fashion. Walpole, in spite of his pacifist policy, had
been compelled to yield to the storm of popular wrath, and had
declared war. Charles of Bavaria, in right of his wife, had
denounced the Pragmatic Sanction, and declared his own claim
to the entire Austrian inheritance. He was also a candidate for
the imperial crown in opposition to Francis of Lorraine, the
husband of Maria Teresa. France and Spain had no sort of
intention of standing by their guarantee of the Pragmatic Sanction : George II of England, as Elector of Hanover was entirely
on the side of Maria Teresa.

At this point the king of Prussia, upsetting all the calculations
of Fleury and Walpole, launched his troops into Silesia, and
announced to Maria Teresa that if she would acknowledge his
sovereignty in that province he would stand by her. In 1741 he
proved his own importance and the value of his troops by winning
the battle of Mollwitz over the Austrians, the queen having
naturally repudiated his proposals with indignation. France
intervened, sending her troops to fight, under the curious fiction
that they were merely auxiliaries for Bavaria ; and though Great
Britain sent troops to help Maria Teresa, theoretically Great
Britain and France were not at war with each other. Perhaps the
motive most strongly actuating George II was the fear that
Frederick of Prussia might attack Hanover.

George's position made him anxious to remove the Prussian
menace to Hanover by persuading Maria Teresa to buy him off with

a substantial portion of Silesia. In fact, she found her position so critical that, although the usually turbulent Hungarians proclaimed their enthusiastic support for her cause, she did for a time neutralize Frederick by ceding Lower Silesia, though a little later he returned to the attack and obtained better terms.

Each of the belligerent states was seeking some gain for itself, so that neither of the coalitions worked in real cooperation. In 1744 the tide had so far set in favour of Maria Teresa that she was disinclined for peace, except on terms of recovering what she had been obliged to give up. George's efforts to procure a pacification failed, new leagues were formed, and France entered the war, no longer as an auxiliary, but as a principal, so that at last the governments of Britain and France were actually formally at war —a circumstance deriving special importance from the fact that it opened the way, hitherto closed, for the French and British East India Companies to attack each other in India.

The Young Pretender. In 1745, although Charles of Bavaria died and his son came to terms with Austria, resigning his claim to the imperial succession, so that Maria Teresa's husband Francis was elected emperor, France was prospering in the Netherlands, and Frederick would give up nothing of what he had gained. Since Prussia and France, on the one side, and Austria, on the other, could not come to terms, the war went on. For Great Britain the interest was varied by the great Jacobite insurrection headed by Charles Edward Stuart, the young Chevalier, or Pretender, as his friends and enemies respectively called him, on behalf of his father, James Edward. Charles led his Highlanders into the heart of England, but his advisers refused to advance farther than Derby. The prince was compelled to retreat, and in the next year the hopes of the Stuarts were finally blasted by the decisive victory of the established government at Culloden ; the prince was a fugitive, and finally escaped from England disguised as a woman.

Peace of Aix-la-Chapelle. A pacific king, Ferdinand, succeeded to the Spanish throne. He at once sought to withdraw from the war, while Frederick also held his hand, indignant because France played her own game regardless of his. In the course of the war Britain had proved her own decisive superiority at sea. French and English had been fighting in America, where the British had taken Louisburg, which lies just outside the mouth of the St. Lawrence. They had been fighting in India, where the French had turned the British out of Madras. But all the parties were tired of a struggle which seemed to promise a result satisfactory to none of them. The War of the Austrian Succession was brought to an end in 1748 by the peace of Aix-la-Chapelle. The one solid gainer was Frederick of Prussia, who retained Silesia. To counterbalance the loss of Silesia, Austria had little except the recognition of Francis as emperor and of his wife Maria Teresa as her father's heiress. There was no doubt that she would merely await her opportunity for endeavouring to recover Silesia and to crush Frederick. Practically everyone else restored such conquests as they might have happened to make. The war had settled practically nothing, beyond proving the ascendancy of British fleets on the seas and the military power of Prussia.

British Government in India. Meanwhile, despite the peace, British and French companies were fighting each other in India in support of rival claimants to native thrones, not avowedly against each other. The British East India Company had three "presidencies": at Bombay, at Fort William (Calcutta) on the Hooghli, one of the mouths of the Ganges, and at Madras in the Carnatic. The headquarters of the French company in India were also in the Carnatic, at Pondicherry. The French governor, Dupleix, wished to establish his influence at the courts of the Nizam of Hyderabad and of the Nawab of the Carnatic at Arcot. His plans were frustrated by the brilliant audacity of Robert Clive (1725–74), and after the capture and defence of Arcot (1751), while the French got their candidate on to the throne of Hyderabad, the British got theirs at Arcot, and the prestige had passed from the French to the British in India. Hostilities were stopped temporarily by the recall of Dupleix in 1754. It had, however, become certain to shrewd observers that when the inevitable fighting should be resumed, not only between the two companies, but between the two nations, the command of the sea would be the decisive factor, and that nothing but hopeless mismanagement and inefficiency could in that event deprive the British of ultimate victory. But when the struggle did come, the European combinations had become entirely rearranged. Austria, Russia and France were united by Austrian diplomacy for the destruction of Frederick of Prussia, whereas Great Britain was unexpectedly found to be allied with Frederick and in opposition to Austria. Spain, on the other hand, under Ferdinand, followed the prosperous path of peace, retrenchment, and reform.

LESSON 16

Decisive Battles
of the Seven Years' War

See Plate 58.

A<small>T</small> the beginning of 1756 the Austrian league was all but completed ; in May France and Austria signed the defensive Treaty of Versailles. The alliance between Prussia and Britain practically involving Hanover had been avowed in the defensive Treaty of Westminster in January of that year ; while it was certain that Saxony, lying on the southern frontier of Brandenburg, would act with the Powers which were bent on crushing Frederick. The first move was made by the French, who attacked and captured Port Mahon, in Minorca. The next blow was struck by Frederick, who suddenly marched into Saxony, hoping to force it into immediate submission, and, when he had paralysed it, to fling himself upon Bohemia before the Austrians were ready for the attack. Saxony offered a more stubborn resistance than he had anticipated, and he was not able to advance against Austria until the following year, 1757. For nearly a year Britain, under the guidance of an incompetent administration, accomplished nothing. Then the control passed to William Pitt.

William Pitt. From the moment of Pitt's ascendancy the war took on a definite character. Pitt threw his energies into the most vigorous development of a naval policy which was to secure not merely an ascendancy, but very nearly a monopoly on the seas. He planned and organized campaigns in America, to be supported by the fleet, which should destroy the French power in Canada. He made it impossible for French reinforcements to reach India. By perpetually threatening a descent upon the French coast he compelled France to retain large defensive forces at various points, instead of concentrating armies for the overwhelming of Prussia. Only small contingents were sent to swell the Prussian army, which covered the west of Brandenburg from attack, but large subsidies were poured into the treasury of the Prussian king. Pitt's contribution to the war on the Continent materially enabled Frederick to maintain the contest against a circle of foes, which included Russia, Austria and France.

Black Hole of Calcutta. In 1756, before the declaration of war in Europe had reached India, the Nawab of Bengal, a man of feeble intellect and inflamed by bitter hatred of the English, massacred the British residents at Calcutta, shutting 146 of them up in a cellar where there was barely standing room, and the only inlets for air were small gratings. Only 23 survived the night's imprisonment in the " Black Hole of Calcutta."

Clive was dispatched with the available troops from Madras to demand reparation. He captured Calcutta, allied himself with the leading natives, who had formed a conspiracy for the deposition of the Nawab, marched against him with 3,000 men, and scattered the native army of 60,000 men at Plassey (1757). At least one-third of the enemy had intended to desert if they saw any reasonable probability of the British success. Terrific as the odds seemed, Plassey was, in fact, an easily won victory. But the impression which it produced upon the native mind was tremendous ; and the practical result was that actually, though not formally, Clive, as general, not of the Crown, but of the East India Company, became master of Bengal. In 1760 he went back to England, and Macaulay (Historical Essays : " Lord Clive ") observes that during the next five years " the misgovernment of the English was carried to a point such as seems hardly compatible with the very existence of society." Clive returned to India in 1765, and in his stay of eighteen months he achieved " one of the most extensive, difficult, and salutary reforms that ever was accomplished by any statesman. . . . He called up all the force of his mind for a battle far harder than that of Plassey. . . . When he landed in Calcutta in 1765, Bengal was regarded as a place to which Englishmen were sent only to get rich, by any means in the shortest possible time. He first made dauntless and unsparing war on that gigantic system of oppression, extortion and corruption."

The contest began again between French and British, but there were no reinforcements for the French, since the British held the seas, and in 1760 the battle of Wandiwash practically brought the struggle to its foregone conclusion, although Pondicherry was not taken till next year.

Capture of Quebec. In America, too, the French and British colonists had been fighting before the war was actually declared. Pitt's plan of crushing the French in Canada by converging columns was at first foiled by the incapacity of the commanders.

The British fleets, however, cut off the French from receiving effective reinforcements. The real key of the French position in Canada was Quebec. In 1759 Quebec was captured by a brilliant feat of arms, the scaling of the Heights of Abraham, by General Wolfe, and the routing of the French forces under Montcalm on the summit. The fall of Quebec was followed by that of Montreal, and the conquest of Canada was virtually completed. In the same year the British fleet, which, since the beginning of the war, had generally kept the French squadrons in port, and had almost put a stop to French commerce, annihilated the French Navy by the two victories of Boscawen at Lagos and, still more notably, that of Admiral Hawke at Quiberon.

Successful Campaigns of Frederick. Meanwhile, Frederick had been carrying on his amazing struggle against the united Powers. The one advantage he possessed was that of occupying the central position, from which he could strike with extreme rapidity at one point after another of the enclosing circle. In 1757, while his enemies were slowly moving up on every side, he dashed upon Prague, in Bohemia, with his main force, won a great victory, laid siege to Prague, and, when the great Austrian army, much larger than his own, was brought on the scene, lost what he had won in a disastrous defeat at Kolin. However, he managed to retreat through Saxony, unpursued by the slow-moving Austrian, Daun.

By this time a great French army was moving up from the south under Soubise ; Frederick, with his reorganized forces, shattered it at Rossbach. Within a few weeks he was in Silesia again, and won a brilliant victory over the Austrians at Leuthen. In 1758 he had to check the Russian hosts in a desperate battle at Zorndorf and then to hurry back to Saxony, where, in spite of a defeat at Hochkirchen, he succeeded in forcing Daun to fall back to Bohemia. The frightful strain of the perpetual pitched battles had reduced his Prussian forces to very small numbers, but in 1759 Frederick was saved by a decisive victory on the west, won at Minden against the French by Ferdinand of Brunswick, in command of the British, Hanoverians and Brunswickers. On the other hand, the Russians inflicted a severe defeat upon Frederick at Kunersdorf. If the victors had followed up their advantage, the fate of Prussia must have been sealed. In 1760 the exhaustion of Prussia was still more marked ; Frederick began to despair of finding recruits or provisions for his army, but while the means of sustaining and destroying life remained he was determined to continue.

Results of the Struggle. Two events then changed the affairs of Europe : the resignation of Pitt from office and the death of the Empress Elizabeth of Russia. Pitt's successor, Bute, arranged the Peace of Paris, followed by that of Hubertsburg, in 1763, and Russian hostility was removed or suspended. France was exhausted by the struggle with Britain, whose fleets had captured piecemeal all the transmarine possessions of France and of Spain, which had been induced by France to join in the conflict when it had already become hopeless.

The broad outcome of the Seven Years' War was that Britain was established as a territorial power in India, where France no longer had any effective foothold. Canada was ceded to Great Britain, which, by the treaty, resigned a good many conquests. In Europe there were no territorial rearrangements, but Frederick remained in possession of Silesia. The Prussian monarchy had permanently taken its place among the Great Powers of Europe. The war was over. It had undoubtedly proved Frederick's superiority against odds and " the utmost spite of fortune " ; it had, however, resulted in destruction and decay in his victorious country. Macaulay in his essay on Frederick the Great, writes :

"The ruin of private fortunes, the distress of all ranks, was such as might appal the firmest mind. Almost every province had been the seat of war, and of war conducted with merciless ferocity Clouds of Croatians had descended on Silesia. Tens of thousands of Cossacks had been let loose on Pomerania and Brandenburg. . . . The fields lay uncultivated. The very seed corn had been devoured in the madness of hunger. Famine and contagious maladies produced by famine, had swept away the herds and flocks. . . . Near fifteen thousand houses had been burned to the ground. The population of the kingdom had in seven years decreased to the frightful extent of ten per cent. . . . The currency had been debased ; the authority of laws and magistrates had been suspended ; the whole social system was deranged. For, during that convulsive struggle, everything that was not military violence was anarchy."

LESSON 17

Birth of the U.S.A. and Britain's Indian Empire

(See plate 59)

A LONG interval was to elapse before there was another European war. The British Government involved itself in what was at first a constitutional contest with the old colonies in America, which issued in the American War of Independence, lasting from 1775 to 1783. For all practical purposes, Britain throughout this period ignored Continental politics. France and Spain, however, did not ignore British politics, and presently used their opportunity, so that the British Empire was only saved from destruction by the fleet.

France, Austria and Prussia, at the moment, found sufficient scope for their energies in devoting themselves, with more or less success, to recuperation after the exhaustion of the Seven Years' War. Russia continued under the empress Catherine the process of consolidation and expansion southwards and eastwards which since the days of Peter the Great had been most active under the empress Elizabeth. For a long time past, however, the three eastern Powers—Prussia, Russia, and Austria —had turned greedy eyes upon Poland. Russia wanted the eastern provinces of that kingdom, Austria those on the south, while Frederick wanted West Prussia, the Polish province which isolated his own dominion of East Prussia by cutting it off from Brandenburg. In 1772 the three Powers came to an agreement among themselves for the partition of a considerable portion of Poland, Austria appropriating the southern province, while the Prussian kingdom took West Prussia, and Russia absorbed a tract of territory on the east. Poland was not as yet wiped out. There was enough left for two further partitions in 1793 and 1795, when Poland was obliterated. In 1772 Great Britain was too fully occupied with colonial and domestic quarrels to intervene, even if disposed to do so, while France had lost interest in Poland. On the other hand, France had four years earlier acquired Corsica from Genoa with the good will of the Corsicans, who had previously offered themselves to England. Owing to this Napoleon was born a French and not an English subject.

RIVALS FOR GERMAN HEGEMONY. Frederick II of Prussia (1712–86), seen here in a portrait executed in 1739 by Antoine Pesne, succeeded his father on the throne of Prussia in 1740 and almost at once embarked on a career of the most unscrupulous aggression. One of his greatest coups was his seizure of Silesia, part of the dominions of the Austrian empress, Maria Teresa (1717–80), depicted on the left. MODERN HISTORY 15

JENKINS' EAR. The Anglo-Spanish War of 1739 is often called "The War of Jenkins' Ear," owing to the fact that a contributory cause was the popular indignation aroused by the case of Robert Jenkins, an English merchant sea-captain trading with the West Indies, who asserted that the Spaniards boarded his vessel off Havana in 1731, accused him of smuggling, and cut off his ear. Walpole resisted the clamour for war as long as he could, and this contemporary caricature shows him waving aside Captain Jenkins, who is showing him his severed ear, while a servant ejects another merchant complainant and Fleury's emissary offers his country's mediation. MODERN HISTORY 14

ROBERT, LORD CLIVE (1725–74).
Going to India in 1744 as a clerk in the
service of the East India Company, he
joined its army and after some sensational victories became Governor of Bengal. He retired in 1766 owing to ill-health
and died by his own hand. More than
any other he laid the foundations of British rule in India. MODERN HISTORY 15

SITE OF THE BLACK HOLE OF CALCUTTA. Within the railings shown
in this picture is enclosed the site of the cellar 22 feet square, known as the
" Black Hole," at Fort William, Calcutta. On June 20, 1756, the nawab of
Bengal, to whom the British fort had surrendered, confined 146 prisoners in
this narrow space. Only 23 survived until the morning. MODERN HISTORY 16

Plate 58   *Volume III*

When Frederick the Great died in 1786, he had raised Prussia, by the diplomacy of his latter years almost as much as by his wars in the past, to be practically the premier power in Germany, by posing as the champion of the rights of the German princes in the face of the unconstitutional efforts of the emperor Joseph II to establish an effective imperial control ; but his nephew and successor, Frederick William II, rested on his uncle's laurels. Joseph was a man of lofty but confused ideals, conspicuous as one of the " benevolent despots " of the period, but also as having failed in everything he undertook.

War of American Independence. In its influence on world-history, the supreme event of this period was the birth of the North American Republic. The real grievance was the denial by the British Government of the right of American colonists to settle in the territory acquired as a result of the French war. The colonial population was rapidly expanding   As the frontiersmen stood on the Alleghanies and, looking over the vast regions which the Americans had helped to win for the Empire in eight years of fighting, realized that the government 3,000 miles away denied them right of free occupation because of indecision as to its future administration, they looked on the denial as an act of pure and simple tyranny.

There were other minor causes of dissatisfaction. The projected setting up of Anglican bishops in America had antagonized the Nonconformist element, which was in the overwhelming majority. The Parliamentary laws against the issue of colonial paper money had also embittered Americans, there not being enough currency to carry on trade or daily affairs. In 1765 Parliament passed the first law attempting to establish imperial internal taxation in the colonies. This act, the Stamp Act, imposing a stamp duty on all legal documents, was clearly a revenue measure, and affected individuals in all classes. So violent was the reaction that the act was repealed, but the repeal contained a clause asserting the right of Parliament to pass laws which should bind the colonies. In America was raised the cry " No taxation without representation."

There was abstract justice in the demand that the colonies should share the burden of cost of imperial defence, but the ministers of George III unwisely pushed the matter to extremities. The fatal disputes went on. Sam Adams, the propagandist, and James Otis, the lawyer patriot, fomented separatist feeling by their brilliant speeches, pamphlets and state papers. New taxes were imposed by the government in England. In 1773 occurred the celebrated " Boston Tea Party," as a result of which other repressive measures were passed. The "tea party " had consisted of throwing overboard £10,000 worth of tea, which English merchants were trying to force into the colonies against the wishes of the " patriot " party. The colonists took up arms to maintain their rights in 1775, still declaring themselves loyal to the British connexion. When once war had begun, the Americans dropped the theory of loyalty, and, at the inspiration of Benjamin Franklin and Thomas Jefferson, issued their Declaration of Independence on July 4, 1776. With indomitable patience and perseverance their great leader, George Washington, succeeded in keeping the colonial armies under his command from dissolving, while Thomas Paine, an English journalist, kept up their morale by his expositions of the American case.

The British operations were conducted without intelligence or vigour, probably in the expectation that the colonial resistance would presently collapse of itself. Instead of collapsing, the Americans ruined the British plan of campaign in 1777 by trapping a British force at Saratoga, and compelling it to capitulate. The French saw their opportunity, and allied themselves with the Americans. The American armies were reinforced by French volunteers. French fleets sailed to the West Indies— France had in the interval realized that, to fight the British power, a great fleet was essential—and it was the presence of a French fleet which compelled the surrender of the British commander, Cornwallis, at Yorktown, the blow which destroyed all prospects of the victory of the British over the Americans.

British Naval Victory of The Saints. Spain joined with France, but Spanish energies were mainly devoted to a vain attempt to capture Gibraltar, which stubbornly defied her utmost efforts. When it was designed that a great Spanish fleet should join the French fleet in the West Indies it seemed as though Britain's maritime power would be annihilated, but before the junction could be effected the British admiral, Rodney, destroyed the French fleet at the battle of The Saints. The British maritime supremacy was saved ; but the peace which was negotiated in 1783 left Britain shorn of American colonies, with the exception of Canada, where the French population had been conciliated by wise government.

Hastings the Empire-Builder. While the future nation of the United States was cutting itself loose from the British Empire, the British position in India, as the leading territorial power, was established, mainly by the genius of the Governor-General, Warren Hastings (1732–1818), a man of great qualities, who rendered good service to the Empire. His reputation suffered during his administration as servant of the East India Company owing to the Company's habit of verbal insistence on honesty and practical insistence on what could not honestly be accomplished. Clive, in the 'sixties, had done as much as one could do towards organizing in Bengal a government for which his victory at Plassey had forced the responsibility upon the British. The position had been legalized by obtaining from the Mogul at Delhi formal recognition of the Company as the official authority in control of Bengal. Then the British Parliament, awaking to its responsibilities, created a sort of Constitution, which left the British possessions in India under the three presidencies of Bombay, Madras and Bengal, while the Governor of Bengal exercised a not very well defined authority as governor-general of the whole.

Warren Hastings, as first Governor-General, found before him a very heavy task, for which he had no adequate resources, while his action was hampered at every turn by the Council with which the British Regulating Act had fettered him. By actions which were often high-handed, and by some which could only be excused because the alternative would have been the disappearance of the British from India, Hastings succeeded in maintaining authority and in counteracting the disastrous results which would otherwise have attended the perpetual blundering of the Governments in the other two presidencies.

Of his administration with all its blemishes Lord Macaulay says in " Historical Essays : Warren Hastings " :

" But whoever seriously considers what it is to construct from the beginning the whole of a machine so vast and complex as a government will allow that what Hastings effected deserves high admiration. To compare the most celebrated European ministers to him, seems to us as unjust as it would be to compare the best baker in London with Robinson Crusoe, who, before he could bake a single loaf, had to make his plough and his harrow, his fences and his scarecrows, his sickle and his flail, his mill and his oven."

India Act. As yet only a fragment of India was under direct British control. Before Hastings left India in 1785, the younger Pitt had passed in England the India Act, which reorganized the government of the British possessions in India, and placed the ultimate control in the hands of a Government committee in London, directly responsible to Parliament; the general control in the hands of the Company in London; and the practical management of affairs in the hands of the Governor-General with his Council on the spot. Recalled in 1785, Hastings was charged with hiring out British troops to exterminate the Rohillas, with robbing the Begums of Oudh and being responsible for the murder of the Brahman Nuncomar. Unanimously acquitted by the House of Lords after a trial which had lasted from 1788 to 1795, the House of Commons also formally acknowledged his distinguished services before his death.

LESSON 18

The Story of the French Revolution

(See plate 60)

THE French Revolution was a revolt against the social order which was universal in Europe, and in France was more pronounced than anywhere else—the order which divided the world socially and politically into classes separated from each other by almost insuperable barriers, appropriating to these exemptions, privileges, and authority; to those burdens, disabilities, and subjection.

Like the Reformation, it was a rebellion against authority conventionally accepted for centuries, but now it was the political rather than the religious authority that was called in question. Europe had substituted absolute monarchy, supported by an aristocracy which was bound up with it, for the disintegration of political feudalism.

England had led the way by blotting out of her system the theory of the divine authority of monarchs, and had substituted in diverse forms the conception of something in the nature of a contract between the crown and the people—a theory that the government must in some sort express the popular will, that the monarch's right to rule depended, in effect, on his agreement with the popular will. In other European countries, however, the monarchical theory still ran on the lines that the monarch was divinely appointed to rule; that he was bound, as God's viceregent, to rule righteously and to act as the father of his people, but that if he neglected to do so he was within his rights as far as his subjects were concerned, and was accountable to no one but his Creator.

On the whole, the leading monarchs of Europe were quite inclined to be benevolent despots, though their benevolence was mitigated by a great sensitiveness where their own interests were concerned. Upon these theories were impinging novel humanitarian notions concerning the " rights of man," urgent beliefs that Man in his natural, unsophisticated condition was a much nobler creature than Man misshapen by social pressure. The somewhat arid doctrines of the Whig philosophers in England were taking a new emotional shape—in effect, a demand for the restoration of the social contract to the original form out of which it had been distorted by the rich and powerful till it had become merely an instrument for their own convenience.

Features of the ' Ancien Régime.' The Englishman is apt to make little account of theories, and to fix his attention on immediate practical grievances. Very much more than in England, the great bulk of the population in the countries of Europe suffered from practical grievances. In France the noblesse and the clergy were practically exempt from taxation, of which the whole burden was borne by the bourgeoisie and the peasantry. In England the law recognized no distinction between classes, however rigidly such social distinction might be enforced by custom. In France the law emphasized such distinctions. Society was divided into three estates: the clergy, the nobility and a third estate composed of the bourgeoisie or responsible citizens— merchants, manufacturers and professional men—the artisans and the peasants. Although many of the bourgeoisie were wealthy, they were subjected to hampering taxation and restrictions, and thus had their own grounds for discontent and revolt.

The artisans were a large class, whose products went all over the world. Some were independent workers, turning their cottages into workshops in which the whole family slaved for a bare living. They bought raw materials from a middleman and usually sold the products to the same or another middleman. Other artisans worked in the factories which were either " royal "— that is, run by shareholders enjoying privileges under a royal charter—or private concerns without privileges. In the royal factories the workers were signed on for and guaranteed four years' service, but were subject to fines, a twelve-hour day and restricted liberty. The artisans in the free factories were more independent, but were subject to unemployment and reduced wages according to the fluctuations of the labour market. Strikes and lock-outs occurred and the beginnings of combination occurred under workers' guilds or " compagnonnages."

The peasantry living directly on the produce of the soil were the bulk of the population. They held their land from overlords, the rentals complicated by feudal tenures, forced labour conditions, and burdened by unfair taxation. Some were miserably poor ; others, the peasant farmers, were disgusted at the lack of correspondence between economic realities and the legal forms that imposed on them the obligations of a dead social system.

Besides the arbitrary distinctions of class there were at least three other causes of profound discontent under the *ancien régime* : anomalies in the public administration, those in the law and those in commercial and industrial affairs. But the supreme immediate grievance lay in the grinding poverty of the poor, and the financial chaos which had been produced by the interminable wars in which the country had been involved for generations past. The natural and immediate remedy lay in a readjustment of the burdens of taxation which should diminish the extortions from the poor, and compel the rich and powerful to pay their share ; but fundamentally any change must carry with it the principle that the mass of the people should have their voice in the government, instead of being excluded from it altogether.

Louis XVI and the States General. The revolution may be said to have begun when Louis XVI, an amiable monarch with the best intentions, but somewhat lacking in intelligence, was persuaded to revive an institution which had dropped out of use for the best part of two centuries, and to summon the States General —a sort of Parliament of the Three Estates, the noblesse, the clergy, and the Commons, who were to undertake the task of reconstruction (1789). The noblesse and the clergy, or, at any rate, the higher clergy, did not want reconstruction. The Assembly of the Third Estate (the Commons) succeeded in carrying the principle that the Three Estates should vote together, whereby the Third Estate obtained preponderance, instead of in three separate chambers, which would have ensured that the two

Privileged Chambers, acting in concert, would outvote the third. This composite Chamber called itself the National Assembly. Among its first decrees were those abolishing the censorship. Journalism thus released exerted a great influence until the Press was again censored under Napoleon.

Fall of the Bastille. When it appeared that the Government intended to pay no serious attention to the Assembly thus constituted, a great volunteer force, known as the National Guard, was enrolled and the Parisian populace found themselves practically free to do what they liked so long as the National Guard was on their side. They marched on the Bastille, the fortress-prison which was the material symbol of arbitrary rule, stormed it, and destroyed it (July 14, 1789).

Palpably force was on the side of the National Assembly, which proceeded to enact the abolition of one after another of the privileges of the noblesse and the clergy, including the abolition of feudal rights and the suppression of religious orders. The Church was dispossessed of all property and tithes were withdrawn. Many of the aristocrats made haste to escape out of the country. The National Assembly found that it was not, like English Parliaments, modifying and defining, securing what it conceived to be the historical principles of the Constitution ; it was, on the contrary, abolishing the base on which the whole Constitution was built up. It was necessary to create from the beginning a new Constitution to take the place of that which was being destroyed.

Mirabeau. When the Comte de Mirabeau appeared in the Chamber of the Estates on May 5, 1789, a representative of the Third Estate, whom the nobility of Provence, his native province, had refused to admit, he was well known for his scandals—duels, love affairs, quarrels with his father, lawsuits and imprisonments ; his genius as an orator, pamphleteer and political organizer was little suspected. During the early months of the Revolution, as leader of the Third Estate, he opposed with great force—from June to October, 1789—the privileged classes and the Court. Mirabeau, always in the centre of the stage, became the head of an intelligence department. Over against the royal ministry, he secured acceptance, by sheer force of his powerful personality, of what was really a ministry although it had neither legal authority nor title. The misfortune was that Louis XVI could not co-operate with Mirabeau, who tried to enter into negotiations with the Marquis of Lafayette, the commander of the Parisian National Guard, himself a firm believer in reform, though a moderate and devoted to the royal family. Together they might have been strong enough to obtain and maintain control.

At the critical hour, when Lafayette might perhaps have persuaded the Court to summon himself and Mirabeau, the Constituent Assembly took alarm, and, fearing to lose its newly found authority, voted the decree of November 7, excluding from the royal ministry all members of the Assembly—Mirabeau in particular. For the next two years—until his death in 1791—he devoted himself to the fulfilment of his forlorn hope—reconciliation between the king and nation for the common weal.

Flight to Varennes. Lafayette had been powerless to prevent the populace of Paris from rushing upon the Château of Versailles. All he could do was to save the king and queen—the beautiful, brave, extravagant and dignified Marie Antoinette—who were brought back to the Tuileries by the crowd. Afterwards, in spite of his devotion, Lafayette was unable to be of assistance to the queen, because he was shorn of the authority necessary to keep law and order. The flight of the king to Varennes (June 4, 1791), in which he was a responsible agent, and the killing of citizens, at the Champ de Mars, who protested against the refusal of the Assembly to proclaim the deposition of Louis, lost Lafayette his popularity. He withdrew temporarily from politics ; and after his failure to stem the violence of the Jacobins (the extreme revolutionary party) in 1792, rode into the neutral territory of Liége and was seized and imprisoned by the Austrians.

The king, after the abortive attempt to escape from the country—he was recognized at Varennes with his wife and children and brought back to Paris—accepted the new Constitution, and the government was vested in a new Legislative Assembly, from which the members of the old National Assembly had excluded themselves by a self-denying ordinance, so that its members were wholly inexperienced in the conduct of affairs of State. The real leaders of the party of revolution were not members at all.

War Declared on Austria. Meanwhile the émigrés, the aristocrats who had made their escape from the country, were clamouring for foreign intervention, and calling upon the monarchs of Europe to restore by force the old monarchical order. The Emperor Leopold (the French queen's brother) and the King of Prussia issued a warning declaration which the Legislative

Assembly regarded as an unwarrantable and insolent interference with the domestic affairs of France. Consequently it compelled Louis to declare war upon Austria, Leopold having been succeeded at that moment by his son Francis II.

The troops were dispatched to the front—that is, the north-western or Netherlands frontier. Then Paris was seized with a panic, in belief that the " aristocrats " were organizing a *coup de main* in conjunction with the foreign invaders. The Jacobins captured the Commune or Government of Paris ; they made the whole of the royal family prisoners, and then, in the September Massacres (1792), a large number of " suspects " were put to death in the prisons of Paris by the mob, now thoroughly dehumanized and frenzied by the menace of foreign interference, though almost at the same moment the news arrived that the advancing Prussians and Austrians had been driven over the frontier after their failure at Valmy.

At the end of the month the Legislative Assembly was dissolved, and its place was taken by a newly elected National Convention. In the Convention the Republicans were overwhelmingly dominant. It proceeded at once to proclaim the abolition of the monarchy, which had been hitherto preserved in name, and the establishment of the republic. The extraordinary success which attended the troops in every theatre of the war which was now in progress was accompanied by a declaration that the populations were being set free from their tyrants. Finally, at the close of the year, the leaders, in the words of Danton, the bourgeois leader who had taken the place of Mirabeau, " flung down to the kings of Europe the head of a king as the gage of battle " ; Louis, after a form of trial, was guillotined in January, 1793. In October the guillotine also claimed Marie Antoinette.

At this stage Pitt, who had hitherto held aloof, not without some sympathy for what was believed in England to be a genuine if blundering attempt to copy British precedents, had become definitely convinced that the French Republic was as much engaged upon a war of unmitigated aggression as ever Louis XIV had been.

France had assumed the right to tear up bygone treaties which Britain was pledged to maintain. War was declared ; and from thenceforth Britain remained the most persistent and consistent enemy of France.

Our Course in Modern History is continued in Volume 4.

LESSON 11

The Empiricism of Locke, Berkeley and Hume

(See plate 59)

TRADITIONALLY opposed to the Rationalistic philosophers, Descartes and Leibniz, are the Empiricists, Locke, Berkeley and Hume. The common starting point of these three philosophers is a thoroughgoing criticism of Rationalism. Denying the existence of *a priori* knowledge, they affirm that we cannot by reasoning alone arrive at the truth about the universe. Reasoning may tell us what ought to be, but it cannot inform us of what is. Therefore, if we want to know what the universe *is*, we must leave the study and go and look ; in other words, we must adopt the methods of science. Our knowledge is, they hold, founded on the experience that comes to us through the five senses ; in fact, we never have any knowledge other than that which is provided by the raw material of sense experience.

The philosophy of Locke (1632–1704) begins with a criticism of innate ideas, these being the tools or weapons with which the Rationalists conceived mind to have been fitted initially, and by the exercise of which it obtained *a priori* knowledge, independently of experience. Locke in his philosophical writings sought to show that such ideas did not exist.

Similarly, Berkeley argues against abstract or general ideas. What is it, he asked, that is before the mind when we think of something abstract and general, like triangle ? Plato's answer was the Form of a triangle, and most philosophers have invoked the existence of some kind of general concept or universal idea to explain abstract thinking. This course was not, however, open to Berkeley, since as we do not experience general ideas with our sense organs, it would have involved the admission that we know something that we have not experienced through the senses. Hence, Berkeley argues, when we think of a triangle, what we actually have in mind is some actual particular triangle that we have experienced.

Representationalism. Believing all knowledge to consist of sense experience, the Empiricists were led to consider in detail the nature and analysis of such experience as it comes to us in knowledge of the outside world. Locke's philosophy is, in fact, a sort of psychology. The following is a brief summary of his view of the nature of perception, a view known as Representationalism. The external world consists of entities possessing only primary qualities, such as size, shape, number and occupancy of space. These entities, impinging upon our senses, cause representations or images of themselves to appear in consciousness. It is these representations, called by Locke ideas, and not the external objects that cause them, that the mind knows. But the ideas, unlike the external objects, are invested by mind with secondary qualities such as temperature and colour, which the mind then projects outside itself into the world of objects. The mind is thus conceived after the model of a dark cabinet containing a brightly lit screen illuminated by the light of consciousness. What we know are not objects external to ourselves, but the images of them which are cast by the senses upon the screen of consciousness.

The following quotation from Professor Whitehead's " Science and the Modern World " admirably sums up Locke's view :

" Thus the bodies are perceived as with qualities which in reality do not belong to them, qualities which in fact are purely the offspring of the mind. Thus nature gets credit which should in truth be reserved for ourselves : the rose for its scent : the nightingale for his song ; and the sun for his radiance. The poets are entirely mistaken. They should address their lyrics to themselves, and should turn them into odes of self-congratulation on the excellency of the human mind. Nature is a dull affair, soundless, sceneless, colourless ; merely the hurrying of material, endlessly, meaninglessly."

What, according to Locke, there really is in the external is a kind of featureless stuff called substance, which, though itself without qualities, serves as a substratum or foundation for the primary qualities.

Denial of Abstract Ideas. Berkeley abolished the distinction between primary qualities and secondary ones. Whatever reasons there were for believing that the latter were ideas in the mind applied, he held, also to the former. Secondly, and consequentially, he abolished the external world of things, which, though itself unknown to mind, was supposed by Locke to be the cause of the ideas which mind knows. But, if we do not, and never can know the external world directly, we cannot, said Berkeley, know anything about it ; we cannot, therefore, know that it has the property of being able to cause the ideas we do know ; and we cannot know that it exists. Putting the point in another way, we may say that, as we never have any sense experience of the external world, but only experience our own ideas, we can only know the external world *a priori*. But *a priori* knowledge for the Empiricist does not exist.

This consideration applies also to Locke's substance, which *ex hypothesi* cannot be known, since it is devoid of qualities by virtue of which alone things can be known. Hence, for Berkeley to say of a thing that it exists is the same as to say that it is known, since whatever is known turns out to be an idea in the mind of the knower. Thus, the existence of things consists in their being perceived or known. Berkeley's conclusions and the reasons for them will be considered in greater detail in Lesson 12.

Hume's Scepticism. Hume proceeds still farther along the same lines. Berkeley held that the world continues to exist when we are not perceiving it, because it is perceived by God, who puts the ideas we experience into our minds. But, as Hume pointed out, we have no sense of experience of God, and if, therefore, we are consistent in our rejection of *a priori* knowledge, we cannot invoke His existence to sustain the world when we are not perceiving it. Therefore, there is no reason to believe in the existence of anything other than the ideas we momentarily perceive.

Secondly, we have no experience of a self in and to which the ideas occur. If we try to perceive the self, all that we in fact come across are separate psychological states, e.g. a willing, a fearing, a hoping, or, in the case in question, an endeavouring to see whether we can perceive a self. It is these psychological states that we actually meet ; what we never come across is a continuing thread to hold them together ; they remain, therefore, distinct isolated entities, a necklace of beads without the thread. Thus Hume reduces subjective Idealism, the position of Locke and Berkeley, to the position known as Solipsism, that is to say, the view that the isolated momentary experiences of the perceiver are the only things that are known to exist in the universe. In fact, they constitute the universe, while it must be remembered that, in the light of Hume's criticism of the self, even " the perceiver " is only invoked by courtesy. Much subsequent philosophy consists of different attempts to refute this conclusion. It may be said here that, although it cannot be refuted, there is no reason to believe it to be true.

Suggestions for reading are : Hume's " Treatise of Human Nature " (Parts I and II, Everyman ed.) ; Locke's " Essay concerning Human Understanding " (early chapters only) ; Berkeley's " Theory of Vision and Other Writings " (especially the three dialogues between Hylas and Philonous. Everyman ed.).

LESSON 12

Bishop Berkeley's Doctrine of Idealism

THE philosophy of Idealism, which we began to sketch in the last Lesson, is something of a stumbling-block to those who are making their first acquaintance with the subject. The doctrine has had a chequered history and, as put forward by Berkeley, won little acceptance at the time. Pope has a line, " And coxcombs vanquish Berkeley with a grin." His views have been " laughed at, written at, taught at, shrieked at." Everyone is familiar with the story of Dr. Johnson, that incarnation of the limitations of common sense, who thought he had disposed of Berkeley by kicking a stone.

Every student of philosophy must know from his own experience that there is a stage of mental development in which Idealism appears to be the most monstrous of absurdities. Some will remember having heard at school the quaint notion that the world only exists in our minds or in some Higher Mind than ours ; and probably, after the fashion of schoolboys, we characterized this notion as " rot." Whatever it is, it is not " rot," and whatever our conclusions may finally be, let us remember the advice of Lord Acton—" to understand what we reject as thoroughly as what we accept."

Idealism and Matter. When we say that Berkeley denied the existence of matter—or, as he would now have to say, physical energy—we do not mean that he denied, or acted as if he denied, the existence of appearances. The difference between him and his opponents is that, while they postulate something behind appearances, Berkeley says this is superfluous. He finds no need to suppose that there is an inaccessible substance underneath

(557)

all the properties by which we know a thing in the outside world. Those properties are themselves the whole thing. Subject to the qualification to be mentioned below, there is for Berkeley nothing beyond the world of sense, *but*—a world of sense.

What we commonly do, however, is to group together in our minds certain of the properties or qualities from which we infer the external world, and then declare that these inhere in something which we agree to call matter—or, nowadays, energy. According to Berkeley, this matter is a creation of our minds, and has no existence outside them. It is our minds that have put together these qualities and properties, compared them, and then explained them in terms of something behind. But there is no such something behind ; to suppose that there is, is a delusion born of our way of thinking. As Berkeley points out, once we admit the existence of such a something, we find ourselves in all sorts of difficulties. The farther we pursue it the more certainly we find ourselves in absurdities and contradictions ; but, says Berkeley :

" Upon the whole, I am inclined to think that the far greater part, if not all, the difficulties which have hitherto amused philosophers and blocked up the way to knowledge are entirely owing to themselves—that we have first raised a dust, and then complain that we cannot see."

Berkeley's Doctrine. Here is the famous passage in which, especially in its last sentence, his theory is stated :

" That neither our thoughts, nor passions, nor the ideas formed by our imagination, exist without the mind is what everybody will allow ; and to me it is no less evident that the various sensations or ideas imprinted on the sense, however blended or combined together, cannot exist otherwise than in a mind perceiving them. . . . The table I write on, I say, exists—i.e. I see it, and feel it—and if I were out of my study I should say it existed, meaning thereby that if I was in my study, I might perceive it or that some other spirit actually *does* perceive it. As to what is said about the existence of unthinking things, without any relation to their being perceived, that is to me perfectly unintelligible. Their *esse* is *percipi ;* nor is it possible they should have any existence out of the minds or thinking things which perceive them."

If we perceive nothing but our own ideas and sensations, it is impossible to imagine that any one of these ideas, or any combination of them, should exist *unperceived*. Their *esse* is *percipi*—their being is the being perceived. Furthermore :

"When we do our utmost to conceive the existence of external bodies, we are all the while only contemplating our own ideas."

Followed out in its logical entirety, this theory leads Berkeley to the famous passage :

"In a word, all the choir of heaven and furniture of earth— all those bodies which compose the mighty frame of the world— have not any subsistence without a mind ; their *esse* is to be perceived or known, and consequently, so long as they are not actually perceived by me, or do not exist in my mind, or that of any other created spirit, they must either have no existence at all, or else subsist *in the mind of some eternal spirit.*"

Significance of God to Berkeley. It is sometimes asked : "Does the room in which we are sitting alone go out of existence when we leave it and therefore cease to perceive it ? " The implication of the question is that, since, on Berkeley's view, the room consists entirely of ideas in the mind of the perceiver, when it ceases to be perceived there ceases to be a room. The implication does not follow because of the part played by God in Berkeley's scheme. Because God continues to perceive the room it continues to exist. The difference between real things and imaginary ones for Berkeley is that real things are those perceived both by God and by us ; imaginary ones are perceived by us only. If we ask how Berkeley knows that God exists, his answer is that we have a " notion " of God. Since this " notion " does not come to us through the senses, it is perilously like a re-introduction through the back door of the *a priori* knowledge which Berkeley had expelled from the front. It is, however, clear that, unless we are prepared to follow Berkeley in introducing God to give independent reality to a world whose existence, apart from knowledge, has been destroyed, we are reduced to the position that the only things which exist are our mental states and our knowledge of them. His belief presupposes that we are in an intelligible and trustworthy universe.

The Problem of Perception. The philosophy of Berkeley is chiefly famous because it raises in an acute form what is known as the problem of perception. We saw in Lesson 11 how the logical development of the philosophy of Locke, Berkeley and Hume is Solipsism, or the view that the only things which can be known are the ideas in the mind of the knowing self.

Many people hold that, if we take our start from the Representationalism of Locke—if, that is to say, we hold, as he did, that what we immediately know in perception are not bodies outside ourselves, but representations, pictures or ideas thrown by such bodies on the screen of consciousness—then there is no way of avoiding the solipsistic conclusion. At the same time, it is difficult to see how this view of Locke's can be refuted.

For this reason the problem of perception has become one of the most important in philosophy, especially in modern philosophy, and much of the philosophy that is written today is concerned to answer the question : " Exactly what is it that I am knowing when, as I say, I see my hand ? "

LESSON 13

Subjective Idealism and Material Knowledge

IN the present Lesson it is proposed to consider from a purely common-sense point of view what reasons, if any, may be adduced in support of the conclusion that, whatever exists, exists only in so far as it is known, and that the nature of existence is, therefore, to be an idea in some knowing mind.

Let us suppose that I press my tongue against my teeth and ask the question : " What is it that I experience or am aware of ? " At first sight the answer would appear to be : " I am aware of my teeth." But is this answer really correct ? Is not what one really experiences a feeling in the tongue—a feeling caused by the contact between tongue and teeth, but a feeling, nevertheless, and, being a feeling, something that is mental ? Suppose, now, that I press my fingers against the table, is what I experience the table ? Again, the obvious answer proves on examination to be incorrect. The immediate object of my experience, that of which I am aware, is a sensation in my fingers, a sensation of hardness, smoothness, and coolness.

Let us take a further example. If I stand two feet away from the fire, I experience heat, and say that the heat is a property of the fire. If, however, I move nearer to the fire, the heat increases in intensity, until it becomes pain. Now, the pain is clearly in me and not in the fire ; since, then, the pain is only a more intense degree of the heat, the inference is that the heat also was a sensation of mine, and not a property of the fire. The leg of a cheese mite is so small that, except with the aid of a microscope, one cannot see it. Are we, then, to suppose that the cheese mite cannot see its own leg ? This seems unlikely. We must infer, then, that the size of the cheese mite's leg varies according to the nature of the mind perceiving it—that the leg has one apparent size for the cheese mite and another for ourselves. But the leg cannot have two different sizes at the same time. Hence, the size turns out to be a property of our seeing, and not of the object seen ; it is, in other words, not an intrinsic quality of the object seen, but relative to and dependent upon the nature of the perceiver's mind.

Physicists' Account of Perception. By similar arguments it can be shown that all the qualities apparently possessed by material objects in their own right turn out, on examination, to be feelings or sensations or ideas on the part of the perceiver. This conclusion is reinforced by the scientific account of perception. What precisely is it that, according to the scientist, occurs when we see something ? Taking first the case of visual sensations, we find that their causation is roughly described in the following terms : a physical object sends out rays of light, which, after travelling through the ether, impinge on the optical nerve ; the resulting disturbance in the optical nerve is conveyed along neural cords to the brain, where it causes a further disturbance in the cerebral cortex. It is as a result of this disturbance in the cerebral cortex that we have the sensation of seeing the object ; this, in fact, is the physical event which *constitutes* our seeing. Similarly, with regard to hearing. A sound is a vibration in the atmosphere ; this vibration impinges upon our ear-drums ; the effect produced upon the ear-drums is conveyed by the nerves to the brain ; here it causes a disturbance, as a result of which we become conscious, and our consciousness of the cerebral disturbance is called hearing the sound.

Touch Perception. Perception by touch makes the matter even plainer. Suppose that the finger is pressed against the desk. Ordinarily, one would say that there was contact between two material substances. Science, however, lends no countenance to this view. What happens, according to science, is that repulsion is developed between the atoms composing the finger and those composing the desk. The harder the desk is pressed, the stronger the electrical forces which repel the finger. These electrical forces set up in the nerve cells at the end of my finger a current which reaches my brain, as a result of which I experience the sensation of touching the desk. In fact, however, I am not aware of any object external to my body, and, if appropriate parts of my nervous system are suitably stimulated, I shall experience the same sensation of touching the desk, although there is no desk to touch. What is more, I can experience what appears to be a sensation of a pin-prick in the non-existent finger of a hand which has been amputated, provided that the nerve terminals in my arm are suitably manipulated.

It is on these lines, and, it might well seem, only on these lines, that it seems possible to explain the fact of differing perceptions of the same thing. If X sees a carnation blue and Y, who is colour-blind, sees it green, it is very difficult to suppose that the carnation is both green and blue at the same time. On the other hand, there seems no reason to affirm that it *really* is blue merely because it is blue to normal vision, and to deny that its appearance to the colour-blind man is its *real* appearance because the colour-blind man is in a minority. The plain implication seems to be that the difference between the apparent colours is due to a difference in the physiological machinery of the two perceivers. Moreover, if we place santonin in our eyes, we see everything yellow. Since it cannot be supposed to be the case that this alteration in our visual apparatus has produced a corresponding alteration in that which we see, we can only suppose that the yellowness is the result of a peculiar condition of our seeing. But, if this is true in regard to yellowness, there is no reason why it should not be true in regard to all the colours which we believe ourselves to perceive in the outside world.

Qualities and Substance. It would seem, therefore, that the apparent qualities of things are not possessed by them in their own right, but are effects produced in the mind or the brain of the person perceiving the thing. But if the qualities of a thing are mental, what is left in the outside world ? We normally think of an object as consisting of a lump of featureless stuff to which certain qualities belong. It is Matter, to revert to Aristotle's phrase, and the qualities taken together constitute its Form. But let us suppose that you take an object, and one by one strip away all its qualities. What is left ? Consider, for example, a chocolate. A chocolate is brown soft, sticky, and sweet to the taste. Let us abstract these qualities one by one and consider what remains. What is it that had the qualities, but now has them no longer ? We may say, of course, that what is left is the chocolate minus its colour, consistency and taste. But is this residue anything at all ? If it is, it is only so in virtue of such qualities as we may have left remaining in it ; if these qualities, too, were taken away, there would be literally nothing left. There is, that is to say, no substratum or foundation in which the qualities inhere, which is itself without qualities and other than they. If, therefore, the qualities turn out to be ideas in the mind of the perceiver, and, if there is no substance or material foundation besides the qualities, there is nothing left except mind. Matter, therefore, is an illusion. This is not to say that the tables and chairs which we know in everyday life do not exist ; merely that they turn out on analysis to be ideas in the mind of the perceiver. Hence, as Berkeley said, their existence consists in their being perceived or known.

LESSON 14

Introduction of the Kantian Philosophy

ONE of the most important questions in philosophy is the fundamental, sceptical question : can we know anything at all, or rather, can we know it as it really is ? Hume's sceptical conclusions had made this question very acute. There is, it is obvious, no necessary reason why the human mind should be an instrument capable of discovering the truth about the universe. The human mind works in accordance with certain prescribed laws of logic, certain rules of reasoning. It holds, for example, that a thing cannot both be and not be at the same time. It holds that if a thing has a quality X, it cannot at the same time not have the quality X. It holds that, if p implies q, and q implies r, then p also implies r. These are laws of logic. There are also mathematical laws : that 3 and 2 make 5, that $a^2 - b^2 = (a + b)(a - b)$, that the three interior angles of a triangle are equal to two right angles.

Now it is a fact that we believe that these laws apply to the universe outside us. The universe is, we are accustomed to believe, such that a tree cannot both be and not be a beech, and that any three things in it, if added to two things, will make five things. But, for all we know to the contrary, these laws may be laws about the workings of the mind, and not in any sense laws about the workings of the universe. It may be merely that our *minds* are constituted in such a way that they are bound to think that a tree cannot both be and not be a beech, that three and two must make five, and that every cause must have an effect. How do we know that these laws of thought really apply to things ? Unless we do know this, we have no guarantee that our knowledge will give us truth about reality. Clearly, then, an inquiry is necessary into the nature and capacities of knowledge, so necessary that, it may be said, all kinds of philosophizing are premature until we have ascertained something about the instrument which we mean to employ. In what sense do we know anything and to what extent ?

Kant's Critical Philosophy. To answer this question was the object of Immanuel Kant (1724–1804), and it is one of the most amazing facts in the history of thought that the answer should have waited for so long. It is because the work of Kant constitutes a criticism of men's thought and of the conditions of their thinking that it is generally described as the " critical philosophy." A somewhat uncouth word has also been employed—and is, indeed, now found indispensable—in order to indicate the study with which Kant chiefly concerned himself. This word is *epistemology*, from the Greek word *episteme* (knowledge). Just as biology, then, is the science of life, so epistemology is the science of knowledge. It is the department of philosophy which concerns itself with the knowing process, the conditions, the limits, and the validity of all that we know or think we know.

Certainly, we know something of the external world. Daily life demonstrates the fact. We act on the assumption that an unsupported object will fall, and we are found to be right. So far, so good. There is, at least, open to Man some proximate, practical, working kind of truth. There may be more, but at any rate there is this empirical truth—the word empirical meaning experimental or dependent upon experience. We know that under the present conditions of things the sun will rise tomorrow. That is an empirical truth, demonstrated to be true by experience. But we have still no guarantee that this empirical knowledge of ours is really knowledge about reality. May it not be merely knowledge of the conditions imposed upon reality by our own minds ?

This, very briefly, was Kant's position. Our knowledge of the external world, he held, is limited and conditioned by the limits and conditions of our own minds ; it is knowledge not of reality, but of appearances. The reality which lies behind those appearances is and must remain unknown.

The two opposed words which Kant employed for appearance and reality were *phenomenon* and *noumenon*. The word, phenomenon, which is so familiar to us, is one of the most important words employed in philosophy, since it expresses for all those who know its meaning one of the most important ideas in philosophy. In common use the word means anything that is out of the way or wonderful, and we apply the adjective phenomenal to anything which we wish to signalize as extraordinary. But these employments of the word are unfortunate. The adjective phenomenal should be confined to its proper philosophic use as a description of anything that has the character of a phenomenon. We shall see in a moment how convenient the word may be. A phenomenon, then, is literally an appearance or something that appears ; and, whenever we use the word, we are to associate with it in our minds the idea of a something else which, though hidden from us and not apparent, is yet the reality, the self, or the thing-in-itself, lying behind the appearance or phenomenon.

The universe, then, is divided into two sorts or categories of things, the real or the noumenal and the apparent or the phenomenal. Our knowledge is only of what appears to us, and is, therefore, only phenomenal knowledge. It is not suggested that there is necessarily any opposition or contradiction between the real and the apparent. It is asserted merely that our knowledge of reality must always be inferential and can never be direct.

An analogy may serve to make the matter plainer. Let us suppose that I am born with a pair of blue spectacles permanently affixed to the bridge of my nose. Then everything that I shall see will appear blue. This will not be because things really are blue, but because their appearing to be blue is a condition of my seeing them at all—a condition which is imposed upon them by the peculiarities of my visual apparatus. If everybody else is in the same predicament, Mankind will take the same view as I do, namely that everything is blue, because blueness will be a universal attribute of things seen by human eyes.

Kantian Categories. In much the same way, Kant held that the mind was fitted initially with a whole number of sets of mental spectacles, whose peculiarities it inevitably imposed upon everything that it knew. These spectacles are known as the Kantian " categories." It is, he held, a condition of our knowing anything at all that it should be in space and time, of a certain quantity, exhibiting certain qualities, the effect of a preceding cause and the cause of some succeeding effect. But this is the case, not because space, time, quantity, quality and causality belong to reality as it is, but because they are categories necessarily imposed by us upon reality as it appears. Of reality as it is, the noumenal world, we can have no knowledge, because in the very process of knowing it we transform it into the phenomenal world, the world as it appears, by the categorizing activities of our own minds.

LESSON 15

Kant's Theory of the Moral Sense

IN the preceding Lesson Kant's theory of knowledge was briefly described, and some account was given of the distinction which he makes between the world of appearance, the phenomenal world, and the world of reality, the noumenal world. Briefly, we know, and can know, only the world of appearance, because we construct it in the very act of knowing it by imposing the categories of the mind upon it. On the basis of this distinction we are in a position to give Kant's answer to the question asked at the beginning of the previous Lesson : What right have we to suppose that the laws of thought necessarily apply to the behaviour of things ? Kant's answer is that they must inevitably apply to the behaviour of the things *that we know*, because the things that we know are the products of the minds which know them. By the very fact of knowing the world we have put causality, identity, mathematical relations, and so on into it. Inevitably, therefore, it is found to conform to the mental requirements of logic and mathematics. It is for this reason that science is possible. What we understand by science is simply knowledge of the phenomenal world. Science deals with appearances, with what Kant called " co-existences and sequences between phenomena," and science, a product of the human mind, is, therefore, true of the phenomena, which are also products of the human mind. But science does not give us knowledge of reality, which, Kant held, is obtained primarily in moral experience.

Intuitionism in Philosophy. The moral theory occupies a key position in the Kantian system of philosophy, because while our knowledge of the external world is, in Kant's views, phenomenal —that is to say, is knowledge of appearance only—he conceives that when we will and act morally, we are in direct touch with reality. The moral self, Kant held, is truly real, and in experiencing it we establish a direct contact with reality.

Ethical philosophy is discussed at the end of this Course, but Kant's theory is included here because of the closeness of the connexion between his ethics and his philosophy. The theory illustrates a certain type of ethical theory of which it is an extreme example. The type of theory to which it belongs is called " intuitionist."

Many writers on ethics have held that actions possess in themselves some intrinsic quality in virtue of which they have ethical value. This quality is recognized as belonging to the action by a special faculty known as the moral sense or conscience. The verdicts of conscience are intuitional ; that is to say, though they may be defended by, they are not based upon, reason. They are also final. The moral sense is thus arbiter over all that pertains to the moral sphere, just as the sense of sight is arbiter over what pertains to the visual sphere. Our eyes tell us what is beautiful, and the moral sense tells us what is right, and there is no appeal against either verdict. Now, Kant's theory is intuitionist in the sense that it holds that moral actions are those which proceed from a good will. The essence of the theory is a distinction made by Kant between Man as a moral agent and Man " from the point of view of anthropology."

" From the point of view of anthropology " Man is a creature of tradition, environment and training. Morality is the name which he gives to actions of which his society approves, and his own actions are determined by his desire to stand well with his society and by the fear of its disapproval. From this point of view our opinions on morality are formed not by us, but for us. We get them ready-made, as we get our clothes and boots, from the social shop, being fitted with a code which assures us that it is right to marry one wife and that slavery is wrong, if we are born in a bedroom in Balham, as surely as we are fitted with the contrary beliefs that we may have four wives and, if we are rich enough, a similar number of slaves, if we first see the light in a bedroom in Bagdad.

Aristotle's Doctrine of Self-Determinism. Not only our beliefs, but our desires are, from this point of view, determined. There is a famous doctrine called self-determinism, bequeathed to us by Aristotle, which puts very clearly the reasons for this view. Aristotle is concerned with the question : why does a man come to have a good character ? His answer is : because he has continually performed good acts. But he cannot continually perform good acts unless he is the sort of man whose nature it is to perform them ; unless, that is to say, he has the good character from which the good acts necessarily spring. This good character will, in its turn, proceed from and be formed by a preceding series of good acts. Retracing our steps by this method over the past history of the individual, we shall see that the actions which he performs at any given moment spring from, and are conditioned by, his being the sort of person that he is at that moment ; and, further, that he is the particular sort of person that he then is because of the impulses which he experiences and the tendencies which he exhibits.

If, therefore, we go far enough back we can show that the tendencies and impulses which were originally his on the first occasion on which he acted are those which really determined the whole subsequent tenor of his life. If we leave out of account the bearing upon the issue of theories of transmigration, we may say that the tendencies and impulses which the individual possesses on the first occasion on which he acts lie outside his control. These tendencies and impulses, which we are accustomed to call hereditary, acting in conjunction with and reacting from the environment in which he finds himself, determine his future actions. By these actions his character is formed. But, since he is responsible neither for his heredity nor for his environment, it would appear that he is not accountable for the actions which these two factors jointly determine, or for the character which is formed by these actions.

Summing up, we may say that our thoughts, desires and impulses are, in every case, the result ot what we may describe as a push from behind, for the strength and direction of which we cannot hold ourselves responsible.

Our Course in Philosophy is continued in Volume 4.

LESSON 7

Introduction to the Molecular Theory of Matter

IF we release a small volume of ammonia in one corner of a large room, it is only a matter of a few minutes before the smell of the gas reaches the opposite corner. This transference of the gas takes place when the air of the room appears to be quite still, so that it is not brought about by a regular movement of the air. We say that the gas has diffused through the air. A similar process takes place when the gas is separated by a porous membrane. For example, if we take a porous pot, such as is used in electric cells, and fill it with coal-gas and cork it up, we find that the gas escapes through the pores at a quicker rate than the air enters, and consequently the pressure inside is reduced.

The process of diffusion is not confined to gases only, as may easily be shown by a simple experiment. A clean glass jar is half filled with water and, by means of a funnel which leads to the bottom of the water, a concentrated solution of blue copper sulphate, which is heavier than water, is poured gently to the bottom of the jar. If this is done carefully, we have in the jar two distinct layers. The lower one is blue and the upper one colourless. If the jar is again examined after some days it is found that the surface of separation has become indistinct and has moved upwards. The penetration of the blue copper sulphate upwards has been brought about against gravity, so that the possible explanation in terms of gravitation is eliminated. This is an example of diffusion in liquids.

In solids, diffusion takes place at a very slow rate. Lead and gold blocks, which were resting together for some years, were found at the Mint to have inter-diffused. More recently, some experiments of this kind were discovered to work at a quicker rate. Thus we see that diffusion takes place in all forms of matter, the distinguishing feature being the time taken. In gases it is usually a matter of minutes, but the heavier the gas, the longer the time ; in liquids, it is a matter of days, and in solids it requires years to produce a small measurable effect.

Osmosis. A most important phenomenon, *osmosis*, can be best explained in terms of a simple experiment. A long glass tube is taken and at one end, which widens out, a sheet of parchment is stretched and fastened to the rim of the tube, to make a drum-like seal to the end. A thistle tube serves well for this purpose. Holding the tube vertically with the parchment at the bottom, the container so formed is filled with a strong sugar solution, so that the surface of the solution in the tube can be marked. When the parchment end of this tube is immersed in a glass of clean water it is found that the level of the liquid in the tube gradually rises. This is due to osmosis. What happens is: water enters through the membrane, making the solution weaker, of course, but definitely raising the column against the effect of gravity, and so producing an increasing pressure on the membrane. If the tube is long enough it will be found that in time the liquid within the tube comes to a level at which it remains constant. The pressure so created is called osmotic pressure. In some cases it may happen that the pressure becomes so large as to break the parchment. This can be well seen if, instead of the glass tube, we take a pig's bladder, fill it with a strong sugar solution, and immerse the tied-up bladder in clean water. The bladder will increase in size and in time may burst. This is due to the water entering at a quicker rate than the water of the solution inside leaves the bladder.

Referring again to the glass tube experiment, it is a fact that, if we use two sugar solutions of different strengths, the solution inside will rise if it is stronger than the outside. There is always the movement of the water tending to equalise the strength of the solutions, and thereby increasing the pressure opposing further change.

Incidentally, this process of osmosis is of extreme importance to all living cells. It accounts for the movement of sap in the cells of a plant, and is one of the important factors in the rise of sap up very tall trees against the pull of gravity.

If dried currants are placed in water it is found that they swell and become rounded; this is due to water entering by the process of osmosis. In human beings, too, osmosis plays a most important rôle. The alimentary tract and the blood stream are contained in membranes which allow the passage through their walls of solution when the difference in concentration is suitably arranged. The administration of salines after operations and numerous other examples could be quoted of the most vital importance of the process of osmosis to our daily routine. The laws to which osmosis conforms have been studied at length by physicists, and many important theoretical as well as practical discoveries have been involved.

Osmosis is also dealt with in Lesson 12 in Botany (volume 2, page 94) and in Lesson 12 in Biology (volume 2, page 72).

During the review of the properties of matter which has been given in these Lessons since dealing with definitions, the writer has had a strong desire to explain the phenomena described in terms of the accepted theories, and it is hoped that the student has also had a desire to know *why* this or that happens in the experiments described. Speculations as to the nature of matter began long before the Christian era, and are still being made. The theories can now be tested because we have a large mass of experimental data against which to check them.

Atoms and Molecules. Two theories concerning matter alternated in favour. According to the first, matter is infinitely divisible, that is to say, however small a piece of it is taken it retains its individuality. If, for instance, we take a piece of iron and cut it into small pieces, however small we make the pieces, they have the properties of iron. In answer to the question, "What happens in the limit when we are dealing with ultramicroscopic particles ? " the upholders of this theory maintained that we should still have iron, and the process could go on indefinitely. According to the other school of thought, this process of division would lead us to a unit which is the smallest portion of that kind of matter which could exist as such. This unit is regarded as differing from element to element, and is called the *atom*. It has the property of not being divisible and yet retaining the property of the element concerned. In compounds the unit is the *molecule*, which is made of a group of different atoms, just as the molecule of an element is made of one, two or more atoms. When the molecule repeats itself the accumulation is the matter we see. This theory is the one which seems to fit the observed experimental fact to the nearest degree of approximation. The old idea was to regard the molecules as solid elastic spheres, but, as we shall see later, this has been considerably modified in recent years. For the moment we will not concern ourselves with the structure of the atoms or molecules, but just regard them as extremely minute particles. They are so small, in fact, that it would need one hundred million of them in a row to measure 1 cm. In the same way we will not consider a possible shape for them, but regard them as being located by their centres.

The number of molecules in a cubic centimetre of a gas at normal pressure and at 0°C. is assessed at about 3×10^{19}, or thirty million million million. This number is too large to mean much to us, but when we remember the size of the molecule 10^{-8} cm. in diameter we see that there is plenty of room between the molecules.

Since we saw, when discussing gravitation in Lesson 3 (volume 2, page 577), that all matter attracts matter with a force that can be calculated from the equation given in page 578, it is clear that, if this attraction were the only force acting, all the molecules would gravitate together and, in spite of their number, would form a solid mass in the space.

Now actually we know this is not so. The experiment on diffusion in gases which we quoted earlier in the Lesson definitely disposes of this. The extra factor which is introduced is a random velocity. All the molecules move about in a haphazard manner with a velocity which is really great. If we confine our attention to a single molecule it will fly off in a definite direction until it hits a second molecule, which will cause it to change its direction. This process will be repeated at every collision. Now at one pressure the average distance a molecule will go without having a collision will be fixed. It is called the *mean free path*. When the pressure is reduced, as inside an ordinary valve, the mean free path might be as long as 10 to 25 cms., but at atmospheric pressure it is a fraction of a centimetre. Now we know further that each cubic centimetre of gas has a definite mass, so that if the number of molecules in that centimetre is known, the mass per molecule may be found.

When a gas is turned to liquid its volume is very much smaller, and so the molecules do not have the same freedom of movement —they have a greater influence on each other. In the change to solid state we find that the molecules are usually closer packed together, and now their mutual attractions become a very important factor. For example, if we think of a steel wire holding up a 2-ton load we realize that the attraction between molecules in the wire is at least equal to the pull of the earth on the 2-ton load on the wire, otherwise the molecules would separate, or, in commoner language, the wire would break.

LESSON 8

More on the Molecular Theory

IN the previous Lesson we saw that, according to the accepted molecular theory, the molecules have a random velocity which is great ; that in spite of the very large number of molecules per cubic centimetre (c.c.) of a gas at normal pressure and o°C., there is a large space between them as they are so very small. The average distance between successive impacts we called the " mean free path," and this depends on the pressure of the gas.

Now it seems clear that, if the molecule has a mass and moves with a velocity, it also possesses momentum (m.v.). If we consider a gas kept in a closed space it follows that the molecules will hit against the walls of the space and so have their momentum changed. The rate of change of momentum is force, so that on each unit of wall area of the containing vessel there will be a pressure which is equal to the momentum changed on that area per second.

If the volume is halved, there will be twice the number of molecules per c.c., and consequently twice as many hits per second, and consequently twice the pressure. This is what we saw to be the case, and it is stated in so many words in Boyle's Law.

The molecules of one sort—say oxygen—have the same mass (with the exceptions to be described later when considering isotopes), and if the temperature remains constant they have an average velocity which has a definite value. In spite of this being true, the individual molecules may have vastly varying velocities, just as a form in a school containing a number of boys of the (alleged) same intellectual level (corresponding to temperature) is said to have an average age of 16 ; whereas individual members may vary from $14\frac{3}{4}$ to 17 years.

Molecular Behaviour in Liquids. If the temperature is raised the result is an increase in the average velocity of the random movement of the molecules. The same applies in liquids. The closer associated molecules have an average random speed which depends on the temperature ; the velocity of individual molecules may be much greater or less.

(573)

When a molecule moves in a liquid it also has collisions, and, as in gases, the result is a rebound in another direction, or a spin is given to it as well as a movement in a straight line. The attractions between the molecules balance out, as there is a pull equally in all directions. When the molecule approaches the surface, however, the attractions no longer balance out. If we imagine that an instantaneous picture of one molecule shows it just on the surface, it seems clear that there is a big pull from the molecules under it, which is not compensated by a pull from above, where there is no liquid. The result is a pull back into the liquid. In fact, it makes the surface appear to behave as if it were a membrane. If a small drop of water be suspended, then the pull on the surface molecules is inward, directed to the centre, and the water forms a drop of spherical shape in consequence. These will be recognized as two of the effects we have discussed in dealing with surface tension. Most of the surface tension effects can be similarly explained.

Now if we return to consider the water surface, it is clear that if a molecule could arrive at the surface with sufficient speed it could overcome the attraction of the remaining liquid and break through the surface. Once away, it is free moving, and is said to form a vapour. It is a common experience that this actually takes place in evaporation. One thing which should follow, since it is the quickly-moving molecules which are able to get out of the liquid, is that the remaining liquid should have a lower average velocity—or the liquid should be cooler, since the temperature depends on the average speed. This effect is very noticeable if a little ether or petrol is placed on the hand. The rapid evaporation produces a very marked cooling effect.

In solutions, the molecules of the solids intermix with those of the liquids, which are usually smaller. Now, if a solution is against a wall containing very minute holes, the chance of a water molecule getting through a small hole is hindered by the presence of the larger solid molecule. Therefore, if on two sides of such a partition we have pure water and solution respectively, it is clear that there is a better chance of the pure water passing to the solution than of the water of the solution passing the other way. In fact, osmosis is to be expected.

'Brownian Movement.' These examples of the way in which the molecular theory fits the observed facts could be multiplied considerably. But perhaps the most convincing experiments are those which Perrin developed from the simple observations of Robert Brown, an English botanist.

If a solution of ordinary gamboge water colour be viewed by a high-power microscope it will be found that the granules or particles of gamboge in suspension move about in a most erratic manner. This movement is called *Brownian movement*. The same kind of thing can be observed with gum arabic and other substances. After eliminating all possible explanations of the curious movement it was established that it was due to the liquid itself and not to any outside cause.

It is definitely established that what we see is simply due to the uneven bombardment of the gamboge granule by the molecules of the liquid. The granule happens to be hit on one side only by a molecule and moves away. Then another molecule hits the granule and causes it to move in some other direction, and so on.

If the granule is very large the chance of this erratic movement being imparted to it by molecular bombardment is much smaller. This is due to the fact that, as the granule becomes larger, it receives a greater number of direct hits by molecules coming from all directions, and the result is no net force on it in any direction. Of course, even with a large granule, an occasional chance of an unbalanced impact occurs. When we consider large objects, this chance of Brownian movement becomes very small.

Mathematical Tests. Perrin made a careful experimental study of Brownian movements and was able, by applying relatively simple mathematical treatment, to calculate from his observations the number of molecules per cubic centimetre, the mean free path, etc. Einstein, who is better known through his theory of relativity, also made it possible to find molecular constants from observations of the *positions* of the granule after measured times. The mathematics there is similar to the problem of finding how far a drunken man would go if he started in a given direction and then fell. After each fall he gets up and starts again in a random direction and has a " mean free path " between falls. It can be shown how far he will go from his starting point by calculation analogous to that used for the random-moving granules. The granules are *seen*, their movement is measured, and molecular constant calculated. It is small wonder we always think of the phrase " Molecular Reality " when thinking of the Brownian movement, and we feel that—at any rate, in broad outline—the molecular theory must be very near the truth.

If at one temperature the average velocity of the molecules is fixed, it is clear that the average kinetic energy ($\frac{1}{2}$ mv^2) is also fixed. If, therefore, we wish to raise the temperature of the substance, we must increase the kinetic energy of this random movement. The only way of doing this is by supplying the equivalent of the energy gained. In other words, we must do work equal to that gained. We say that we supply heat. We, therefore, implicitly state that heat is a form of energy. In the old days heat was thought to be a massless fluid called *caloric*, which passed from the fire to the body, whose temperature was raised. But we know that by doing work we can produce heat. For example, if we rub a piece of wood on a table we impart a regular movement to the molecules of the wood ; we overcome the friction between them, and the work so done converts the regular movement into random movement of the molecules, and the temperature goes up. From an experimental side this was verified in the classical experiments of Dr. Joule, of Manchester, who showed that every 42 million ergs of work, if all converted to heat, produced one unit of heat, called the *calorie*. The calorie is the unit used to measure heat, and is the amount of heat which will raise the temperature of 1 gramme of water through 1°C. We usually call the relation " the mechanical equivalent of heat," or " Joule's equivalent," and write it in the form $4 \cdot 2 \times 10^7$ ergs per calorie.

LESSON 9

Heat as the Physicist Sees It

OUR considerations of the molecular theory in the preceding Lesson led us to associate with the temperature of a body the mean kinetic energy of the molecules of that body, but this does not lead to a very ready method for the measurement of temperature. Defined as the " degree of hotness " of a body, temperature is usually measured by means of a thermometer. Quantities of heat are measured in terms of the calorie ; temperature, or heat level, is measured in terms of an arbitrary scale of temperature. The Fahrenheit scale serves in everyday use engineering and medicine, and the Centigrade scale is used for scientific purposes. The estimation of temperature by the sense

GEORGE WASHINGTON
(1732 – 99), commander in
chief of the American army
in the War of Independence
and first president (1789–96)
of the U.S.A. MODERN
HISTORY 17

Metropolitan Museum of
Art, N.Y.

MAKERS OF THE UNITED STATES. Left to right : Thomas Jefferson
(1743–1826), Virginian lawyer, who helped to frame the Declaration of
Independence and was president 1801–9 ; Benjamin Franklin, who was born
at Boston, became a printer and publisher, achieved prominence as a politician,
investigated electricity and suggested lightning conductors, acted as the
Colonists' plenipotentiary in Europe and played a great part in the early
history of the republic ; Thomas Paine (1737–1809), English Deist and
Radical, who emigrated to America and by his pamphlets " Common Sense "
and the " Crisis " did much to arouse and sustain the ardour of the revolting
states. MODERN HISTORY 17

A PHILOSOPHIC TRIAD. George Berkeley (1685–1753), who was bishop
of Cloyne from 1734 to 1752 and is generally regarded as founder of the
philosophy of Idealism ; David Hume (1711–76), whose scepticism found
expression in his " Treatise of Human Nature " (1737) and " Essays " (1741):
and John Locke (1632–1704), famous not only for his philosophy but for
his pleas for democracy and toleration PHILOSOPHY 11

LAFAYETTE AND MIRA-BEAU. M. J. P. du Motier, Marquis de Lafayette (1757–1834), helped the American colonists 1777 and played a leading part in the early days of the French Revolution. Left, Gabriel Honoré Riqueti, Comte de Mirabeau (1749 – 91), leader of the Third Estate in the States General of 1789. MODERN HISTORY 18

LOUIS XVI AND MARIE ANTOINETTE. Louis XVI (1754–93) succeeded his grandfather, Louis XV, on the French throne in 1774 and reigned until the kingly office was abolished in 1792. Shortly afterwards " Louis Capet " was accused of treason against the republic, tried, found guilty, and guillotined (January 21, 1793). Nine months later he was followed to the scaffold by his queen, Marie Antoinette (1755–93), who was a daughter of the Empress Maria Teresa and married Louis in 1770. MODERN HISTORY 18

Plate 60   *Volume III*

of touch is a simple, but very unreliable method, which does not enable us to measure in a quantitative manner.

To establish a scale of measurement of temperature we take any physical property which varies regularly with temperature ; we then find the magnitude at two fixed points, and subdivide the change into a convenient number of divisions. To make this clear, let us see how the Centigrade scale is actually defined in the case of a mercury thermometer. We select the expansion of mercury in glass as the physical property—we know quite well that substances increase in size as the temperature rises. When the thermometer is placed in melting ice, the mercury remains at one volume so long as any ice is left ; the level in the thermometer stem is noted and is taken as the lower fixed point. When the water and ice mixture is heated the mercury expands and rises up the stem as soon as all the ice is melted ; this goes on until the water boils, when again no further increase in volume and consequent rise occurs. This level of the mercury in the stem is taken as the second fixed point. Actually the stem of the thermometer should be in the *steam* from the boiling water, and the pressure should be 76 cms. of mercury.

The distance on the stem of the uniform bore tube of the thermometer between these points is then divided into 100 parts, and each division is called a degree Centigrade. It is merely a matter of agreement—any subdivision could have been taken. For example, the Fahrenheit scale is made by calling the melting ice level 32° F. and the boiling water level 212° F. ; there are thus 180° F. between melting ice and boiling water, corresponding to the 100° on the Centigrade scale.

The thermometers we have considered are suitable for the measurement of temperatures from near the freezing point of mercury to near the boiling point of that liquid. For accurate work the expansion of air is used in the " air thermometer," and for high temperatures the variation of other physical properties is utilized.

Clinical Thermometers. For special cases, where accurate measurement is required over a limited range, special forms are used. A well-known example is the clinical thermometer, which is used to measure a range of only 15° F. The normal temperature of the human body is 98·4° F., and variations from this form a most useful indication to the medical practitioner in diagnosis. This range is obtained by using a very fine bore tube, so that

(577)

expansion in volume of the mercury takes up a large length of stem. The bulb of the thermometer is not fully filled, so that expansion taking place up to 94° F. merely fills the bulb. When the temperature reaches 95° F. the mercury comes to the first graduation on the stem, and so the further rises of temperature to 110° F. may be measured. To prevent the mercury slipping back when the instrument is taken from the mouth there is a constriction in the bore, and the mercury must be shaken back past this constriction. It is obvious that the instrument must not be put into boiling water to clean it, otherwise the mercury will expand sufficiently to burst the thermometer.

In Lesson 8 we learnt that heat is a form of energy ; that if mechanical work be all converted to heat we can calculate the heat produced by making use of the " mechanical equivalent " as found by Joule in his classical experiments, viz. $4 \cdot 2 \times 10^7$ ergs per calorie. In such calculations, as we shall see later, we deal with large numbers, and so we must often use a larger unit of work than the erg, called the *joule*, which is 10^7 ergs. In this unit we say that the mechanical equivalent is $4 \cdot 2$ joules per calorie. To form some idea of the amount of work required to produce one calorie, let us consider a pan containing about $1\frac{3}{4}$ pints of water at room temperature, 20°C. Heat is supplied by a gas ring, and the water is gradually brought to the boiling point (100° C.). Now $1\frac{3}{4}$ pints are approximately equal to 1000 c.cs. (1 litre), so we may readily find the heat taken from the gas flame to be $1000 \times$ rise in temperature $= 1000 \times 80$ calories. This is equivalent to $80000 \times 4 \cdot 2$ joules, or $33 \cdot 6 \times 10^{11}$ ergs. To realize what this means, let us consider what mechanical task could be accomplished by the work. For example, suppose we apply it to lifting a 3-ton rock. The work would be used in giving the rock a potential energy m g h, where h is the number of feet the rock is raised, i.e. since 1 ton $= 1016000$ gm. and 1 ft. $= 30$ cms., we may say :

$(3 \times 1016000) \times 981 \times (h \times 30) = 33 \cdot 6 \times 10^{11}$ or h is just over 37 ft. ! It seems rather astounding to consider that the energy required in such a commonplace operation as boiling $1\frac{3}{4}$ pints of water could, if suitably applied, lift 3 tons from the ground to the top of a tall wireless mast, but such is the case.

Specific Heat. If we consider substances other than water we find that the heat required to raise the temperature of 1 gm. 1 degree Centigrade is not 1 calorie. For copper it is about

1/10 cal., for paraffin oil about 1/2 cal., and so on. We say that the *specific heat* of water is 1, of copper is 1/10, of paraffin oil is 1/2, etc. This is well exemplified in sand and sea water. When both are exposed to the intense heat of the sun for the same time the sand, being of low specific heat, becomes much warmer than the sea water, a fact we verify when bathing on a summer's day.

For large-scale phenomena, where mass is measured in pounds and temperature in degrees Fahrenheit, a larger heat unit is employed called the British Thermal Unit (B.Th.U.). This is the amount of heat required to raise the temperature of 1 lb. of water 1° F. For example, on the reverse side of many gas bills the heating power of the gas supplied is expressed as so many, say x, B.Th.U. per cubic foot. This means that if 1 cu. ft. of the gas were burnt under conditions of complete combustion x B.Th.U. would be obtained. As we have seen, this is equivalent to a definite amount of energy. The therm, which in 1933 began to be used in the Press to create an interest in gas, is the name given to the unit of supply of gas in terms of the B.Th.U., and is equal to 100,000 B.Th.U. ; so that if the consumption of gas is 1000 cu. ft., and each cu. ft. happens to be equivalent to 470 B.Th.U. under the conditions stated, the number of therms is $\frac{470 \times 1000}{100,000} = 4.7$ therms. The excellence of this method of gas supply is that, if the calorific power of gas varies, the payment is still for the thermal equivalent of the energy, as the number 470 is adjusted by the company to be equivalent to the actual heating value of the gas supplied.

Latent Heat. If we put a thermometer into a pan containing ice and water we find that it reads 0° C., and if the pan is placed on a gas flame the temperature remains the same until all the ice is melted. Then there is a rise in temperature until the water boils, when again the temperature remains constant until all the water is boiled away. Now it is clear that the gas flame supplies heat all the time, and the question arises, what becomes of the heat when the thermometer stands at 0° C. and at 100° C. ? In terms of the molecular theory the answer is not far to seek. The molecules of ice, changing to water, are split apart to be more free-moving, and there must be a certain amount of work done to overcome the attraction of the molecules to each other. The mechanical equivalent of the heat is used on this separation. In the same way work is done tearing the water molecules apart to make steam, only in this case more work is required, because in the gaseous state the molecules are free of each other. We say the heat supplied is *latent* or *hidden*. Each gramme of ice at o° C. changing to water at o° C. requires 80 calories (approx.). In the same way, if 1 gm. of water at o° C. changes to ice at o° C. there is a liberation of 80 calories. We say that the *latent heat of fusion of ice* is 80 cals. per gm. In the change from water to steam each gramme of water at 100° C. requires 540 cals. (approx.) to convert it to steam, and in the reverse operation each gramme of steam gives up 540 cals. on condensing to boiling water. The *latent heat of evaporation of water* is said to be 540 cals. per gm.

A well-known example of the high value of the latent heat of evaporation of water is seen in the intense scalding which takes place if, say, the hand is placed in steam. The condensation of the steam on the hand is brought about with a consequent liberation of 540 calories for each gramme condensed to boiling water. If a gramme is condensed and cools to 20° C. the number of calories is $540 + (100 - 20) = 620$, whereas if the hand merely had 1 gramme of boiling water poured on it, the heat received would only be $100 - 20 = 80$ cals.

Whenever a change to vapour from liquid takes place it is always necessary to supply heat equivalent to the latent heat. This is smaller, the lower the temperature at which the change takes place ; but in all cases, as we saw in Lesson 8, we could anticipate the existence of latent heat from the molecular theory.

LESSON 10

What Happens to Matter When it is Heated

WHEN we considered the construction of a mercury thermometer in the last Lesson, we assumed that there is an expansion of the mercury when the temperature rises. We know as a matter of common observation that most substances do indeed change in size under these conditions of temperature change. The gap left between lengths of railway lines to allow for expansion in hot weather is a simple application of this.

The exact increase in length of a substance is usually expressed in terms of what is called the Coefficient of Linear Expansion (a), which is defined as the increase in length of 1 cm. when heated through 1°C. For example, the coefficient of linear expansion of iron is 0·000012 per degree Centigrade. That is, the fractional increase per degree Centigrade rise is 0·000012. If the length of metal rod is l_0 at 0°C., the increase in length at t°C. is $a\, l_0\, t$, and therefore the new length, l_t, at t°C. is $l_0 + a\, l_0 t$ or $l_t = l_0 (1+at)$. We thus see that, if the value of a is known, we can calculate the changes in length when the temperature changes. To facilitate such calculations, tables of constants are available, in which are tabulated the coefficients of linear expansion of different substances. Each figure in the table has been found by a set of careful experiments on the substances.

Over ordinary ranges of temperature it is not necessary to use the formula, deduced above, to refer strictly to lengths initially measured at 0°C., if an approximate answer is required. For example, if a steel bridge is a quarter of a mile long at 10°C. $(= 32° + \frac{9}{5} \times 10 = 50°F.)$ we can see what the expansion is when the temperature rises to 40°C. $(= 32° + \frac{9}{5} \times 40 = 104°F.)$, if we take l_0 to be the original length (i.e. not at 0°C. but at 10°C.), and take t to be the *rise* in temperature, viz. $40 - 10 = 30°C$. The expansion in feet then becomes $(440 \times 3) \times 0·000014 \times 30$, since a for steel is 0·000014 and l_0 is 440×3 ft., i.e. the expansion or increase in length is 0·554 ft. = 6·65 inches. For ordinary small values of temperature, therefore, we write :

$$l_2 = l_1 \{ 1 + a(t_2 - t_1) \}$$

where l_1 and t_1 refer to the lower temperature, and l_2 and t_2 refer to the higher temperature.

It is seen that the increase of length in ¼ mile in the above case is 6½ inches, and provision must be made in construction to allow for this length change. In the same way, in the example quoted at the beginning of this Lesson, the expansion in a long length of railway line would lead to serious warping of the line if it were all laid as a continuous length for, say, 100 miles, for here the expansion, of over 2 ft. per mile, would be 200 ft. In our conditions of climatic variation of temperature a bigger range has to be catered for.

Another application of this kind of expansion is seen in the pendulum of a clock. The time of swing, T, of a simple pendulum, is the time for a complete swing—there and back again—and is equal to $2\pi\sqrt{\dfrac{l}{g}}$ where $\pi = 3\tfrac{1}{7}$ (approx.) and g is the acceleration due to gravity, and l is the length of the pendulum. Obviously, in summer the length l increases and so T increases, and therefore the clock does not make as many swings in a day as in cold weather—in other words, we say the clock loses in summer. Now in most clocks the pendulum is not a simple one—i.e. a heavy very small mass on a light cord—but is compound : there is a *rod* which carries a massive bob. The same type of change occurs in its time of swing, however, and it is often corrected against temperature changes by allowing the bob to be free moving against an end stop on the rod (Fig. 1). When the rod expands, the centre of mass of the bob is lowered, but, at the same time the bob, which is made of a substance having a large coefficient of expansion, expands upwards to a greater extent, and is arranged so that the centre of gravity just keeps the same distance from the point of support, and thus keeps the same time of swing however the temperature changes.

Varying Expansion of Metals. There are many devices in common use which make use of the differences in the linear coefficient of expansion of metals in other ways. If we take a strip of iron ($a =$ 0·000012 per °C.) and a strip of brass ($a =$ 0·000018 per °C.) of the same dimensions and rivet them together, it will be found that at a higher temperature the compound strip takes up a curved form : the brass, expanding more than the iron, is on the outer side of the curve.

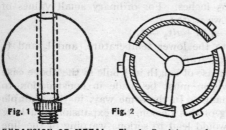

Fig. 1 **Fig. 2**

EXPANSION OF METAL. Fig. 1. Pendulum safeguarded against rise of temperature by tree-moving bob. **Fig. 2.** Balance wheel of watch with expansible rim.

This principle is made use of in such things as fire alarms, where the rise in temperature causes a double strip to bend and close an electric circuit and so cause an alarm bell to ring. The same principle, using other metals, is employed in the compensation of balance wheels of watches and clocks against temperature changes. The method of doing this is shown in Fig. 2. The rim which contains the bulk of the mass is divided and made of a compound strip whose more expansible component is on the outer side. For a rise in temperature the rim moves inward, and thus the mass moves nearer the axis of oscillation. Offset against this is the outward expansion of the spokes. The adjustment is made so that the net result is a complete compensation in this respect, and also to a great extent in respect of the change of stiffness of the hair spring.

In making the early form of electric lamps the difference in the coefficient of expansion of glass and the material of the filament presented a serious problem. It was found that when the lamp was switched on the glass cracked, as it had not expanded to the same extent as the filament. This difficulty was overcome by the use of short lengths of platinum wire to " seal in " the filament, since, over ordinary ranges of temperature change, the expansions of glass and platinum are the same.

There is always a bigger risk of breaking when the heated substance is a bad conductor of heat. We are all familiar with the breaking of a tumbler by too sudden a change in temperature. When boiling water is poured into such a vessel the glass is heated locally and expands ; if the expansion is too local it breaks.

If a tumbler is made of fused silica it is possible to heat it up to dull red heat and then pour in cold water without any fracture taking place ; this is because the coefficient of expansion of the silica is so very small. In metals an alloy called invar has been made which also has such a small coefficient of expansion that changes in length over ordinary ranges of temperature are negligible. Invar, therefore, is an ideal substance for pendulums.

Liquids and gases expand to a greater extent than solids, and in their case there is a new feature, viz. they must be contained in a vessel made of some substance which also expands. The measurement of the expansion is, therefore, not quite as straight-forward as in the case of solids.

For example, if we observe an expansion of a liquid in a glass vessel there is the expansion of the vessel, tending to make the liquid appear to take up less space, and then the expansion of the liquid increases its size. So if we observe the net result, it is the real expansion of the liquid minus the expansion of the vessel.

In volume changes we express the expansion by means of a coefficient called the Coefficient of Cubical Expansion. This is the volume change per unit volume for 1°C. rise in temperature, e.g. if a volume V increases by an amount v when the temperature is raised by t°C., the coefficient of cubical expansion is $\dfrac{v}{Vt}$

For the liquid we have just considered there are two coefficients of cubical expansion ; the first, dealing with actual expansion, is called the Real Coefficient of Expansion. When we measure the rise of a liquid in a vessel, we have seen that the observed amount is less than this, and the corresponding coefficient, calculated in the manner shown above, is called the coefficient of Apparent Expansion. It happens that the vessel expands as though it were solid, and the coefficient of cubical expansion for the solid material is very nearly three times the linear coefficient.

We have, therefore : The coefficient of real expansion = coefficient of apparent expansion + coefficient of cubic expansion of the glass of the vessel.

To see the difference in these two coefficients, consider water in a glass vessel. The real coefficient is 0·00015 between 10°–20°C. ; for glass the linear coefficient is about 0·000007 ; the apparent coefficient for water in glass is 0·00015 − 3 × 0·0000017 = 0·0001449 per °C.

Temperature Changes in Gases. In the case of gases the expansion is so large that it is customary to neglect the effect of the containing vessel entirely, except in specially accurate work. This will be appreciated if we consider the order of the expansion : air has a coefficient of expansion (" cubical " is implied as this is the only possible case for gases) of 0·00366, and if we take away the cubical expansion of the glass vessel, viz. 0·0000051, it is only a matter of 5 in 3600, or approximately 0·1 per cent. Offset against this simplification for gases there is a more serious complication. We have seen that the volume of a gas changes with pressure, so that it is clear that a change in volume which takes place on heating will be related to the possible pressure conditions as well as temperature.

To make things clear, it is customary to deal with rises in temperature of a gas under two headings : (1) at constant volume, and (2) at constant pressure. In the first case the result of a temperature rise is an increase in pressure ; in the second, in volume.

Our Course in Physics is continued in Volume 4.

LESSON 5

What Isobars and Isotherms Tell us About Climate

THE chief factors in climate are the variations, at different times of the year, and in different regions, of temperature, atmospheric pressure, winds and rainfall. By dealing with these four factors in the order given here, we shall be able to show how temperature affects the distribution of atmospheric pressure as recorded by the barometer. Pressure, again, affects the direction and strength of the prevailing winds, which in turn are directly responsible for the distribution of rainfall.

In the Lesson on the seasons (volume 2, page 601) we learnt that the amount of warmth reaching a particular area of the earth's surface varies according to the latitude at which the sun is overhead at noon. Were the earth's surface all land or all sea, variations of warmth would therefore depend on latitude only. But this is not so. Land is heated more quickly than water, because it is heated at the surface only. Water is heated more slowly than land, because the warmth spreads through the whole mass. Therefore land reflects more heat, because it absorbs less ; water reflects less heat, because it absorbs more. The result is that land cools fairly quickly and water cools fairly slowly.

It is well known that climbers, balloonists, and aircraft pilots often suffer severely from cold at high elevations. Thus it is evident that temperature is dependent, not only on latitude, but also on the irregular distribution of land and sea, as well as on height above sea level.

Temperature is generally shown on a map by means of isotherms, i.e. lines of equal warmth, drawn so as to connect all points having one and the same temperature, the lines being more or less numerous according to the scale of the map. By means of isotherms, then, we can show the temperature in a given region at any particular time, or we can show the distribution over that region of the average temperature for a long or short period.

Before we draw the resulting isotherms on our map, it will be necessary to introduce a rather important modification in our temperature figures. If we took account of such differences of temperature as exist between the summits of the Himalayas and the plain of the Ganges, or between the great plateau within the Rocky Mountains and the prairies lying east of them, our map would be so crowded with detail as to be useless.

Observation has shown that, on an average, temperature decreases by 1° Fahrenheit for every 300 feet rise in elevation.

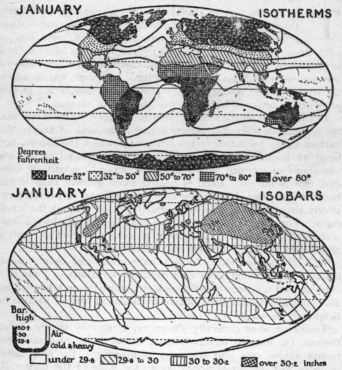

JANUARY   ISOTHERMS

Degrees
Fahrenheit

▨ under 32° ⬚ 32° to 50° ◫ 50° to 70° ▥ 70° to 80° ▦ over 80°

JANUARY   ISOBARS

Bar.
high
30·2
30
29·8   Air
cold & heavy

▢ under 29·8 ◫ 29·8 to 30 ▥ 30 to 30·2 ▦ over 30·2 inches

If, therefore, to the temperature recorded by the thermometer at an elevated station we add 1° for every 300 feet of its height above sea level, we shall get the temperature recorded at the hill station as reduced to sea level.

These reduced temperatures are those we record on our maps, and on which we base our isotherms. The final result, then, in the present Lesson, takes the form of the two maps, which show the mean, or average, temperature over the earth's surface during the months of January and July.

If temperature were dependent on latitude alone, we should find the isotherms, the lines of equal temperature, running round the globe parallel to the equator. Our maps, however, give us a very different picture. Both in July (northern summer) and in

JULY   ISOTHERMS

Degrees
Fahrenheit

▓ under 32° ░ 32° to 50° ▨ 50° to 70° ▤ 70° to 80° ■ over 80°

JULY   ISOBARS

Air
hot
Light
30·2
30
29·8
Bar.
Low

☐ under 29·8 ▨ 29·8 to 30 ▥ 30 to 30·2 ▨ over 30·2 inches

January (southern summer) the isotherms of 80° are closer together over the sea than over the land, which means that the hottest area is more extensive on land than at sea. For example, over the Pacific Ocean there is no area with an average temperature of over 80°, either north or south of the equator. Even mere nearness to the sea affects temperature in this way as is illustrated by the cooler strips running south along the west coasts of South America and South Africa during the southern winter, or along the west coast of North America during the northern summer.

North Africa, during this latter season, provides a striking illustration of the conditions described above. This great land mass appears on our map as the most extensive area with this very high average temperature, while off its west coast the isotherms are so close together as almost to make the region of cooler air continuous from north to south over the Atlantic.

When we come to consider the areas with low temperature, we find the same thing. During the northern winter, nearly half North America and more than half the immense area of Asia have an average temperature of below 32° (freezing point). Between the two, however, under the moderating influence of the Atlantic Ocean, the isotherm of 32° is bent so far north that all north-western Europe, nearly to the Arctic circle, is included in the warmer area, with a mean temperature, for January, of over 32°. Note also how the isotherm named turns sharply north along the coast of eastern Asia.

A comparison of the facts stated here gives us an illustration of what is meant by continental and oceanic climate respectively. Continental climate is characterized by extremes (hot summers, cold winters), because air over a land surface becomes hot or cold quickly. Oceanic climate, on the other hand, is more moderate, because air over the sea is warmed or cooled more slowly.

The distribution of atmospheric pressure is shown on a map by means of isobars, i.e. lines of equal weight (of air). They are drawn so as to connect all points having equal atmospheric pressure—the lines, as in the case of the temperature maps, being more or less numerous according to the scale of the map.

The two lower charts show the average atmospheric pressure over the earth's surface (land and sea) for the months of January and July. Hot air is light and tends to rise, while cold air is heavy and presses downwards. As temperature is observed by means of the thermometer, so atmospheric pressure is recorded by the barometer, i.e. measurer of weight (of air). The small inset diagrams illustrate the effect of light and heavy air respectively on the barometer, and will serve to explain the meaning of the reference to inches appearing under the two maps.

LESSON 6

Prevailing Winds and Ocean Currents

THE weight of the air and its pressure on the earth's surface vary within narrow limits. This pressure, as we learned in the preceding Lesson, is measured by the barometer, and under average conditions may be taken as equal to the pressure of a column of mercury just under 30 inches high.

Air over a surface heated by the sun is warmed quickly over the land, more slowly over the sea. When air is warmed it expands and rises, as does the air in a chimney when the fire is lighted. If it rises, it must be lighter than it was before. Hence it exerts less pressure, and as it cannot support as large a column of mercury as it formerly did, the barometer falls. As hot air is light, so cold air is heavy and tends to sink. It can support more mercury than it could before, and the barometer will rise.

These are the phenomena which the two maps of atmospheric pressure, in pages 586–7, show for the whole surface of the globe, in the shape of the averages for the months of January and July. By comparing the maps referring to the same month, we see how changes of temperature affect atmospheric pressure.

In January (northern winter) the cold areas of North America and Asia are represented by two areas of heavy pressure, with areas of lighter pressure between them, because air over the sea keeps warm longer. In July (northern summer) the areas of light pressure are over the land, because air over the land becomes hot, and so light, more quickly than it does over the sea.

AIR: Hot & light Minimum   BAROMETER: Low   BAROMETER: High   AIR: Cold & heavy Maximum

On the southern hemisphere, January (southern summer) shows very clearly how the heating of South America, South Africa, and northern Australia makes for light pressure over those regions, while the Pacific, Atlantic, and Indian Oceans have corresponding areas of heavier pressure. Conditions are not quite so clearly marked in the southern hemisphere during July (southern winter), as the land areas are comparatively small, and have not so strong an influence as the vast land mass of Asia.

The diagram in page 589, showing how a barometer works, should help to make clear the connexion between atmospheric pressure and the direction of the wind. If the air rises over a certain area, winds will blow inwards towards the centre of that area, to take the place of the air which has risen. Similarly, when

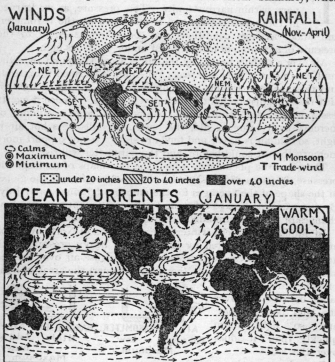

the air over an area sinks, winds will blow outwards. For further information concerning the barometer the student is referred to Lesson 4 in Physics (volume 2, page 581).

If temperature and, consequently, pressure were influenced by latitude only, there would be winds blowing constantly from north and south towards the latitude at which the sun, being overhead at noon, warms the earth's surface most quickly and thoroughly.

The irregular distribution of land and sea affects the distribution of temperature, and consequently of pressure also. Finally, as we have now to learn, it influences the direction of the prevailing winds, shown, again for the months of January and July, in the maps given in this Lesson.

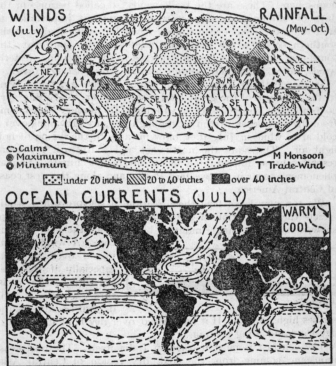

For the sake of clearness the chief centres of high pressure (maxima) and of low pressure (minima), from or to which the chief wind currents are directed, have been marked on these two maps. Winds do not, however, blow directly outwards or inwards from or to these points. The earth's rotation causes them to incline to the right on the northern hemisphere and to the left south of the equator. In other words, a north wind blowing towards the equator becomes a north-east wind, while a south wind blowing towards the equator becomes a south-east wind.

The above explanation should enable the student to trace the origin of the winds shown in our maps as blowing regularly from the north-east in the Pacific and Atlantic Oceans north of the equator, and from the south-east in all three oceans in the southern hemisphere. These are the trade winds, so called because in the days of sailing ships they were of paramount importance to traders on the great ocean routes. Over the vast expanse of the southern ocean which surrounds the Antarctic continent the south-east trade winds become merged in the prevailing westerly winds, called, from their average latitude, the Roaring Forties.

In the northern Indian Ocean conditions are different, owing to the influence of the great land mass of inner Asia, being very cold in winter and very hot in summer. In January winds come from the north-east, driven by the high pressure prevailing over a cold area, while in July they blow inwards to the region of hot, light air. These are the north-east and south-west monsoons respectively, so important a factor in India's climate. Similar phenomena occur in the western Pacific and along the west coast of Central America.

We can now learn how the direction of the prevailing winds affects the distribution of the world's rainfall, which our maps show, not for two single months, but for half the year in each

case. A wind blowing inland over the sea, especially if that sea be warm, carries moisture, which it will deposit as rain when it strikes high ground. If it has passed over dry land it will be a dry wind and bring no rain.

The contrast is most marked in India itself. The north-east monsoon, coming from the cold, dry region of Central Asia, carries no moisture. This is India's dry season. The south-west monsoon, on the other hand, has traversed the warm Indian Ocean and brings to India the wet season, with the monsoon rains so necessary to the livelihood of millions of small cultivators.

The student should be able to find for himself other examples, as shown in the maps, notably the regions covered by the two great equatorial rain forests of South America and central Africa. The movement north and south of the areas of heaviest rainfall is due to the fact that the hottest area is north or south of the equator, to correspond with the northern and southern summers.

Ocean Currents. Yet another phenomenon is illustrated by the maps, namely, the ocean currents. The wind, acting on the surface of the sea, not only causes ripples and waves, but also, if continuous, sets up regular currents, shown here in simplified form.

Again it is in the northern Indian Ocean that we find the most striking and interesting example. The north-west monsoon drift of January changes, with the changing wind, into the south-west monsoon drift of July, and it is the moisture-laden winds of the latter month which bring to the Western Ghats and the southern slopes of the Himalayas in particular, as well as to south-eastern Asia generally, some of the heaviest rainfall to be found anywhere on the earth's surface.

The maps show how the prevailing west winds of the northern Atlantic set up the Gulf Stream, warmed by its passage through equatorial regions, and bring to western Europe mild winters and heavy rainfall.

LESSON 7

How Landscape Features Originated

THE present Lesson and that which follows it are devoted to a consideration of the more important of those surface features of the land, such as mountains, rivers, lakes and glaciers, which not only give us what we call landscape, but which play such an important part in influencing the distribution and mode of life of the human race.

The stratified rocks, which cover so much of the earth's surface, were originally deposited horizontally (Fig. 1), in the form of mud, the product of erosion, carried into lakes and the sea by rivers, and falling to the bottom in the still water. In the Grand Cañon of the Colorado river the strata are plainly to be seen in their original horizontal position, being easily distinguishable by their various colouring.

Evidence of the changes of level by which such tracts have now become dry land is of various kinds. Fossil remains of sea or lake animals and vegetation are found at quite considerable heights above present-day sea or lake level; while such a formation as the Roads of Glenroy, near Ben Nevis, probably marks three successive positions of the shore of a lake.

These changes of level, however, can be only very slow and gradual, and would not have produced the much diversified landscape which the earth possesses today. There would have been no mountains. These features are due to movements of a more violent nature and are classified in four types : folded mountains, block mountains, highlands of erosion, and volcanoes.

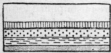

Fig. 1. Horizontal Strata.

Fig. 2. Folded Strata.

Fig. 3. Fan-like Folding.

Mountain Formations. A characteristic example of folded formation is that of the Jura mountains, along the Franco-Swiss frontier. The horizontal strata of which they consist now cover a much smaller area than formerly, with the obvious result that they have been thrown into the shape of waves or folds by pressure in a horizontal direction. From time to time the earth's crust has been thus affected and more or less regular ridges have been formed (Fig. 2). If the force and extent of compression are very great, we may have an almost fanlike shape (Fig. 3), a well-known example of which is on the shores of lake Titicaca in South America. Most of the earth's greatest mountain systems, such as the Himalayas, Alps, Carpathians, and the American Rockies, were created in this way, although other agencies, especially

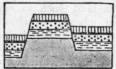

Fig. 4. Block Mountain.

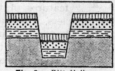

Fig. 5. Rift Valley.

erosion by water or ice, have been at work, to shape their details and give them their present outline.

The term block mountains is usually applied to a range which has been raised above the general level, or left standing as isolated blocks by the sinking of the surrounding country. A striking example is seen in the Harz mountains, which not only overlook the great plain of northern Germany, but are flanked by low-lying districts of smaller extent. The earth movements which bring about such formations often work violently in a vertical direction and are known as " faults." A mass of sedimentary rock, deprived of its foundations by the collapse of some great subterranean hollow, sinks down, leaving one or more blocks of strata in their original position (Fig. 4). The great rift valley of East Africa has a similar origin, while another example is the Rhine valley between Bâle and Mainz (Fig. 5). The geological formation of the highlands (such as the Vosges and Black Forest), for nearly 200 miles along either side, shows clearly that the strata were once continuous, though now separated by a valley nearly 20 miles wide.

Folded mountains may be worn down into rugged peaks and ridges by the action of water or ice. This action, when applied to undisturbed sedimentary rocks, will not perhaps produce such fantastic shapes as that of the Matterhorn, but in some parts of the globe the details of the surface features are due entirely to their glacial covering. The English Lake District has been carved out of a block of sedimentary rock by the action of water and ice, which removed the softer materials, so that the shape of the mountains is only partly due to their original structure. Norway is just such another block of which the fjords—and the narrow valleys continuing them inland—owe their existence and shape to erosion. An example of an isolated block is Table mountain, Cape of Good Hope.

Rivers. A bucket of water emptied on the side of a hill will take the shortest way it can find to the bottom. If the soil is soft it will absorb all or part of the water. If it consists of hard rocks, the water will run over them, still taking the shortest possible way. The inequalities we may expect to find on any hill will not only give to the water a course winding from side to side to avoid obstacles, but may also change its gradient, as the slope varies.

In fact, the water from the bucket will exhibit, on a small scale, the phenomena that are observable in a mountain brook or a great river. It will run smoothly over ground of a regular slope ; it will form bends to avoid stones lying in its path ; a steep ledge will produce a waterfall ; and should it find its way into a hollow capable of holding water, it will form a pool, just in the same way as the river forms a lake. The river, however, will not only take the shortest and easiest way it can find, but will also be continually at work trying to make that way shorter and easier still. It does this by means of erosion and deposition.

Mechanics of Erosion. Erosion signifies the wearing away of the banks of a river (lateral erosion), or the deepening of its bed (vertical erosion). If the nature of the rocks is suitable to such a process, they may actually be chemically dissolved, as is the case with such materials as limestone or salt. This work is mainly of a mechanical character; but whether in the form of mechanical erosion or chemical solution, whether working laterally or vertically, the object is, and the result will be, to make the stream's course easier and more direct.

In doing this work, a stream will make use of fragments of rock, large and small, to wear out its bed and banks, and just as rough fragments are worn down by the sea waves to the rounded pebbles of our shingle beaches, so the fragments rolled along by a stream not only become smooth and round themselves, but also help to wear away and smooth the ground over which the stream takes its course.

The amount of material which a river can carry along with it obviously depends both on the volume of water and on the speed of its flow. The carrying power increases as the sixth power of the velocity; this means that if the rate of flow is doubled, the carrying power will be multiplied by 64, so that a stream able to carry a pebble weighing an ounce will, if its speed be doubled, be able to shift a stone weighing four pounds. When a mountain stream reaches level country it begins to drop the débris brought from the upper reaches owing to the reduction in speed of its flow.

While the wearing away of the banks tends to straighten a river's course, the wearing down of the bed, also effected with the help of débris carried along, will gradually even out the channel and give it a uniform slope. The extent to which a river will be able to perform this grading must depend largely on the varying hardness of the rocks over which it passes. It is not to be expected, therefore, that we shall find any river with a perfectly uniform gradient from source to mouth. Moreover, particularly hard rocks may resist erosive action so successfully as to remain in the shape of small rocky islands or reefs in the river bed. A well-known example of this is the Iron Gates through which the Danube passes from the plain of Hungary to the lowland region of its lower course. A river which approaches a uniform gradient is said to be " well graded." If a river had a perfectly straight course, deposition of its débris would take place with perfect regularity throughout ; the larger fragments would be dropped first, then the smaller ones, while the sand and mud would be carried down to the mouth and even out to sea. A river with a winding course will have its swiftest current not always in the middle (as would be the case with a straight course), but on one side or the other. The current being swifter on the outside of a bend, that part of a river will be able to carry the sediment away, thus keeping its bed clear and its channel deep. On the inside of the bend, in the more sluggish water, deposits of sediment will take place.

When a river overflows its banks and floods the surrounding country, the sediment which it has brought down from its upper reaches will be dropped by the comparatively sluggish water of the flooded area outside the regular course. It is in this way that the Nile every year performs its work of fertilization, by spreading over the surface of the land the rich volcanic mud brought down from Abyssinia. When a river finally reaches a lowland plain it will be flowing too slowly to carry any but quite small particles of erosive products. The dredging operations necessary in the lower reaches of such rivers as the Rhine, Elbe, Rhône, and many others, are evidence of this. But the most striking result of sediment reaching the mouth of a river manifests itself in the formation of deltas, as in the case of the Ganges, Nile, etc.

LESSON 8

Nature's Methods of Lake Formation

HEAVY rainfall or the sudden melting of snow in an upland area may cause a river, in its course through level country, to overflow its banks. When the water has had time to drain away the river will return to its normal size and course. Under certain conditions this surplus water might have been prevented from draining away. The temporary flooding would then have become permanent, and we should call it a lake. The large and small lakes dotted over the earth's surface owe their existence to a variety of causes, and we may distinguish three geological phenomena which have brought into existence hollows capable of holding water. These causes are erosion, deposition, and movements of the earth's crust, but lakes owing their origin exclusively to one of the three are comparatively rare.

A lake formed by erosion may generally be recognized by the fact that it is completely surrounded by rather hard rock. When a river passes over a bed of soft rock, this will be eroded more quickly, forming a hollow which must be filled before the river can proceed on its course.

Erosion by a river may, as we have learnt, take the form of actual chemical solution, and this occurs not only at the surface, but also by means of underground streams, which easily dissolve such material as limestone and salt. Underground hollows are formed, which ultimately collapse and, when filled with water, become lakes. Of this nature are the " polyes " of the Dalmatian limestone, of which the lake of Scutari is an example, and probably also the meres of the Cheshire salt area. Often, however, it is only the deeper portion of a lake basin which has been formed in this way, and we shall generally find that deposition has contributed to the formation of the lake as we see it today.

Deposition most frequently takes the form of building a dam of sediment across a valley or at its mouth, which may either form a new lake or increase the extent and depth of an already existing rock-basin. In addition to the sediment carried by the streams, there is the débris brought down, in the form of moraines, by a glacier and deposited at its foot. Most of the Alpine lakes are of this nature.

Lagoons and Broads. Lakes formed by deposition in lowland areas frequently take the shape of lagoons, cut off from the sea by river deposits, or by the products of sea erosion, transported by current and tide. Of this character are the lagoons of the Adriatic coast between Ravenna and Trieste, the " haffs " of eastern Prussia, and the lagoons of the Camargue, at the mouth of the Rhône. The Norfolk Broads, though now mostly at some distance from the sea, were formed in this way, and some of them are still within reach of the tide.

Deposition may take the more violent form of a landslide extending right across a valley and so building up a dam, as in the case of Lake Gohna in Kashmir. A view of the eastern side of Wastwater, in Cumberland, shows clearly how the screes of Scafell, which may be described as a permanent landslide, have altered the original shape of the lake.

Lakes in the volcanic areas frequently take the form of crater-lakes, as in the Eifel district of the Rhineland, where the lake of Laach is an example, or as in the case of Lake Avernus near Naples. The small gulf of Baiae, in the same district, was probably a crater-lake till its wall collapsed to admit the sea.

The animal kingdom also plays a part in this work. The lagoon of a coral island owes its existence to the reefs built up by the coral polyp. Another lake-forming animal is the Canadian beaver, with its dam-building habits.

In the preceding Lesson we referred to rift valleys, formed by the sinking of blocks of sedimentary rock. In the lower portions of such valleys water will naturally accumulate to form lakes. The best-known example is the Jordan valley, the lowest portion of which is filled by the Dead Sea. Lake Baikal in Siberia is another instance of a lake formed by a geological fault, as are also Lakes Nyasa and Tanganyika, and other smaller East African lakes in the great rift valley.

Very often the strata have been tilted to form the furrow in which the waters of the lake have collected, as in the case of Lake Titicaca in South America. The great lakes of North America were probably formed (at least partly) in this way, though here we find, in old shore-lines (once horizontal, but now tilted), evidence of earth movements since the lakes originally formed.

Changes of level over large areas may also lead to the formation of lakes. The Caspian and the Sea of Aral, now inland drainage areas, were once part of the sea, since cut off by a rising of the land. The whole of the shores of the Caspian, as well as part of the bottom of the Aral Sea, lie below the general ocean level.

LESSON 9

Volcanoes of Today and Yesterday

(See plate 61)

A FAVOURITE theory as to the immediate cause of volcanic action is that cracks in the earth's crust admit the sea to subterranean reservoirs of land, the explosion being brought about by the sudden formation of vast quantities of steam which follows. This theory, however, leaves two things unexplained. First, there are some volcanoes at a considerable distance from the sea, such as Mt. Teleki and Mt. Kirungo, near Lake Rudolf in East Africa, and Koh-i-Tafdan in eastern Iran. Secondly, there are considerable stretches of coast without volcanoes.

This theory is, therefore, now generally regarded as erroneous, and the immediate cause of a volcanic outburst is sought rather in such occurrences as the development of gas or steam, due to the cooling of molten rock, or even to the purely mechanical pressure exercised by the collapse of some great subterranean hollow filled with molten matter. The simplest way of defining a volcano is to describe it as a hole in the earth's surface through which masses of molten matter are thrown up. But there is considerable variety in the phenomena which accompany the eruption.

Volcanoes of the type of Mt. Vesuvius seem to follow a regular programme, beginning, fortunately, with warning earthquakes. The liberation of gas and steam is then followed by the throwing up of ashes, accompanied by rain and even thunderstorms, and concluding with a generally quiet and steady outpouring of lava.

Vesuvius was believed to be extinct till A.D. 79, when the eruption in which Pliny the Elder lost his life overwhelmed Herculaneum with mud and Pompeii with ashes. The eruption of 1631 was even more terrible than that of 79, and destroyed two towns with most of their inhabitants. Since then the character of the mountain's activities has changed. Eruptions have been more frequent, but individually less alarming.

Mount Etna, the loftiest of Europe's volcanoes, came into existence as an island volcano close to the east coast of Sicily. By filling up the narrow strait with the débris of successive eruptions it ultimately joined itself to the main island. Of eighty recorded eruptions, that of 1669 was the worst, especially in the matter of the outpouring of lava. Vesuvius has one main crater, with a few subsidiary outlets scattered over its extensive surface. In the case of Etna, the actual main crater has fallen in on one side, forming a gorge with steep sides, the Val di Bove, while eruptions now take place through small scattered craters, of which there are nearly 200. Etna's most recent destructive eruption was in 1928.

The eruptions of Krakatoa, between Java and Sumatra (1883), of Mt. Tarawera in New Zealand (1886), and of Bandaisan in Japan (1888) were quite different from those described. They were really explosions—in the true sense of the word—of subterranean accumulations of gas and steam, which, in the cases of

VOLCANOES

Krakatoa and Bandaisan, blew away a large part of the mountains in which they occurred, and then threw up vast quantities of rock fragments and ashes, but no lava.

Lava eruptions, pure and simple, are comparatively rare. The best-known examples are the Hawaian volcanoes. A characteristic Hawaian eruption takes place without anything in the nature of an explosion. An enormous mass of lava, in a very liquid state, simply rises until it overflows the crater's edge.

A quite different phenomenon was witnessed at the eruption of Mt. Pelée, in the island of Martinique, French West Indies (1902), which ended, not with an outflow of lava, but with what can only be described as an avalanche in the shape of a cloud of water-vapour laden with glowing ashes, which rolled down the side of the mountain and destroyed the town of St. Pierre.

Extinct Volcanoes. When we speak of a volcano being extinct or dormant, we do not mean that volcanic activity has ceased altogether. It may manifest itself in various ways, though not so violently as in an actual eruption. Instances of this kind are the so-called solfataras, from which issue clouds of steam laden with sulphurous gases, as in the case of La Soufrière, in the island of St. Vincent, British West Indies, which erupted in 1902 and devastated nearly half the island. The geysers of the Yellowstone National Park, in the United States, and of Iceland belong to this class of volcanic activity.

Perhaps the most interesting example of what we may call expiring volcanic action is to be found in the Rotorua district of New Zealand (North Island), where these phenomena may be studied in all their various forms of solfataras, geysers, fumaroles or smoke geysers, hot springs and lakes, and mud volcanoes. The wonderful pink and white terraces of Lake Rotomohana were destroyed by a terrible eruption of Mt. Tarawera in 1886.

Hot springs of various kinds are to be found at several places in western Europe—which was, in prehistoric times, a region of considerable volcanic activity—as also in the Azores, in Iceland and elsewhere.

A very interesting form sometimes taken by an extinct volcano is that of a crater-lake. Lake Taupo in New Zealand is an example, and others are to be found in the United States—such as Lake Mazama in Oregon—in the Auvergne, central France, in the Eifel district of Germany, and in the West Indies.

Our Course in Physiography is continued in Volume 4.

LESSON 11

Digestion: How Food is Absorbed

(See plate 62)

THE transit of the chyme through the small gut takes place normally in about four hours, though it may be three or four hours longer before the last traces of a meal are passed into the large intestine into which the small intestine opens at its lower end. During this time the chyme undergoes the greater part of preparation for absorption into the body proper. This is effected by the intestinal juice and by two other juices which are poured into the first loop of the gut, the duodenum. Into this loop, which is about a foot long and curves away from the stomach to encircle the end of the pancreas or sweetbread, opens a double tube or duct. One part of this duct conveys the secretion from the pancreas, the other conveys bile from the liver.

The pancreas is a glandular structure consisting of groups of gland cells supported by areolar tissue; it measures about 6 to 8 inches in length, and about $1\frac{1}{2}$ inches in breadth and thickness, and weighs about 3 ounces. It lies in front of the spinal column, behind the stomach. Most of its cells secrete a digestive fluid, the pancreatic juice; but certain special cells in it manufacture a hormone or messenger substance known as insulin, which passes into the blood and regulates the use of sugar by the tissues. Disease of these cells causes diabetes. Bile is derived from the liver and is collected by ducts in the liver substance into the gall bladder, from which it passes by the bile duct into the duodenum.

Action of Ferments. The pancreatic juice is strongly alkaline and contains ferments which act on all classes of foodstuffs. One, called trypsin, acts more potently than the pepsin of gastric juice on protein substance. It not only completes the partial work of the latter in splitting these elements of the food into what are known as amino-acids—the form in which they are capable of being made use of by the tissues—but also deals with protein that has escaped change in the stomach. A second ferment, known as amylopsin, converts starch into a sugar called maltose ; and yet another ferment converts the maltose into the still more absorbable sugar, glucose. A fourth ferment, lipase, deals with fat, splitting it into glycerol and fatty acids, the latter combining with the alkaline salts of the juice to form a soap.

Secretion of pancreatic juice is activated by a hormone known as secretin, derived from glandular cells in the wall of the duodenum in response to stimulation of these cells by the acid chyme. The secretory activity of the pancreas is, like that of the stomach, also under the control of the higher nerve centres.

Bile is a greenish alkaline fluid, the digestive action of which is confined to its solvent action on fats and soaps ; it also assists the digestive action of the pancreatic juice on fats by its physical action on the fat globules. Bile has, too, some slight antiseptic action, and also stimulates the peristaltic movement of the gut. The intestinal juice, or *succus entericus*, has a similar action to that of the pancreatic juice on sugar, and powerfully reinforces the action of this latter juice on proteins.

Practically all the nutritive material except water is absorbed from the small intestine. Starch and sugar, converted to glucose, pass direct by way of the portal veins to the liver. Here they are converted into the substance glycogen, and stored as such for future use. Proteins are absorbed as amino-acids, and pass as such direct into the blood stream and are carried to all the body cells. As we shall see later, there are several kinds of these acids required for different kinds of cell. Fat is split up into glycerol and fatty acid. Glycerol is absorbed as such, and the soaps, as they enter the villi, are reconverted into fat. The fat passes into the lacteals of the villi, which finally conduct it into the thoracic duct and so into the blood stream. Some of the absorbed fat, however, appears to pass direct into the blood.

The Large Intestine. The last loop of the small gut enters the single loop of the large intestine or colon low down on the right side of the abdomen. The opening is guarded by the ileo-caecal sphincter, which prevents return of the contents of the colon into the small gut. Below the opening the colon has a blind end or sac called the caecum ; and close to the juncture of the caecum, colon, and small gut is the appendix, a worm-like hollow tube with a blind end, and about 4 inches long and $\frac{1}{2}$ inch round. It represents the remains of the much larger colon of purely vegetarian animals. From this point the colon passes up in the right flank, crosses the abdomen at the level of the navel and descends in the left flank to the pelvis, where, after forming an open loop—the sigmoid flexure—it becomes the rectum and opens to the surface at the anus. The colon is about 70 inches in length and, cut open, measures 6 inches across. The wall has a mucous lining in which are glands secreting mucus for purposes of lubrication. There are two layers of muscle tissue—one circular, the other longitudinal—collected into three bands which run the length of the colon. An elaborate network of nerves and nerve cells, and a capillary field of blood vessels and lymphatics provide for the active movements of this part of the gut, and for the limited amount of absorption that takes place from its interior.

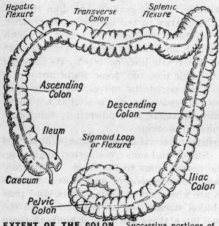

The wall of the colon is puckered into pouches and folds—an arrangement permitting a retention of its contents which, to

EXTENT OF THE COLON. Successive portions of the large intestine are named the ascending, transverse, descending, iliac and pelvic colon.

a certain extent, is normal but may easily become of harmful duration. Two kinds of movement occur. The circular muscle exercises a kneading action on the contents, and the longitudinal muscle sets up at long and regular intervals a mass peristaltic wave, which propels them onwards into the sigmoid flexure, and thence into the rectum. This movement should occur after taking a meal. The presence of the faecal mass in the rectum gives rise to the desire for evacuation, and if a suitable voluntary response is made to the stimulus, the wall of the rectum contracts and the powerful sphincter muscle which guards the anus relaxes. If the stimulus is not attended to, this mechanism soon becomes faulty.

Digestion in the Colon. The digestive work of the colon is confined to dealing with foodstuffs which have escaped digestion in the small bowel because of their fibrous nature. The cellulose of vegetable and fruit fibre is here acted on by micro-organisms which, by setting up fermentation, break up the cellulose and liberate mineral and other constituents of the vegetable cells. These, together with water, are absorbed through the colon wall. So numerous are these microbes that a considerable part of the faeces consists of them, alive or dead. The process is a slow one, and food remnants normally lie in the colon for 24 to 48 hours. If constipation is present this time may be extended to several days. Putrefaction of the contents of the colon ensues, with formation of poisonous substances, which, being absorbed into the blood stream, are carried to all parts of the body and are the cause of many diseases. Hence the necessity of regular and complete evacuation of the food remnants.

LESSON 12

Nutritional Value of Food Substances

HAVING briefly surveyed the workshops and transport arrangements for the preparation and conveyance of food in the body, we will now consider its nature and purposes. Food, so far as its greater part is concerned, provides the body with the energy which appears either as bodily heat, as mechanical work, or as electrical currents, and, possibly, also in other forms not yet understood. A smaller proportion provides for growth and the reconstitution of the tissues, which are constantly breaking down as the normal result of their activity. The chemical changes which produce the liberation of the energy contained in food—energy that is derived ultimately from the radiant energy of the sun—are spoken of as metabolism. They are at their lowest state of activity when the body is at rest—as during sleep—and this rate of activity is known as the basal metabolic rate.

It provides for the activities of such vital organs as the heart and lungs, which know no rest, and for unceasing changes proceeding in the vast community of cells. It can be measured in terms of the heat given out, the chosen unit of measurement being called a calorie. A calorie is the amount of heat required to raise the temperature of a kilogramme (approximately 2 pounds) of water by 1 degree Centigrade. The heat given out, i.e. the basal metabolism, varies with a person's age and the surface area of the body. The younger the individual the higher the basal metabolic rate, and a tall, stout man has a higher rate than a short, thin man. A man weighing 70 kilos (11 stone) gives out about 1 calorie of heat per hour per kilo of weight when completely at rest. In practice, the basal metabolism is usually estimated by measuring the amounts of oxygen consumed and carbonic oxide given out by the lungs, energy production being due to the breaking down of the food substance into simpler compounds by oxidation, in effect, by food being burned. Foods are classed under three headings—proteins, carbohydrates, and fats.

Proteins. These consist of highly complex combinations of carbon, hydrogen, oxygen, nitrogen, and sulphur. Of these the nitrogen is the essential and characteristic constituent, and it is this element which enters so largely into the make-up of the protoplasm of the cell. Hence protein is essentially the building material of the body. Its carbon is burnt as fuel, the protein being broken down in digestion into sugar, glucose, and urea, the last being excreted by the kidneys. In this way protein can supply about 15 per cent of the total energy in an ordinary mixed diet.

Most of it is, as we have seen, broken down by digestion into amino-acids. These are nitrogenous substances of various kinds and of varying values as building material—that is to say, some proteins contain better types of building material than do others. Proteins of various kinds and values and in very varying amounts are found in all animal products, in cereals and in most vegetable and fruit foods. Those of animal origin are of the highest value in human nutrition.

Carbohydrates. These consist of carbon, hydrogen and oxygen, the last two elements being combined in the same proportions as in water, viz. 2 atoms of hydrogen with 1 of oxygen. This enables all the carbon to combine with the oxygen of the blood—hence the high fuel value of these foods. The carbohydrate foods are sugars and starch, the latter, as we have seen, being converted into sugar in the process of digestion. The principal product of the digestion of all carbohydrate foods is the sugar glucose. It is either quickly used, or is stored in the muscles and liver as glycogen and forms a readily available source of fuel under the influence of the pancreatic secretion, insulin, without which it cannot be utilized.

Carbohydrate furnishes about two-thirds of muscular energy. If it is not available the body uses the protein of its own muscles and organs to furnish the necessary fuel, the protein breaking down to form glucose. Excess of carbohydrate is converted into and stored as fat. The common sources from which it is derived are the cereals, root vegetables, tubers such as the potato, the various forms of sugar—cane, beet—milk, fruit, etc. These foods, especially the cereals, are the best and most economical sources of energy, since they are less costly and better adapted for the purpose than foods of animal origin. Moreover, if they are used in sufficient quantity, much less protein is required to maintain the tissues than if protein foods such as meat are used in their stead for production of energy. They are protein sparers.

Fat Foods. These consist of complex combinations of carbon, hydrogen, and oxygen, and have a relatively high energy value. They do not, however, burn as readily in the body as do carbohydrates, and, indeed, are dependent on the presence of an adequate amount of sugar in the blood for their complete combustion. They, as it were, burn in the fire of carbohydrates. With an insufficient amount of carbohydrates in the diet the incomplete combustion of fat produces poisonous acid products, a condition known as ketosis or acidosis. The condition is common among children and may readily occur in diabetes.

Amount of Food Required. The basal requirements of the body for fuel substance, i.e. when the body is at rest, can, as we have seen, be accurately estimated. It is merely a matter of mathematical calculation. When muscular work is undertaken, the additional amount required to supply the additional energy can be as readily ascertained. The chemical make-up of foodstuffs being known, and it also being known how much energy in the form of heat a given quantity of protein, carbohydrate or fat will give out when burnt, the fuel value of a particular food can be accurately estimated. The amount of energy expenditure involved in performing muscular actions of various kinds has also been carefully estimated. It only remains to adapt the quantity of fuel to the energy to be expended, and to see that all three classes of food are made use of. A given weight of fat will provide more than twice the amount of energy, if it is fully burnt, as the same weight of carbohydrate or protein.

So far as actual foodstuffs are concerned, some contain much more water than others and are correspondingly less valuable as fuel, weight for weight, than those that contain little or no water. Sugar and fat are water free, but vegetables and fruits may consist of up to 93 per cent of water and are, therefore, poor fuel. From the above facts the calorie requirements of various individuals with varying activities can be estimated. Thus, of two men whose basal requirements are, say, 1,400 calories, one who is doing sedentary work most of the day may need only an additional 1,000 to 1,500 calories, while the other, doing heavy manual labour, may need a further 3,000 to 4,000. Children require more fuel in proportion to their size than adults owing to their brisk metabolism and unceasing activity. Under ordinary conditions and in health, appetite is a sufficient guide by which to adjust fuel food requirements to energy expenditure with sufficient accuracy. Excess of fuel in relation to energy expenditure leads to undue increase in weight and vice versa.

LESSON 13

Foods that Build and Renovate

WE saw in the preceding Lesson how the fuel requirements of the body are met and how the necessary quantity can be estimated. Protein requirements for growth and repair involve several factors. The quality of the protein has to be considered, and there is an amount that is the minimum compatible with life, as well as a larger amount calculated to promote the maximum vigour, resistance to disease and prolongation of life. As to quality, we have already noted that the nutritive value of proteins is variable, and depends on the number and kind of amino-acids, or building stones, contained in them. Certain of these amino-acids are necessary, for example, in the manufacture by the body of the hormones, of other glandular secretions and of certain tissue cells. A diet deficient in them cannot produce perfect health.

Proteins. The best quality proteins, in their completeness for human nutrition, are those of milk, meat and eggs. Of lower value are those of plants. The proteins supplied by the cereal grains and by the pulses, such as peas and beans, while of great

(608)

VOLCANOES OF TODAY. The lower photograph shows the main stream of lava which, in an eruption of Mauna Loa in Hawaii, in April, 1926, made its irresistible way through miles of tropical forest until it reached and entirely obliterated the native fishing village of Hoopuloa, 13,900 feet below it. Above is a photo of the crater of Vesuvius, during a recent period of activity. PHYSIOGRAPHY 9

Photos, The Times and Tai Sing Loo, Honolulu.

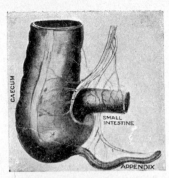

APPENDIX. The vermiform appendix, a hollow tube with one blind end, situated at the base of the caecum. PHYSIOLOGY 11

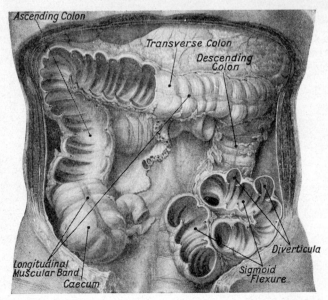

COLON OR LARGE INTESTINE. The inner surface of the colon wall presents a regular series of ridges projecting into the interior, between which the bowel bulges out into pouches or diverticula. PHYSIOLOGY 11

Plate 62

Volume III

value in nutrition, cannot be depended on as the sole source when used alone, although, used in combination, they supplement to some extent each other's deficiencies in one or another amino-acid. They may, however, be supplemented by milk, eggs or meat with the best possible results. As to the minimum quantity of protein necessary, there is some difference of opinion among scientists. According to some, not more than 40 to 50 grammes of dry protein are required daily; others—and these are more numerous—assess it at least at 100 grammes. Other authorities recommend for perfect health and superabundant vigour an even larger amount. There is undoubtedly, however, some danger attached to the use of an undue amount of meat foods, especially of muscle meat. There is additional strain thrown on the kidneys; putrefactive processes are apt to be set up in the colon, with consequent absorption of poisons into the system, and the diet is apt to become badly balanced. Excess is not so likely if dairy produce is used as the main source of animal protein.

In practice, and using the more moderate estimate of require-ments, the daily need for protein can be well met by consuming daily half a pint of milk, one egg, two ounces of cheese, and four to five ounces of meat or fish. These will supply the best quality protein, and the cereal foods—bread, rice, flour, etc.—and the vegetable foods—potatoes, greens, pulses, etc.—taken to supply energy, may be depended on for the rest. Growth in children demands a more generous supply of animal protein than do the repair requirements of adults. Increased physical work calls for a higher consumption of carbohydrates and fats, but not of protein as such.

Mineral Salts. We must now turn to the consideration of other nutritional factors of fundamental importance. The important rôle played by mineral substances in the food has long been recognized. They are concerned with growth and repair, with the proper functioning of every organ and system in the body, and enter into the make-up of all the tissues, fluids and secretions. When a food substance is burnt an ash remains which is composed of the salts of a variety of mineral elements. A salt is the com-bination of a chemical element with an acid. Of the dozen and more of these chemical elements which are found in the body, the more important and in the greatest quantity are sodium, potassium, magnesium, calcium (lime) and iron. They are com-bined with acids to form sulphates, phosphates and chlorides.

Thus we find the sulphates, chlorides and phosphates of soda in the ash of animal and cereal foods.

These salts are predominantly acid salts and tend to diminish the natural alkalinity of the blood and tissues. The salts of vegetables and fruits are principally the carbonates of soda, potash and magnesium. They are alkaline salts and tend to preserve a favourable reaction of the blood and body fluids. Of the mineral elements, iron and copper (a trace only) are necessary to furnish the haemoglobin of the blood. They are best found in meat, eggs and whole cereals. Lime and phosphorus form the basis of the structure of bones and teeth, and their salts play an important part in the general economy of the body. Lime helps to regulate muscular activity and, especially, the action of the heart. It promotes coagulation of the blood, and deficiency of this mineral occurs in many forms of disease. Lime is present in good quantity in milk, cheese, fruits and vegetables. Phosphorus forms a vital part of the nucleus of every cell and also of the plasma and other body fluids. It occurs in the body in combination with the organic substances—proteins, carbohydrates and fats—and is the most widely distributed inorganic element in the body. It occurs in good quantity in eggs, milk, whole cereals and most vegetables.

Iodine is another mineral constituent of great importance. It enters into the make-up of the juice of the thyroid gland, which controls metabolic activity. The parts played by other mineral substances, some of which are present only in very minute quantities, are not fully understood, but are doubtless of equal importance with those we have mentioned. Though minerals are present in most natural foodstuffs, the methods of preparing the foods for marketing and consumption are often responsible for depriving the foods of their mineral value. The prolonged boiling of vegetables in much water dissolves out the mineral substances, and, unless the water is used, these are wasted. The milling of cereals, as in making white flour, removes the part of the grain that is rich in salts. A diet in which white flour, sugar and margarine form a large part is likely to be very poor in mineral substances.

A further variety of food substance remains for consideration without which a diet, though it may be composed of ample fuel-building and mineral substance, is of no avail for health or even to sustain life. They are the vitamin substances.

LESSON 14

The Vitamins' Part in Nutrition

THE presence in foodstuffs of vitamins or, as they were originally termed, accessory food factors, was proved when it was found that an artificial mixture of good protein, carbohydrate, fat and minerals in correct proportions was unable to support life in rats. If, however, a few drops of milk were added to the mixture the rats throve and survived. This discovery was then linked up with the known, but little understood, fact that certain diseased conditions were associated with faulty diets. Thus scurvy was known to be due to want of fresh food and to be curable with orange juice. It then came to be recognized that fresh, living foods supplied substances of vital importance—hence the name vitamins. Only very recently these substances have been isolated from foodstuffs in the form of what appears to be nearly the pure vitamin substance itself, and they are found to be of fairly simple chemical nature and closely allied to substances already well known.

Vitamins are derived from plants, and are the products of biological activity in their leaves, seeds and fruit, under the influence of sunlight. Science has labelled them with the letters of the alphabet, those designated A to E being now well known. Others are still being sought for.

Vitamin A. This is essential to growth, and also influences the health of the epithelial cells lining the cavities of the body and their power of resistance to invasion by micro-organisms. Absence or deficiency of this vitamin in the food is followed by inflammation of the eyes and infections of the mucous membranes. Young animals fed on a diet in which it is deficient fail to grow. Its original source is the green leaves of plants, from which animals obtain it to be stored in their liver and fat. Hence it occurs richly in the fat of milk, in egg-yolk, the liver oil of fishes, and the liver and fat of grazing animals. Vegetable oils do not contain it, but it is found in juicy fruits. It is closely associated with the yellow colouring matter of vegetables, such as the carrot, and of fat. This substance is called carotin, and it is probably the chemical precursor of the vitamin.

Vitamin D. Usually associated with Vitamin A as being also soluble in fat, this vitamin is found in greatest abundance in fish oils, such as cod and halibut liver oil, and in less amount in milk, butter and egg-yolk. If some kinds of food are exposed to the ultra-violet rays of light, Vitamin D appears in the food which did not previously contain it. It also forms in the fat underlying the skin of a human being when the person is exposed to these rays. The principal function of this vitamin is to control the metabolism of lime in the body. In its absence the lime salts are defective in the bones and teeth and other parts of the body. This is the cause of the disease known as rickets, which can, therefore, be cured by giving fish oil and by irradiating the skin. Vitamin D is derived from ergosterol, which is itself a derivative of a substance in fat call cholesterol.

Vitamin B. Also concerned with growth, this vitamin has as its chief function the preservation of the health of the nerves. If it is absent from the food the animal becomes paralysed, the heart weakens and the stomach and intestines lose their muscular activity. The wall of the digestive tract becomes thin and weak, the digestive secretions are impaired and food is no longer properly absorbed. Death ensues from paralysis and exhaustion. Vitamin B is widely distributed in food but is most abundant in the leaves of green vegetables and in cereal grains and nuts. Milk and egg-yolk also contain it in good quantity. For most people its main source should be in bread, but when the germ and branny coverings are removed in milling to make white flour the vitamin is also removed. There is probably a considerable deficiency of this vitamin in the average dietary, and hence the prevalence of indigestion, constipation and nervous weakness.

Vitamins C and E. Responsible for protecting the body from scurvy, an insufficient supply of Vitamin C causes general weakness, rheumatic pains, disease of the gums with bleeding, and a low resistance to infection. The vitamin is found in raw, young vegetable leaves and juicy fruit, especially the orange, lemon, and tomato. It is very susceptible to being heated in the presence of air, so that boiled vegetables are deprived of it. Vitamin E is concerned with the activity of the reproductive system. Animals deprived of it are sterile. It is found in meat, egg-yolk, seeds and green vegetable leaves.

Water and Roughage. Two other factors of fundamental importance in nutrition remain for consideration. First, an adequate supply of water is essential. It is the vehicle which conveys to the cells the nutritive elements, removes their waste products and forms the medium in which all the chemical processes of the body are carried on. Water is being continually lost from the body in the breath, from the kidneys and bowels and from the skin. Evaporation from the lungs and skin is, as we have seen in Lesson 4 (volume 1), responsible for regulating the heat of the body. This loss must be constantly made good. Though most foods supply their quota of water, it is necessary that at least 3 pints of additional fluid should be taken into the system daily. The second remaining important factor is roughage. This is the term applied to the indigestible residue of food ; it chiefly consists of the woody fibre or cellulose of plants and fruits. Its purpose is to give bulk to the contents of the colon and act as a mild stimulant to the nerve-muscle of the colon wall. Absence of a proper amount of this material leads to constipation.

Having thus briefly reviewed the principal constituents of food, it remains to point out that satisfactory nutrition, that is to say, a constant supply of all the material required by the body cells, can only be secured by ensuring a correct balance in the daily dietary. Not only must the need for fuel be met—and for this appetite is usually a sufficient guide—but an adequate amount of good class protein must be taken, and a full supply of each of the vitamins and minerals be ensured. For this purpose dairy produce, vegetables both raw and cooked, and raw fruits must enter into the dietary in good quantity. Milk is an invaluable supplement to the diet.

LESSON 15

The Kidneys' Place in the Human Mechanism

THE bodily functions we have been considering, respiration and digestion, have one main purpose : that is, to provide a constantly favourable and suitable medium in which the cells of the body can live, flourish and perform their several functions. This medium is the blood and its intermediary the lymph. Not only must these be kept supplied with nutriment and oxygen for the cells, and the waste products of their activity be removed, but this supply and removal must be constantly maintained in the face of varying conditions in the external environment. The cell will only survive for a few minutes if deprived of its regular oxygen supply; we have seen in the mechanism of respiration and the circulation of the blood how Nature has ensured this constant supply. Food and water are taken at intervals, but Nature has also contrived that the vital substances, sugar, protein, fat, minerals and water, are maintained at a level in the nutritive fluid, varying only within very narrow limits despite the irregularity with which they are taken into the body.

If these limits are exceeded in either direction serious consequences ensue. Nature has, therefore, devised agencies which, automatically brought into action, restore the conditions to the normal before these limits are reached. Failure of these agencies to act normally is one of the common aspects of disease. Hunger is a device of this kind. Deficiency of nutritive material in the blood—and, more especially, of sugar—causes violent contractions of the muscular wall of the stomach to occur, and it is these that give rise to the sensation. In civilization hunger has been largely replaced by appetite, a less imperious and more habitual sensation, which we have taught ourselves to substitute for the more primitive stimulus to the taking of food.

Similarly, thirst is a protective effort of the body to ensure an adequate amount of water in the body. Dryness of the mouth due to lack of saliva occurs, this mechanism giving the first indication of a lack of water in the body. We have already referred to the vital importance of water in the dietary and in the bodily economy. It constitutes roughly two-thirds of the body weight—brain issue, for instance, is 85 per cent water. A loss of 10 per cent of the water of the body is a serious matter, while a loss of 20 per cent means death. Through the skin and lungs not less than two pints of water are lost from the body daily, and the loss from the kidneys is not less than another two pints.

Physiology of the Kidneys. This brings us to the consideration of the kidneys, which play an all-important part in the maintenance of the purity and consistency of the nutritive fluids of the body. Their office is to provide a living and selective filter through which excess of any particular substance in the blood is removed, whether it be a nutritive substance or the waste matter from the activity of the cells. The kidney consists, for the greater part, of millions of minute tubules. One end of each tubule lies in the outer part of the kidney and forms a microscopic cup, and in this cup lies a tuft of capillary blood vessels. The cup is known as a glomerule. The other end of each tubule opens into a hollow space in the concave side of the organ known as the pelvis of the kidney. Fluid, i.e. urine, passing down the tubule, collects in this space and is drained away from it through the ureter, a tube 12 to 16 inches long which passes down from each kidney to end in

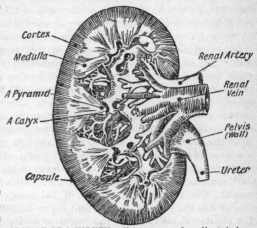

SECTION OF A KIDNEY. Urine emerges from the tubules into the calyces, whence it reaches the ureter.

the urinary bladder. Here the urine collects until discharged by the act of micturition.

The Kidneys' Selective Action. The essential filtering apparatus is the glomerule and its contained tuft of capillary blood vessels. Water, in which are dissolved urea (the end product of the disintegration of protein material derived from breaking down cells or from food), salts and sugar, passes through the capillary walls into the cups of the tubules and thence down the tubules themselves. These are lined with cells, which are able to exercise a selective action on the substances in the contained fluid. They absorb back again into the body a mixture of salts, sugar and water such as is normally present in the blood. The waste material, urea and uric acid, dissolved in water, is allowed to pass on down the tubules as urine, for discharge from the body as unwanted matter. If there is a great excess of sugar or salts or of water in the blood, these are also allowed to pass until normal amounts are present in the blood. Under certain circumstances protein material is also allowed to pass out, giving rise to the condition known as albuminuria. In this manner, through the selective action of the kidney tubules, the nutritive, waste and water content of the blood is regulated and kept constant so far as the removal of excess of any constituent is concerned. There is, however, a limit to the power of the cells of the tubules to absorb sugar and salts from the fluid passing over them. This is spoken of as the " threshold " of the kidney for the particular substance.

Sugar in the Body. Normally, there should be about 100 milligrams of sugar in 100 cubic centimetres of blood. Eating a large amount of sugar may cause this to rise to 180 milligrams. Some of this amount will pass the threshold and appear in the urine. The amount of sugar must not be allowed to fall below a certain point. With only 70 milligrams per cent in the blood symptoms of serious illness ensue. Nature ensures a steady supply from the stores of sugar laid up in the cellular spaces of the skin, a source of supply that is constantly being drawn on. Also, as we have seen, sugar is stored in the form of glycogen in the liver and muscles. This storage takes place under the influence of insulin, the hormone substance of the pancreas. Glycogen is released in the form of glucose and taken up into the blood under the combined influence of the secretion of the suprarenal glands (adrenalin) and the sympathetic nervous system. These are considered in a later Lesson.

When muscular effort is made, these factors come into play in order to flood the blood with the stored-up sugar and render it available to the muscles. Constancy in the amount of water in the blood, in the face of the steady loss that has been referred to, is brought about by soakage of water into the capillaries from the reservoir constituted by the cellular spaces under the skin and in the tissues, in which water taken at intervals is collected and stored. This soakage into the vessels occurs whenever the water content of the blood falls below the normal.

Other mechanisms exist which ensure in a similar way the constancy of protein, fat, lime and other substances in the nutritive fluids. Space will not permit of a detailed description of these, but enough has been said to demonstrate the fact that, by one means or another, the nutritive medium on which the well-being of the cells depends at every moment is kept at a standard composition, which varies only within narrow limits, and that this is effected by a self-regulating mechanism, so rendering the organism largely independent of environment.

Our Course in Physiology is continued in Volum. 4

A First Lesson on the Arthropods

NATURE'S crowning successes in the invertebrate section of the animal kingdom are to be found in the great phylum of jointed-limbed animals known to the zoologist as the *Arthropoda*. Such triumphs have been brought about by numerous experiments—if this term be permitted—with more species of animals than are contained in all other animal phyla together. For this reason we find the *Arthropoda* abundantly represented in both salt and fresh water, on the land and in the air. Wherever we search for animal life—in the unending monotone of darkness and cold in depths of ocean ; in sunlit rock-pools or on sandy expanses of seashore ; near rivers or in the merest pond ; on the naked rocks of the mountain summit or in luxuriant valleys—we are certain to meet with members of this very important and interesting group of animals. Some of the more beautiful existent creatures—butterflies and dragon-flies, for instance—are here included, as are some of the most hideous parasites ; baneful carriers of disease, like the dreaded mosquitoes, which endanger human life ; and some of the most formidable pests which ravage agriculture.

Arthropod Affinities. Careful examination shows that the animals included in this phylum have much in common with the *Annelida*, and must have been derived from the same stock of animals which gave rise to the bristle-worms (*Polychaeta*). The body is divided up into a series of rings, or segments, which, however, are of limited number and many fewer than in worms. The body is enclosed in a thick cuticle, and the great thickness of this formidable armour has necessitated the development of flexible joints between the segments. In addition, we see that some means had to be devised for moving the rigid armour plates, and we find that the continuous muscle layers of the worm's body wall have become modified into systems of separate muscles. The stump-like appendages of the worm have been transformed into well-developed limbs, which differ in nature in the various sections of the phylum. Bristles embedded in the skin are quite common in worms, but unknown in the Arthropods ;

though hollow outgrowths of the cuticle, which receive this name, are of general occurrence.

We shall appreciate the principal differences between the Annelid and the Arthropod by making the following comparison. If we open an earthworm by an incision along the upper middle line of the body, we cut into a cavity, the coelom, which is divided into as many chambers as there are external body rings. The most important organs of the earthworm's body project into the coelom. The digestive canal runs through it suspended from its upper wall, and the nerve cord runs along its lower boundary. Two sets of organs are more closely related to the coelom, being derived from its wall : these are the reproductive organs and the excretory organs, or nephridia. The coelom contains colourless fluid in which amoeboid corpuscles float, but as we have previously observed, this cavity is completely separated from the closed network of blood vessels which contain red blood.

If now we open an Arthropod—an insect, spider or crayfish, for instance—we at once perceive that there is no coelom, the organs of the body lying in an irregular system of spaces filled with blue-tinged fluid, which is blood containing the copper-bearing pigment, haemocyanin. In the Arthropod there is no distinction between the body cavity and the blood vascular system, the former being derived, incidentally, from the greatly dilated blood channels which surround the organs of the body. After the early stages of development the true coelom, such as occurs in Annelids, is found solely in the hollow sac-like reproductive organs, its main part having vanished. The mystery of its disappearance has not yet been fully elucidated, but we know that in soft-bodied animals, like the worm, the fluid-filled coelom serves an important mechanical function, protecting internal organs from injury by external pressure. In the Arthropod such protection is afforded by the rigid integument.

Before passing on to the evidences which lead us to believe in the derivation of *Arthropoda* from *Annelida* we might mention the principal types of animals included in the former phylum. These types are for convenience arranged into subphyla, of which the following are the most important : (1) *Onychophora*, primitive forms we regard as connecting links between the two phyla, represented by the single genus *Peripatus ;* (2) *Myriapoda*, those friends and foes of the farmer known as centipedes and millipedes ; (3) *Insecta*, which constitutes the great world of insect life ; (4) *Arachnida*, which includes scorpions, mites and spiders as well as the ancient king-crabs and the fossil *Eurypterids ;* (5) *Crustacea*, which is typified by lobsters and crabs, but contains also lesser-known forms, such as barnacles and fish-lice.

Onychophora. *Peripatus*, the sole representative of the *Onychophora*, occurs as several species with a very wide distribution through the hotter parts of the globe, being represented in South America, the West Indies, South Africa, the Malay Penin-

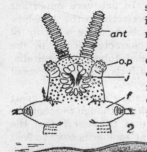

sula, Australia and New Zealand. It is an animal of great antiquity and might almost be described as an Arthropod in the making. This archaic creature lives in rotten tree-stumps and other dark places, and might easily be mistaken for a caterpillar on cursory examination. Many of its characters indicate its obvious relation to the Annelids. The body, though not clearly divided into rings or segments, bears numerous pairs of conical stumps, which are not divided into proper joints and which carry each a pair of sharp

RUDIMENTARY ARTHROPOD. Fig. 1 (below). General view of Peripatus. **Fig. 2** (above). Lower aspect of front end ; ant., pre-antenna ; o.p., oval papilla ; j., jaw ; f., first trunk appendage.
After Sedgwick

claws at the tip. The mouth is on the underside of the head and is provided with a single pair of jaws, formed by modification of a pair of legs. The jaws of Arthropods in general are not, like those of backboned animals, part of the framework of the head, but are modifications of the jointed limbs typically borne in pairs by the segments. They bite on one another from side to side, while the lower jaw of a backboned animal is moved up and down.

A second pair of limbs in the head region have given up the locomotor function and form blunt projections upon which peculiar slime-secreting glands open. The slime can be ejected to some distance, serving to secure small insects as food, and also as a means of protection. Rising from the soft, velvety surface of the body on the head two feelers or antennae may be seen ; these are organs of touch. Near the base of each antenna is a small, ill-formed eye, which is built on a simple plan and resembles the eye of the worm rather than the compound faceted eye of the Arthropod.

On opening *Peripatus* we might at first sight judge it to be a typical Arthropod. The body cavity consists of a number of irregular spaces containing blood, and no internal segmentation is apparent as in worms. Moreover, the heart is an elongated tube perforated by openings, or ostia, as in the typical jointed-limbed animal, and the reproductive organs are built on the complex plan found in such animals. In one very important respect, however, *Peripatus* conforms perfectly to the Annelids' plan. In almost every segment of the body there is a pair of excretory organs such as are found characteristically in the Annelid. These organs are simple coiled tubes, or nephridia, which open by funnels clothed with cilia internally and by small pores at the bases of the legs externally.

A study of the development of the genus *Peripatus* is of great importance to the serious student of Zoology, though too complex to embark upon here. Let us be content to observe that the researches of some of the most competent zoologists have proved beyond doubt that the embryo develops a true segmented coelom exactly as does the embryo worm, but that this cavity does not realize its full potentialities and is represented in the adult solely by the cavities of the reproductive organs and the segmentally arranged nephridia. *Peripatus* is thus deemed to be a real connecting link between the Annelid and the Arthropod in the nature of the body cavity and the blood vascular system. The relationship of this animal to both Annelid and Arthropod is more clearly shown than that between the higher groups of the phylum of jointed-limbed animals.

Myriapoda. The animals included in this subphylum, like *Peripatus,* are air-breathing Arthropods and typical land animals. Such air-breathing types were at one time known as *Tracheata,* a name derived from the fact that the breathing organs most commonly present are in the form of delicate tubes or *tracheae,* which ramify throughout the tissues of the body and communicate with the exterior by series of small openings called *stigmata.* *Insecta* and certain members of the *Arachnida* possess these characters also.

Myriapoda are decidedly more specialized than *Onycophora.* I he body is clearly divided into segments, the limbs are distinctly

ARTHROPODS

jointed, and three pairs of them have become converted into jaws. A pair of fairly long antennae and two groups of simple eyes are to be found on the head. The system of trachea is well developed and each air-tube has a spiral thickening in its lining, so that its walls are prevented from collapsing. The stigmata lie on either side of the body. The two types of *Myriapoda*, centipedes and millipedes, show well-marked differences in structure and habit.

Centipedes are exceedingly active creatures of highly carnivorous habit. They are flattened from above downwards, and each

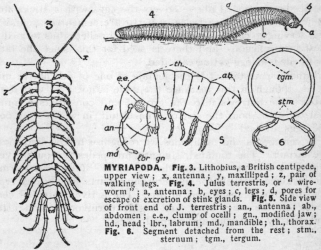

MYRIAPODA. Fig. 3. Lithobius, a British centipede, upper view; x, antenna; y, maxilliped; z, pair of walking legs. **Fig. 4.** Julus terrestris, or " wireworm "; a, antenna; b, eyes; c, legs; d, pores for escape of excretion of stink glands. **Fig. 5.** Side view of front end of J. terrestris; an., antenna; ab., abdomen; e.e., clump of ocelli; gn., modified jaw; hd., head; lbr., labrum; md., mandible; th., thorax. **Fig. 6.** Segment detached from the rest; stm., sternum; tgm., tergum.

segment of the trunk bears one pair of jointed limbs, while every other one is perforated by a pair of stigmata. The two legs next to the jaws have become converted into formidable poison claws, rendering some of the tropical species—like *Scolopendra*, which may attain a length of 8 inches—dangerous even to Man. The commonest British form is *Lithobius*, a small and rather shortened form. *Geophilus*, another of our native centipedes, is extremely long and slender, and is said to be a relentless enemy of earthworms.

Millipedes are slow-moving myriapods of vegetarian habit, devoid of poison fangs and perfectly harmless. Their bodies are cylindrical and well segmented, but we observe an important difference from the segmentation in centipedes. Each apparent segment is really the result of fusion of two adjacent segments, which explains why we find two pairs of limbs and two pairs of stigmata to each body-ring. Some of our native species—like *Julus*, which is common in hedgerows—curl up if alarmed, while certain greatly shortened millipedes, like *Glomeris*, roll themselves up into a ball under similar conditions.

We should scarcely expect the creatures under discussion to be capable of much parental solicitude, yet such is the case, at least as far as the mother is concerned. The small British centipede mentioned above covers the eggs with a sticky fluid, by means of which particles of earth are cemented around the egg, serving to camouflage it. The small pellets thus formed are most inconspicuous, and there is need for this, since the father centipede is an egg-eating cannibal.

Equally painstaking is the female of one of our native millipedes, though in this instance the male is not a perverted egg-eater. She burrows into the ground and constructs a minute nest of earth about the size of a hazel nut, in which from 60 to 100 eggs are laid.

In centipedes and millipedes we recognize friends and foes of the farmer. The rounded, sluggish millipedes are purely vegetarian, and some of them—the so-called " false wire-worms," for instance—attack the underground parts of various crops, and are thus pests of agriculture. The active, flattened centipedes, on the other hand, are highly carnivorous and attack and destroy numerous agricultural pests.

LESSON 13

Some Common Forms of Insect Life

THE ubiquitous group of arthropods called the *Insecta* includes more species than all other groups of animals together. Yet the animals in this group are closely similar to one another. The general plan upon which the insect body is built renders insects clearly distinct from all other animal types. The body is short and made up of comparatively few segments, which form three well-marked regions. These are called head, thorax and abdomen respectively.

COMMON FORMS OF INSECT LIFE

The head of an insect comprises six segments—not obvious in the adult—and bears a number of appendages. A pair of feelers, or antennae, and two large compound eyes (sometimes, in addition, several simple eyes) are seen in front, while three pairs of jaws, which differ greatly according to the habits of the insect, are found in front and below. The thorax is composed of three segments, and has three pairs of jointed legs and usually two pairs of delicate wings. Lastly, the abdomen generally consists of eleven segments, and is devoid of walking appendages.

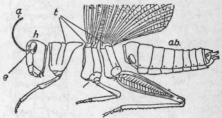

The legs of an insect are made up of five sections, and in many instances end in a pair of claws embracing a cushion of soft tissue.

TYPICAL INSECT. Sketch of grasshopper to show external segmentation typical of insects; ab., abdomen; a., antenna; e., eye; h., head; t., thorax. *From Borrodaile, Eastham, Potts and Saunders, " The Invertebrata," Camb. Univ. Press.*

Legs may be adapted to a variety of habits. *Dytiscus*, the giant water beetle, has legs modified for swimming purposes ; the grasshopper has jumping legs ; the cockroach has running legs ; and the fore-legs of the praying mantis are adapted for grasping prey. Limbs may assist in the production of characteristic sounds made by insects, and may be used for the collection of food—as are the pollen baskets of the bee.

The wings of insects are thin folds of skin horizontally flattened and arising from the soft joint between the armour plates on the upper and lower sides of the thorax. The space between the upper and lower layers contains a blood chamber into which the tracheal tubes grow. The veins—so conspicuous on the wings, and constituting the strengthening framework of these organs— are merely tough-walled spaces around the trachea, and during development of the wings they carry blood and nerve fibres.

The tracheal system is exceedingly complex and opens to the exterior by small openings, or *stigmata*, on the soft membrane between the upper and lower armour plates ; two pairs of stigmata are found in the thoracic region, eight pairs in the region of the abdomen. The tracheal tubes branch repeatedly, and the finest branches, or *tracheoles*, always end in the cells composing the body, never blindly in the blood. Life-giving oxygen is carried to the cells independently of the blood. The great success of insects in the struggle for existence is largely due to this perfect arrangement for the exchange of gases. Carbon dioxide is eliminated as fast as it accumulates, and fresh oxygen taken up in its place. The nature of the respiratory mechanism also determines the small size range within which all insects must remain. The laws of gaseous diffusion, upon which the conduction of gases to and from the tracheoles depends, break down just beyond the size limit of existing insects, so that this means of respiration is impossible in larger animals. Insects are thus of necessity small.

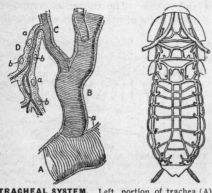

TRACHEAL SYSTEM. Left, portion of trachea (A) of a caterpillar. B, C and D, branches; a, cellular layer; b, nuclei. Right, principal trunks of tracheal system of the cockroach.

Parker & Haswell, " Textbook of Zoology," Macmillan

The remaining internal organs of insects are very complex, and we should require much space to discuss their details. We can but touch upon them here. There is invariably a digestive canal, which, while short and straight in the larva, is often long and much coiled in the adult. It shows differentiation into three important regions, called fore-, mid-, and hind-gut respectively. These regions are further subdivided into smaller regions, each with a definite function to perform. Salivary glands, which may produce secretions very similar to those of the glands of the same name in vertebrates, open into the fore-gut. The task of digestion and absorption of food materials is delegated to the mid-gut, while the hind-gut is the tube through which indigestible residues pass to the exterior at the anus.

In the nature of its blood-vascular system the insect is a typical arthropod, for this system is a set of ill-defined spaces which cause the organs of the body to be bathed with blood. There is a definite heart, however, which lies in the upper part of the body. It is an elongated tube of thirteen chambers, each of which is the derivative of a segment and has a pair of minute openings, or *ostia*, in its walls. Blood is propelled forwards in the heart, and passes into a fine vessel towards the head, whence it is forced into the blood spaces of the body.

Regulation of the movements of the body and co-ordination of impressions received from the world around, as well as responses called forth by them, are carried out by means of a nervous system. This includes a brain and a number of clusters of nerve cells, or *ganglia*, connected to form a chain by threads built up of nerve fibres. The brain lies on the upper side of the fore-gut, while the nerve chain runs along the lower part of the body.

Many characters are made use of in classifying insects, the best known ones having reference to the mouth parts, the wings and the life history. With respect to this last, an insect—the butterfly, for instance—may hatch out from the egg as a larva totally dissimilar to the adult, into which it is transformed by radical changes constituting a metamorphosis. Or, as in the cockroach, the young animal may resemble its parents from the first, and becomes adult by comparatively slight changes, which are chiefly in size.

Wingless Insects. Space limitation forbids our dealing at length with the many kinds of insects known to Entomology, and we must be content to glance briefly at some of the commoner forms. The *Aptera* are wingless insects. This division of the *Insecta* does not include all insects devoid of wings—some of these belong to other groups, for the good reason that their ancestors possessed powers of flight—but only certain primitive forms representing an early wingless stage in the racial history of the sub-phylum. The *Aptera* include small insignificant creatures which lurk under stones or bark, or live in other similarly sheltered places, where they are likely to escape the attentions of their enemies. The mouth parts are feebly developed and there is no metamorphosis. Two insect types are met with here, the bristle-tails (*Thysanura*) and the springtails (*Collembola*).

Bristle-tails are so named because of the jointed bristles at the hinder end of the body, but a more interesting feature is the presence of small limbs on the abdomen. There are reasons for supposing that insects have arisen from centipede-like creatures by a shortening of the body, the establishment of three regions, and the suppression of many limbs—especially those of the abdominal region. Bristle-tails come closest to the ancestral type visualized by the evolutionist.

Springtails get their name from the " spring and catch " arrangement found as a sort of fork which lies folded under the abdomen with its prongs projecting forwards and held in place by a minute projection. When liberated from its catch the elasticity of the fork hurls the insect into the air.

Straight-Winged Insects. Some members of this group, the *Orthoptera*, are generalized and very suitable for study by those who wish to grasp the complexities of insect structure. The cockroach, for instance, has a biting mouth, in relation to which three typical pairs of jaws are made out : (1) the hard-toothed first jaws (mandibles) ; (2) the second jaws (first maxillae), with a cutting blade and a feeler ; (3) the third jaws (second maxillae), also possessing feelers and partly fused together into what is called the " lower lip," or *labium*. The so-called " upper lip " or *labrum*, is a plate overhanging the first jaws.

The forewings are modified into horny wing-covers, under which the delicate wings fold fanwise when not in use. The limbs vary in nature. The *Orthoptera* are divided into Runners (*Cursoria*) and Leapers (*Saltatoria*). In the former all three pairs of legs are alike, but among the latter the hind limbs are enlarged and serve as leaping organs.

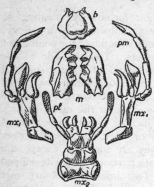

Cockroaches, soothsayers, stick and leaf insects and earwigs are included in the *Cursoria*. The first of these—sometimes erroneously referred to as " beetles "—though emitting a disagreeable smell, are perfectly harmless creatures. Our common kitchen pest is not native to Britain, being a destitute alien, while the larger ship cockroach belongs to a different species. Soothsayers, or praying insects—

MOUTH PARTS OF COCKROACH b, labrum , m., mandible ; mx_1, first pair of maxillae ; mx_2, second pair of maxillae ; pl, labial palp; pm, maxillary palp.

Parker & Haswell

rapacious creatures found in warmer parts of the world—derive their name from the fact that the front legs are turned up and serve to grasp prey, leading to a supplicatory attitude responsible for many superstitious ideas. Stick and leaf insects are vegetarians of warm climates; they resemble the objects after which they are named both in colour and shape—no doubt a protective device. Earwigs differ in many ways from other *Orthoptera*—to which they are closely related, however—and are sometimes segregated as the *Dermaptera*.

The *Saltatoria* include grasshoppers, locusts and crickets. The first of these have short antennae and possess organs of hearing in the base of the abdomen. The pleasing chirp of our field grasshopper is the love-call of the male, and is produced by rubbing a beaded ridge on the inner side of the thick part of the hind leg against the wing-cover. Locusts are notorious on account of the immense swarms in which they appear from time to time, with disastrous results to vegetation. Crickets differ in minor respects from other *Saltatoria*. There are jointed bristles projecting from the tip of the tail. Our house-cricket is the best known form; the burrowing mole-cricket is the most extra-ordinary one. The latter is a carnivore with forefeet modified into spades.

Bugs. Despite the unpleasant associations conjured up by the common name of this group, the *Hemiptera*, many of its members are very attractive in appearance and quite unobjectionable in their habits. The mouth parts are highly characteristic, forming a long-pointed " beak " used for piercing and sucking. The first jaws are sharp stylets, grooved on their inner sides for conducting fluid to the mouth, and the second jaws are also pointed rods. The third jaws form a kind of sheath, which encloses the others.

HEMIPTERA: MOUTH PARTS. Sagittal section through head of Graphosoma italicum; lm, labium; lr, labrum; s, stylets.

Borrodaile

Plant bugs feed upon vegetable juices. The largest of them are the cicadas of warm climates, noted for the loud chirping of the males. Plant-lice are familiar objects in greenhouses, where they play havoc among cultivated plants. They are small and have a complicated life history, including winged and wingless forms. During the summer numerous generations are produced independently of sexual processes (*parthenogenesis,* or virgin birth), and these young are born alive. Fertilized eggs are laid on the approach of autumn in tremendous numbers. It has been estimated that if all the individuals of the tenth generation produced from a single egg were to survive, the collective weight would equal that of 500 million men.

The curious scale insects include some familiar British pests, and are so called because the female is sheltered under a scale-like shield. The exudations from the bodies of some species are of economic value. Scale insect products are shellac, white wax and cochineal. The " manna " of the Old Testament was probably of similar origin. Bugs and lice, wingless types, are sometimes grouped together as *Mallophaga*.

Fringe-Winged Insects. These are the *Thysanoptera*, small insects with sucking mouth parts and four narrow, fringed wings. The feet are swollen into bladders at their tips. Such insects may be seen creeping about in flowers. One species injures our corn crops and is called the corn thrips.

Net-Winged Insects. In this interesting group, the *Neuroptera*, the members of which have four membranous wings and biting mouth parts, we find dragon-flies, mayflies, ant-lions and lace-wing flies. Dragon-flies are sometimes classified separately as *Odonata*. They are beautiful four-winged creatures, which glitter like silver and jewels in the sunshine. Their eyes are of enormous size ; their powerful jaws are able to take insects on the wing. The female lays her eggs on water plants, and the wingless young leads an aquatic life. The young are among the most formidable of Nature's " infants," feeding avidly by means of the lower lip (united third jaws), which is modified into a grasping organ. Ant-lions look like abbreviated dragon-flies but lack brilliance and speed. They are nocturnal in habit. The wingless larva— to which the name " ant-lion " is properly applied—captures prey with its formidable first jaws in an ingenious manner. It digs a conical pit in sandy ground, throwing out excavated material with its broad head, and lurks at the bottom of this pit, entirely buried except for the powerful jaws. Unwary insects which step on the sides of this treacherous pit promptly slide down, and are dispatched immediately by the waiting larva.

LESSON 14

More About Insect Life

AN enormous host of insects—some 150,000 species—belong to the group of *Coleoptera* or beetles. Such insects have a particularly thick horny investment, and possess strong biting jaws, which differ in some respects from those of the cockroach and its allies. The third pair, for instance, are much more intimately fused together into a lower lip. The fore-wings are modified into hard wing-covers, while the hind-wings are membranous—as in straight-winged insects like the grasshopper. There is one important difference, however ; the hind-wings of *Orthoptera* fold up along a set of longitudinal pleats, while those of *Coleoptera* are relatively long and require a transverse fold as well. Further, in the life history of a beetle there is a well-marked metamorphosis. From the egg hatches out a grub, which, after a time, passes into a motionless pupal stage, and the pupa is ultimately transformed into the perfect insect.

The beetles known as " chafers " include dung beetles, cock-chafers, Hercules beetles and rose chafers. Perhaps the most interesting dung beetles are the scarabs, of which one species was sacred in Egypt. Their fore-legs are broadened into powerful digging organs, with which subterranean chambers are excavated to serve as larders for the storage of dung, and as nurseries, the eggs being laid in masses of the same unsavoury material. Hercules beetles are among the largest of insects, and are remarkable on account of the curious horn-like projections on the body of the male. Rose chafers are insects of a metallic green colour.

Water Beetles. Water beetles are carnivorous types which have become adapted to life in fresh water, though the adults have not lost the power of flight. In our native great water beetle, *Dytiscus marginalis*, the large hind legs are fringed with bristles and serve as oars, while the wing-covers form a store-place for reserves of air. The unattractive larvae both pierce and suck their prey by means of the large first jaws (mandibles). Whirligig beetles are also aquatic. Their spinning movements are due to the action of the second and third pairs of legs, which are broadened into beautifully constructed paddles.

In this group are found also the pretty little ladybirds, readily seen on account of the red, black-spotted body. They lay their eggs on various plants, and the larvae which hatch out devour plant-lice, scale insects, and other pests with avidity, thus entitling them to the affection of the agriculturist. Of an entirely different habit are the beetles of an allied family—called *Dermestids*—the larvae of which devour articles of food and clothing, as immature fur beetles, bacon beetles and horsehair beetles. Nearly related also are the larger death-watch beetles, which appear to make some of the mysterious tickings heard in old houses, and which ravage woodwork.

Fireflies and glow-worms have long attracted attention on account of the light they emit. In the Italian firefly the males are by far the more brilliant, and fly about of an evening in large swarms, scintillating like so many tiny lamps. The source of light in our own native glow-worm, on the other hand, is the wingless female, which doubtless attracts a mate thereby. Probably the same is true of the railway beetle of South America, which is so called because it has a red light at each end of its body and a series of smaller green ones along each side. Blister beetles are so named because a highly irritant substance can be extracted from their bodies—as in the typical case of the Spanish fly, the source of cantharides.

Among beetles we recognize numerous agricultural pests. The seed beetles are small, inconspicuous forms, of which the larvae live in peas and beans, often damaging these crops considerably. Leaf beetles are still more notorious pests. Of these the Colorado potato beetle has caused more than one scare in this country, while the greedy little turnip flea-beetle—thus named because of its springing powers—is constantly with us. Long-snouted vegetarian weevils include a host of small beetles, the ravages of which are only too familiar. Our nut weevil deposits its eggs in hazel nuts and acorns, within which the larvae find an abundance of nourishing food ; while the larvae of grain -weevils are extremely destructive in granaries.

Butterflies and Moths. For beauty and variety of coloration the group of insects known as *Lepidoptera* is quite unrivalled. The attractive appearance of these insects is due primarily to the presence on the four wings of overlapping scales of different kinds. The mouth parts are specialized to form a suctorial organ, which is made up of the second jaws (first maxillae), while the first and third jaws are greatly reduced. Each second jaw becomes a half tube, and the halves are hooked together to form a proboscis, sometimes of great length, the parts of which can be separated for cleaning purposes.

The life history exhibits a very typical and familiar metamorphosis. From the egg, which is often beautifully sculptured, a larva, known as a caterpillar, hatches out, and this possesses not only the three pairs of jointed legs characteristic of the class, but also a varying number of unjointed *pro-legs* terminating in suckers. After feeding voraciously for a time by means of its powerful biting first jaws, and undergoing a number of moults, which enable it to grow, the caterpillar passes into the motionless pupal stage. The pupa, called a *chrysalis*, may be invested in a protective cocoon.

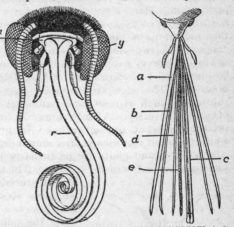

MOUTH-PARTS OF TWO GROUPS OF INSECTS. Left, of Lepidoptera ; a, labrum; y, eye ; r, sucking tube. Right, of Diptera (Culex) ; a, labrum ; b, first pair of maxillae; c, proboscis ; d, mandible ; e, hypopharynx.
From Parker & Haswell, " Text-book of Zoology,"
Macmillan

The skin of the chrysalis ultimately splits to allow of the escape of the perfect insect or imago.

Butterflies are typically distinguished from moths by the club-shaped thickenings at the ends of the feelers or antennae, and by the fact that when settling the wings are folded together over the back. In moths the antennae may be of various forms, but are very rarely club-shaped, and the resting position of the wings is horizontal or sloping downwards, while in certain instances the wings may be to some extent wrapped round the body.

Flies. The enormous assemblage of insects known as *Diptera*, most of which are minute, include many species that have earned an undesirable reputation as blood-suckers and pests. Except in fleas and a few others, there are two membranous front wings, the hinder wings having become reduced into vestiges called balancers, which appear to be sensory organs. The mouth parts of the females are often piercing and sucking organs of great efficiency, the first and second jaws being slender lancets protected above and below by upper and under lips respectively. But in other types, like the house-fly, the jaws are modified into a proboscis used for sucking juices and devoid of powers of perforation. Here, a droplet of digestive fluid is ejected on to the fragment of food, and partially digested food materials are then sucked up by the proboscis. In this habit lies the chief danger of the two-winged fly as an enemy of Man.

The life history exhibits a marked metamorphosis, which may be illustrated by reference to the blow-flies (*Calliphora*) or the house-fly. The elongated whitish eggs are laid in animal substances, such as meat, and hatch out into limbless maggots of extreme voracity. After growing to a certain size, the maggots become quiescent pupae, enclosed in firm investments, from which the adult flies escape after metamorphosis.

Mosquitoes and gnats are particularly notable for the blood-sucking propensities of the females. The larvae are small worm-like creatures, which may be seen wriggling about in stagnant water; they possess a breathing tube at the tip of the tail, which can be pushed above the water surface to procure air. The pupa floats at the surface with two breathing tubes projecting from its head. If alarmed, it is able to dive. After a time the pupal skin opens and the perfect insect makes its way out. Midges are minute gnats of which the aquatic larvae are known as blood-worms. Crane-flies are familiar to us in the daddy-long-legs (*Tipula*), well adapted for climbing among grasses. The larvae—called leather-jackets—gnaw at the roots of grasses and become pupae in the ground. Sand flies are small gnats of bloodthirsty disposition which have aquatic larvae.

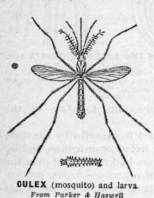

CULEX (mosquito) and larva.
From Parker & Haswell

Fleas are wingless *Diptera* (sometimes considered as a distinct order, the *Aphaniptera*) whose agility fully compensates for the loss of powers of flight. There are many species infesting different mammals and birds. The females of tiny sand-fleas or chiggers of tropical America deposit their eggs in the feet of human beings or other animals, and the painful swellings thus brought about may develop into dangerous festering sores.

Membrane-Winged Insects. The vast group of the *Hymenoptera* includes, among many other types, ants, bees and wasps—the most instinctively clever of all insects. They are readily recognized by the presence of four transparent wings traversed by a comparatively small number of veins, the hinder ones being much smaller than the foremost ones, to which they are in many instances attached during flight by means of a row of minute

RED ANT. Three individuals of Formica rufa : left, male ; centre, imperfect female or worker ; right, perfect female. Each form is specially adapted for the part it plays in the community.
From Parker & Haswell

hooks. The hinder end of the female's body is commonly provided with a piercing apparatus, which may serve either for boring small holes in which eggs are laid—in which case it is called an *ovipositor*—or as a poisoned sting, useful for purposes of offence and defence.

The larvae may resemble caterpillars, or may be pale, helpless, limbless maggots, for the welfare of which more or less elaborate provisions are made by the mother insect. Later on a quiescent pupal stage is reached, from which the winged adult triumphantly emerges. The highest members of the group live in communities comprising several castes, as in termites. These include males, perfect females or queens, and one or more kinds of imperfect female workers, sometimes called soldiers.

Wood-wasps resemble true wasps imperfectly, for they do not possess the characteristic waist and sting. The giant wood-wasp is a typical species, in which the female has a powerful boring apparatus with two long blades that serve as augers for perforating the trunks of sickly or felled pine trees. The eggs hatch out into wood-eating larvae, and the life history is somewhat prolonged, as is testified by well-known cases of the escape of the perfect adults from wooden furniture after the lapse of several years. Like wood-wasps, female saw-flies possess ovipositors, which here consist of elegant, curved, saw-edged blades, sliding on supports. The larvae somewhat resemble little caterpillars, and attack various types of vegetation.

Gall-flies. Gall-flies are minute black insects, the females of which lay eggs in soft vegetable tissues, first pierced by the ovipositor. A kind of irritation is set up and results in the formation of an abnormal swelling, known as a gall, within which the larva lives and feeds and grows. The oak tree is victimized by a large number of species. The most familiar case is afforded by the spherical brown bodies known as oak-apples, while other common oak galls look like currants, or circular brown scales (oak-spangles) on the backs of the leaves.

Ichneumon flies make up a host of mostly inconspicuous creatures which go far to check the ravages of vegetarian insects, and are, therefore, among the most valuable friends of the farmer, market gardener and forester. Their eggs are laid near, on, or in the immature stages of other insects, the juices of which are absorbed by the growing larvae. The caterpillars of butter-flies and moths (sometimes the eggs also) are familiar objects of attack, while the destructive *aphides* come in for a good deal of attention. Some of the larger kinds check the ravages of the wood-wasp, piercing infested timber with their powerful ovi-positors. In this way they are able to deposit their eggs in the galleries of the wood-wasp larvae, to which their own larvae later attach themselves.

LESSON 15

Scorpions, Spiders and Their Relatives

A WELL demarcated subphylum of the *Arthropoda* is the *Arachnida*. This includes many terrestrial animals like scorpions, spiders, mites, and ticks, false scorpions and harvesters—as well as the strange marine creature, *Limulus*, the king crab, and its near relatives, the now extinct sea scorpions or *Eurypterida*, which flourished in the remote geological past.

Terrestrial arachnids are sometimes confounded with insects, from which they differ, however, in several obvious structural details. Arachnids never have feelers or antennae. The head and thorax are invariably fused together to form a unified head-thorax or *prosoma*, consisting of six adult segments bearing characteristic appendages. The first segment, which lies in front of the mouth, has a pair of delicate three-jointed pincers (*chelicerae*) ; the second segment has a pair of limbs, which may be powerful pincers or, on the other hand, slender sensory appendages (*pedipalps*) ; while the remaining four segments bear each a pair of walking legs. The extra pair of walking limbs here noted serves to render arachnids clearly distinct from insects, while the wingless body is a further criterion of distinction. Moreover, the young arachnid, unlike most young insects, generally closely resembles the adult at hatching.

The hinder part of the adult body consists of thirteen segments (though rarely, as in spiders, is it unsegmented), which form the abdomen or *opisthosoma*. In some arachnids—scorpions, for instance—the opisthosoma is modified into two distinct regions, a wide *mesosoma* in front, and a narrow *metasoma* with a sharp terminal sting behind.

Scorpions. These arachnids (*Scorpionidea*) are found commonly in the hotter parts of the globe, and some of the smaller species live in south Europe. They lurk under stones and in other dark places, their dull, dark bodies harmonizing well with their drab surroundings. They are generally nocturnal in their habits, and feed upon insects and spiders, also accepting other small creatures, which are seized by the first two pairs of appendages. Grasped in these claws, the prey is helpless. The scorpion then raises its narrow tail over its back and brings the sharp, curved sting into operation. Near the tip of this is a minute aperture, the opening of two poison sacs located in the swollen tail. The secretion of the poison gland is injected into the wound made by the sting and immediately has a fatal effect. The prey is not masticated and swallowed, for the scorpion's mouth is exceedingly small ; but its juices are extracted by the action of a stomach which acts like a suction-pump, and which draws fluid into the food canal as water is drawn into a syringe.

The structure and arrangement of the blood vascular system, digestive system and nervous system are typically arthropodan, but the respiratory system shows differences from that of the insect. A scorpion does not breathe, like an insect, by means of air-tubes, but by means of four pairs of lung-books, the slits opening into which are easily seen on the under side of the mesosoma. These organs are chambers, kept filled with air, within which numerous delicate plates, resembling the leaves of a book, are contained. Within the leaves blood circulates, separated from the chamber of the organ merely by a thin sheet of delicate tissue, through which respiratory gaseous exchanges are made.

Spiders. These familiar arachnids (*Araneida*) differ from scorpions in several respects. The abdomen, instead of being elongated and clearly divided into rings, is of rounded form and shows no trace of segmentation. The jaws do not terminate in pincers. The chelicerae have a claw-like end joint, which can be bent down like the blade of a pocket-knife, for grasping purposes. The pedipalps are used as feelers. But, as in scorpions, there are several simple eyes upon the upper part of the prosoma, though the arrangement of these differs in the two classes.

Spiders are every bit as rapacious as scorpions, and likewise suck the juices of their victims. But the prey of the spider is killed or paralysed by the secretion of poison glands that open on the first jaws, which compensate for the absence of a tail-sting. The colours and marking, as in scorpions, render the animal inconspicuous and make it a dangerous enemy and an obscure prey.

Respiration in spiders provides many problems to the embryologist. Some spiders possess two pairs of lung-books, while others possess only one pair, but have stigmata and trachea in addition. In one family trachea alone occur. Spiders have passed through a primitive lung-book stage of respiration to a higher tracheal grade, but all spiders have not emerged from the lower grade completely. In the class all stages of the substitution of trachea for lung-books are indicated.

The most familiar spiders construct webs of various kinds to serve as snares for their insect prey, a device which fully compensates for the absence of wings. Some spiders use silk for cocoon spinning—a device which protects the eggs—others to form retreats, to bind up their prey, to anchor themselves, or to form a " gossamer " drifting line. In the common garden spider, *Epeira*, the silk glands open on six small teat-like projections, the spinnerets, situated on the under side of the abdomen near its hinder end. The ends of these are studded with over six hundred minute tubes, some larger than the rest. The fluid which exudes from each tube at once hardens into a thread of inconceivable tenuity. Every line of the web is exceedingly complex, consisting of numerous strands woven together and coated, in some instances, with adhesive material. The silk threads are thus very much stronger than they would otherwise be, and hardening takes place more rapidly.

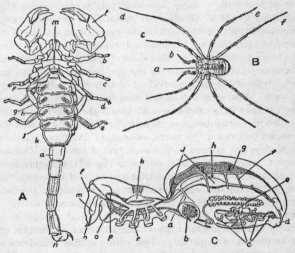

FORMS OF ARACHNIDS. **A,** scorpion ; a, first segment of metasoma ; b, c, d, e, walking legs of the prosoma ; f, g, h, j, stigmata of right side ; k, last segment of mesosoma ; l, pedipalp ; m, chelicera ; n, tail. **B,** a phalangid, misnamed harvest " spider " ; a, chelicera ; b, pedipalp ; c, d, e, f, walking legs. **C,** diagram of a spider ; a, vessel bringing blood from lung-book to heart ; b, lung-book ; c, silk glands ; d, anus ; e, ovary ; f, artery ; g, heart ; h, ducts of digestive gland ; j, mid gut ; k, sucking stomach ; l, eye ; m, chelicera ; o, mouth ; p, brain ; r, lobes of stomach.

From Borrodaile, Potts, Eastham & Saunders, " The Invertebrata." Cambridge University Press

The sheet webs and tubes found in country lanes are made by *Agelena*, a near relative of the house spider, *Tegenaria*. Other spiders make hammocks and labyrinths, while in the common garden spider—which makes wheel-like snares—the art of spinning is brought to perfection. The web is vertically disposed in a hedge or in some other convenient place—often near water, where flies and gnats abound—and is made by the female. To begin with, a roughly quadrangular frame is constructed of foundation lines, and firmly fixed to supports. Then radial strands, arranged like the spokes of a wheel, are laid down. Later, the radial threads are united by a spiral thread, which commences near the middle of the hub and runs outwards. This first spiral is gradually removed and replaced by a second spiral, coated with adhesive material, which runs towards the centre of the hub, without reaching this point—where the non-viscid first spiral is allowed to remain. The spider takes up occupation either on the hub of the snare or in a near-by retreat connected with the hub by special threads.

The viscid secretion of the second spiral is laid down as a continuous secretion of special glands, but soon breaks up into minute droplets, some 120,000 of which are to be found on a large web. The spider does not become trapped in its own web partly because it is careful not to touch the adhesive parts with legs or body, partly because its legs appear to be covered with an oily secretion which prevents adhesion. A glass rod smeared with oil does not adhere to the web, but if the oil is then washed off with carbon disulphide it clings to the web tenaciously. The great naturalist, Fabre, found that the legs of the spider appear not to adhere to the viscid spiral unless washed in this way, or otherwise robbed of their oily surface secretion.

The floating lines of silk which drift through the air in spring and early autumn are spun by young spiders of various species to serve as means of dispersal. The young spider stands on a firm object, facing the wind, and spins mooring strands. The end of the abdomen is then turned up and a thread is woven which streams out into the wind. When the thread is sufficiently long to support the weight of the spider, the moorings are cut and the spider drifts away ultimately to land far from its starting point.

The water spider constructs a web under water for the protection of its eggs. The web is really a thimble-shaped nest, moored to water plants and smeared externally with liquid silk to make it airtight. The nest is filled with air, brought down from the surface of the pond in successive bubbles adhering to the hairy body of the spider.

Some spiders do not construct webs but use their silk merely for lining their dwellings, which are commonly underground. The tarantula spider stalks its prey and seizes its victims by a sudden spring when sufficiently close. The clever trap-door spiders are hunters, noted for the neat way in which their underground retreats are constructed. A cylindrical burrow is excavated and lined with silk, intrusion being forbidden by the circular trap-door made of particles of earth cemented together with silk and provided with a durable silken hinge. Bird spiders are of immense size and can dispatch frogs and small birds, which are hunted along with insects and other spiders.

Many arachnids which do not belong to the *Araneida* are often wrongly called spiders. The long-legged harvest spider or harvestman is not a spider at all, as we readily see when we study its characters. The abdomen is segmented and is united with the prosoma by its entire width—that is to say, there is no "waist." There are no spinning glands and the chelicerae are pincer-like. This arachnid belongs to the class *Phalangida*. Another form which is commonly miscalled a spider is the minute red-spider, which causes so much damage to our greenhouse crops. This belongs to the class of mites and ticks known as the *Acarina*.

Mites and Ticks. These are mostly of very small size, and all three regions of the body are fused together into an ovoid mass. The mouth parts are typically suctorial. In many free-living forms the chelicerae are piercing claws, while the pedipalps are leg-like. But in the familiar cheese-mite, *Tyroglyphus*, the chelicerae are pincer-like and the pedipalps are no longer leg-like.

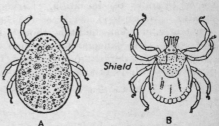

Ticks all belong to a single family of the *Acarina* known as the *Ixodidae*, all other acarines being so-called mites. An adult

TWO FORMS OF TICK. A, Argas ; **B,** Amblyomma. The former is distinguished by its leathery skin, the latter by the hard shield which covers the whole body of the male, and the front part of that of the female, as shown here.

From Borrodaile, etc., " Invertebrata," Cambridge University Press

tick may attain the size of a hazel-nut, while the mites are generally very much smaller. We recognize two kinds of ticks and call them " hard " and " soft " ticks respectively. The former have a hardening of the upper surface which takes the form of a shield, but the latter have soft flabby bodies. Both kinds are parasitic on a wide variety of vertebrated animals.

Soft ticks remain on the body of the host only until gorged with its blood, and usually spend the light part of each day sheltered in crevices near the habitat of the host. *Argas* is a genus of bird ticks with species parasitic on fowls, ducks, geese, turkeys and pigeons the world over. Hard ticks develop through a series of interesting stages. The eggs are laid on herbage and hatch out in two to six months into larvae with only three pairs of legs. The larva seeks a host, on which it becomes gorged with blood, later to fall to the ground. Moulting takes place on the ground, the moulted animal possessing the full number of legs but imperfectly formed sexual organs. It is called a " nymph." This seeks a host, gorges itself with blood, and falls to the ground in order to moult and to become mature. The reproductive act (*copulation*) takes place on the ground, and the fertilized female must again seek a host and feed, and must once more come to the ground in order to lay the eggs.

In view of the slender chance any individual larva has of completing its life history, it is scarcely surprising that the number of eggs laid is very large. Of the 5,000 to 20,000 eggs produced very few will reach the adult stage, despite the great resistance shown by ticks to starvation. Larvae are known to live six months without food, while adults have remained alive and apparently in good condition though kept in corked tubes for five years. The dangers of extinction due to the difficulties of finding hosts are largely met, however, by the immense numbers of potential adults produced.

Our Course in Zoology is continued in Volume 4.

END OF VOLUME THREE